Livestock
and
Meat Marketing

other AVI books

Food and Field Crops Technology

Edmond	Sweet Potatoes: Production, Processing, Marketing
Hall	Drying Farm Crops
Hall	Processing Equipment for Agricultural Products
Inglett	Corn: Culture, Processing, Products
Matz	Cereal Science
Ryall and Lipton	Handling, Transportation, and Storage of Fresh Vegetables and Melons
Schaible	Poultry: Feeds and Nutrition
Schneidau and Duewer	Symposium: Vertical Coordination in Pork Industry
Smith	Potatoes: Production, Storing, Processing
Teskey and Shoemaker	Tree Fruit Production, 2nd Edition
Wall and Ross	Sorghum Production and Utilization
Woodroof	Peanuts: Production, Processing, Products
Woodroof	Coconuts: Production, Processing, Products
Woodroof	Tree Nuts: Production, Processing, Products, Vols. 1 and 2

Milk and Milk Products Technology

Arbuckle	Ice Cream, 2nd Edition
Brink and Kritchevsky	Dairy Lipids and Lipid Metabolism
Hall and Hedrick	Drying of Milk and Milk Products, 2nd Edition
Henderson	The Fluid-milk Industry, 3rd Edition
Webb and Johnson	Fundamentals of Dairy Chemistry
Webb and Whittier	Byproducts from Milk, 2nd Edition

Food Technology

Desrosier	The Technology of Food Preservation, 3rd Edition
Desrosier and Desrosier	Economics of New Food Product Development
Greig	Economics of Food Processing
Junk and Pancoast	Handbook of Commercial Sugars
Kramer and Twigg	Quality Control for the Food Industry, 3rd Edition, Vol. 1
Matz	Cereal Technology
Pomeranz and Shellenberger	Bread Science and Technology
Smith and Circle	Soybeans: Chemistry and Technology, Vol. 1 Proteins
Tressler and Joslyn	Fruit and Vegetable Juice Processing, 2nd Edition
Tressler, Van Arsdel and Copley	Freezing Preservation of Foods, 4th Edition, Vols. 1, 2, 3, and 4
Weiss	Food Oils and Their Uses

Food Chemistry and Microbiology

Pederson	Microbiology of Food Fermentations
Pomeranz and Meloan	Food Analysis: Theory and Practice
Schultz and Anglemier	Proteins and their Reactions
Schultz, Cain and Wrolstad	Carbohydrates and Their Roles
Weiser, Mountney and Gould	Practical Food Microbiology and Technology, 2nd Edition

LIVESTOCK
AND
MEAT MARKETING

JOHN H. McCOY, Ph.D.

Professor of Agricultural Economics,
Kansas State University,
Manhattan, Kansas

WESTPORT, CONNECTICUT
THE AVI PUBLISHING COMPANY, INC.
1972

381.41
M131 l

Library of Congress Catalog Card No. 72-78910
ISBN-0-87055-120-5

Printed in the United States of America

Dedication

Dedicated to M. A.

Preface

The task of directing production and of moving some 38 billion pounds of highly perishable products into the hands of consumers requires a vast and complex market system. In the years immediately following World War II much criticism was levelled at the system for its lack of change and adaptation in a rapidly changing world. Not all of the criticism was warranted for the historical record shows change. Nevertheless, the pace of change has quickened in recent years and, like many other aspects of current economic and social life, possible developments in livestock and meat marketing challenge the imagination.

This book is designed to present a balance of descriptive analysis of the marketing system together with the basic economic principles underlying its operation. The text is intended for undergraduate students. It is assumed that readers have an acquaintance with elementary economic theory, but some of the more relevant principles are reviewed in applying them to this particular field. Emphasis is placed on practical aspects rather than academic discussion. This text is the product of a number of years of classroom give and take with students from all agricultural curricula, but the predominant student influence has been from majors in agricultural economics and animal science. The book is intended to provide the chief reference for courses dealing exclusively with livestock and meat marketing. Relevant chapters may be utilized as supplementary reference material for appropriate sections of general agricultural marketing courses. Readers who wish to delve deeper in the various subject matter areas will find additional references at the end of each chapter.

The author acknowledges the contribution of former students and colleagues of Kansas State University and the University of Arizona in their numerous suggestions for improvements in content and organization. Indebtedness also is acknowledged to the many authors of publications cited throughout the text.

John H. McCoy

January 10, 1972

Contents

CHAPTER 1

Introduction

LIVESTOCK AND MEAT IN THE ECONOMY

The U.S. livestock-meat industry produced 36 billion pounds of meat during 1970, and the marketing system moved it to consumers—an average of 185.5 lb for every man, woman, and child in the country. This is an immense amount of product, and the quantity is increasing at the rate of about 3% per yr. While meat is the main output, the industry also produces substantial quantities of joint products and by-products (hides, wool, lard, tallow, inedible fat, etc.). Those also were processed and moved to ultimate users.

Most people take for granted that retail meat cases will be routinely stocked with a good selection of wholesome meat and meat products. Many are unaware that the vast and complicated production and distribution system which brought those products within their reach is one of the largest and most important industries in the United States.

The importance of an industry can be viewed in many different ways. In an economic sense, importance is attached to such factors as the number of people employed (directly and indirectly), amount of investment, quantities of physical resources used, and quantities of products produced. From the standpoint of physical health of the nation, concern is attached to wholesomeness and nutritive aspects of the products of that industry. Governmental agencies are concerned with the contributions an industry may make to tax revenues; and in recent years concern has become pronounced with social costs in such aspects as environmental pollution. Importance also may be attached to an industry's contribution to national defense. Some aspects of importance are capable of quantitative measurement, but some cannot be measured objectively. Some could be measured, but data have not been assembled. These limitations apply to the livestock-meat industry. However, enough information is available to show that, by any reasonable standards, livestock and meat are big business in the United States.

Assets

Total assets of U.S. farmers and ranchers were $317 billion at the beginning of 1971 (Table 1.1). That was the current value of all equipment, livestock, land, buildings, and savings of farmers and ranchers.[1] Farm and ranch assets were some 3 to 4 times greater than the combined assets of the 10 largest U.S.

[1] It should be pointed out that farmer indebtedness also is increasing. Farm real estate debt on Jan. 1, 1970, was $28.7 billion and other debt was $29.4 billion. While the rate of increase in farm mortgage debt was down in 1969 compared to recent years (5.7% in 1969, 6.5% in 1967, and 9.4% in 1966), there is considerable apprehension over the increase in debt burden.

TABLE 1.1

U.S. FARM AND RANCH ASSETS OF THE 48 CONTINENTAL STATES, 1969, 1970, 1971

Item[1]	1969	1970 (Billion $)	1971[2]
Physical assets			
Real estate	202.7	209.0	212.4
Nonreal estate	73.4	78.6	80.4
Financial assets	23.0	23.8	24.4
Total	299.1	311.4	317.2

Source: USDA (1971A).
[1] All items are for Jan. 1 except real estate which is for Mar. 1.
[2] Preliminary

corporations, including such industrial giants as General Motors, U.S. Steel, Ford Motor Co., Chrysler Corp., Standard Oil of New Jersey, General Electric, International Business Machines, Mobil Oil, Texaco, and Gulf Oil. Information is not available to indicate the proportion of farm and ranch assets applicable to livestock. Any such determination would show that, in addition to assets used directly in livestock production, the bulk of those assets devoted to forage and feed grain production indirectly are an integral part of the industry.

In addition to farm and ranch assets, the total industry includes the packing, processing, and distribution sectors. Beyond that are many associated, or supplementary, sectors which are entirely or partially devoted to functions of the industry. Among the latter are substantial assets in facilities for transportation (truck and railroad), marketing (auctions, terminals, concentration yards, futures markets, etc.), banking and credit, veterinary services, manufacturing of veterinary equipment and supplies, feed manufacturing, livestock and meat processing equipment manufacturing, insurance companies, publication of

TABLE 1.2

U.S. CASH FARM AND RANCH RECEIPTS, 1968, 1969, 1970

Product	1968	Year 1969 (Million $)	1970
Cattle and calves	11,241	12,522	[1]
Hogs	3,807	4,667	[1]
Sheep, lambs, and wool	387	402	[1]
Total meat animals and wool	15,435	17,591	17,976
Dairy products	5,955	6,172	6,470
Poultry and eggs	3,828	4,423	4,333
Other livestock items	266	253	310
Total livestock and products	25,484	28,439	29,089
Crops	18,733	18,790	19,589
All commodities	44,218	47,229	48,678

Source: Data for 1970 from USDA (1971A); for earlier years from USDA (1970).
[1] Not available at the time this table was compiled.

numerous magazines and newspapers, etc. No one has ever calculated the combined value of assets devoted to livestock and meat, but there is no doubt that this industry, if not the leader, is near the top of all U.S. industries.

Cash Receipts

Cash receipts from farm and ranch marketings totaled $49 billion (exclusive of government payments) in 1970 (Table 1.2). Of this total 60% was from livestock and livestock products—with meat animals (cattle, calves, hogs, sheep, and lambs) and wool comprising the largest share (these are the "red meat" animals which constitute the "livestock" under discussion in this material). Meat animals are steadily increasing as a source of income. Cash receipts were about $11 billion (or 30% of total farm marketing) during the early 1960's and almost $18 billion (or 37%) in 1970.

The importance of meat animals and wool varies considerably among states—both in absolute amount and as a percentage of cash farm and ranch receipts (see Table 1.3). Iowa was high in total dollars of receipts in 1970 with

TABLE 1.3
CASH FARM AND RANCH RECEIPTS FROM MEAT ANIMALS
AND WOOL FOR SELECTED STATES, 1969

State	Meat Animals ($1,000)	Wool ($1,000)	All Commodities ($1,000)	From Meat Animals (%)	From Wool (%)
Illinois	1,122,008	914	2,702,957	41.5	[1]
Iowa	2,532,997	8,014	3,788,020	66.8	0.2
Missouri	794,638	733	1,445,960	55.0	[1]
Nebraska	1,297,474	980	1,933,345	67.1	0.1
Kansas	1,027,712	1,030	1,717,753	59.8	0.1
N. Carolina	164,413	46	1,406,161	11.6	[1]
Georgia	214,142	14	1,147,877	18.6	[1]
Florida	155,374	11	1,343,115	11.5	[1]
Alabama	193,056	14	722,554	26.7	[1]
Mississippi	207,412	26	807,246	25.6	[1]
Arkansas	138,451	15	1,038,908	13.3	[1]
Oklahoma	570,150	301	939,279	60.7	[1]
Texas	1,318,995	14,561	2,905,261	45.4	0.2
Montana	319,775	4,451	534,206	59.8	0.8
Wyoming	171,013	7,506	224,620	76.1	3.4
Colorado	714,602	4,031	1,015,808	70.3	0.4
N. Mexico	266,862	3,122	390,322	68.4	0.8
Arizona	369,398	1,285	662,004	55.8	0.2
California	885,635	5,262	4,371,260	20.2	0.1

Source: USDA (1970).
[1] Less than 1/2 of 1%.

slightly over $2.5 billion, while Wyoming was tops as a percentage of receipts with a combined meat animal and wool total of almost 80%.

A large share of the income received by farmers and ranchers is pumped back into the economy in payment for production expenses, and most of the remainder is spent for household and personal items. As meat and wool moves through marketing channels, value is added by slaughtering, processing, and distribution. Sales at retail were estimated at $28.5 billion in 1970.[2] Thus, the value added in slaughtering, processing, and distribution pumped an additional $10.5 billion into the economy ($28.5 − 18.0 = $10.5). At these magnitudes it is apparent that the livestock-meat industry is an important component—not only in U.S. agriculture, but in the national economy as well.

Interrelationships with Other Industries

Livestock is important, not only in absolute terms, that is from the standpoint of the number of dollars turned over by the industry, but even more so in additional business activity generated in other economic sectors in servicing livestock and meat producers. This commonly is referred to as the "multiplier effect". It applies to income generated in other sectors, as well as output of goods and services in other sectors. No national studies have been made comparing the multiplier effect of meat animal sectors with other sectors, but this was done by Emerson *et al.* (1969) in a study of the Kansas economy. There is reason to believe the Kansas results would apply to other important U.S. livestock areas.

Emerson and his co-workers made a comprehensive input-output analysis in which they separated the Kansas economy into 69 major sectors, or components, to study interrelationships among economic sectors. Cattle and hog production were treated separately, but sheep production, unfortunately, was not. Meat packing and processing were handled as one sector. Other agricultural sectors consisted of the major crops, dairying, poultry, grain milling, etc. Nonagricultural activity was broken down into a number of industrial and service sectors, government, and households.

Income Multiplier.—This study showed that the Kansas beef cattle industry had an income multiplier of 5.00. This means that every additional $1.00 worth of output in the beef cattle industry generated 5 times as much income in other industries as it did in the cattle industry itself. In hog production the income multiplier was 3.29, and in the meat packing and processing industry it was 6.95. Of all Kansas industries, including nonagricultural industries such as petroleum, coal, gas, building construction, aerospace and other manufacturing, only grain milling had a higher (i.e., slightly higher) income multiplier than meat packing-processing. The grain milling multiplier was 7.18, compared to 6.95 for meat packing and processing. It may be noted this also is an agricultural sector. By comparison, the income multiplier effect of several other important sectors was: petroleum and coal products manufacturing, 4.99; dairy products manufacturing, 4.73; crude oil and natural gas mining, 4.58; nonmetalic mining, 3.74;

[2] Official data were not available when this was written. During 1969, retail sales were 1.585 times the amount of cash farm receipts for meat animals. This same factor was used in estimating 1970 retail sales. The result ($28.5 billion) was identical with 1969 retail sales and probably is a conservative estimate.

dairy farming, 3.39; and building construction, 3.11 (see Table 1.4). The income multipliers of crops were considerably lower than those of livestock activities. For example, wheat, corn, and milo farming had income multipliers of 1.80, 1.67, and 1.71, respectively.

TABLE 1.4

INCOME AND OUTPUT MULTIPLIERS FOR LEADING KANSAS ECONOMIC SECTORS, 1965

Sector	Multiplier
Income Multiplier	
Grain mill products manufacturing	7.179258
Meat packing and processing	6.948381
Cattle farming	5.001746
Petroleum and coal products manufacturing	4.922734
Dairy products manufacturing	4.733268
Crude oil and natural gas manufacturing	4.577211
Nonmetalic mining	3.735876
Dairy farming	3.386584
Building Construction	3.110438
Other mining	3.607454
Output Multiplier	
Meat packing and processing	2.590568
Maintenance and repair construction	2.218130
Dairy products manufacturing	2.205620
Cattle farming	2.031102
Hog farming	1.974438
Dairy farming	1.930507
Petroleum and coal products manufacturing	1.853648
Grain mill products manufacturing	1.786472
Building construction	1.706107
Electric, gas, and sanitation services	1.636593

Source: Emerson *et al.* (1969).

Output Multiplier.—Another measure of interrelationships among economic sectors is the output multiplier. The output multiplier of the cattle sector was 2.03. This means that each additional $1.00 output in the cattle sector generated 2.03 times as much output in other sectors as it did in the cattle sector itself. In hog production the output multiplier was 1.97 and in meat packing-processing it was 2.59. As Table 1.4 shows, meat packing-processing had the highest output multiplier of any economic sector, cattle production ranked virtually at the top among all industries of the state, and hog farming was fifth.

It is readily apparent from these data that the livestock and meat sectors are highly interrelated with other industries in the state of Kansas. Logically, comparable relationships would be expected in other important livestock states or regions. The significance of these relationships lies in the indicated importance these sectors have in the economic development of a state or region. They provide the clue that economic development of the state could be enhanced by research and extension activities which would promote development of livestock and meat production.

Land Utilization

Livestock production utilizes a greater area of land than any other activity in the United States. Of the entire land area 41% (922,985,000 acres) is used solely for pasture and grazing (U.S. Dept. of Com. 1964). In the western states, a much higher percentage is devoted to grazing. The production of supplementary pastures, forages, and feed grains necessitate additional vast acreages. A major share of the feed used by western livestock comes from native range, pastures, and meadows on land which, under present conditions, has virtually no other feasible alternative use. The same situation prevails through the Sand Hills region of Nebraska, the Flint Hills and Osage Pasture areas of Kansas and Oklahoma, and many other localized areas in all parts of the United States. Livestock (primarily cattle and sheep) utilize this native vegetation and enormous quantities of roughage and crop aftermath, etc., which otherwise would contribute nothing to the food supply. While the forages, both native and cultivated, provide an economical means of growing livestock preparatory to finishing for slaughter, consumers have indicated a distinct preference for meat from grain-finished animals. Requirements of the grain-finishing operation support virtually the entire feed grain industry which in itself is a major user of much of the best land in the United States. Consumers spend more for meat than any other food item, which attests to the importance attached to the end product.

Employment

Published data are not available on the number of people employed in the production and marketing of livestock and meat. Directly or indirectly, nearly all farmers and ranchers have a hand in it. Most of those who do not produce livestock are involved in feed production to a greater or lesser degree. The relationship is obvious for those in feed grain and forage production. It is less obvious in such crops as cotton and sugar beets, but many crops do have feed by-products such as cottonseed meal and beet pulp. Even fruit and vegetable producers are involved in a minor way because limited quantities of pulp and refuse are used for livestock feed. According to the 1964 agricultural census 72.4% of the farm firms had cattle and calves, 34.3% had hogs, and 7.4% had sheep and lambs. As a rough estimate, it appears likely that 80%, or 4.8 million, of the 6 million people classified as farmers and ranchers by USDA in 1965 were engaged directly or indirectly in livestock production. In that same year, USDA data show 8 million persons engaged in marketing agricultural products. In all of agriculture there were 8 people in marketing for every 6 engaged in production. If this same ratio holds true for the livestock sector, there would be 6.4 million people engaged in the marketing of livestock and meat. In total, then, there would be 11.2 million people employed in the livestock and meat industries.

MARKETS AND MARKETING

Marketing—the Concept

Marketing is that area of economics concerned with the exchange and valuation of goods and services.[3] This definition encompasses (1) activities associated with the physical movement and transformation of goods and (2) the pricing of goods and services. In some aspects the physical functions of marketing are related to production. Production, in economic jargon, is defined as the creation of "utility" or usefulness. Utility may be created by changing the form, location, availability over time, or possession (ownership) of a product. In a narrow sense, marketing sometimes is construed to apply only to exchange of title (Bakken 1953). This would limit it to problems of possession utility including pricing and activities associated with buying and selling. However, by long tradition marketing has been considered to be broader than this. By the so-called functional approach to the study of marketing it would include, in addition to buying and selling, such functions as transporting, storing, processing, packaging, advertising, collecting and disseminating market news, standardizing and grading, inspecting, financing, and risk bearing. This would appear to include the creation of all types of utility listed under the definition of production; and prompts the question of whether there is a difference between production and marketing. There is little to be gained in belaboring this point. For administrative purposes, the USDA considers marketing to be limited to those activities which take place from the time products leave the farm gate. Activities performed prior to that are considered to be production. But, clearly, there can be a direct relationship between the two. A marketing program may be influenced by prior decisions that determine the quantity, quality, or timing of production. Even prior to that, a decision which determines the quality of feeder livestock purchased may directly affect the feeding program. Marketing and production are closely intertwined. There is a growing awareness that efficiencies may be gained by considering production and marketing as one integrated or coordinated system. This is one application of the so-called systems approach to economic as well as noneconomic problems, which has received increasing attention in recent years. We will not attempt to draw a firm distinction between marketing and production.

What Is a Market?

At first thought, the concept of a market may appear rather straightforward. One can see the livestock auction building and pens on the outskirts of his home town, or the big office building and yards of public terminal livestock markets at

[3] Agreement is not universal on an acceptable definition of marketing (or of the term market). The usefulness and validity of a definition is associated with its application. A different definition may be perfectly proper and correct depending upon the use made of it.

such places as Kansas City or Omaha. But it also is rather common to hear references to the "cattle" market, the "corn" market, and the "automobile" market. On other occasions the reference may be to the "futures" market and the "cash" or "spot" market. In the first instance, a market was associated with a particular place; in the second, the association was with a commodity; and in the third, with an element of time. In other cases a market has been defined as: a particular group of people, an institution, a mechanism for facilitating exchange, the perfect market, and the imperfect market. The market concept also has been linked to the degree of communication among buyers and sellers and the degree of substitutability among goods. While there are differences among these concepts, any one could be correct for the purpose for which it might be used. The concept of a perfect market is an abstraction used by economists as a benchmark for evaluating performance of market situations that deviate from its specifications. Further reference will be made to the perfect market in later sections.

Our application here of the term market does not necessitate a single choice of definitions. Depending upon the particular context, reference will be to certain geographically located markets; on other occasions to markets for particular class, grade, and weight of livestock. Various aspects of the cash and futures markets, as well as the agencies and institutions that make up these markets will be analyzed at some length. In other words, a comprehensive concept of the market will be used. It is generally agreed that a viable, competitive market requires more than physical facilities. The assembly and concentration of salable livestock may tend to promote competition. But the essential ingredients are people and a communication system—people who are adequately informed with respect to (1) the quality of livestock being offered (2) the current or prospective value of that quality of animals, and (3) bargaining techniques. If all parties interested in transacting business are adequately informed and have an efficient communication system, it is apparent that the concept of a market would need little reference to geographical location or space. Some recent developments in livestock marketing are making this more and more obvious.

Role of Markets and Marketing in the Economy

It was implied in previous paragraphs that we are concerned with marketing under competitive conditions. This normally is taken for granted for we live in a market economy—also sometimes called an exchange economy, a competitive economy, or capitalism—where competitive forces are "relatively" free to exert their influence in the formation of prices and in direction of the economy. This is not the case throughout the world. While all countries have some degree of government regulation or control over marketing activities, the situation is one of degree. The United States is at one end of the spectrum with a relatively low degree of government control. Such countries as the Soviet Union, Red China,

Albania, and Cuba are at the other end with a relatively high degree of central planning.

Regardless of the economic system, certain functions must be performed. Goods must be produced and distributed. Income must be distributed among the participants. In a market economy, competitively-determined prices are the guiding force which gives direction to what is produced, what technologies are used in production, where production takes place, when production is carried out, when and where consumption takes place and who gets the proceeds from the whole process. In a completely centralized economy such decisions as these would be dictated by the government through administrators, committees, boards, etc., responsible for operation of the economy. The attainment of an optimum which meets or approaches economic, social, and political objectives is an extremely complex problem. The problem is no less complex in a market economy, but the approach is vastly different. Here, chief dependence is placed upon impersonal, competitive market forces which generate prices that give direction to the economy—again with the expectation that economic, social, and political objectives will be met to a satisfactory degree. This places a tremendous burden on the markets. If markets do not operate efficiently, resources used in production may be misallocated; consumers may not have goods available in the form, quantity, quality, place, and time desired; and inequalities may occur in the distribution of income among individuals. Departure from generally-desired objectives or goals prompts government intervention in the name of public interest, or general welfare. Intervention may take many forms, e.g., inspection, licenses, regulations designed to curb monopoly or enhance competition.

Marketing Problems

Problems which have arisen in the system stem directly from the functions marketing is expected to perform in directing the economy. These may be grouped under three general classifications—determination of consumer demands, reflection of these demands back through market channels to processors and producers, and physical movement of goods through market channels to consumers. Problems arise with respect to the efficiency with which these functions are performed. From an analytical standpoint, the first two are encompassed in the study of problems of "pricing efficiency" and the latter under problems of "operational efficiency". In actual operation the two are often interrelated.

Operational Efficiency.—Operational efficiency in marketing is analagous to the engineer's concept of physical efficiency, i.e., it is concerned with measuring input-output relationships. In marketing, the relevant relationships are in the physical movement of products from point of production to point of consumption. An improvement in marketing technology that permits an increase in quantity of goods marketed without a proportional increase in resources devoted to marketing or, what amounts to the same thing, a decrease in resources used in marketing without a proportional decrease in quantity of goods handled, would represent an increase in operational efficiency. In either case, it is assumed that unit costs of marketing would be lower with improvement in operational efficiency. There are many examples of this. Studies have revealed that labor requirements, per unit of livestock handled, can be reduced at many livestock auctions by improvements in pens, alleys, gates, scales, and sale ring layouts which facilitate the movement and sale of livestock (McNeeley *et al.* 1953). Modernized methods and office equipment can reduce bookkeeping costs per livestock unit handled in larger marketing operations. Another example is the use of multiple-deck and drop-center trucks which lead to a reduction in unit costs of transportation.

But not all types of operational efficiency lend themselves to such straightforward measurement. Suppose the output were marketing services instead of physical quantities. Service cannot be measured in physical units. Yet, services most certainly are an output of the marketing system. The commission agent engaged to sell livestock on a terminal market is expected to perform a service, as is the order buyer engaged to purchase feeder cattle. One approach would be to consider that the value of the commission agent's services is the additional value he obtains for livestock over that which could have been obtained without his services. Likewise, the value of the order buyer's services may be presumed to be the difference between the value (cost to you) of feeder cattle purchased by the order buyer as compared to the value (cost to you) if you had not used his services. The principle is clear enough, but quantification can be difficult in some cases.

In a broader sense, value added in manufacturing can be used as an imputed value of services performed by a firm engaged in manufacturing. Calculated marketing margins of farm products, defined as the margin between farm prices and retail prices, is an approximation of the value of services performed in processing and moving goods from farm to consumer. Both value added and marketing margin are crude measures of operational efficiency. The general assumption involved is that competition is high enough to prevent inclusion of excess profits in value added and/or in marketing margins. This may be a valid assumption but conclusive evidence is hard to come by. In spite of recent investigations which failed to uncover existence of unreasonable profits in food industries,[4] many farmers and ranchers feel they are disadvantaged in bargaining for the sale of their products and suspect excess profits in the processing and distributing sectors.

Farmers and ranchers are interested in marketing livestock at the lowest cost consistent with price received (i.e., as long as marketing economies enhance the

---

[4] Investigations carried out by the National Commission on Food Marketing, an investigating agency formed by Congressional action in 1964. Relevant reports by this commission are discussed in later chapters.

net price). Over the years, producers generally have questioned whether gains in operational marketing efficiency accrue to them, to the market agencies, or to consumers. In a competitive economy, any reduction in marketing costs, which results in above normal profits, will attract additional competitors. With the possibility of increased profits, competition for products to handle tends to enhance prices paid to producers. Competition by buyers, farther down the marketing channels, to get products as cheaply as possible will also tend to lower selling price. Lack of adequate competition anywhere in the system may permit above normal profits for some time; but if competition is keen, an improvement in operational efficiency will benefit all parties in the long run.

Nevertheless, farmers and ranchers on occasion have been dissatisfied with what they considered exorbitant marketing costs. Probably the most extensive counteraction has been the organization of farmer-owned marketing agencies, such as cooperatives.[5] There are examples of cooperative livestock commission agencies, cooperatively-operated auctions, various types of cooperative livestock and wool pooling arrangements, and cooperative packing plants. Early history is replete with examples of farmer agitation for the lowering of freight rates. And, largely as a result of farmer dissatisfaction, the Packers and Stockyards Division of the USDA exerts a degree of control over the level of commission and yardage and feed charges at public livestock markets.

Pricing Efficiency.—In the traditional sense (Phillips 1961), "Pricing efficiency . . . is concerned with the price-making role of the market system. It concerns how accurately, how effectively, how rapidly, and how freely the marketing system makes prices which measure product values to the ultimate consumer and reflects these values through the various stages of the marketing system to the producer . . .

"Economic theory suggests that prices which reflect more accurately the preferences of consumers will do a more efficient job in allocating productive resources to maximize consumer satisfaction and producer incomes."

Thus, pricing efficiency is concerned with such questions as how well the price system interprets changes in consumer demands, how well prices transmit changing demands back to producers and induce a proper allocation of resources among alternative productive uses, and how well the price system distributes income among producers and marketers.

If consumers have a preference for meat with certain quality specifications it is presumed that competitive market forces, acting through the pricing mechanism, will transmit this message through market channels back to producers and induce an increase in production of meat with those specifications—and vice versa with meat of less desirable qualities. A much-discussed example of this is

[5] Not all cooperatives were organized solely in the interest of operational efficiency. Cooperatives may also be designed to improve pricing efficiency or to act in dual capacity for both operational and pricing objectives.

consumer reaction to overfat pork. An efficient pricing system would be expected to record this situation in consumer willingness to pay more for leaner pork. Thus, a price differential would be transmitted from the retail level back through distribution channels—processors, packers, and market agencies to the producers. The differential, if it were of significant magnitude, would be expected to induce swine producers to increase production of lean, meat-type hogs relative to the production of lard-type hogs. This assumes the increase in price equals or exceeds any associated increase in production costs. This is an example of prices directing a reallocation of resources. Presumably, producers and consumers both would benefit from such a change. Whether market agencies or packers and processors would benefit would require an analysis of their costs and returns. In spite of considerable criticism over the speed and effectiveness of pricing efficiency in the hog market, records show that over a period of years a substantial increase has occurred in the production of leaner hogs (Agnew 1969). This is not to say that the market exhibited perfect pricing efficiency, but it serves as an example of the principle. Further improvement undoubtedly can be made, and if consumer preferences change, the market will be expected to transmit those changes.

Classical economic theory, built around a model of perfect competition, was able to show that self-generating competitive forces would optimize the allocation of resources, the production and distribution of goods, and returns to factors of production, i.e., wages, rent, and interest. There would be no pure profits, but management would receive a minimal, normal profit. From the beginning, the prevailing economic philosophy in the United States has been based on relatively free and competitive markets. However, it also was apparent from the beginning that unbridled competition produced some undesirable social results, and regulations of many sorts have been incorporated into the system. The attributes of perfect competition never existed and no one has argued that they did. It always has been obvious that from the private, individual standpoint, advantage could be gained by introducing or developing imperfection in the system, e.g., developing inequality in bargaining power. In other words, private interest is not necessarily compatible with the general interest. As a member of society, each person is presumed to be cognizant of social responsibility. At the same time experience has shown that individuals or firms, by and large, will go about as far as the law allows (or as far as personal moral convictions allow) in the enhancement of personal or private interest, which generally means enhancement of profit.

The recent increase in concern about farmer bargaining power is, in reality, concern about pricing efficiency. A term used in this connection is "market performance". Farmers have shown dissatisfaction with the distribution of returns. Some would resort to greater governmental intervention, directly or indirectly. Others recommend voluntary farmer organization with the exercise of self-discipline in marketing. This area will be discussed later in relevant chapters, but it should be noted here that market organization (the structure which gives rise to the behavior or conduct of firms and their performance in terms of pricing efficiency) is not a static phenomenon. As noted by Farris (1965), producers of most farm products ". . . traditionally have had readily available to them markets in which prices, though subject to various kinds and degrees of imperfections, were generated in a relatively impersonal manner. This is changing; such markets are fading from the scene."

BIBLIOGRAPHY

AGNEW, D. B. 1969. Improvements in grades of hogs slaughtered from 1960-61 to 1967-68. USDA Econ. Res. Serv., Marketing Res. Rept. *849*, May.

AMERICAN NATIONAL CATTLEMEN'S ASSOCIATION. 1965. Proc. 3rd Coordinated Beef Improvement Conf., July. Texas A & M Univ.

BAKKEN, H. 1953. Theory of Markets and Marketing. Mimir Press, Madison, Wisc.

EMERSON, J. *et al.* 1969. The interindustry structure of Kansas. Dept. Econ. Analysis, State of Kansas, Topeka.

FARRIS, P. L. 1965. Talk given at 3rd Coordinated Beef Improvement Conf., July. Texas A & M Univ.

FOWLER, S. H. 1961. An introduction to livestock marketing. *In* The Marketing of Livestock and Meat, 2nd Edition. Interstate Printers & Publishers, Danville, Ill.

McNEELEY, J. *et al.* 1953. Texas livestock auction markets—methods and facilities. Texas Agr. Expt. Sta. Misc. Publ. *93*.

PHILLIPS, V. B. 1961. Price formation and pricing efficiency in marketing agricultural products: The role of market news and grade standards. Proc. 26th Ann. Conf. Natl. Assoc. Social Sci. Teachers, Econ. Sect., April 20, Howard Univ., Washington, D.C.

USDA. 1955. Guide to agriculture, USA. USDA Econ. Res. Serv. Agr. Inform. Bull. *30*, Revised.

USDA. 1966. Agricultural markets in change. USDA Econ. Res. Serv., Agr. Econ. Rept. *95*, July.

USDA. 1970. Farm income State estimates, 1949-1969. USDA Econ. Res. Serv. *FIS-216*, Suppl. Aug.

USDA. 1971A. Agricultural finance outlook. USDA Econ. Res. Serv. *AFO-10*, Febr.

USDA. 1971B. Farm income situation. USDA Econ. Res. Serv. *FIS-217*, Febr.

U.S. DEPT. OF COMMERCE. 1967. 1964 Census of agriculture. Bur. Census, U.S. Dept. Com., Washington, D.C.

WILLIAMS, W. F., and STOUT, T. T. 1964. The role of marketing and measures of performance. *In* Economics of the Livestock-Meat Industry. Macmillian Co., New York.

CHAPTER 2

Historical Perspective

Many changes have occurred in methods of marketing livestock and meat in the United States, and the dynamic nature of the industry practically assures that changes will continue. The following thumbnail sketch of historical development is presented, not so much in the interests of history per se, but rather to point out factors which were responsible for changes in the marketing system. In many respects the marketing system developed in conjunction with and as an integral part of the production process. For both it has been a gradual, but steady evolution.[1] Among the more important factors influencing market development were shifting geographical centers of livestock production and population; shifting import-export opportunities; changes in technology of transportation and refrigeration; changes in structural characteristics of the producing, packing, wholesaling, and retailing components of the industry; developments in grading, and in the collection and dissemination of market intelligence.

Marketing was of little significance in the self-sufficient, subsistence economy of the early settlers. Meager surpluses of livestock and meat were readily bartered for other necessities. In time, a continuous influx of immigrants gave rise to population concentrations in cities in the present Central Atlantic states. Simultaneously, livestock production expanded in the eastern coastal region and slowly pushed westward and southward. Cattle were introduced in the southwest—through Spanish influence and largely by missionaries—as early, if not earlier, than on the East Coast, but the pattern of a marketing system which was to emerge as the prevailing model had its origins in East Coast livestock development. As specialization of labor increased, there quickly developed a need for trade. Barter between producers and consumers soon was replaced by merchants (middlemen) who, for a fee, acted as the go-between for producers and consumers. As long as distances were not too great, most slaughtering was done by producers who delivered dressed carcasses to local retail merchants. As both distances and demand for meat increased, the feasibility arose for another intermediary—a merchant who would buy live animals. This person might slaughter the animals and retail the meat himself, or slaughter and sell dressed carcasses to a retail merchant. Thus in our earliest period, direct marketing—producer to slaughterer—was the rule. As will be

---

[1] The introduction and subsequent development of domestic meat animals is an extremely important and interesting chapter in U.S. annals. For those who may be interested, a considerable body of literature is available on the subject. Examples are: Clemen (1923), Duddy and Revzan (1938), Thompson (1942), Wentworth (1948), and Williams and Stout (1964).

pointed out later, the trend for some years has been back to direct marketing of slaughter livestock.

At first, all movement of livestock was on foot. No other means was available. In time, limited river and coastal water transport was used. Slaughtering was limited to winter months. Meat preservation was crude, being limited to smoking, salting, and pickling. The meat was packed in barrels for storage and shipment. It was these techniques which gave rise to the term meat "packer," a term which has remained and is now used synonymously with slaughterer. Commercial trade in "packed" meats got under way around the mid-1600's with shipments to the British West Indies and the provisioning of sailing vessels (Clemen 1923). The West Indies trade was initiated by New England colonies, but in time the geographical advantage of Virginia and the Carolinas gave the latter the competitive edge—an early U.S. example of regional competitive advantage. (Probably the latest analogous example is the development and introduction of hybrid grain sorghum in the Southern Plains States, which gave that region a competitive advantage over others in cattle feeding.)

As a rule, curing and packing was done by individuals, farmers or merchants, until about 1662. At that time William Pynchon launched what is purported to be the first commercial venture in meat packing (Clemen 1923). The plant was located at Springfield, Mass. Prior to that, Pynchon had been a cattle drover. According to Webster's New World Dictionary, the word "drover" has two meanings: (1) a person who takes a drove of cattle to market, and (2) a cattle dealer. This occupation is worthy of mention because at this time, and for some time later, it was an important element in the marketing system. Many farmers drove their own livestock; but as distances lengthened this became more of a problem. Additionally, some preferred to sell at home for a known price and let the professional drover carry the risk from there on. As the definition indicates, drovers would drive farmers' livestock to market for a fee; or, acting as dealers, they would buy livestock from farmers and market them on their own account. The definition given above implies that droving applied only to cattle. While used most extensively for cattle, it also was used to some extent for hogs and sheep and, in some cases, even for turkeys.

From a dealer's standpoint, droving was a risky profession. Market information was almost nonexistent; there were physical hazards on the trail; and marketing consisted basically of locating a slaughterer who wanted livestock at that particular time—at best an uncertain proposition. Nevertheless, drovers continued to be a significant link in the marketing system until the advent of railroads and emergence of terminal markets.

Marketing apparently continued on an informal, unorganized basis until the mid-1700's although there is no question that the pace of activities and the volume of trading increased significantly with the passing years. While a number of cities emerged as market centers, Boston was particularly active and it was there, or nearby, that the formalities of organized marketing were first reported. This happened for meat a few years prior to live animals. In 1742 in Boston, a meat market known as Faneuil Hall was erected. Here "...the old-fashioned ways came to an end...Regulations were...voted regarding the quality of meat sold and as a result both the producer and consumer were greatly aided" (Clemen 1923). The thriving meat market fostered the meat packing business and this, in turn, fostered livestock marketing in the vicinity—or possibly the order of causation was reversed. In any event, the Brighton, Mass., Market is cited as a leader. Brighton is now a part of the Greater Boston area. This market was established by Jonathan Winship, who "...established a large slaughter house there, and producers of beef cattle soon began to find their way to this place to effect a sale. Other butchers came here to compete with him in making purchases, and in a short time the business became centered here, Mr. Winship having wisely encouraged and fostered it. This is believed to have occurred at the time of the old French War (1756) or very soon after. From that time this was the cattle market of New England...

"Brighton Market was the model for many others in the East and later in the West. [It was] ...an example of the old-fashioned market institution which was the forerunner of the great, modern centralized livestock market..." (Clemen 1923).

Following the War of Independence, settlement rapidly spread westward over the Allegheny Mountains and into the rich Ohio Valley. Shortly after the beginning of the 19th Century the center of livestock production shifted to this region. Droving continued as a means of transporting cattle to eastern markets. The distances, however, necessitated development of the packing industry, particularly for hogs. The activity originally centered at Cincinnati, which became known as "Porkopolis." Not only was Cincinnati in the heart of a rich production area, but it also was on the Ohio River. River transport down the Ohio and Mississippi provided an outlet for livestock and meat to southern cities and for export. As livestock production spread westward, the packing industry also spread and the packing of beef increased with the westward movement, although at this stage beef packing was limited. As production spread into Illinois and beyond, the distances to eastern markets became too great for the droving of fat cattle. This necessitated the movement of stock cattle eastward for finishing in Ohio or beyond. But New England no longer could successfully compete with the west in fattening cattle and was rapidly being industrialized. Simultaneously the south was specializing in cotton.

The region now known as the Corn Belt virtually took over livestock production. But the southern meat market soon proved to be the most lucrative, and the movement of meat and livestock down the Ohio and

Mississippi rivers increased to the detriment of eastern markets. This provided a stimulus for eastern interests to promote improved transportation to the east. Canal construction was greatly expanded during the first half of the 1800's and canals became important links in the transport system. Private toll roads and public roads were pushed throughout the settled area. But more importantly, the drive for trade gave a great impetus to railroad construction. By the 1850's railroads had reopened the eastern meat trade and quickened the pace of livestock-meat industry expansion.

It was about this time that livestock auctions gained recognition. The auction method, of course, was not new. It had been used in Great Britain for centuries. Early American colonists used auctions to some extent, but apparently they were not used extensively for livestock. Auction marketing was reported with development in the Ohio Valley. The first mentioned was the Ohio Company for Importing English Cattle, in 1836 (Henlein 1959). Others were organized in the following 25 yr or so in Ohio and Kentucky in connection with the sale of imported purebred cattle (Henlein 1959). And Clemen (1923) reported that they were used for cattle, mules, jacks, jennies, horses, sheep and swine. The extent of auction marketing is not specifically reported. However, after a relatively short period of growth this method waned for new factors were shaping the marketing system. Among these were the influence of railroads in association with locational aspects of production and a growing need for yarding facilities at points of assembly.

The railroads were pushed through the Ohio, Mississippi, and Missouri River Valleys. With an ever-growing volume of livestock, drovers and shippers were finding it increasingly inconvenient that no public stockyards were available for holding stock during its sale. Earlier, this was a minor problem as stock generally could be sold upon arrival; but with time this changed. One privately-operated yard, the Bull's Head Market, was reported in Chicago as early as 1848. By the early 1860's each of the five major railroads serving Chicago had constructed yards individually as an enticement of business. Livestock was a major source of freight revenue. A multiplicity of railroads converging in Chicago from the heavy production areas to the west and south soon made Chicago the major market center.

Another simultaneous development of major significance about this time was the emergence of the livestock commission agent. Prior to this the owner (drover or farmer) acted as his own agent in selling. This was time-consuming and owners were often ill-informed on market conditions. Drovers undoubtedly could see that use of an agent would relieve them of expenses of accompanying livestock to market and allow them more time to solicit business. Another advantage to drovers and farmers lay in financing. Commission firms were able to remit full receipts upon sale of livestock, while drovers formerly bought on credit and sold on credit with delayed payment all down the line. The first bona fide livestock commission firm began operation in

Chicago in 1857 (Clemen 1923). This must be considered a major milestone in livestock marketing.

The Civil War (1861-1865) brought on unprecendented demands for meat. Many rail-oriented markets were operating by this time but Chicago was the greatest in volume. However, it was painfully apparent that the individually rail-owned stockyards, scattered about the city, were inadequate and inefficient from both an operational and pricing standpoint. Buyers could be at only one yard at a time. Shippers often had only one choice of rail line and ran the risk of arrival at a yard devoid of buyers. This was soon remedied. At the urging of virtually all interests—although a trifle belatedly on the part of railroad officials—the Illinois legislature in 1865 incorporated the Union Stockyards and Transit Company. This was a single facility to accommodate all rail lines and it served as the model of public terminal livestock markets for many other cities. Thus, the tendency toward centralization of marketing, which already was moving under individual auspices, received a shot-in-the-arm through public sponsorship. At that time Chicago had all the ingredients for a great market, a position it held for many years. Railroads converged on Chicago from the tremendously productive regions to the west and south, directing livestock into the city like an enormous funnel. The Union Stockyards provided physical facilities for handling the stock, and rapid expansion of slaughtering and processing plants provided packing capacity. Outgoing rail and water transportation facilitated shipments of meat and reshipment of live animals. And credit resources were available to finance necessary investments and operations.

Other centrally-located cities also possessed certain advantageous attributes and quickly came to prominence as terminal markets. Among these were East St. Louis, Kansas City, Wichita, St. Joseph, Omaha, Sioux City, and Indianapolis, to mention only a few. The stream of cattle flowing into these markets by this time had gained additional sources of supply. These were the vast range lands of the Southern Plains States and the Southwest. The Northern Plains States followed in a short time. Droving continued to be a vital link, for the railroads had not yet penetrated that far. Figure 2.1 shows the principal trails over which thousands of cattle were driven to reach these markets.

Prior to the Civil War, cattle production in Texas had expanded faster than available markets warranted. Southern coastal cities provided about the only outlets beyond the state itself and these outlets were severely restricted by monopoly tactics of shipping interests. With the outbreak of the Civil War these markets were virtually eliminated. The cattle industry of Texas suffered a severe depression. Wartime demands inflated the price of cattle in eastern markets, while range prices dropped. This, of course, provided a tremendous incentive for the range cattlemen to reach the lucrative eastern markets. The only alternative was on foot to a rail head. Many obstacles lay in the way, but

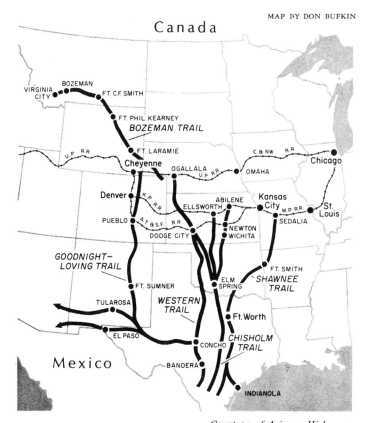

MAP BY DON BUFKIN

Courtesy of Arizona Highways
FIG. 2.1. MAP OF THE PRINCIPAL CATTLE DRIVES

in time they were overcome. Trails were established and thousands of cattle were delivered. As the rails were extended, the drives shortened, so by about 1880 this era ended. In the process, however, some of the loading points (which also were market points like Abilene and Dodge City) gained fame and a sort of notoriety that seems destined to continue.[2]

The year 1857, mentioned earlier as the beginning of commission firm operation, also marked the inauguration of another innovation of incalculable significance. Summer meat packing made its debut by use of natural ice refrigeration. The use of natural ice had obvious limitations but it soon was augmented by artificially-produced ice and this, in turn, by mechanical refrigeration. The use of mechanical refrigeration was well established by 1890 (Ives 1966). The use of refrigeration revolutionized the meat packing industry.

[2] For an interesting account of this period see *Historic Sketches of the Cattle Trade of the West and Southwest* by Joseph G. McCoy published in 1874 by Ramsey, Millet and Hudson of Kansas City and reprinted in 1932 by the Rare Book Shop, Washington, D.C.

It could now be a year-round business, which added greatly to operational efficiency. Storage and shipment of fresh meat became possible and feasible. Not only was the quantity of meat available increased on an annual basis, but the quality also was enhanced which undoubtedly boosted demand. Recognition of quality, however, did not come about automatically. Eastern packers were averse to inshipments of fresh western beef. Railroads had cattle cars, but not refrigerated box cars, and they resisted change. Rumors were spread of objectionable quality and unwholesomeness of refrigerated meat. There may have been some basis for this at the beginning, but techniques were soon perfected. Year-round markets were opened for producers, although the seasonality of production was to continue—and continues to this date at an abating rate.

Centralized terminal marketing remained the dominant method until after World War I. However, even before that, other factors were at work which were to verify the proposition that, in the world of economics, "things never stay put for long." Improved varieties permitted the northwesternly expansion of corn production. Consistent with previous tendencies, the packing industry was prone to follow livestock production. A number of other factors were involved in this movement but probably the most significant was expanded use of motor trucks and improvements of roads and highways. A sharp drop in livestock prices following World War I made farmers relatively cost-conscious and more critical of marketing charges and practices at terminals. Improvements in market news services and adoption of grade standards made possible a wider dissemination of market information (Duddy and Revzan 1938). The trend toward decentralization of markets became obvious following the close of World War II and is continuing to date. As packing plants were constructed nearer to the point of production, producers tended to revert to direct marketing of slaughter livestock. The movement initially was much more extensive with hogs than with cattle or sheep. In later years it has spread more and more to cattle and sheep. This movement is particularly apparent with the expansion of finished cattle production in the southwest, on the west coast and in the Southern Plains States. It is significant that in May, 1970, Chicago, the former "hog butcher of the world," stopped accepting hogs at the Union Stockyards. Trading in cattle and sheep ceased in August, 1971.

Auction markets which were known in colonial times and came on with a flurry about the mid-1800's, only to fade into obscurity, came back in a big way following World War I. While of only limited use for slaughter livestock (there are exceptions to this), they assumed significant proportions in the marketing of feeder livestock and cull cows. The 1930's was a period of very rapid expansion, with a slowing of the growth rate during the 1940's and a slight decline in the number of auctions during the 1950's. Annual data are not available but it appears that the number of livestock marketed through auctions has tended to stabilize in recent years.

During the period since World War I structural changes at the retail level have changed materially the wholesale and retail system of meat marketing. This was associated with the emergence of large chain supermarkets and their influence on the relative competitive position of retailers versus packers. Their attempt to obtain a steady supply of uniform quality meat has been felt back through channels (through packers to the producer level). The increase in bargaining power of the retail sector, as exemplified by chain stores, is a near reversal of the situation prior to World War II.

Producers have always been concerned with their relative position in bargaining. This concern has come to the foreground with particular emphasis during the last decade. Farm organizations are attempting, by various means, to improve their bargaining position. This will be discussed in some detail in a later chapter.

Over the years the import-export balance also has reversed itself. While there was considerable variation in earlier periods, exports were an important element in the livestock-meat industry during the latter half of the 1800's. From that time on, however, exports dwindled and, with the exception of war periods, were a minor fraction of total meat production, but did remain of major proportions for certain items, such as lard, variety meats, and hides. In recent years, however, the United States has become a major importer of meat. The livestock interests have been instrumental in the passage of national legislation designed to limit imports. This continues to be a matter of national concern.

As stated at the beginning of this chapter, only a panoramic view was intended. The objective was to show major historical changes that have occurred in the evolution of our livestock and meat marketing system and relate to these changes the circumstances or forces which were associated with the changes. The brief outline presented here omits many details. A detailed historical review would constitute a volume in itself.

It is obvious that change has characterized the livestock-meat industry. It is a dynamic industry. If the past is any criterion of the future, we can look for more change.

BIBLIOGRAPHY

CLEMEN, R. A. 1923. The American Livestock and Meat Industry. Ronald Press, New York.

DUDDY, E. E. and REVZAN, D. A. 1938. The Changing Relative Importance of the Central Livestock Market. University of Chicago Press, Chicago.

HENLEIN, P. C. 1959. Cattle Kingdom in the Ohio Valley, 1783-1860. University of Kentucky Press, Lexington.

IVES, J. R. 1966. The Livestock and Meat Economy of the United States. American Meat Institute, Chicago.

THOMPSON, J. W. 1942. A history of livestock raising in the United States, 1607-1860. USDA Agr. History Ser. *5*, 1, 14-15, 37, 54, 108.

USDA. 1966. Agricultural markets in change. USDA, Econ. Res. Serv., Agr. Econ. Rept. *95*, July.

WENTWORTH, E. N. 1948. America's Sheep Trails. Iowa State College Press, Ames.

WILLIAMS, W. F., and STOUT, T. T. 1964. Economics of the Livestock-Meat Industry. Macmillan Co., New York.

CHAPTER 3

Economic Theory and Principles

Use of the word "theory" has a tendency to disturb many people who have only a layman's concept of its meaning. One way to avoid an issue on the point would be to avoid use of the word. But it is a perfectly legitimate word and in an academic setting, at least, there is justification for common agreement on its meaning. In the vernacular, theory has come to be synonymous with "impractical" or "nonfactual." This is a totally distorted view from the standpoint of a scientist, and this would hold for scientists of any discipline, be it economics, chemistry, animal science, physics, etc. In briefest terms "theory" to a scientist is a "systematic explanation." It is an explanation " . . . which describes the workings and interrelationships of the various aspects of some phenomenon" (Baumol 1961). Used in this sense it would be contradictory to label theory as impractical, per se. If a theory gives an accurate explanation, it by definition cannot be classed as nonfactual. A determination of whether it is practical or feasible may require additional analysis.

There is no guarantee, of course, that every theory is a satisfactory or adequate explanation. In some instances it simply can be bad theory—an inaccurate explanation. But this is not equivalent to being impractical or nonfactual. In other cases a theory may appear to be an adequate explanation of a phenomenon, given the state of knowledge at that point in time, but turn out to be inaccurate or inadequate at a later time when additional knowledge is available. Many such examples exist in the physical and biological sciences. Before man landed on the moon various "theories" had been advanced regarding the nature of its matter and origin. The moon landings produced evidence which showed that some of these theories were wrong.

In economics it is recognized that some of the theoretical models of various market situations do not precisely correspond to the real world. The widely-used, perfectly competitive model is an example.[1] It is an abstraction of the real world—a simplified model used as an illustration of certain principles and as a guideline or benchmark with which other market situations may be compared.

In a previous chapter a quote was presented which indicated that the traditional, relatively impersonal market is fading away. By implication this means we are drifting toward a situation where more prices and terms of trade are being set by negotiation, formula, or some other institutional arrangement.

[1] It is assumed that readers have a knowledge of elementary economics. Readers who have not had recent work in economics should review a modern elementary text on price theory.

The markets for a number of agricultural commodities already have faded considerably from the traditional, impersonal, free, and open market. Examples are milk, eggs, and a number of fruits, vegetables, and specialty crops. These are commodities marketed under federal or state marketing orders and agreements. To a degree, farm price support programs also have altered the working of the traditional market. This is an example of an attempt to set up an institutional arrangement (i.e., the support program) within the traditional market—to supplement without eliminating or replacing it.

Livestock marketing is influenced to a lesser degree by personal or institutional arrangements than are other major agricultural commodities. However, even here some contracting is being done by farm organizations and individuals under negotiated conditions. In the wholesale meat trade substantial quantities are sold by formula. These arrangements do not obviate the need for a knowledge of economic principles. When negotiators sit down around the bargaining table or individuals take it upon themselves to do their own buying and selling, the need for an understanding of economic theory and principles is as great as it is in the free and open market, if not more so. Foremost among marketing theories are those which explain the relationships between demand and supply.

THEORY OF DEMAND

Demand—the Concept

"Demand" is another word that means different things to different people. During periods when prices of, say slaughter steers, are increasing or are at a relatively high level, one often hears the comment that "demand is high." Conversely when prices are low the comment may be that "demand is low" or "demand is dropping." Under certain circumstances these comments may be partially correct but they are loose, nontechnical concepts of demand. For effective communication among market analysts and for consistent use in economic analysis we need a precise, rigorous meaning. Fortunately, there is an accepted definition: Demand is the functional relationship between prices and quantities of a product that consumers will purchase in a specified market, ceteris paribus. Note that "prices" and "quantities" are used in the plural. "Ceteris paribus" refers to the assumption that all other factors—in addition to price—that can influence the quantity purchased, remain unchanged. Under this definition demand is a series of prices and quantities, not just the quantity at a particular price or the amount of money spent for some particular quantity. One of the earliest axioms established in economics was that an inverse relationship exists between quantities taken by consumers and prices of a product. Or to put it another way, consumers will buy more at lower prices than at higher prices. This is the law of demand.

The "functional relationship" may be expressed (1) in table form often referred to as a schedule, (2) as a mathematical function or (3) in graphic form. For example, the prices at which consumers will purchase various quantities of a hypothetical product may be expressed in schedule form as follows:

Price per unit $	Quantity
1.00	180
2.00	160
3.00	140
4.00	120
5.00	100
6.00	80
7.00	60
8.00	40
9.00	20

If we consider that the quantity consumed is a function of price (i.e., that quantity purchased depends upon price), by rather elementary mathematical calculations we can "fit" a function to the above data. It would be as follows:

In general form $Q = f(P)$
In specific form $Q = 200-20P$
where Q = quantity, and
P = price

This series of prices and quantities also can be shown in graphic form as in Fig. 3.1 where line D_1-D_1 is a demand curve illustrating this functional relationship.

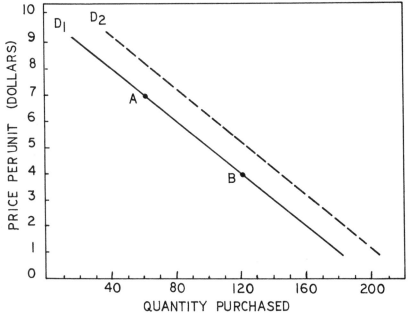

FIG. 3.1. HYPOTHETICAL DEMAND CURVES

The above three forms of expression simply are different ways of presenting the same data—the same functional relationship. All three are used extensively in economics.

Conceptually we speak of individual demand and aggregate or market demand. The latter simply is the sum of the demands of individuals who make up the market.

The ceteris paribus condition, "other factors being equal or unchanged," requires some clarification. It is obvious that price is not the only factor which determines the quantity of goods consumers buy. Among the more important "other factors" are: population (the number of buyers); income levels (the purchasing power of buyers); personal preferences or tastes; the price, quality, and availability of substitute or complementary products that compete with the product under consideration for the buyer's dollar; buyer's expectations of future prices of the product under consideration and his expectation of prices for substitute or complementary products. What we mean by the ceteris paribus assumption is that at a given time in a given market these things will be at some observable level. Their effect upon quantities purchased will be incorporated in the price-quantity relationship, but at that time the only thing which is considered to vary is price. We want to know the effect on quantity purchased due solely to price variation when everything else is constant.

This does not mean that we are uninterested in the effect "other factors" have on quantity purchased. On the contrary, we are intensely interested and also try hard to determine the relationships between these factors and quantity purchased. In economic parlance they are called "demand shifters" or it may be said that a change in one (or more) of these factors results in a "change in demand" or a "shift in demand." A change in the factor implies that some time elapses from one set of ceteris paribus conditions to another.

Using the same data presented in the previous illustrations, let curve D_1-D_1 in Fig. 3.1 represent a demand curve where all the so-called demand shifters are at some given level. Points A and B do *not* represent different demands, nor do the different locations of A and B represent change in demand. They both are on the same demand curve. What these points mean is that at $6.00 per unit, buyers will purchase 80 units, but *if* the price were $4.00 they would purchase 120 units. They simply represent 2, among an infinite number of price-quantity relationships on that demand curve, only 1 of which could be realized in a given market at 1 time.

Now, assume that some time elapses and incomes of buyers increase. With higher incomes buyers would be expected to pay higher prices for any specified quantity (or what amounts to the same thing, purchase a greater quantity at any specified price). Buyers may now purchase 90 units at $6.00 per unit where originally they would have purchased only 80 units, or at

$4.00 per unit they may now purchase 130 units where originally they would have purchased only 120—and so on at other price levels. Thus, the change in income (the increase in income) shifted the entire demand curve from D_1-D_1 to D_2-D_2. The changed demand shows that greater quantities would be taken at all possible prices (or what amounts to the same thing, higher prices now would be paid for all possible quantities). In this example it was considered that only income increased. But the same reaction could occur from changes in any one or any combination of the demand shifters. (An increase in demand is indicated by a shift to the right on the graph—a decrease would show up as a shift to the left.)

Population in the United States has increased year by year, providing one of the most stable and important shifters (increasers) in the demand for farm products. On the average, per capita personal disposable incomes have increased fairly consistently for a number of years. Studies show that consumers have a strong tendency to increase purchases of beef as incomes increase, but the same relationship does not hold for pork. These relationships will be discussed in some detail at a later point.

Derived Demand

Consumer demand for meat makes itself felt at the retail level—at the supermarket. To be more specific, a demand exists for each separate cut of meat. How is this demand transmitted to livestock producers? From the farmer's standpoint, the demand for slaughter steers, for example, is a "derived demand"—that is, the demand derived from consumers' demand for beef. The aggregate retail value of all retail cuts establishes a value for the carcass at the packer level. The carcass value, in turn, establishes the value of the live steer. The same sort of derived demand exists for hogs and lamb and, as a matter of fact, for the various classes, grades, and weights of animals within each species.

This is an oversimplified statement, but it contains the essential features of the concept of derived demand. It is obvious in this situation that the degree of pricing efficiency throughout market channels is of considerable importance in transmitting to producers the demands of consumers.

Elasticity of Demand

A knowledge of the functional relationship that exists between prices and quantities of a particular product is valuable to market analysts. But probably of even more importance is a measure of the degree of sensitivity of change in quantity purchased occasioned by a change of price. This is·what is meant by elasticity. Traditionally, in the study of demand we have taken quantity as the dependent variable.[2] In the study of price elasticity we are interested in determining the percentage change in quantity purchased, occasioned by (or associated with) a specified percentage (say 1%, or 10%) change in price. Of major importance, also, is income elasticity which is the percentage change in expenditures for a product (or quantity purchased, depending upon model used by the researcher) associated with a specified change in income. And still another elasticity concept of substantial importance is cross elasticity. An excellent example of cross elasticity of direct interest among livestock producers is this: What effect would a decrease in pork prices have on the quantity of beef purchased by consumers, assuming beef prices remain unchanged? Thus, there are three concepts of elasticity to be noted (1) price elasticity, which if written fully and more precisely would read, "price elasticity of demand," but normally is shortened to price elasticity, (2) income elasticity, which again more precisely would be written as "income elasticity of demand," and (3) cross elasticity, a cross-price elasticity.

Price Elasticity.—The importance of price elasticity lies in its association with total revenue (i.e., total expenditures of purchasers). Total revenue is the total amount of money spent by consumers for a product. It is the total of product times quantity purchased (or sold). If, for the moment, we ignored costs of production it would be apparent that the sellers of a product would want to maximize total revenue received. It readily can be shown that under conditions of an elastic demand, total revenue can be increased by cutting price (or by increasing the quantity for sale, which amounts to the same thing viewed from a different angle). If demand is elastic, a given cut in price will result in a more than proportionate increase in quantity sold, and hence, an increase in revenue.

Before proceeding, we must present methods of calculating elasticity and clarify some terms. Price elasticity is calculated as a numerical measure which is referred to as the coefficient of price elasticity. It is calculated by dividing percentage change in quantity by the associated percentage change in price, or

$$e_{D/P} = \frac{\%\Delta Q}{\%\Delta P}$$

where $e_{D/P}$ = coefficient of price elasticity of demand
Δ = change
Q = quantity
P = price

Thus, $e_{D/P}$ is a ratio of the two percentage changes. The sign of the ratio normally is expected to be negative since price and quantity usually move in

[2] It may be noted that in graphic analysis the vertical axis traditionally is used for the dependent variable. But in graphing demand curves it is conventional to put price on the vertical axis. In a sense this is inconsistent. However, there is nothing sacred about these conventions. The graph would be equally valid one way as the other. Our major concern is with the relationship between variables—not which one is the dependent variable or which axis is used for one or the other.

PRICE PER UNIT

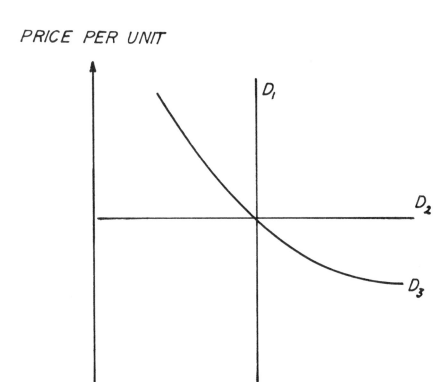

QUANTITY PURCHASED

FIG. 3.2. ILLUSTRATION OF DIFFERENT DEGREES OF PRICE ELASTICITY

opposite directions. This was referred to earlier as an inverse relationship. Some authors omit the sign of the elasticity coefficient—it is universally understood to be negative. The magnitude of the coefficient can range from zero to infinity (negative infinity). If price changes were associated with no change in quantity purchased, elasticity would be zero or perfectly inelastic. Graphically this would be a vertical line (curve) such as D_1 in Fig. 3.2. This might be visualized as some unique, absolutely necessary product, but a case this extreme is unlikely. If an unlimited quantity would be purchased at a given price, elasticity would be infinite or perfectly elastic. This would show up as a horizontal curve (see D_2 Fig. 3.2). Viewed from the standpoint of an individual farmer, this is the situation he faces in selling most products. No individual hog producer, for example, sells enough hogs to influence the price. For all practical purposes, any one farmer can sell all the hogs he may have without depressing prices. In the aggregate, however, prices and quantities normally move in opposite directions.[3] Most demand curves fall somewhere between the limiting extremes—sloping downward to the right on a graph—such as D_2 in Fig. 3.2. Within this in-between area is a dividing line which separates the "relatively elastic" (often shortened simply to "elastic") from the "relatively inelastic" (often shortened to "inelastic"). The separation occurs at an elasticity of −1.0, or unit elasticity. This would occur where percentage change in quantity was exactly equal to the percentage change in price. Here demand would be unitarily elastic. For example, if a 5% decrease in quantity was associated with a 5% increase in price, price elasticity would be −1.0; that is

$$^e D/P = \frac{-5.0}{5.0} = -1.0$$

Here the change in price is exactly offset by the change in quantity purchased. This situation can occur where a firm or family budgets a certain amount of money for a given item and sticks to the budget whether prices rise or fall.

For those with a knowledge of the calculus, determination of the coefficient of price elasticity is a simple calculation, providing the mathematical function is known. For illustration purposes we use the demand function presented earlier, i.e., $Q = 200 - 20P$. The formula for calculating elasticity is

$$^e D/P = \frac{dQ}{dP} \frac{P}{Q}$$

where $\frac{dQ}{dP}$ = the first derivative of Q with respect to P (from the demand function).

   P = price (any relevant, specified price)
   Q = quantity consumers would purchase at the specified price

For the demand function used here $\frac{dQ}{dP} = -20$. With this, the formula becomes $^e D/P = -20 \frac{P}{Q}$ and we simply plug in applicable pairs of P and Q. A number of relevant price-quantity pairs were shown earlier. Others may be calculated by inserting any relevant price in the demand function and calculating its associated Q. We complete the illustration by calculating $^e D/P$ where P = $6.00 and Q = 80 units:

$$^e D/P = -20 \frac{6.00}{80} = -1.50$$

Thus, $^e D/P$ is −1.50 at the point on the demand curve where P = $6.00 and Q = 80.

To calculate $^e D/P$ at another point we take P = $2.00 and Q = 160:

$$^e D/P = -20 \frac{2.00}{160} = -0.25$$

---

[3] There are exceptions to the normal situation. Some goods with high "snob" appeal sell greater quantities at higher prices than at lower prices. These cases are rare and are of no concern to this discussion.

These two calculations should serve to show that the coefficient of elasticity may vary at different points on the same demand curve. This is further illustrated in Table 3.1 where the coefficient of elasticity is shown for nine points on the demand curve. The coefficient varies from one point to another. On only one unique type of demand curve—the rectangular hyperbola—does elasticity remain constant throughout the entire curve.

For those who do not have a knowledge of the calculus, the coefficients can be calculated by elementary arithmetic, again providing the demand schedule is known. For illustrative purposes we will use the schedule of prices and quantities in Table 3.1, which is the same schedule presented earlier. In this case we assume a movement from one point on the demand schedule to

TABLE 3.1
HYPOTHETICAL PRICE, QUANTITY, ELASTICITY, AND TOTAL
VALUE RELATIONSHIPS

Price ($)	Quantity	Coefficient of Elasticity	Total Revenue ($)
9.00	20	−9.00	180
8.00	40	−4.00	320
7.00	60	−2.33	420
6.00	80	−1.50	480
5.00	100	−1.00	500
4.00	120	−0.67	480
3.00	140	−0.43	420
2.00	160	−0.25	320
1.00	180	−0.11	180

another point, calculate the percentage change in price and the percentage change in quantity, then divide percentage change in quantity by percentage change in price. This is the ratio that produces the coefficient of price elasticity. The formula is:

$$e_{D/P} = \frac{\dfrac{Q_2 - Q_1}{Q_2 + Q_1}}{\dfrac{P_2 - P_1}{P_2 + P_1}} = \frac{\%\Delta Q}{\%\Delta P}$$

where Q_1 = quantity before change
Q_2 = quantity after change
P_1 = price before change
P_2 = price after change, and
Δ = change

To complete this illustration we shall assume price and quantity were: price = $6.00 and its associated quantity = 80 units before change; then price drops to $5.00 which has a corresponding quantity of 100 units

$$e_{D/P} = \frac{\dfrac{100 - 80}{100 + 80}}{\dfrac{5.00 - 6.00}{5.00 + 6.00}} = \frac{\dfrac{20}{180}}{\dfrac{-1.00}{11.00}} = -1.22$$

The same procedure could be repeated at alternative places on the demand schedule to obtain measures of price elasticity throughout the schedule.

As pointed out in elementary economics, this is a measure of "arc elasticity." It represents an arc, or area, of the demand curve rather than a point as was obtained by the method involving the calculus. The method involving calculus is more precise and therefore considered to be preferable but is not necessary for an understanding of the concept.

Any coefficient of elasticity within the range 0 to −1.0 (noninclusive) is classified as relatively inelastic. Any coefficient greater than −1.0 is classified as relatively elastic. These two categories encompass virtually all goods and services that enter market transactions. Some elementary graphic explanations of elasticity purport to show that a steeply sloped demand curve is inelastic and that a gently sloped curve is elastic. This can be misleading. The slope of a curve is not equivalent to elasticity. The linear (straight line) demand curve drawn on arithmetic graph paper will have the same slope throughout its entire length, but when elasticity is calculated at various points along that demand curve it is found that the coefficient changes continuously throughout the length. Do not confuse slope with elasticity.

It was mentioned earlier that total revenue is associated with elasticity. The price-quantity schedule presented earlier is repeated in Table 3.1 along with calculations of the coefficient of elasticity and total revenue at various points throughout the demand schedule. Note that the coefficient of elasticity varies throughout the demand schedule. It ranges from −9.00 to −0.11. The schedule became less elastic with movement from higher prices (lower quantities) to lower prices (higher quantities). Total revenue also varies. It rises from $180 to a peak at $500 and then declines to $180 again. Note that total revenue rises until elasticity reaches unity. As the coefficient becomes less than unity, total revenue decreases. The lesson to be learned here is that a firm, or an industry, which has (or which can obtain) sufficient control over prices *or* production can maximize total revenue by proper manipulation of these variables. If demand is relatively elastic it can, by cutting prices, increase sales and total revenue up to the point where demand becomes unitarily elastic. If it is operating in an inelastic demand it can increase total revenue by raising the price and cutting back the quantity offered for sale, to the point where demand becomes unitarily elastic.

Maximization of total revenue does not automatically maximize profits. The firm or industry also would need a knowledge of cost behavior to maximize profits. Generally, a reduction in production would not increase per unit costs. An increase in production could lead to higher, lower, or constant cost per unit depending upon characteristics of the cost functions of that particular firm or industry.

The price elasticity faced by individual firms is greater than that faced by an entire industry. This clearly is the case for farmers. Individual farmers face a perfectly elastic demand for hogs, or cattle, or corn, etc., but the demand faced by any one of these sectors of the entire industry is substantially less. Demand at retail ordinarily is greater than at any earlier stage in the marketing-production process. For instance, the price elasticity for ham or pork chops is greater than for hogs at the farm level.

Income Elasticity.—The concept of income elasticity is analagous to that of price elasticity in that it refers to sensitivity of change in expenditures for a product associated with a change in income, everything else remaining constant. It is known that as incomes increase, consumers will buy more of some products, but less of others. Products that fall in the former category are classed as superior products while those in the latter are classed as inferior products. Hamburger may be considered an inferior product by people who already have relatively high incomes. That is, they probably would eat less hamburger with further increases in income. But people in low income brackets likely would increase hamburger consumption if their incomes were increased. To the latter, hamburger is a superior product.

Studies several years ago showed pork to be an inferior product on the basis of average incomes in the United States. This presumably was associated with an image (at that time) of pork as a relatively fat cut of meat. This means that consumers would spend less for pork as average income increased. With substantial improvement in quality of pork in recent years it is possible that consumers would now react differently than they did at an earlier period. This problem points up the difficulty in empirical studies of distinguishing the effect of income from the effect of consumer preferences or tastes.

Livestock producers and meat marketers obviously have no direct control over consumer incomes. Indirectly they have some control in fostering (or opposing) national economic policy that may have an impact on employment and wage rates. On the other hand, producers and marketers do have direct control in improvement of the quality of a product which may, in turn, improve its income elasticity. In a sense, this is changing the product rather than changing the income elasticity, but the net result to producers and marketers may be the same.

The coefficient of income elasticity is calculated in a manner similar to that of price elasticity. The formula for income elasticity by the arithmetic method is:

$$e_{D/I} = \frac{\%\Delta E}{\%\Delta I}$$

where $e_{D/I}$ = coefficient of income elasticity of demand
Δ = change
E = expenditures (for a specified product)
I = income

By use of the calculus the formula is:

$$e_{D/I} = \frac{dE}{dI} \frac{I}{E}$$

FIG. 3.3. CROSS RELATIONSHIPS BETWEEN GOOD X AND GOOD Y

The sign of the coefficient is positive for superior products and negative for inferior products.

Cross Elasticity.—Cross elasticity refers to price-quantity relationships between or among different products. As mentioned earlier, beef producers are interested in knowing what will happen to the quantity of beef purchased if the price of hogs declines. Beef and pork are "substitutes" for one another, or in other words, they are competing products. It is not enough simply to know that a drop in pork prices will hurt beef consumption and cause a lowering of beef prices. A market analyst needs to know in quantitative terms how much a specified drop in hog prices (say 10%) will affect beef consumption and beef prices. The general relationship between substitute products is shown by curve A, Fig. 3.3. If products are substitutes, an increase in the price of product Y will result in increased purchases of product X, assuming no change in the price of product.

While the vast majority of products are substitutes in a greater or lesser degree, this is not true of all. Some products are "complementary." In this case, an increase in the price of product Y will be associated with a decrease in the purchase of product X (see curve B, Fig. 3.3). Automobiles and gasoline provide an example. An increase in the price of automobiles would be expected to result in decreased sales of gasoline, because fewer autos would be sold and hence less gasoline would be needed. A decrease in the price of sweet corn probably would lead to an increase in purchases of butter (or margarine). More sweet corn would be sold and since most people butter sweet corn, more butter would be purchased. Included in this category also are "joint" products. Beef and cattle hides are joint products. An increase in the price of beef (assuming this would result in fewer cattle being purchased) would lead to fewer hides being sold. This could, of course, bring about a longer term effect. If the increased price of beef persisted, farmers and ranchers would be induced to produce more beef cattle and thus lead to increased sales (and purchases) of hides—though prices of both might decline in the process.

In another class are "supplementary" products. Supplements are products whose demands are unrelated. This means that the quantity purchased of product X has no relation to the price of product Y (curve C in Fig. 3.3). Products that comprise a minor element in the purchases of a firm likely would fall into this category. Supplementary products are not of particular importance in this study of livestock and meat marketing.

THEORY OF SUPPLY

The concept of supply, like demand, is widely misunderstood. In a technical sense supply is the functional relationship between prices and the quantities of a product that producers are willing to place on a market. Like demand, this concept envisions a schedule of alternative prices and quantities which can be shown in Table form, as a mathematical function, or in graphic form. It also envisions the situation where quantity marketed is a function of price alone—all other factors which can influence the quantity marketed are assumed to be constant. In the calculations by which supply (and demand) functions are determined, these other factors are held constant by statistical processes. We logically expect a supply curve to have positive slope, i.e., we expect producers to place more of a given product on the market at relatively high prices than at lower prices. Figure 3.4 illustrates a supply curve.

A supply function looks like a demand function except for algebraic sign. Following is a hypothetical example:

$$Q = 1.45 P$$

The constant is omitted in this function to indicate that at zero price nothing would be marketed. The similarity of supply and demand functions may prompt the question of how one differentiates between the two. This is the so-called problem of "identification."

FIG. 3.4. HYPOTHETICAL SUPPLY CURVE

"Identification (Breimyer 1961) is the term given to the principle that few observed values are of either pure supply or pure demand. Price changes in the market place do not carry any labels accommodating to analysts which explain whether they were due to demand forces or supply forces. Elmer Working's (1927) article of more than 30 yr ago remains the basic reference. Working concerned himself with how to identify supply and demand forces as represented in statistical data, and with how to separate slopes of demand and supply curves from shifts in their positions.

" . . . as Working (1927) pointed out in his article on identification, it is not necessary that true demand and true supply curves be constructed if the analyst only wants a method that will help him forecast future trends in prices" (Breimyer 1961).

The concept of elasticity of supply is comparable in meaning to that of demand. Supply elasticity refers to the sensitivity of change in quantity marketed to specified changes in price. The formula for calculating elasticity of supply is the same as that for demands:

$$e_{S/P} = \frac{\%\Delta Q}{\%\Delta P}$$

where $e_{S/P}$ = coefficient of elasticity of supply
Δ = change
Q = quantity
P = price

By use of calculus, the formula is

$$^{e}S/P = \frac{dQ}{dP} \frac{P}{Q}$$

The coefficient of supply elasticity normally carries a positive sign while that of demand normally is negative. In some instances $^{e}S/P = O$. This can be the case if a certain stock of a product is available for a market and no more can be made available at any price. Here the supply would be perfectly inelastic. When the $^{e}S/P$ is less than 1 but greater than zero (i.e., $O < ^{e}S/P < 1$) supply is said to be relatively inelastic—usually referred to simply as "inelastic." When $^{e}S/P = 1$ the supply is unitarily elastic, and when $\infty > ^{e}S/P > 1$ the supply is said to be relatively elastic or simply "elastic." The limiting case on the upper end is $^{e}S/P = \infty$ or infinitely elastic. In this limiting case the quantity offered has no relation to price.

While the notion of supply abstracts from the effects of everything except price, it is well known that "other factors" do affect the quantity offered. These other factors are "supply shifters" and are conceptualized and handled in a manner comparable to demand shifters. Among the supply shifters are (1) technical innovations (improvements in physical input-output conditions), (2) changes in factor prices, (changes in prices of inputs), (3) development of new technology, and (4) changes in opportunity costs.

ORGANIZATIONAL CHARACTERISTICS

An area of market research which has received increasing attention in recent years is the study of market organization or market structure analysis. This approach holds that relationships exist between structural characteristics of an industry and the competitive behavior of firms in that industry, and beyond this, these attributes are associated with economic performance.

Performance is the critical issue. This was touched upon in Chap. 1 in the discussion of pricing efficiency and operational efficiency. Individual producers as well as the general public have a stake in this matter because the degree of efficiency attained affects producer prices and profits. It affects the costs to consumers, and thereby their real income; and it affects general resource utilization. Society as a whole has an interest in optimum utilization of resources. Performance has many other facets such as the degree of price stability in the industry, equitability of income distribution among people, degree of economic progress, and level of employment.

There is substantial evidence that, for decades, farmers have been dissatisfied with the economic performance of markets for farm products. Of recent origin is the National Farmers Organization (NFO) which was organized in an attempt to improve farm income. The recent inauguration of the American National Cattlemen's Association CATTLE-FAX program is another example of an attempt to improve prices and incomes.[4] Through the years, history is

[4] The CATTLE-FAX and NFO programs will be discussed in later chapters.

replete with other examples, both private and public attempts to alleviate farm problems. To the extent that these problems are associated with structural characteristics and firm conduct or behavior, market structure analysis is a legitimate area of marketing.

Market Structure

Among the major structural characteristics of firms or an industry are: (1) Degree of concentration. This refers to the number of firms, size of firms, and their size-distribution. Is the industry composed of only a few large firms—such as automobile manufacturing? Is the industry composed of many firms, but dominated by a few large ones? Is the industry composed of many small firms? Economic theory indicates that such characteristics can influence output and profit rates. They also may influence income distribution, progressiveness of the industry, and other measures of performance.

The multitude of relatively small farmers does not have the control over output or of profits that the steel industry has, for example.

(2) Product differentiation. Do individual firms have the power, by advertising or otherwise, to convince consumers that their products are different from those of competitors? Is there a relation between the degree of concentration and the ability of firms to differentiate their products? Not only is farming characterized by a low degree of concentration, but its products are relatively homogenous. There is little opportunity for individual farmers to differentiate products. Exceptions occur such as purebred livestock breeders who have been able to show excellence in their stock. Citrus growers have been successful in differentiating "Sunkist" oranges as have walnut growers in marketing "Diamond" brand walnuts.

Processors of farm products, of course, make extensive use of brand names. This is particularly true in canned vegetables and fruits. Some large meat packers have successfully identified their brands of processed meat. Progress has been slow in differentiating fresh meat, although Swift & Co. apparently has made some headway with its Proten Beef[5] through an advertising campaign over a number of years.

While there are a few examples of differentiating agricultural products at the farm level (accomplished largely by farmer cooperatives) the vast bulk leaves the farm unbranded and undifferentiated. Outside of agriculture, differentiation is the rule.

(3) Barriers to entry into the industry. The relative ease (or difficulty) for a firm to gain entry into an industry is closely associated with degree of concentration. Traditionally, farming has been an industry with easy entry. Nearly anyone who wished could start farming. This no longer is true for commercial-sized farms. Capital requirements associated with economies of size necessitate large-scale financing that is not available to everyone.

[5] A registered trademark of Swift & Co.

In nonfarm sectors, successful differentiation of product by already-established firms may be an effective barrier to entry by new firms. In other instances absolute cost advantages and/or economies of scale already obtained by existing firms may prevent new firms from entering that industry.

Firms in an industry with effective barriers against new competitors exercise a different sort of behavior than firms in a highly competitive industry.

Market Conduct

Market conduct refers to the behavior of firms—the strategy they use (1) individually in competition with other firms, in purchasing inputs and selling output, and (2) in conjunction with other firms which may take the form of informal cooperation or collusion. The practices arising out of market strategy generally are related to price or product manipulation. The objective usually is to optimize profits.

Farmers acting individually, for all practical purposes, can exercise no positive market strategy. No one individual has any effective control over price, industry output, or differentiation of product. In contrast, where a few firms dominate an industry they can, by informal agreement or through collusion (explicit or tacit), exercise some degree of control over output and prices. They can differentiate products. They can divide the market. They can carry out advertising and promotional programs.

Market Performance

It has been apparent for years that, in the market arena, farmers have been operating at a competitive disadvantage relative to other economic sectors (Clodius 1959). The implication is that market structural characteristics are associated with the differences in conduct and performance. It follows that there are two logical approaches available to alleviate the situation: (1) make the nonagricultural sectors more like agriculture, i.e., make them conform more to the structure, conduct, and performance of the more highly competitive model that typifies agriculture, or (2) make agriculture more like the nonagricultural sectors, i.e., allow agriculture a degree of economic power more commensurate with that of nonagricultural sectors. There is nothing new or novel in these approaches. They have been discussed for decades. Over the years numerous actions on both approaches have been taken by both private and public (government) means. Among the public actions are freight rate regulations, antitrust laws, legislation aimed at unfair competition and price discrimination, farm price and income support legislation, specific legislation designed to regulate livestock marketing charges and to promote competition on public markets, laws providing for standardization in grading, laws that implemented market news reporting, specific restrictions on certain large meat packers under a "Consent Decree," and legislation which facilitated the organization of farmers' cooperatives. This is merely a sample of public actions which presumably were aimed at correcting or alleviating unsatisfactory conduct and performance of firms and industries. There are many more. Some are directly related to agriculture and some are not.

Private efforts on these problems probably are best exemplified by cooperatives. The organization of a farmer cooperative is recognition that a joint effort may provide farmers with some economic power where individually they have none. There are many types of cooperatives including some devoted exclusively to livestock marketing. The activities of the National Farmer's Organization are conducted as a cooperative effort.

A number of commodity-oriented organizations also illustrate private efforts. Among these are the National Swine Association with a check-off program for financing promotional programs, The American Sheep Producers Council with a similar program, and the American National Cattlemen's Association with its subscription-financed CATTLE-FAX.

There appears to be a growing recognition among livestock producers (and other farm sectors) that the eventual attainment of economic power (bargaining power) necessitates a joint effort in order to gain "countervailing power" (Galbraith 1952) in the market place. If this is an indication of the trend, it will mean a further fading of the impersonal open markets. Opportunities for joint efforts increase as the number of producers becomes smaller (and operations become larger)—a trend which has been in evidence for many years.

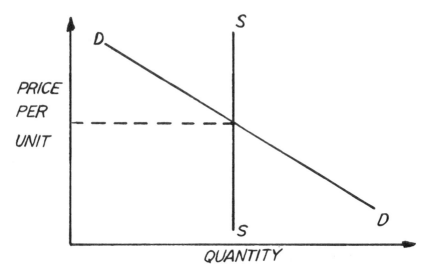

FIG. 3.5. SHORT-RUN EQUILIBRIUM PRICE, FIXED SUPPLY

PRICE FORMATION

Price formation is related to the degree of competition in the market. A considerable body of price theory has been developed covering perfect competition, oligopoly, duopoly, and monopoly. The available theory generally is satisfactory except for the case of oligopoly, i.e., an industry dominated by a relatively few large firms. Under these conditions it is difficult to generalize because the action one firm takes will depend upon the action his competitor takes. This can make price and output indeterminate except for special cases under rigid assumptions.

We present here only the basic concept of price formation as generated by the interaction of forces of demand and supply in a highly competitive market situation. It is noted, however, that institutional factors such as structural characteristics and market conduct discussed in the previous section may permit price modification or manipulation, particularly in the short term.

It sometimes is argued that the supply of livestock is relatively fixed for any given day or even for longer periods.[6] This is based on the assumption that for a short period there is a certain number of livestock on hand and price cannot influence that number. If this were the case, supply would show up on a graph as a perfectly inelastic, i.e., vertical curve. This is illustrated in Fig. 3.5. The aggregate demand almost always will be a negatively sloped curve (as D–D in Fig. 3.5) which will intersect the supply curve at some point. This point represents the market clearing price for that number of livestock.

The assumption of fixed supply, however, is not very realistic for livestock. Producers can withhold or rush livestock to some degree. Given some time they can make animals heavier or lighter depending on timing of marketing and variations in feeding programs. A positively sloping supply curve, even for the short period, probably is normal for livestock markets.

Normal, short-period industry supply and demand curves are shown in Fig. 3.6 Industries, of course, are made up of firms, and these industry supply-demand functions are derived from firm supply-demand functions. The intersection of D–D and S_1-S_1 mark the short-period equilibrium price, P_1, at which quantity Q_1 would clear the market. Demand and supply can shift as was discussed earlier. An increase in supply would shift the entire curve to the right as shown by S_2-S_2. If demand remained unchanged, the new point of intersection with D–D would be at a lower price, P_2, and an increased quantity, Q_2. A simultaneous increase in demand and supply can have offsetting effects on price, and an increase in demand without proportionate increase in supply can result in a higher price. It should be readily apparent that the effect on price of a change in either supply or demand will be related to the degree of elasticity associated with supply and demand.

[6] The fixed supply assumption may be appropriate for a commodity which is harvested at one particular time, thereby setting the quantity available for the subsequent year.

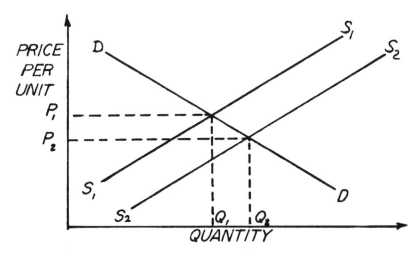

FIG. 3.6. SHORT-RUN EQUILIBRIUM PRICE, NORMAL SUPPLY FUNCTION

Over the long run, prices, under highly competitive conditions, are associated with long-run costs. Costs must be covered in the long run for firms to stay in business. Anything above normal profits would attract new firms. But it takes time for adjustments to be made. There are lags between the time decisions are made and carried out, and uncertainties exist even in the most competitive markets. Imperfections in the market system result in continuous price variations about a moving long-period equilibrium. Moving equilibrium has been compared to "...a man riding a bicycle" (Shepherd and Futrell 1969).

BIBLIOGRAPHY

BAUMOL, W. J. 1961. Economic Theory and Operations Analysis. Prentice-Hall, Englewood Cliffs, N. J.

BREIMYER, H. F. 1961. Demand and prices for meat. USDA Econ. Res. Serv. Tech. Bull. *1253*.

CLODIUS, R. L. 1959. Opportunities and limitations of improving bargaining power of farmers. *In* Problems and Policies of American Agriculture. Iowa State University Press, Ames.

GALBRAITH, J. K. 1952. American Capitalism—The Concept of Countervailing Power. Houghton Mifflin Co., Boston.

SHEPHERD, G. S., and FUTRELL, G. A. 1969. Marketing Farm Products, 5th Edition. Iowa State University Press, Ames.

WILLIAMS, W. F., and STOUT, T. T. 1964. Economics of the Livestock—Meat Industry. Macmillan Co., New York.

WORKING, E. J. 1927. What do statistical demand curves show? Quart. J. Econ. *XLI*, No. 2, 212-235.

CHAPTER 4

Livestock Production and Supply

Livestock market analysis necessitates a thorough knowledge of supply and demand conditions. It is important to know the current situation at any given time, but of greater importance is an understanding of trends and forces behind change. Knowledge of this sort provides a basis for anticipating or projecting future changes. Market outlook, a subject of substantial interest among producers, basically is an attempt to evaluate the impact of ever-changing market supply and demand factors on livestock prices. This chapter will examine some of the more important supply characteristics. A similar study of demand will be made in the following chapter.

GEOGRAPHIC DISTRIBUTION OF PRODUCTION

Cattle, hogs, and sheep are produced in every state but the geographical distribution is not uniform. Not only is the distribution different for each of the three species, but for a given specie the density of production varies substantially. The density of human population also varies. It is not surprising that the human population density does not correspond with livestock production, but the fact that this is so complicates the marketing system. For example, production of beef in the states east of the Mississippi River comprises 20% of total production, but the population in those states accounts for approximately 70% of total consumption of fed beef. Beef must be moved in vast quantities to satisfy this demand. In a general way, Fig. 4.1, 4.2, and 4.3 show the variation in relative geographic concentration of production for cattle, hogs, and sheep, respectively.

The location of areas of concentration follows the principle that governs industrial location. As a general rule, an area of concentrated production develops where that industry has a comparative advantage, or where it has the least comparative disadvantage. The availability and cost of inputs, transport charges on both inputs and outputs, and the location of existing and potential demand are controlling factors in industry location. Feed is by far the major input in livestock production. It almost is axiomatic that a region which possesses a comparative advantage in producing feed of a particular type also will have a comparative advantage in producing the specie and class of livestock adapted to the consumption of that feed.

Vast areas of range and pasture land, in the absence of irrigation, are adapted only to the indigenous vegetation. The native forage of the Plains and Mountain States is adapted only to cow herds, cattle growing programs, and

FIG. 4.1. GEOGRAPHIC CONCENTRATION OF CATTLE AND CALVES, 1964

HOGS AND PIGS, 1964

UNITED STATES
TOTAL
54,080,194

1 DOT = 10,000 HEAD

MAP NO 64A-M57
U.S. DEPARTMENT OF COMMERCE
BUREAU OF THE CENSUS

FIG. 4.2. GEOGRAPHIC CONCENTRATION OF HOGS AND PIGS, 1964

FIG. 4.3. GEOGRAPHIC CONCENTRATION OF SHEEP AND LAMBS, 1964

ewe flocks. Most of this land has no other feasible commercial use.[1] The relatively light density of cattle and sheep production in these areas is shown in Fig. 4.1 and 4.3. This should not obscure the fact that the areas typically are rather fully utilized. The nature of livestock production systems adapted to these areas is classified as extensive (in contrast to intensive) from the standpoint of land use.

Areas of highly concentrated red meat animal feeding (finishing) programs mirror areas of highly concentrated feed grain production. It was pointed out in Chapter 1 that livestock feeding followed feed grain (corn) production as farming spread westward.[2] Feeding activities still are following geographic changes in feed grain production that more recently have resulted from the development of hybrid feed grains, irrigation, and the impact of government crop restriction programs. The Corn Belt became the Corn-Hog Belt. That region also became the major cattle finishing area. This was logical from an economic standpoint. The demand from population concentrations in the east required an eastward flow of livestock and meat. The Corn Belt was strategically located from a geographical (freight cost) standpoint. Subsequently, population concentration increased on the west coast. Coincident with this was increased irrigated feed grain production in California, Arizona, and the Milo Belt of the central and southern Plains States. Farm program acreage restrictions on wheat also encouraged increased production of grain sorghum, especially in the winter wheat region.

Clearly, it made economic sense to feed western-produced grain to cattle for west coast beef consumption. However, in time cattle feeding in California and Arizona exceeded local feeder cattle supplies and feed grain supplies, and importation of both feeder cattle and feed grains became necessary.[3] In this situation the freight rate structure became a significant factor, although climatic conditions as they affect cost of production also is an important factor. The freight rate structure has been such that the combined cost of shipping feeder cattle and grain to the west coast is greater than the cost of shipping meat on an equivalent converted basis. Van Meir (1963) calculated that a Nebraska feeder had a locational advantage of $1.70 per cwt (excluding consideration of nonfeed costs) of fed carcass beef compared to a California

[1] It is recognized that with increasing affluence of an increasing population, pressures are mounting for both commercial and public recreational use of land suitable for those purposes. In some particular areas, residential development is taking substantial acreages. With the passage of time, nonagricultural demands will take additional acreages.

[2] The location of broiler production is not oriented to feed grain production to the extent of red meat animals. Feed inputs are significant in broiler production, but are relatively less important. The feed conversion ratio is more favorable for broilers than for red meat animals and other factors, e.g., labor requirements, can be more easily filled in areas other than feed grain-producing regions.

[3] Urban development in California also has been an important factor in curbing cattle feeding operations. Not only do residential developers outbid crop producers and feedlot operators for land, but feedlot odors are not compatible with residential use.

feeder who shipped in feed grain and feeder cattle. If this figure is correct for a Nebraska feeder, it is highly probable that a feeder in southwestern Kansas or the High Plains area of Texas would have an even greater advantage. Livestock interests on the west coast periodically petition for a revision in freight rates which would cheapen the cost of imported feed grain but, as of 1971, the Interstate Commerce Commission has been reluctant to grant such a change. Cattle feeders in the Plains area are somewhat vulnerable in this situation and in protection of their interest oppose a change in freight rates which would benefit a competing region. This is an example of institutional factors modifying competition.

Population increases on the west coast and in southwestern states for some years have been greater than in other areas of the United States necessitating greater and greater shipments of meat to those areas.[4] The USDA periodically calculates an imaginary north-south "balance line" between eastward and westward shipments of meat (see Fig. 4.4). These lines are calculated production-consumption balances. Actual shipments cross the lines in both directions, but the charts do emphasize the fact that a greater proportionate growth in population (i.e., demand) than in meat supplies of a particular area results in shifts in marketing patterns. The balance line for all three species has moved progressively eastward.

FIG. 4.4. LINES BETWEEN EASTWARD AND WESTWARD SHIPMENT OF CATTLE AND CALVES, SHEEP AND LAMBS, AND HOGS

[4] Florida is another area of relatively rapid population expansion.

There is a tendency to visualize the production of various crops in a relatively set geographic pattern. Type-of-farming areas have been delineated on the basis of consistency in geographic production patterns. On a year-to-year basis, or in the relatively short period, this probably is a valid assumption. For certain uses, such analyses serve useful purposes. Over a period of time, however, shifts do occur in feed production patterns which contribute to geographical shifts in livestock production. Other factors also are instrumental in shifting livestock production, but feed production probably is the major one.

The development and adoption of hybrid corn in the Corn Belt increased that region's competitive advantage relative to some of its fringe areas. As a case in point, corn and hog production dwindled in Kansas. Kansas still has not regained its pre-hybrid-corn position in hog production. However, the development of hybrid grain sorghum and its early adoption in Kansas and other Plains States has again changed the relative competitive situation (Brandner 1969). The resultant expansion of cattle feeding in the Milo Belt is well known. Not so well know is a reversal of the downtrend in Kansas' hog production. These are examples where break-throughs in plant breeding and development of irrigation triggered changes in livestock production—not only in the extent of feeding operations but also in its location. The potential development of hybrid wheat, possibly a hybrid feed wheat, could result in additional shifts.

PRODUCTION AND PRICE MOVEMENTS

Three types of production and price movements are of concern to livestock market analysis: (1) secular, (2) cyclical, and (3) seasonal. Such movements are observable in inventories, market supplies, and prices. Seasonal variations are those that tend to follow a more or less uniform pattern within the year (i.e., a 12-month period, but need not start in January) and, furthermore, conform to this pattern over a period of years. This means peaks and troughs tend to come at about the same time each year. A cyclical movement, as the name implies, is one that tends to follow a pattern that repeats itself.[5] As defined here, a cycle requires more than 1 year (it tends to repeat itself over a period of years). Secular trends are long-time trends that persist over a period of several cycles. A fourth type of production and price movement is random, or erratic variation. This has no uniformity, hence little or no predictability. Over a period of time it is expected that random variations will cancel out and, hence, usually are ignored.

Price and production data as generated and reported in the markets at any given time represent the combined effect of secular trend, cyclical movement,

[5] The term "cycle" implies a degree of regularity that is not actually found in livestock. Cyclical tendencies exist but successive movements are not identical.

seasonal movement, and random variation. As mentioned above, random variations usually are ignored. A first task in a study of the others is the problem of isolating the effect of each separately. Statistical techniques are available to do this, although no attempt will be made here to present the statistical treatment. In the discussion which follows, the notion of secular trend is fairly obvious. Fig. 4.5 is presented as an aid in visualizing the concept of cyclical and seasonal movements. Line A represents original data, adjusted only for secular trend. Line A has both cyclic and seasonal influences combined in it. In line B the cyclical effect is isolated, i.e., seasonal influences have been removed. Line C represents the isolated effect of only seasonal variation.

Federal Reserve Bank of Kansas City (1962)

FIG. 4.5. ORIGINAL, ADJUSTED, AND SEASONAL CHANGES IN AVERAGE PRICES OF ALL CATTLE SLAUGHTERED UNDER FEDERAL INSPECTION

Cattle–Secular Trends

The total of all cattle and calves on hand Jan. 1 of each year since 1867 (the year annual records were begun) is shown in Fig. 4.6. This includes both beef and dairy cattle, and for purposes of this discussion, both should be considered. Over the years the slaughter of dairy stock has contributed substantial quantities of beef, although it has been of declining importance since about the mid-1940's. It is obvious that the secular, or long-time, trend in cattle numbers has been upward. Superimposed on the secular trend are cyclical variations. While the overall trend is upward, the rate of growth has not been uniform. The total period can be logically broken into two segments, with the breaking point in the late 1920's. DeGraff (1960) reported the secular growth to be 350,000 head per year from 1880 to the late 1920's and

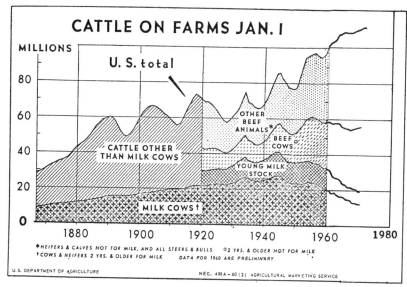

FIG. 4.6. CATTLE ON FARMS JAN. 1, 1880 TO 1970

Data after 1961 added by author from USDA annual livestock inventory reports.

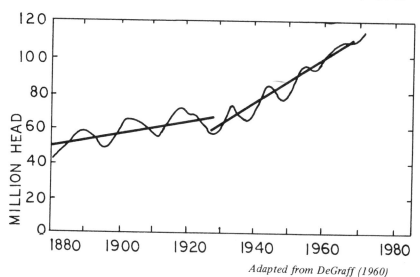

Adapted from DeGraff (1960)

FIG. 4.7. NUMBER OF CATTLE ON FARMS, JAN. 1, 1880-1970

1,150,000 head per year from the 1920's to 1960. (see Fig. 4.7). It is apparent from Fig. 4.6 that the latter trend can be extrapolated to 1970.

Production per head also has increased so the secular trend in production has increased at a faster rate than have numbers of cattle (see Fig. 4.8). A

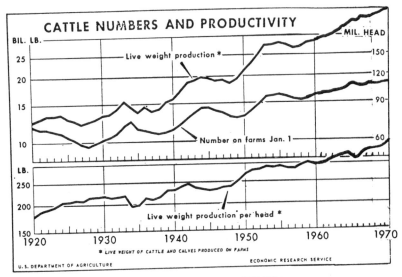

FIG. 4.8. CATTLE NUMBERS AND PRODUCTIVITY
Data for 1961-1970 added by author

From USDA data

number of factors have contributed to the increase in productivity. Among
the more important are:

(1) An increasing proportion of the cattle population is composed of beef
cattle, and meat output per head is greater for beef cattle than for dairy
cattle. The ratio of beef cows to dairy cows has changed rapidly during the
past 25 yr. A generally overlooked fact is that dairy cows outnumbered beef
cows by more than 2 to 1 during the 1930's. By the early 1950's, beef cow
numbers equaled dairy cows, and in 1970 beef cows outnumbered dairy cows

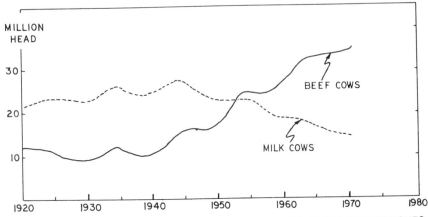

FIG. 4.9. NUMBER OF BEEF COWS AND MILK COWS ON FARMS AND RANCHES,
JAN. 1, 1920-1971

by more than 2 to 1. By almost any standard, this has been a very rapid change. The number of dairy cows reached a peak about the mid-1940's and has been declining steadily since, while beef cow numbers have been on an increasing trend since the 1930's (see Fig. 4.9).

(2) An increasing proportion of slaughtered cattle is composed of grain-fed cattle. The slaughter of vealers and calves has declined steadily and slaughter of "grass-fat" cattle has about disappeared. Included in the increased numbers and proportion being grain fed are substantially more heifers than previously. Output of meat per head, of course, is increased substantially by holding cattle through the growing period, and finishing out on grain.

(3) Improved breeding, feeding, and management are factors in increased productivity. The effects of these improvements show up in many ways, such as size of animal, conformation, carcass yield, yield of lean meat, feed efficiency, rate of gain, death loss, and percentage calf crop. Fig. 4.10 illustrates the increasing trend in percentage calf crop. Death losses have decreased 20 % since the mid-1940's (DeGraff 1960).

Adapted from USDA, ERS, Neg. 201-61 (6)

FIG. 4.10. MEASURES OF PRODUCTIVITY OF CATTLE INVENTORY—CALF CROP

The net effect of these factors is not only an increasing trend in average dressed weight (Fig. 4.11), but also an improvement in beef quality. In 1970, approximately 70% of the total cattle slaughter was composed of grain-fed beef. It was half that much 25 yr. ago.

In an analysis of slaughter cattle prices, Franzmann (1967) calculated an average secular increase of $0.0063 per cwt per month for the period Jan. 1921-Aug. 1967. This was based on monthly prices which had been deflated—a process whereby the effects of inflation and deflation are removed. This long-run increase in price occurred during the time that the quantity of beef supplied (consumed) per person also was increasing. When prices increase simultaneously with quantity over a period of years, it is apparent that demand is increasing, and at a faster rate than supply. These trends have

Adapted from USDA, ERS, Neg. 201-61 (6)

FIG. 4.11. MEASURES OF PRODUCTIVITY OF CATTLE INVEN-
TORY—DRESSED WEIGHT PER HEAD, CATTLE SLAUGHTER

important implications for the beef industry. There is an element of risk in extrapolating any trend into the future, but all statistical projections are based on historical data. There are no statistics available for the future. Used in conjunction with other evidence, it is valid to project a continuation of these trends; and while they do not guarantee a profit to beef producers, an increasing demand must be considered a favorable situation.

Cattle—Cyclical Variations

Cattle cycles have been observed since late in the 19th Century. Over the entire period, cycles have averaged about 12 yr. in length, but earlier cycles were longer than later ones. Each cycle may be divided into two phases: (1) the upward or accumulation phase, and (2) the downward or liquidation phase.

The cyclical nature of the cattle industry may be observed in inventory numbers, in slaughter, and in prices. Even a casual observation of Fig. 4.6 reveals the upswings and downswings in cattle numbers. It also can be seen that the peak of each succeeding cycle was higher than the preceding peak, and each trough is higher than the preceding trough. Fig. 4.12 is an alternative means of illustrating the cycles. Here the individual cycles are shown separately. It may be observed that cycles tend to become shorter in length, and, furthermore, the shortening is due primarily to a reduction in the downswing, or liquidation phase.

Theory of Self-Generating Cycles.—No two cycles have been identical, but a remarkable similarity exists. This degree of consistency and uniformity suggests some underlying causal forces. There are underlying causes, but analysts have never reached unanimous agreement on them. The major difference in opinion centers on whether the forces are self-generating within the cattle industry (i.e., endogenous) or arise from forces outside the industry

FIG. 4.12. CATTLE ON FARMS BY CYCLES

(i.e., exogenous). Analysts in the former camp hold that farmers' and ranchers' price expectations are the key. "The industry (Walters 1965) seems to be seized periodically with 'spontaneous optimism.' During these periods, usually following favorable prices, the growth rate of cattle numbers exceeds an equilibrium growth rate. Cattle numbers in the optimistic periods are increased by adding cows to the basic breeding herds and by keeping feeder cattle longer than usual, consequently to heavier weights. This increasing production finally exceeds the increasing demand, causing first slaughter prices and then feeder prices to decrease.

"With the advent of lower prices, the industry becomes subject to a kind of 'simultaneous pessimism.' The pessimistic cattle producers then reduce the size of their basic breeding herds (because they are less profitable) by selling cows from these herds and not replacing them with heifers. This adds even more to total production and further lowers slaughter prices. Feeders retain the cattle that they are feeding in hopes of better prices. However, after it becomes apparent that prices have stabilized at the lower levels, the fed-cattle producer must then sell his cattle at heavier weights than usual. These cattle are heavier because they have been retained for a longer time on a concentrate ration. Again this adds to the already towering production."

The notion of self-generating cycles has prompted various attempts to explain them in terms of economic behavior. One such effort is the "cobweb" theorem. Original work was done by Ezekiel (1938). Later applications were developed by Harlow (1962) and related work has been done by Ehrich (1966). The cobweb theorem provides an explanation of how, under certain conditions, prices and quantities supplied and demanded move around the hypothesized equilibrium point specified by the intersection of demand and supply curves as producers and consumers react to price changes. One of the conditions inherent in the theorem is a time lag in the response of production (quantity) change to price change. The livestock industry seems to provide such an example. In the case of hogs it takes a year or more before a production change gets on the market as a result of a price change. With cattle the lag is considerably greater.

An abbreviated description of the theorem is as follows. It may be assumed that a system at one point in time is in disequilibrium. In the real world this would not be unusual. We assume a given supply curve SS and a demand curve DD as in Fig. 4.13 with price out of equilibrium at point A. This represents a price well above the level at which producers are willing to produce a considerably larger quantity as would be indicated by a horizontal movement to the right until intersection with their supply curve (point B). With a sufficient time lag it may be assumed they would respond in that manner. But that output will be taken by consumers only at a substantially lower price, indicated by a vertical movement downward until intersection with the demand curve (point C). At that price, however, producers are off their supply curve and, in an effort to get back on it, they reduce production (to point E). Consumers, however, will pay a higher price (point F) for that quantity and at the higher price producers will increase production; and so the system goes off on another round. The cobweb appearance is apparent—hence the name. As drawn in Fig. 4.13 the movements are converging toward an equilibrium. It can be shown very easily that, by changing the shape of the curves (a rough indication of relative degree of elasticity), the movements can be changed to an explosive or divergent system.

In a somewhat sophisticated model, Ehrich (1966) concludes that the cobweb theorem is an inadequate model of dynamic economic behavior in either the hog or cattle economy. He states, "The characteristic behavior of production and prices suggests that harmonic motion is an appropriate model of cycle-generating forces in the U.S. beef economy. Essentially, true harmonic motion involves stimulus, response, and 'feed-back' which serves to alter the stimulus after a fixed delay. It appears that the physical characteristics of beef-cattle growth, uncertainty regarding future prices, and producers' behavior in the face of uncertainty, combine to produce harmonic behavior in annual fluctuations in cattle prices and numbers. In particular, producers respond to prices (stimulus) by changing the rate of planned production (increasing or decreasing the breeding herd incrementally), the

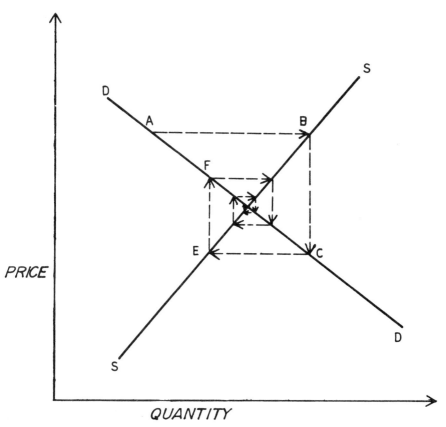

FIG. 4.13. ILLUSTRATION OF "COB-WEB" PRICE AND OUTPUT MOVEMENTS

change in production is realized after a delay (physical growth limitations), and the price stimulus is altered by realized production (prices are unilaterally affected by predetermined supplies).

"Statistical estimates of the relationships among prices, inventory adjustments, and annual production of beef were consistent with the basic model. Of primary importance, the evidence supports the view that producers respond incrementally to deviations of price from equilibrium and it serves to deny the existence of a conventional supply function for beef cattle. For, of course, the conventional concept of a supply function presupposes that producers adjust to a new level of planned output which is independent of the present level of output, in response to a change in price levels, rather than seeking to change the rate of planned output from current levels.

"Parenthetically, other evidence supports harmonic motion as a model of behavior for the hog economy as well as for the cattle economy. The cobweb theorem, which depends on the existence of a conventional supply curve, is then an inadequate model of dynamic economic behavior in either the hog or cattle economy" (Ehrich 1966).

Exogenous Factors in Cattle Cycles.—Others have contended that cycles are generated by stimuli outside the cattle industry. Among the factors cited are wars, inflationary and deflationary price trends, and variation in feed supplies (Hopkins 1926; Burmeister 1949). Most emphasis has been placed on the availability of feed including, of course, range and pasture forage. There is some historical evidence that, on occasion, drouths have coincided with downturns in cattle numbers. However, this is not the case in all cycles.

Breimyer (1954) sums up the situation as follows, "The feed supply may be an important factor at all stages of the cattle cycle. Some think it is. Approximate overall indices of range and pasture condition and crop feed supply have been included in correlation analyses of cattle production, occasionally with positive results. As a rule, though, the supply of feed is not a restraining influence at early stages of expansion because any increase in feed prices is far overshadowed by soaring prices of cattle. Only after the typical cyclical decline in cattle prices has begun are feed supplies and prices watched more closely. From then on the supply of feed can be a controlling factor."

DeGraff (1960) recognizes the effects of cattle prices and feed prices in generating cycles but relates them to the biological timetable of cattle reproduction. He says, "While such influences as a change in demand or in feed supplies may initiate a cycle, they do not explain the sequence of events which follows. The reason why a cycle follows its standardized pattern is found, not in economics, but in biology. Changes in cattle production, whatever caused their beginnings, are converted into a cyclical pattern by the natural biology of the cattle species.

"The life-span of cattle is long. They reproduce and grow slowly. If a bred heifer is kept for breeding instead of being sent to slaughter, her first calf does not reach the market until nearly 3 yr later. This is indeed a long delay in economic response. To say that cycles in cattle originate largely within the industry itself is not to say that producers are either ignorant or indifferent to the consequences of their decisions. The slow-moving biology of the species is the factor that extends the period between decision and consequence and leads to the patterned nature of the cattle cycle."

Price Cycles.—Coincident with cycles in the cattle inventory have been the cyclical trends in prices. Price cycles, typically, are the inverse of inventory cycles (as numbers advance, prices tend to decline and vice versa). However, the turning points do not occur at identical times. Studies have shown that the turning point in beef production (slaughter) lags the turning point in cattle numbers by about 2 yr (McCoy 1959; Ehrich 1966). Some lag is to be expected. For example, if cattle numbers are declining and prices rising, the decline in numbers will be halted by a withholding of heifers from market—

the heifers to be retained for breeding purposes. This withholding will start an increase in inventory, but another immediate effect will be a further reduction in already-declining meat supplies and continued strengthening in prices. When it becomes apparent that beef supplies are (or will be) increasing from the buildup in cattle numbers then prices turn downward—but this does not occur immediately with initiation of the buildup in numbers. The turning point in cyclical changes in cow numbers also lags the turning point in feeder cattle prices by zero to 2 yr (Ehrich 1966). Thus, beef production (slaughter) turning points lag prices by zero to 4 yr. The reverse situation has occurred on increasing phases of the cattle cycle.

The inverse relation between cattle numbers and prices may be seen in Fig. 4.14. During war periods (World War I, World War II, the Korean War, and the Vietnamese War) cattle prices moved upward with increasing cattle numbers due to exceptionally strong inflationary pressures; but generally at other times prices and numbers moved in opposite directions. The cyclical nature of cattle prices are more readily observable when prices are adjusted for effects of price level changes (when prices are deflated, shown in Fig. 4.15). It should be noted, however, that the price line in Fig. 4.15 still

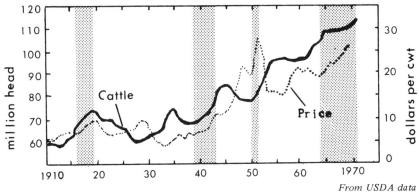

From USDA data

FIG. 4.14. NUMBER OF CATTLE ON U.S. FARMS JAN. 1, 1910-1970, AND PRICE RECEIVED BY FARMERS FOR CATTLE

Franzman (1967)

FIG. 4.15. DEFLATED PRICE OF FEDERALLY INSPECTED SLAUGHTER CATTLE, JAN. 1921-AUG. 1967 contains the effect of the long-time gentle upward trend and the effect of seasonal ups and downs. The latter give the price line the jagged, saw-toothed appearance. Both secular and seasonal trend effects are removed statistically in calculating the true cycle.

Franzmann (1967) reported that, "On the average, the adjusted price paid decreased $2.35 per cwt as the industry progressed from a peak to a trough in the cycle. Conversely, when the industry went from a trough to a peak, price increased by $2.35 per cwt."

The alternating economic booms and busts that have accompanied cattle cycles have been a matter of great concern in the cattle industry. Generally, members of the industry subscribe to the proposition that in a market economy one of the functions of price is to guide production. However, the biological lag, together with lack of precise market knowledge and other market imperfections, have resulted in rather drastic variations in income— from prosperity to bankruptcy in many individual cases. For a number of years the industry has championed self-discipline as a means of smoothing drastic price variations.

There is some evidence that cattle inventory cycles are disappearing. In recent cycles, the liquidation phase has shortened and the magnitude of decline has lessened. It is probable this tendency will continue in the future. The consequences of cyclical variation have been serious enough to warrant a brief review of the characteristics of past cycles.

Six complete cycles have occurred since 1896. These are shown graphically in Fig. 4.11. Annual data for the years 1896-1970 are shown in Table 4.1 with a period divided into alternating accumulation and liquidation phases. Two characteristics of the accumulation phases are apparent: (1) The length of accumulation phases has been remarkably uniform. Accumulation lasted 6 yr during 3 cycles, 7 yr during 2 cycles, and 8 yr in 1 cycle–a range of 6–8 yr. (2) The number of head of cattle added to the inventory also was remarkably uniform. All were within the range 17.2–20.3 million head. The percentage increase in cattle has declined with successive cycles, ranging down from 35% in the first cycle to 20.6% in the latest. This follows from the fact that a fairly constant increase in absolute number has been added to an increasing base.

General characteristics of liquidation phases are (1) a declining trend in length of liquidation phase; (2) a declining trend in number of head liquidated; and (3) a declining trend in percentage of the inventory liquidated. During early cycles the liquidation phases lasted 8–10 yr and in later cycles, 2–3 yr. During early cycles the liquidations amounted to 11–16 million head, while in the latest it was less than 1/2 million head. Liquidation during the last cycle was so small that it can hardly be called a true downturn. Considering limitations on the accuracy of reported inventories (reported numbers are estimates, not actual counts), it appears that cattle numbers

TABLE 4.1

PERIODS OF EXPANSION AND CONTRACTION IN CATTLE NUMBERS FOR
ALL CATTLE AND CALVES ON U.S. FARMS, 1896-1970

Year	No. on Hand Jan. 1 of Indicated Year (1,000)	Increase or Decrease During Year, No. Head (1,000)	Increase or Decrease During Year (%)	Period Increase or Decrease (%)
		Accumulation		
1896	49,205	1,242	2.5	
1897	50,447	2,421	4.0	
1898	52,868	3,059	5.8	
1899	55,927	3,812	6.8	
1900	59,739	2,837	4.7	
1901	62,576	1,842	2.9	
1902	64,418	1,586	2.5	
1903	66,004	438	0.7	
Period total		17,347		35.0
		Liquidation		
1904	66,442	− 331	−0.5	
1905	66,111	−1,102	−1.7	
1906	65,009	−1,255	−1.9	
1907	63,754	−1,765	−2.8	
1908	61,989	−1,215	−2.0	
1909	60,774	−1,781	−2.9	
1910	58,993	−1,768	−3.0	
1911	57,225	−1,550	−2.7	
Period total		−10,767		−16.2
		Accumulation		
1912	55,675	917	1.6	
1913	56,592	2,869	5.1	
1914	59,461	4,388	7.4	
1915	63,849	3,589	5.6	
1916	67,438	3,541	5.3	
1917	70,979	2,061	2.9	
Period total		17,365		31.2
		Liquidation		
1918	73,040	− 946	−1.3	
1919	72,094	−1,694	−2.3	
1920	70,400	−1,686	−2.4	
1921	68,714	81	0.1	
1922	68,795	−1,249	−1.8	
1923	67,546	−1,550	−2.3	
1924	65,996	−2,623	−4.0	
1925	63,373	−2,797	−4.4	
1926	60,576	−2,398	−4.0	
1927	58,178	− 856	−1.5	
Period total		−15,718		−21.5
		Accumulation		
1928	57,322	1,555	2.7	
1929	58,877	2,126	3.6	
1930	61,003	2,027	3.3	
1931	63,030	2,771	4.4	
1932	65,801	4,479	6.8	
1933	70,280	4,089	5.8	
Period total		17,047		29.7

TABLE 4.1 (continued)
PERIODS OF EXPANSION AND CONTRACTION IN CATTLE NUMBERS FOR
ALL CATTLE AND CALVES ON U.S. FARMS, 1896-1970

Year	No. on Hand Jan. 1 of Indicated Year (1,000)	Increase or Decrease During Year, No. Head (1,000)	Increase or Decrease During Year (%)	Period Increase or Decrease (%)
		Liquidation		
1934	74,369	−5,523	−7.4	
1935	68,846	− 999	−1.5	
1936	67,847	−1,749	−2.6	
1937	66,098	− 849	−1.3	
Period total		−9,120		−12.3
		Accumulation		
1938	66,249	780	1.2	
1939	66,029	2,280	3.5	
1940	68,309	3,446	5.0	
1941	71,755	4,270	6.0	
1942	76,025	5,179	6.8	
1943	81,204	4,130	5.1	
1944	85,334	239	0.3	
Period total		20,324		31.1
		Liquidation		
1945	85,573	−3,338	−3.9	
1946	82,235	−1,681	−2.0	
1947	80,554	−3,383	−4.2	
1948	77,171	− 341	−0.4	
Period total		−8,743		−10.2
		Accumulation		
1949	76,830	1,133	1.5	
1950	77,963	4,120	5.3	
1951	82,083	5,989	7.3	
1952	88,072	6,169	7.0	
1953	94,241	1,438	1.5	
1954	95,679	913	1.0	
Period total		19,762		25.7
		Liquidation		
1955	96,592	− 692	−0.7	
1956	95,900	−3,040	−3.2	
1957	92,860	−1,684	−1.8	
Period total		−5,416		−5.6
		Accumulation		
1958	91,176	2,146	2.4	
1959	93,322	2,914	3.1	
1960	96,236	764	0.8	
1961	97,000	3,369	3.5	
1962	100,369	4,119	4.1	
1963	104,488	3,415	3.3	
1964	107,903	1,097	1.0	
Period total		17,824		19.5
		Liquidation		
1965	109,000	− 138	−0.1	
1966	108,862	− 217	−0.2	
Period total		− 355		−0.3

TABLE 4.1 (continued)
PERIODS OF EXPANSION AND CONTRACTION IN CATTLE NUMBERS FOR
ALL CATTLE AND CALVES ON U.S. FARMS, 1896-1970

Year	No. on Hand Jan. 1 of Indicated Year (1,000)	Increase or Decrease During Year, No. Head (1,000)	Increase or Decrease During Year (%)	Period Increase or Decrease (%)
		Accumulation		
1967	108,645	507	0.5	
1968	109,152	733	0.7	
1969	109,885	2418	2.2	
1970	112,303	2167	1.9	
1971	114,470	3446	3.0	
1972	117,916			

Summary

Years (Inclusive)	No. Yrs	Increase or Decrease	
		No. Head	%
	Accumulation Phases		
1896-1903	8	17,237	35.0
1912-1917	6	17,365	31.2
1928-1933	6	17,047	29.7
1938-1944	7	20,324	31.1
1949-1954	6	19,762	25.7
1958-1964	7	17,824	19.5
	Liquidation Phases		
1904-1911	8	−10,767	−16.2
1918-1927	10	−15,718	−21.5
1934-1937	4	− 9,120	−12.3
1945-1948	4	− 8,743	−10.2
1955-1957	3	− 5,416	− 5.6
1965-1966	2	− 355	− 0.3

Source: Data from USDA; calculations by Dept. Econ., Kansas State University.

actually about leveled off in 1965 and held approximately constant until 1969, then started what probably will be another accumulation phase.

Cattle—Seasonal Variations

As defined earlier, seasonal movements, or variations, are those that follow a more or less uniform pattern within the period of a year. Seasonal price movements are a direct reflection of seasonality in marketings and, to a lesser degree, seasonality in demand. Seasonality in marketings is related to biological factors and management practices. The latter are partially a matter of habit but more importantly are related to production costs. The marketing of calves reaches a peak during the fall months at the close of the grazing season. The marketing of cull cows occurs at about the same time as many farmers and ranchers cull their herds during the roundup for calf weaning. These events are related to biological processes associated with the cow-calf production process as well as those of range and pasture forage growth. Calf prices and cull cow prices normally are seasonally low during the period of heavy marketings.

Owners, of course, could hold their cull cows and calves for later sale, or they could sell them ahead of the normal close of the range and pasture season. Some owners do vary time of sale, but most do not. Many market about the same time each year from habit. For those who do not, the decision rests on a market analysis of expected price changes versus associated costs and their effect on net profit. Herein lies the basis for our concern with seasonal analysis. Some classes of livestock have a relatively pronounced and consistent seasonal price pattern; some do not. It does not follow that the producer who adjusts his program to hit the seasonal high price will automatically maximize his profits. Some may be able to make profitable adjustments. For others, cost of production increases may more than offset higher prices. The producer must know the seasonality of his costs as well as seasonality of prices.

Some producers may view prices with greater uncertainty in particular years. But even if future prices were certain, farmers and ranchers would still respond differently to given price situations because of differences in amount and kind of resources available. Seasonal patterns can be broad guides in planning an individual business or marketing program. A producer can alter his marketing program to take advantage of certain favorable price periods without affecting the general seasonal pattern. However, if a large number of producers make the same adjustment to a seasonal trend, they may find the seasonal pattern changing. It will be shown later that such changes have occurred.

Use of Index Numbers.—It will be noted in the following discussion of seasonal movements that the data are presented as index numbers. This is a particularly useful device. It can be used on both prices and production. It is possible to calculate average seasonal price patterns in dollars, and this sometimes is done, but the price level can change rather rapidly even though the pattern of movement may not change. In this case, calculations based on dollars would be of limited use. Conversion of data to index numbers is not a difficult process. Reconversion of index numbers to dollars is a simple calculation, so that once the indices have been developed they may be applied regardless of price level changes. If the seasonal pattern changes, then, of course, a new set of indices must be calculated.

Indices are convenient ways of showing the combined pattern of a large number of seasons. An average month is given an index of 100. High months then will have indices that are greater than 100, such as 105, 110, or 125. Months in which the seasonal lows occur will have indices of less than 100.

One can get an idea of how to use a particular seasonal index by looking at a graph of the index. See Fig. 4.16 for an example. On the graph there is a horizontal straight line which represents an average for the entire year. In other words, the indices for the months of the year are all added together and divided by 12. This value is called 100 merely as a base to compare the indices for other months. The actual value for the index for each month is shown by the heavy black line going up or down from month to month. This is called the seasonal trend line.

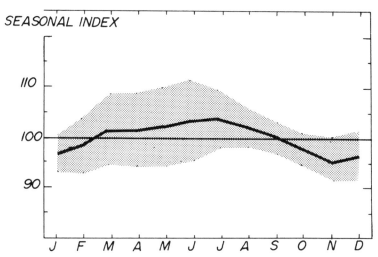

FIG. 4.16. SEASONAL VARIATION IN PRICES OF CHOICE SLAUGHTER STEERS, 900-1100 LB, OMAHA, 1966-1970

A shaded band appears around the seasonal trend line. Technically the shaded band is called an "index of irregularity." This band represents the extremes that the seasonal trend line may be expected to stay within in the majority of years. The width of the band gives some idea of the reliability that can be placed in a given seasonal trend. Other things being equal, the narrower the band, the more reliable the seasonal trend. That is, if the band (shaded area) is quite narrow, one can expect future prices or supplies to vary only slightly in future years.

While a seasonal index gives an indication of the changes that can be expected throughout the year, a more direct application is made in estimating prices in some future month (for example) with current prices. The estimate is obtained by dividing the current price by the index for the current month and multiplying the results by the price index for the future month:

$$\frac{\text{Present Monthly Price}}{\text{Present Monthly Index}} \times \text{Future Monthly Index} = \text{Estimated Future Monthly Price}$$

For example, if the present price for feeder steers is $29.00 per cwt and the current index is 92, then the estimated price 3 months from now (when the seasonal index is 105) would be:

$$\frac{\$29.00}{92} \times 105 = \$33.10$$

One can use the index of irregularity to compute an interval in which prices in the future months might be expected to fall in about 60% of the time.

The method of calculating this interval can be shown by using the feeder steer prices previously computed. The procedure is as follows:

(a) Multiply the estimated future price by the index of irregularity for that price series:

$$\$33.10 \times .028 = \$0.93$$

(b) Add the value obtained to the estimated future price to get the upper end of the interval. Subtract the same value to get the lower end of the interval:

$$\$33.10 + \text{and} - \$0.93 = \$34.03 \text{ to } \$32.17$$

This method of forecasting, of course, depends on the absence of disturbances that seriously alter the general price level, the supply, or the demand situation. It might lead to erroneous results in making estimates for a time when general business conditions are changing rapidly.

Choice Slaughter Steers.—The seasonal price pattern for choice slaughter steers, 900–1100 lb, at Omaha is shown in Fig. 4.16. This shows a tendency for price strength during the spring months with weakness during fall months. However, it must be noted that this pattern is relatively weak. The extent of variation (the amplitude) above the average line (i.e., the index = 100 line) at its highest point during the spring high amounts to only 6 percentage points and the variation below the average line at the lowest point during the period of weakness is just 4.5 percentage points. It also is noted that the monthly index of irregularity is relatively large, indicating a high degree of irregularity. Choice slaughter steer prices in recent years have exhibited a weak, irregular seasonal tendency. This means that little confidence can be placed in this seasonal trend. It is of limited use as a marketing tool. This pattern was influenced considerably by strong prices during the spring months of 1969 and, to a lesser degree, in 1970. It is doubtful that spring prices will continue to consistently show such exceptional strength. The continued expansion of commercial feedlots, with a strong incentive for year-round feeding, tends to level out marketings. There is little doubt that this will continue; and with the leveling, there will be less irregularity in price movements and at the same time a reduction in the amplitude of seasonal trends.

The current pattern differs substantially from earlier periods. Wilson and Riley (1950), using the 1924-1941 period, reported a seasonal weakening of prices through spring and early summer with prices declining to an index of about 94 in June. Their analysis showed a seasonal recovery from the June low to a high of 105.6 in mid-November. This pattern was comparatively reliable at that time, and earlier. Prior to the era of commercial feedlots the customary procedure was to graze feeder cattle until the end of the grazing season. Some were slaughtered at that time as grass-fat cattle; the remainder went into feedlots—usually in the Corn Belt. The length of feeding period was geared to quality of the cattle. So-called "plain" cattle were fed the shortest period and their marketings were bunched just prior to marketing of the next higher grade, and so on to the highest. Thus, the heaviest seasonal marketings and corresponding lowest seasonal prices for successively higher grades came in successive waves through the spring and summer. With the passing of marketing peaks, for the particular grades, price recovery would begin. The price peak for plain cattle would come in the spring or early summer and following next would come the price peak for successively higher grades. This is a matter only of historical interest now, but it did illustrate the relationship between seasonality in marketings and prices. With present conditions tending more and more to level out marketings, there is reason to believe the seasonal price pattern for slaughter steers will tend to flatten out in the future.

Choice Feeder Steers (Yearlings).—The marketing of feeder steers historically has exhibited a relatively strong seasonal pattern. As mentioned in the last section, sales were geared to the ending of the grazing season. Purchases by graziers likewise were geared to the beginning of the grazing season. Consequently, a spring high price and fall low could be depended upon with about as much reliability as the movements of a clock. This basic pattern still persists, but at a somewhat reduced level. The increasing demand by feedlots for feeder cattle on a year-round basis has been instrumental in the change. Fig. 4.17 shows the current seasonal pattern for choice feeder steers, 500–800 lb, at Kansas City. The spring high and fall low are evident. March and April are indicated to be the high period, while prices remain rather uniformly low during the August-January period. The range from high to low is about 10 percentage points. With prices in the neighborhood of, say, $29.00 at the fall low, one could expect a price of about $32.00 for animals of that same weight and grade during spring. An animal purchased at a given weight in the fall usually will be in a different (heavier) weight classification by the following spring. Seasonal price patterns are based on a given weight and grade. To know the probable price differential applicable to animals as they progress through successive increases in weight, one needs an analysis of price margins. This will be presented later.

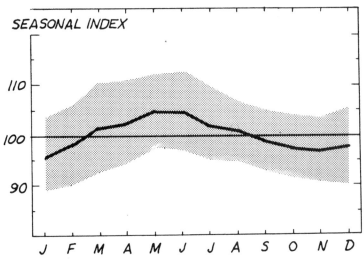

FIG. 4.17. SEASONAL VARIATION IN PRICES OF CHOICE FEEDER
STEERS, 550-750 LB, KANSAS CITY, 1966-1970

There are no absolute standards for evaluating indices of irregularity. On the basis of reasonableness the index of irregularity for yearling feeder steers is relatively small, indicating that a considerable amount of confidence can be placed in expectations that prices in any given year will follow this pattern.

Choice Feeder Steer Calves.—Seasonal prices for steer calves follow essentially the same pattern as for yearling feeder steers (Fig. 4.18). However, the range from low to high (amplitude) is slightly greater and the index of

FIG. 4.18. SEASONAL VARIATIONS IN PRICES OF CHOICE FEEDER
STEER CALVES, 300-550 LB, KANSAS CITY, 1966-1970

irregularity is slightly less for most months. The evidence indicates that one can depend upon this pattern with a substantial amount of confidence.

Utility Slaughter Cows.—The seasonal movement of utility slaughter cow prices is shown in Fig. 4.19. As mentioned earlier, this pattern is the inverse of seasonality in marketing of cows. Cow prices range from a low index of about 93 in December to a high of around 107, which normally occurs in the April-June period. This can be classed as a pronounced seasonal variation. The index of irregularity is larger than that of feeder calves, but is not considered excessive. Again, substantial confidence can be placed in the occurrence of this price pattern.

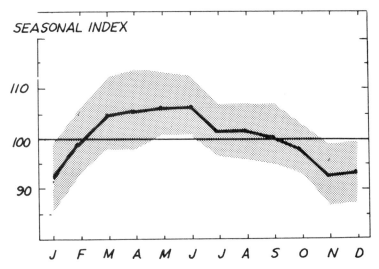

FIG. 4.19. SEASONAL VARIATION IN PRICES OF UTILITY COWS, OMAHA, 1966-1970

Other Cattle and Calf Seasonals.—Calculations have been made for many other classes, grades, and weights of cattle and calves, but the four illustrations demonstrate the basic patterns to be found. It could be shown that prices of "good" grade slaughter steers have a slightly greater amplitude than do prices of choice steers, and that prices of "utility" grade slaughter steers have a higher amplitude than do prices of "good" grade steers, but the highs and lows of each occur at approximately the same time of year. This was not the case in earlier times, as was pointed out previously. The seasonal price pattern for heifers, for both slaughter classes and feeder classes, follows the same general pattern as steer prices of comparable grade.

Hogs—Secular Trends

The long-run trend in hog numbers makes an interesting comparison with that of cattle. As may be observed in Fig. 4.20, growth in the hog inventory

From USDA data

FIG. 4.20. NUMBER OF HOGS ON U.S. FARMS JAN. 1, PRIOR TO 1968; BEGIN-
NING 1968 THE NUMBER ON FARMS DEC. 1

was steadily upward (ignoring the effect of cyclical variations) from 1867 to
the early 1920's. A comparison with the trend in cattle numbers (Fig. 4.6)
shows that the rate of growth was about the same for both cattle and hogs,
and, furthermore, the number of each species was not greatly different. A
significant change occurred during the 1920's. The growth pattern for hogs
became irregular, with a severe drop during the drouth-depression period of
the 1930's, a sharp increase during World War II, and a sharp decline
following the Korean War of early 1950's. A secular trend line through the
1920-1970 period declines slightly. It will be recalled that the rate of growth
in cattle numbers increased during that period.

The long-time trend in pork production (this is weight of hogs slaughtered)
shows a different picture (see Fig. 4.21). The drouth-depression effect and
World War II effect logically can be ignored on the grounds that they were
abnormal occurrences. The secular trend in pork production from 1900 to
1970 comes close to a linear trend with a growth rate of slightly less than
100,000,000 lb of pork per year. Even if one broke the trend around 1930 to
obtain a better fit to the two separate periods, the trend during the latter
definitely would be upward.

The apparent difference between the trend in pork production and hog
numbers during the latter period is due to several factors. Improved breeding
and production practices have increased productivity per head. In addition,
improved feeding and management practices have speeded up the production

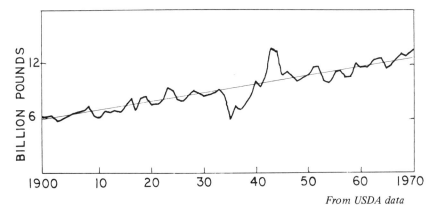

From USDA data

FIG. 4.21. TOTAL PORK PRODUCTION, DRESSED WEIGHT, 1900-1970

and marketing process by finishing hogs at a lower age than formerly, i.e., increased rate of offturn. In spite of these increases in production, supplies of pork per person have trended downward (due to human population increases) and at a slightly faster rate in the latter part of the period than in the former (Fig. 4.22).

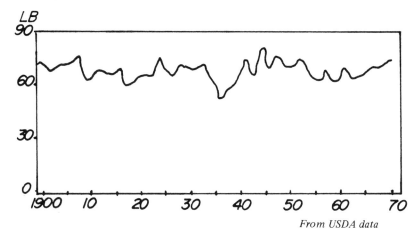

From USDA data

FIG. 4.22. PORK SUPPLIES (CONSUMPTION) PER CAPITA

Hog prices over the long period have followed the general trend of cattle and lamb prices, and prices of all three species have followed the pattern of the "all commodity" wholesale price index (see Fig. 4.23 and 4.24). The effects of inflation and deflation, however, camouflage the trend in "real" prices. Figure 4.25 shows the trend in "real" hog prices (adjusted for price level changes). Visual appraisal of the secular trend may be made by ignoring the short-period ups and downs (which are cyclical variations). It is apparent that the trend has been persistently upward although the rate of increase is

FIG. 4.23. BEEF CATTLE PRICES COMPARED WITH PRICES OF HOGS AND LAMBS
Years 1870-1949 reproduced from materials of the American Meat Institute; later years
added by author.

[1] Prior to 1910: Sheep and Lambs.

FIG. 4.24. BEEF CATTLE PRICES COMPARED WITH PRICES OF ALL COMMODITIES
Years 1870-1949 reproduced from materials of the American Meat Institute; later years
added by author.

[1] Prior to 1910: Sheep and Lambs.

DOLLARS
PER CWT

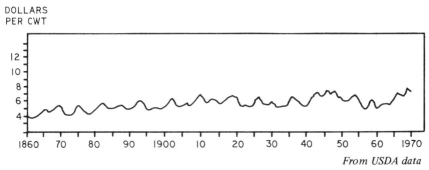

From USDA data

FIG. 4.25. HOG PRICES, CHICAGO, ADJUSTED FOR PRICE LEVEL CHANGES, 1910-1914 BASE

slight. Since 1920 the rate of increase has averaged approximately $0.0025 per cwt per month.

But the pattern has not been uniform throughout the period. Prices tended downward following World War II to the mid-1950's, and possibly beyond—we will not know until more time has elapsed. However, there is some evidence that a significant change may have occurred about the mid-1950's. Since that time consumption per capita has inclined upward. At the same time prices have inclined upward. It is granted that the inclines are very moderate, but at least it is an encouraging sign from the standpoint of the swine industry. Producers have made significant improvements in the leanness and quality of pork as will be pointed out in the following chapter. Much promotional work has been done to increase the demand for pork. Consumers react slowly and there are no studies at this time indicating a change; but temporarily at least, the market has signalled a change.

Hogs—Cyclical Variations

Over the years hog inventories, slaughter, and prices have followed cyclical patterns (see Fig. 4.20 and 4.25). A comparison of Fig. 4.6 with Fig. 4.20 indicates that cycles in hog production have been less regular than in cattle. Prior to World War I the cycles occurred with greater regularity than they have since that time. Hog cycles average about 4 yr, and this holds whether based on earlier or later years. This averages 2 yr of expansion and 2 yr of liquidation. The period 1941–1970 encompassed 7 complete cycles (Fig. 4.26) which varied from 3 to 6 yr. It is obvious that for market planning or price forecasting the cycle has limited usefulness. However, when used with supplemental information, a knowledge of hog cycles can be a useful tool.

Hog cycles have been characterized to some extent by alternating major peaks and minor peaks. That is, there is a tendency for a high peak to be followed by a low peak. This may be seen in the price line of Fig. 4.25,

especially during the period from about 1890 to 1940. It shows up again in
the first two inventory cycles shown in Fig. 4.26.

From USDA data

FIG. 4.26. NUMBER OF HOGS ON FARMS JAN. 1, 1940-1970—WITH LENGTH OF
CYCLE INDICATED

Figure 4.27 illustrates that prices and production move in opposite directions. Due to the relatively inelastic nature of the demand for pork, the
variation in prices is proportionately greater than variation in pork production.
In other words, a given change in quantity produced (and marketed) will
precipitate a relatively greater change in price.

The theory of the cyclical nature of hog production and prices is based on
the supposition that producers respond to prices, and prices reflect quantity
produced—an interaction process. When hog prices are relatively high (profitable) farmers respond by increasing production. As production increases,
prices tend to decline. Inherent lags in the biology of the production process,
lags in reaction by producers, and imperfect knowledge of the situation result
in overreaction—an overshooting of equilibrium on both the upturn and
downturn.

The "hog-corn price ratio," usually shortened to hog-corn ratio, has been

FIG. 4.27. CHANGES IN HOG PRICES AND PORK PRODUCTION

used for many years as an indicator of profitability in hog production and as a tool in forecasting turning points in production and price cycles. The hog-corn ratio is the ratio between the price of hogs and the price of corn, i.e., the price per hundredweight of live hogs divided by the price per bushel of corn. The quotient (ratio) actually gives the number of bushels of corn equal in value to 100 lb of hog:

$$\frac{\text{Price / cwt live hogs}}{\text{Price / bu corn}} = \text{Hog-corn price ratio}$$

It is necessary to specify (1) the grade and weight of hogs, (2) the grade of corn, and (3) the market for which the prices apply. The information needed usually is easy to obtain and calculations are simple. For many years the USDA has calculated and reported hog-corn ratios. One that has been widely used as representative of the Corn Belt is the ratio for No. 1–3 hogs, 220 lb, and No. 2 yellow corn at Chicago markets. With closing of the Chicago public terminal market (hogs in May 1970, cattle and sheep in August 1971) it may be necessary to use another representative market. This will present no particular problem. Any producer can calculate a hog-corn ratio by using applicable market prices for his location.

The hog-corn ratio is only a rough approximation of the profitability of raising hogs. It is based on the notion that feed is the most important production cost and that corn is the most important feed. This undoubtedly is the case. But it does not reflect the situation as well now as it did in former years. Corn (or for that matter, any grain used in the ration) is a smaller proportion of total production costs than formerly.

The hog-corn ratio in recent years has averaged around 16 to 17. Prior to World War II the ratio averaged about 12. The records show that in this earlier period a ratio higher than 12 tended to induce an expansion in hog production. A ratio less than 12 induced a cutback in production—with a lag in both cases. Analyses typically compare, for example, number of sows farrowed in the spring, with the hog-corn ratio during the previous fall. At that time the ratio was a reliable indicator of the direction of change in farrowing (Harlow 1962). This is observable in Fig. 4.28. In the upper part of the chart a horizontal line is drawn at a ratio of about 12. This was the average for the period shown, 1924 to 1960. The actual fall hog-corn ratio is plotted as it varied above and below the average. When above average the area is cross-hatched, when below it is left open. The lower part of the chart shows change in sow farrowing during the next spring. It is readily apparent that above average fall hog-corn ratios were followed by increases in number of sows farrowed the next spring, and viceversa for periods of below average hog-corn ratios. The logic of this type of analysis is that it is not the absolute price of hogs or corn that was associated with changes in number produced, but the relation between prices of hogs and corn.

FIG. 4.28. INFLUENCE OF HOG-CORN RATIO ON SPRING FARROWING
Years 1960-1970 added by author

In recent years, however, the relationship between the hog-corn ratio and sow farrowings has not been as consistent as formerly. This is due in part to the declining importance of grain in total production, as mentioned above. In addition, the government price support program has tended to reduce (but not eliminate) variations in corn prices that formerly were associated with variations in production. Another factor is changing structural characteristics of the hog industry. Many small producers still raise hogs, but the trend is toward larger and fewer operators. The investment required in larger and more specialized units makes those operators more inclined to maintain production near optimum levels for the design of the unit. Producers still make some adjustments in hog production according to the degree of profitability, but output is not as sensitive to relative changes in corn prices as in former years. There is evidence that producers now respond more than formerly to absolute hog price changes. It also is likely that progressive producers attempt to gear production to long-run expectations of supply and demand conditions.

Hogs–Seasonal Variations

Hog prices follow a distinctive seasonal pattern which is directly related to marketings of hogs. This, in turn, is related to time of farrowing and to a lesser degree to feeding and breeding programs. While farrowings are distributed throughout the year, they tend to be concentrated in certain months. This leads to the concentration of marketings. The period of most pronounced concentration in farrowings is during March and April for the spring pig crop and during September for the fall pig crop, with the spring crop being the larger of the two, but this difference also is lessening. The spring crop amounted to 61% of annual production during the early 1940's, it now accounts for about 52%. Further leveling out is expected but a considerable degree of concentration will persist within the spring and fall crop for the foreseeable future.

Figure 4.29 shows the seasonal pattern of farrowings and marketings, using the same scale for both, but the index line for marketing lags (seven months) so that the peak for marketing which occurs in November is matched with the peak in farrowings which occurs in March. It is clear that marketings are more evenly distributed than farrowings, but this is a relative matter. Marketings are far from uniform throughout the year.

Slaughter Barrows and Gilts, No. 2–3, 200–220 Lb.–The seasonal price for barrows and gilts is shown in Fig. 4.30. This is a movement of considerable proportions. The range is 16 percentage points. Prices reach a seasonal peak during the summer (July) when relatively few hogs are marketed. From that peak, prices decline to a fall low (November) as marketings of hogs from the spring pig crop reach a peak. As this peak in marketings passes, prices recover to a minor peak in February, then decline as

McCoy (1958)

FIG. 4.29. INDEXES OF SEASONAL VARIATION IN SOW FARROWINGS AND HOG MARKETINGS FOR THE UNITED STATES, 1953-1957

Note that the same scale is used for both indices.

FIG. 4.30. SEASONAL VARIATION IN PRICES OF U.S. NO. 1-2 SLAUGHTER BARROWS AND GILTS, 200-220 LB, INTERIOR IOWA AND SOUTHERN MINNESOTA, 1966-1970

hogs from the previous fall pig crop are marketed. This produces a second seasonal low in April. Seasonal highs and lows do not always hit exactly the months indicated, as particular characteristics of individual years cause some minor shifting forward or backward. However, the seasonal pattern for hogs is more consistent than that for most farm products. It also has a relatively high degree of regularity—with a higher degree of regularity during summer months than during the winter. There have been exceptions, but it is a rare year when hog prices do not hit a high in the summer and a low in the fall. The winter and spring periods are less consistent.

The price pattern for barrows and gilts has changed over the years, as shown in Fig. 4.31. In the pre-World War II period the summer peak occurred in September. During the immediate post-World War II period it moved to August. Currently it tends to occur in July, although in some years it has been as early as June. This forward movement of the peak probably is a reflection of production changes made by hog producers in their attempts to cash in on higher summer prices.

FIG. 4.31. SEASONAL VARIATION IN U.S. NO. 2 SLAUGHTER BARROWS AND GILTS, 200-220 LB, KANSAS CITY, FOUR PERIODS

Another noticeable change in the seasonal price pattern is a decided reduction in amplitude—a tendency to flatten out. This undoubtedly has resulted from more uniform farrowings (increased multiple farrowings) and more uniform marketings. There is reason to believe this trend will continue in the future.

Slaughter Sows, No. 2–3, 330–400 Lb.—The price pattern for sows is essentially the same as for barrows and gilts (Fig. 4.32). That is, it exhibits a summer high and a fall low. The timing of the turning points, however, tend to be about one month later than for barrows and gilts. The summer high typically occurs in August. The fall low (which might more appropriately be called an early winter low) is in December. A secondary peak occurs in March and this is followed by a low in May. The amplitude is less, and irregularity is somewhat greater than for barrows and gilts.

FIG. 4.32. SEASONAL VARIATION IN PRICES OF U.S. NO. 1-3 SOWS, 300-400 LB, INTERIOR IOWA AND SOUTHERN MINNESOTA, 1966-1970

Feeder Pigs, 40 Lb.—Feeder pig prices, on the average, have a decided peak in early spring, then decline to a July-August low (Fig. 4.33). This is followed by partial recovery in September and October and another dip in December. This general pattern reflects the scarcity of feeder pigs on the market during early spring months; which, of course, is the main farrowing period. As the marketing of these pigs increases, prices decline. A second period of relative scarcity occurs in the fall about the time fall farrowings are highest.

While this seasonal has a high degree of amplitude, it also has a high degree of irregularity. One cannot place a high degree of dependence on its regular occurrence.

Sheep—Secular Trends

The long-time pattern of growth in sheep inventory is shown in Fig. 4.34. The pattern illustrated here is a contrast to that of either cattle or hogs. Sheep numbers were substantially greater than cattle and slightly greater than hog numbers when annual records first became available (1867). The overall

FIG. 4.33. SEASONAL VARIATION IN PRICES OF U.S. NO. 1-2 FEEDER
PIGS, 40 LB, WISCONSIN, 1962-1968

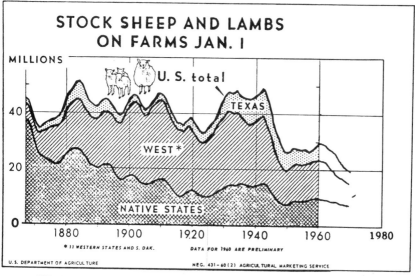

FIG. 4.34. STOCK SHEEP AND LAMBS ON FARMS JAN. 1, 1880-1970
Data 1961 and later added by author from USDA annual livestock inventory reports.

trend since 1867 may be described as irregular with no decidedly general
upward or downward tendency until World War II. At that time inventories
began a precipitous drop that continued until the 1950's. After a minor

recovery, numbers again turned downward. The number of sheep in the United States now is at the lowest point in more than 100 yr.

The trend in total numbers conceals some definite changes within the sheep industry. As may be seen in Fig. 4.34, sheep numbers in the "native" sheep states declined generally throughout the period, while numbers increased in the western states until the 1930's. The drop during the 1940's hit all areas, but was relatively greater in western states. Reasons for this decline are varied, but the ones most usually cited are (1) difficulty in obtaining labor, particularly sheepherders; (2) more attractive alternatives (in some cases a more profitable alternative enterprise; in other cases, a less profitable enterprise but with offsetting noneconomic amenities); (3) problems in predator control (partially related to the labor problem); and (4) reductions in grazing permits on federal lands.

Increases have been made in sheep productivity which have partially offset declining numbers. Death losses have been reduced, the percentage lamb crop has been improved and average slaughter weight has increased. The latter has been accompanied by packer and merchandiser criticism and price discounts. Research by animal and meat scientists at Kansas State University, however, has shown that weight alone is not a valid criterion of lamb values. Improved meat type lambs can be fed to heavier weights without undesirable marketing characteristics.

Increasing importation of lamb and mutton also have partially offset declining U.S. production. During 1969 the importation of lamb amounted to approximately 10% of U.S. lamb production. Imports of mutton were nearly three times U.S. mutton production. The importation of foreign wool and foreign fabrics together with increased domestic production of synthetic fibers have kept competitive pressures on the domestic wool market.

The U.S. sheep industry appears to be at a critical point but it is not necessarily a life-or-death matter. It would take a massive effort to turn production around to the extent that lamb would be made generally available on a regular basis throughout the United States. The sheep industry is cognizant of the situation (Anon. 1970). Further reduction in availability of lamb may eventually put it in the class of a specialty item. This would not mark the end of the sheep industry. Lamb is preferred among certain people and in certain areas, thus assuring a market for lamb on a specialty basis.

Sheep—Cyclical Variations

A semblance of cyclical movements can be seen in Fig. 4.34, although they are not as obvious as in the case of cattle. Prior to World War II there were 7 discernable cycles with an average length of about 10 yr. The sheep cycle is longer than that of hogs, but shorter than cattle, and this is logical in view of the biological timetable of sheep relative to the other species.

The rather drastic changes in sheep numbers since World War II have virtually obliterated cyclical trends. Nevertheless, the changes in production are reflected in corresponding price movements (see Fig. 4.35). If domestic production continues to decline and the importation of lamb continues to increase, variations in domestic production will have less and less influence on prices—except when superior quality of domestically-produced lamb may uphold a specialty market. For the foreseeable future, pronounced or definite cyclical movements are not likely, but variation in domestic production will continue to be the major factor offsetting prices.

From USDA data

FIG. 4.35. PER CAPITA LAMB CONSUMPTION (SUPPLY) AND LAMB PRICES, 1940-1970

Sheep—Seasonal Variations

In market quotation reports, the USDA distinguishes between two classes of slaughter lambs, (1) spring lambs, and (2) wooled lambs. The term "spring lambs" is one of common usage in the trade. However, usual trade terminology for "wooled lambs" is "old crop lambs" or "fed lambs." None of these terms is entirely descriptive of the characteristics of the two classes of slaughter lambs. A major distinction between the classes is in the feeding programs (Cox 1965).

"Spring lambs" are marketed without having been weaned. They are milk-fat lambs. In addition many receive grain, usually by creep feeding arrangements. The production program is such that these lambs begin to reach markets in late spring and marketings increase from that time into the summer.

"Wooled," "old crop," or "fed" lambs are lambs that have been weaned and grain-fed in feedlots. Weaning normally takes place in late summer or fall at the end of the grazing season. These lambs may be "rough fed" for a period or placed in feedlots at weaning time. They normally are marketed in greatest volume during the winter months. The pattern of marketings for each class is instrumental in setting the pattern of seasonality in price movements of the respective classes.

There is some overlapping of marketings of spring lambs and wooled lambs which, if excessive in the spring months, can be detrimental to prices of both classes. The trade considers the two classes to be essentially two separate products. Other things being equal, consumers have a distinct preference for spring lamb. Merchandizers claim that it is difficult to move wooled lambs once spring lambs arrive on the market in volume.

Choice Slaughter Lambs.—The seasonal price patterns for both spring lambs and wooled lambs are shown in Fig. 4.36. It will be noted that this chart is set up with the marketing year beginning in April. Separate price lines are shown for the two classes. The price of spring lambs normally is low early in the season (April and earlier), due to overlapping with wooled lambs. When this ends, spring lamb prices usually are at their seasonal peak. This typically happens in May, but occasionally will vary one month forward or backward. A high at this time of year is very dependable and is due to relative scarcity of marketings. Demand for lamb also is strong at this season. Almost

FIG. 4.36. SEASONAL VARIATION IN PRICES OF CHOICE SLAUGHTER LAMBS, FORT WORTH, 1965-1969

invariably spring lamb prices decline from the early high throughout the summer months.

At the beginning of the season for wooled lambs, prices usually start at a level which is about average for the season then decline to a winter low—typically in December. Following this, à moderate advance sets in as marketings taper off. The seasonal variation of wooled lamb prices is not as pronounced as that of spring lambs, but the degree of irregularity is greater for spring lamb prices.

Choice Feeder Lambs.—Prices for feeder lambs follow a distinctive pattern (Fig. 4.37). Typically, a high occurs at the February-March period. This is followed by a rather drastic decline to early summer (June). Following this, prices can be characterized as generally stable, but indicating a tendency for very slight strengthening to about November, then a definite rising trend to the late winter high. Prices are considerably more irregular during winter and spring months than the remainder of the year.

Seasonal price movements have not been calculated for slaughter ewes. Normally, culling takes place at the end of the grazing season. Substantial numbers go directly to slaughter but many go to feedlots in the "beet belt" (western Nebraska, northern Colorado, Wyoming, and Montana) for fattening. It is a common practice to buy them by the head and sell them by the pound (Fowler 1961).

FIG. 4.37. SEASONAL VARIATION IN PRICES OF CHOICE FEEDER LAMBS, SAN ANGELO, TEXAS, 1967-1970

EMPIRICAL SUPPLY STUDIES

The concept of supply, i.e., quantities which producers stand willing to put on the market at various prices during a given time period, leaves considerable leeway in specifying the time period. For some purposes analysts assume the quantity available for market during, say, the current year to be independent of current prices. The reasoning is that the number of animals available for current marketing was predetermined by prices (and possibly other factors) in a previous period. There is little doubt that greater flexibility—greater response to price—exists in changing quantities for market as the time period is lengthened. The time required for reproduction constrains the domestic production response to price and price changes. Imports, however, may be substituted within limits for domestic production.

Within a period of anything less than a reproduction cycle, some supply changes, even though limited, can be made. Producers can (1) liquidate or add to their inventories and (2) decrease or increase average slaughter weights by adjustment in feeding programs. Generally, it is assumed that the coefficient of price elasticity of supply is positive. That is, producers presumably will sell increased quantities as prices increase and reduced quantities as prices decrease. Given sufficient time this probably is almost universally the case. It is probably correct in most cases in the short-period, but there are exceptions. Livestock feeders with animals approaching market grade and weight often react to a price decline by holding the animals longer than they otherwise would, in hope that prices will rebound. Temporarily, quantities marketed move in the expected direction, but the animals withheld gain weight and the end result is an increase in quantity with decreased prices. But after a period of unprofitable low prices, production will decline. Withholding to build up breeding herds, in response to a price rise, may also appear to be a contradiction to the law of supply, but this short-period phenomenon is followed in time by increased supplies from the larger herds. It stands to reason that elasticity of supply will be less, the shorter the time period specified.

There have been few empirical derivations of the elasticity of supply. An Iowa study reported a coefficient of 0.60–0.65 for spring farrowed pigs (Dean and Heady 1959). This would mean that a 10% change in hog prices would be associated with (in this case it could be said "would result in") a 6-6½% change, in the same direction, in pigs farrowed—all other factors unchanged. This same study also indicated a higher degree of elasticity in post-World War II years than in prior years. A USDA study reported the supply elasticity for spring farrowings to be slightly higher (0.82) than the Iowa study and confirmed an increase in supply elasticity in recent years. In addition, the USDA study noted lower elasticities for fall farrowings than for spring farrowings (Harlow 1962).

Several researchers have investigated the relationship between feed supplies and livestock production. These are supply-related studies. Our previous discussion of the hog-corn ratio, with references cited, is an example. Swanson (1961) reported that a 1% change in the available quantity of feed concentrates (not counting government storage stocks) was associated with a 0.9% change (in the same direction) in feeds fed to livestock. Beyond that he found that a 1% change in quantity of feed fed was associated with about 0.33% change (in the same direction) in livestock production.

Hassler (1962) found an inverse relationship between the quantity of feed concentrates fed and the price of feed concentrates. He reported that a 1% change in concentrate (grain) prices at the farm level was associated with an inverse change of about 0.2% in quantity of concentrates fed to beef cattle and about 0.1% in quantity fed to hogs—given sufficient time for producer response. These findings are consistent with the discussion presented in connection with producer response to the hog-corn ratio. In other words, as feed prices rise relative to livestock prices, fewer livestock will be produced, hence less feed will be fed. It also is likely that producers will attempt to conserve concentrates as concentrate prices rise. The same argument applies to beef as well as hogs. The comparatively low coefficient found by Hassler, however, indicates that the feeding sector is not particularly sensitive to feed concentrate prices.

BIBLIOGRAPHY

ANON. 1970. Special Report Lamb and Wool Industry Developments. Western Livestock Marketing Inform. Proj., Denver. Mar.

BRANDNER, L. 1969. Kansas' investment opportunities or where the economic action is. Kansas Agr. Expt. Sta. Rept. *12*.

BREIMYER, H. F. 1954. 100 million cattle. Proc. Western Farm Econ. Assoc. Meeting, Estes Park, Colo. July.

BURMEISTER, C. A. 1949. Cycles in cattle numbers. USDA Livestock Meat Situation, Mar.

COX, R. 1965. Private communication. Professor Emeritus, Dept. Animal Science and Industry, Kansas State Univ., Manhattan.

DEAN, G. W., and HEADY, E. O. 1959. Changes in supply functions and supply elasticities in hog production. Iowa Agr. Expt. Sta. Res. Bull. *471*.

DeGRAFF, H. 1960. Beef Production and Distribution. University of Oklahoma Press, Norman.

EHRICH, R. 1966. Economic analysis of the United States beef cattle cycle. Wyoming Agr. Expt. Sta. Sci. Monograph *1*.

EZEKIEL, M. 1938. The cobweb theorem. Quart. J. Econ. *52*, 255-280.

FEDERAL RESERVE BANK OF KANSAS CITY. 1961. Is the cattle cycle changing? Monthly Rev. Apr., 3-9.

FOWLER, S. H. 1961. Meat production and consumption. *In* The Marketing of Livestock and Meat, 2nd Edition. Interstate Printers & Publishers, Danville, Ill.

FRANZMANN, J. R. 1967. The trend in slaughter cattle prices. Oklahoma Farm Econ., Dept. Agr. Econ., Oklahoma State Univ. Dec.

GRUBER, J., and HEADY, E. O. 1968. Econometric analysis of the cattle cycle in the United States. Iowa Agr. Expt. Sta. Res. Bull, *564*.

HARLOW, A. A. 1962. Factors affecting the price and supply of hogs. USDA Econ. Res. Serv. Tech. Bull. *1274*.

HASSLER, J. B. 1962. The U.S. feed concentrate-livestock economy's demand structure, 1949-59 (with projections for 1960-70). Nebraska Res. Bull. *203*. Also North Central Regional Publ. *138*.

HOPKINS, J. A., Jr. 1926. A statistical study of the prices and production of beef cattle. Iowa Agr. Expt. Sta. Res. Bull. *101*.

LARSON, A. B. 1964. The hog cycle as harmonic motion. J. Farm Econ. May, 375-386.

MAKI, W. R. 1962. Decomposition of beef and pork cycles. J. Farm Econ. Aug., 731-743.

McCOY, J. H. 1958. Trends in hog prices. Kansas Agr. Expt. Sta. Circ. *368*.

McCOY, J. H. 1959. Characteristics of cattle cycles. Unpublished data, Dept. Econ. Kansas State Univ.

NORDQUIST, A., and OTTOSON, H. 1965. The beef cycle. Nebraska Agr. Expt. Sta. and USDA Cooperating *E.C. 65-827*.

PURCELL, J. C. 1965. Sources of beef and veal supplies and prices of cattle and calves. Georgia Agr. Expt. Sta. Mimeo Ser. *N.S. 233*.

SWANSON, E. R. 1961. Supply response and the feed-livestock economy. *In* Agricultural Supply Functions. Iowa State University Press, Ames.

VAN MEIR, L. W. 1963. Factors in regional location of cattle feeding. Proc. 5th Agr. Ind. Forum, Dept. Agr. Econ., Univ. Illinois, Champaign.

WALTERS, F. 1965. Predicting the beef cattle inventory. USDA Agr. Econ. Res. *XVII*, No. 1, 10-18.

WILSON, C. P., and RILEY, H. M. 1950. Seasonal variation in prices and supplies of livestock. Kansas Agr. Expt. Sta. Unpublished mimeo data, Nov.

CHAPTER 5

Meat Consumption and Related Demand

In a technical sense consumption is not synonymous with demand. As explained in an earlier chapter, demand connotes a relationship between quantity and price. More specifically, demand is the schedule of quantities that purchasers are willing to buy at alternative prices during some given time period. Consumption is defined as the quantity of a product used (consumed) during a specified period without necessarily relating to price.

During a period of 1 yr, for example, the quantity of meat consumed is essentially equal to the quantity available. The quantity available is primarily determined by current production. Storage stocks and net import-export balances are modifying factors. The quantity carried over in storage from 1 yr to the next is only a negligible fraction of total consumption. Some meat is imported and some is exported. While substantial for certain meats and, at particular times, net import-export balances on the average are a relatively small fraction of total meat consumption. International trade in livestock products will be covered in a later chapter.

The price consumers are willing to pay for a given quantity at any particular time is a function of their incomes, tastes and preferences, expectations about future prices, and prices of competing products. Over the long period, the quantity made available by producers at a given time is a function of prices and profit expectations at a previous time.

Consumption trends will be examined, as will factors which influence demand and consumption.

WORLD MEAT CONSUMPTION

Meat consumption in other countries is a matter of interest and economic importance. The United States imports and exports substantial quantities of meat and animal products. Our exports and imports are affected by consumption elsewhere. Within certain limits the world is one big market for meat. Vast areas of the world are capable of producing increased numbers of livestock. Demand for meat increases with increasing incomes and affluence that accompany economic progress. International trade is limited by a number of devices—tariffs, quotas, etc.—nevertheless, large quantities of meat do flow across national borders. While domestic production is the major source of meat consumed in most countries, even a relatively small fraction of imports or exports can be of importance to a domestic market.

The United States ranks high among countries of the world in total meat consumption, but it is not the highest. In 1968 New Zealand was the leader

TABLE 5.1

LEADING MEAT CONSUMING COUNTRIES, 1961-1968[1]

	Meat Consumption per Person				Avg. Percentage Change 1961-1965 to 1968 (%)
	1961-1965 (Lb)	1966 (Lb)	1967 (Lb)	1968[2] (Lb)	
New Zealand	247	222	224	224	− 9
Argentina	198	200	209	220	+11
Uruguay	238	211	227	218	− 8
Australia	210	202	193	204	− 3
United States	167	170	178	183	+10
Canada	141	147	152	158	+12
France	144	152	159	150	+ 4
United Kingdom	143	138	140	138	− 4
West Germany	120	123	124	133	+11
Paraguay	134	133	132	128	− 4

Source: USDA (1969).
[1] Total red meat, carcass weight basis.
[2] Preliminary.

with an average of 224 lb of red meat per person (Table 5.1). This is a position historically held by Uruguay. Following in order were Argentina, 220 lb; Uruguay, 218 lb; and Australia, 204 lb. The United States was in fifth place with 183 lb. Among the five leaders, only in the United States and Argentina was the consumption greater in 1968 than in the 1961-1965 period. The 224 lb consumed by New Zealanders in 1968 was far from a record. In 1953 the people of Uruguay consumed 302 lb per capita. Argentina and Australia have exceeded 224 lb in previous years.

Total meat consumption by the major producing and consuming countries, including those already mentioned, is shown in Table 5.2. Beef and veal consumption by country is given in Table 5.3. Argentina is far ahead in beef consumption with 189 lb. Uruguay is second with 144 lb, and the United States is third with 113 lb.

The consumption level of pork in the top consuming countries does not approach the top beef consumption. However, the distribution of pork consumption is such that in terms of total quantities consumed worldwide (excluding Red China), pork constitutes about 40%, while beef is slightly more than 50%. West Germany was the leader in pork consumption with 81 lb (Table 5.4). Austria was second with 78 lb and Czechoslovakia was third with 70 lb. The United States, with a consumption of 66 lb, tied for fourth with Denmark.

Mutton, lamb, and goat meat comprise about 8% of all meat consumed. Lamb, mutton and goat meat consumption in New Zealand and Australia, at 87 and 84 lb respectively, are in a class by themselves (Table 5.5). Uruguay is third with 57 lb, followed by Greece with 32 lb. Average consumption in the

TABLE 5.2
TOTAL MEAT[1] PER CAPITA CONSUMPTION IN SPECIFIED COUNTRIES,
AVERAGE 1961-1965, ANNUAL 1966-1968

Continent and Country	Avg. 1961-1965 (Lb)	1966 (Lb)	1967 (Lb)	1968[2] (Lb)	Avg. Percentage Change 1961-1965 to 1968 (%)
North America					
Canada	141	147	152	158	+ 8
United States	167	170	178	183	+10
Mexico	40	40	39	40	...
South America					
Argentina	198	200	209	220	+11
Brazil	53	52	53	51	− 4
Chile	64	56	53	51	−10
Colombia	55	48	47	47	−16
Paraguay	134	133	132	128	− 4
Peru	36	35	33	32	−11
Uruguay	238	211	227	218	− 8
Venezuela	49	53	54	53	+ 8
Europe					
Western					
EEC					
Belgium and Luxembourg	116	124	129	132	+14
France	144	152	159	150	+ 4
Germany, West	120	123	124	133	+11
Italy	57	62	66	65	+14
Netherlands	98	108	108	111	+13
EEC	107	113	117	116	+ 8
Austria	120	121	126	128	+ 7
Denmark	113	125	124	111	− 2
Finland	78	82	84	76	− 3
Greece	56	70	73	75	+34
Ireland	110	116	108	108	− 2
Norway	79	82	80	80	+ 1
Portugal	42	45	46	45	+ 7
Spain	47	58	61	68	+45
Sweden	102	100	101	103	+ 1
Switzerland	112	119	117	122	+ 9
United Kingdom	143	138	140	138	− 4
Eastern					
Bulgaria	69	85	89	92	+33
Czechoslovakia	100	106	111	112	+12
Germany, East	99	113	117	121	+22
Hungary	84	83	85	84	...
Poland	82	90	91	94	+15
Yugoslavia	44	46	53	53	+20
USSR	66	74	78	79	+20
Africa					
South Africa, Republic of	79	77	69	71	−10
Asia					
Japan	13	18	19	18	+38
Philippines	24	28	28	28	+17
Oceania					
Australia[3]	210	202	193	204	− 3
New Zealand[4]	247	222	224	224	− 9

Source: USDA (1969).
[1] Carcass weight basis.
[2] Preliminary.
[3] Year ending June 30.
[4] Year ending Sept. 30.

TABLE 5.3

BEEF AND VEAL[1] PER CAPITA CONSUMPTION IN SPECIFIED COUNTRIES,
AVERAGE 1961-1965, ANNUAL 1966-1968

Continent and Country	Avg 1961-1965 (Lb)	1966 (Lb)	1967 (Lb)	1968[2] (Lb)
North America				
Canada	84	92	91	94
United States	99	108	110	113
Mexico	25	25	23	24
South America				
Argentina	169	167	178	189
Brazil	39	37	38	36
Chile	44	36	35	33
Colombia	49	43	42	42
Paraguay	107	104	102	99
Peru	19	19	18	17
Uruguay	179	154	147	144
Venezuela	40	44	45	44
Europe				
Western				
EEC:				
Belgium and Luxembourg	54	54	57	58
France	72	75	80	77
Germany, West	48	49	49	52
Italy	35	40	43	42
Netherlands	45	46	48	47
EEC	51	54	56	55
Austria	43	44	47	49
Denmark	34	44	43	44
Finland	43	44	43	37
Greece	19	27	30	31
Ireland	30	33	27	26
Norway	34	34	33	33
Portugal	15	18	19	19
Spain	16	20	22	24
Sweden	43	44	42	44
Switzerland	53	55	54	56
United Kingdom	57	52	55	53
Eastern				
Bulgaria	20	24	27	29
Czechoslovakia	39	38	41	42
Germany, East	[3]	[3]	[3]	[3]
Hungary	22	19	18	18
Poland	27	29	32	34
Yugoslavia	14	15	17	17
USSR	29	35	39	41
Africa				
South Africa, Republic of	56	54	47	46
Asia				
Japan	4	4	4	4
Philippines	6	7	6	6
Oceania				
Australia[4]	96	94	86	93
New Zealand[5]	111	109	110	107

Source: USDA (1969).
[1] Carcass weight basis.
[2] Preliminary.
[3] Included in total consumption.
[4] Year ending June 30.
[5] Year ending Sept. 30.

TABLE 5.4
PORK[1] PER CAPITA CONSUMPTION IN SPECIFIED COUNTRIES,
AVERAGE 1961-1965, ANNUAL 1966-1968

Continent and Country	Avg 1961-1965 (Lb)	1966 (Lb)	1967 (Lb)	1968[2] (Lb)
North America				
Canada	53	50	56	58
United States	63	58	64	66
Mexico	12	12	13	13
South America				
Argentina	17	21	19	17
Brazil	13	14	14	14
Chile	12	13	12	12
Colombia	6	5	5	4
Paraguay	26	27	28	27
Peru	9	8	7	7
Uruguay	20	18	20	17
Venezuela	9	8	8	8
Europe				
Western				
EEC:				
Belgium and Luxembourg	54	61	64	65
France	61	66	68	62
Germany, West	71	73	75	81
Italy	18	19	20	20
Netherlands	49	58	57	60
EEC	51	54	55	56
Austria	75	76	78	78
Denmark	77	79	79	66
Finland	32	34	38	37
Greece	11	13	11	12
Ireland	56	59	57	58
Norway	34	36	37	37
Portugal	20	19	22	20
Spain	21	28	29	34
Sweden	55	52	56	56
Switzerland	55	60	60	63
United Kingdom	61	62	60	61
Eastern				
Bulgaria	32	38	38	39
Czechoslovakia	60	68	70	70
Germany, East	3	3	3	3
Hungary	59	61	64	63
Poland	52	58	56	57
Yugoslavia	25	26	31	31
USSR	28	32	32	31
Africa				
South Africa, Republic of	6	7	7	7
Asia				
Japan	7	11	12	11
Philippines	18	21	22	22
Oceania				
Australia[4]	23	25	26	27
New Zealand[5]	36	31	29	30

Source: USDA (1969).
[1] Carcass weight basis.
[2] Preliminary.
[3] Included in total consumption.
[4] Year ending June 30.
[5] Year ending Sept. 30.

TABLE 5.5

MUTTON, LAMB, AND GOAT MEAT[1] PER CAPITA CONSUMPTION IN SPECIFIED COUNTRIES, AVERAGE 1961-1965, ANNUAL 1966-1968

Continent and Country	Avg 1961-1965 (Lb)	1966 (Lb)	1967 (Lb)	1968[2] (Lb)
North America				
Canada	4	5	5	6
United States	5	4	4	4
Mexico	3	3	3	3
South America				
Argentina	12	12	12	14
Brazil	1	1	1	1
Chile	8	7	6	6
Colombia	. . .	. . .	. . .	. . .
Paraguay	1	2	2	2
Peru	8	8	8	8
Uruguay	39	39	60	57
Venezuela	[3]	1	1	1
Europe				
Western				
EEC:				
Belgium and Luxembourg	1	1	1	2
France	6	7	7	7
Germany, West	1	1	[3]	[3]
Italy	2	2	2	2
Netherlands	[3]	1	[3]	1
EEC	2	3	3	3
Austria	[3]	[3]	[3]	[3]
Denmark	1	1	1	1
Finland	1	1	1	[3]
Greece	26	30	32	32
Ireland	24	24	24	24
Norway	9	10	9	9
Portugal	6	7	5	6
Spain	9	9	9	9
Sweden	1	1	1	1
Switzerland	2	2	2	2
United Kingdom	25	24	25	24
Eastern				
Bulgaria	17	23	24	24
Czechoslovakia	1	[3]	[3]	[3]
Germany, East	[4]	[4]	[4]	[4]
Hungary	2	2	2	2
Poland	2	2	2	2
Yugoslavia	5	5	5	5
USSR	9	7	7	7
Africa				
South Africa, Republic of	17	16	15	18
Asia				
Japan	1	2	2	2
Philippines	[3]	[3]	[3]	[3]
Oceania				
Australia[5]	91	83	81	84
New Zealand[6]	101	82	86	87

Source: USDA (1969).
[1] Carcass weight basis.
[2] Preliminary.
[3] Less than 0.5 lb.
[4] Included in total consumption.
[5] Year ending June 30.
[6] Year ending Sept. 30.

TABLE 5.6
HORSE MEAT[1] PER CAPITA CONSUMPTION IN SPECIFIED COUNTRIES, AVERAGE 1961-1965, ANNUAL 1966-1968

Continent and Country	Avg 1961-1965 (Lb)	1966 (Lb)	1967 (Lb)	1968[2] (Lb)
North America				
Canada	...	...	...	...
United States	...	...	...	...
Mexico	[3]	[3]	[3]	[3]
South America				
Argentina	...	...	...	...
Brazil	...	...	...	...
Chile	...	...	...	...
Colombia	...	...	...	...
Paraguay	[3]	...	...	...
Peru	[3]	[3]	[3]	[3]
Uruguay	...	...	...	...
Venezuela	...	...	...	...
Europe				
Western				
EEC:				
Belgium and Luxembourg	7	8	7	7
France	5	4	4	4
Germany, West	[3]	[3]	[3]	[3]
Italy	2	1	1	1
Netherlands	4	3	3	3
EEC	2	2	2	2
Austria	2	1	1	1
Denmark	1	1	1	[3]
Finland	2	3	2	2
Greece	...	...	...	...
Ireland	...	...	...	...
Norway	2	2	1	1
Portugal	1	1	[3]	[3]
Spain	1	1	1	1
Sweden	3	3	2	2
Switzerland	2	2	1	1
United Kingdom	...	...	...	...
Eastern				
Bulgaria	[3]	[3]	[3]	[3]
Czechoslovakia	[3]	[3]	[3]	[3]
Germany, East	[4]	[4]	[4]	[4]
Hungary	1	1	1	1
Poland	1	1	1	1
Yugoslavia	[3]	[3]	[3]	[3]
USSR	...	...	...	...
Africa				
South Africa, Republic of	[3]	[3]	[3]	[3]
Asia				
Japan	1	1	1	1
Philippines	[3]	[3]	[3]	[3]
Oceania				
Australia	...	...	...	...
New Zealand	...	...	...	...

Source: USDA (1969).
[1] Carcass weight basis.
[2] Preliminary.
[3] Less than 0.5 lb.
[4] Included in total consumption.

United States was only 4 lb, which was far down the list among countries of the world. Horse meat is a minor component of the total. However, people of Belgium and Luxembourg consumed 7 lb per capita (Table 5.6). This is as much total meat as is consumed by people of some of the less-developed countries.

In total pounds of meat consumed (that is per capita consumption times population) the United States leads all other countries. U.S. consumption accounted for approximately 1/3 of all beef and veal, slightly more than 1/4 of all pork and about 1/10 of all lamb, mutton, and goat meat.

The rate of growth in meat consumption varied greatly among countries. The majority recorded gains, but 1/3 of the countries had a negative growth (consumed less in 1968 than the average of the 1961-1965 period). Note that most countries with a negative growth rate are less developed economically (but there are several exceptions to this, such as Denmark, Finland, Ireland, and the United Kingdom). Countries with greatest gains were Spain, Japan, Greece, and Bulgaria. Japan is cited as an example of what economic development can do to meat consumption. That country is experiencing an almost phenomenal economic growth. Prior to economic take-off, the Japanese were not known as meat-eaters. Even as late as the early 1960's total meat consumption was only 13 lb per capita. With growth in per capita income, the Japanese have shown a distinct preference for meat. Current consumption, at 18 lb per capita, still is low by Western standards but is increasing rapidly. The significance of the situation is that this is a large concentration of people who are developing a demand for meat. With limited natural resources available for livestock production, there is practically no chance of Japan producing both feed grains and livestock. Japan already is importing substantial quantities of feed concentrates and the United States is a chief supplier. Substantial quantities of meat also are imported, with Australia and New Zealand the chief suppliers. Japan's decision on whether to import meat or its raw products in the future will be a matter of both economics and politics. Currently, Japan imports some meat from East African countries largely as means of balancing payments for merchandise sold to those countries.

Economic growth has been generally widespread in European countries since overcoming the disasters of World War II. These countries, also, are increasing consumption of meat. When one considers the relatively low level of current consumption, and the large numbers of people involved, it becomes readily apparent that significant market development awaits only the increase in incomes that come with further economic development.

The less-developed countries of Africa, Asia, and Central America hold vast numbers of people who consume only a few pounds of meat per person per year. Aside from those whose religion forbids the consumption of certain meats (e.g., Moslems and Hindus) these people want more meat. They would purchase more meat if their incomes were higher. The potential of this immense latent market challenges the imagination, just as the formidable array of barriers to economic growth challenges those who are so vigorously pursuing it. Progress will be made and eventually these countries will be brought into the world market economy. Some Central American countries presently are attempting to expand exports. Additional efforts can be expected in the future. In the immediate future, however, foreseeable developments will not significantly affect meat consumption in the less--developed countries. This is a long-range situation.

U.S. MEAT CONSUMPTION

Per capita consumption of red meat was high in the United States in the early days, which is typical of frontier countries. Around 1900, however, total meat consumption began a slight downturn as population increased faster than meat supplies. This trend was reversed following the drouth-depression period of the 1930's and the upward trend established then still is continuing. Consumption of all red meats in 1970 was 184 lb per person—an all-time high. Trends since 1910 are shown in Fig. 5.1. The term "all red meat" or "total red meat" is a composite or aggregation of beef, veal, pork, lamb, and mutton. The trend in total meat consumption covers up some significant differences among individual meats.

A decline in beef consumption from the early 1900's to mid-1930's largely accounted for the decline in total meat consumption. In terms of absolute

FIG. 5.1. MEAT CONSUMPTION PER PERSON

quantity, beef consumption now is far ahead, although this has not always been the case. As may be noted in Fig. 5.1, pork consumption generally was higher than beef consumption until the early 1950's. Prior to that, beef consumption had temporarily exceeded pork consumption on several occasions, but since the early 1950's beef has dominated. Since the early 1950's beef consumption has increased about 50%. U.S. consumers ate 112 lb of beef per capita in 1970 and there is every indication it will go higher. Pork consumption has varied around the 65-lb level most of the time since the early 1950's and only in the most recent years has it shown a tendency to increase.

Veal, lamb, and mutton have always comprised a relatively minor fraction of total meat consumption. Consumption of each was on a slightly increasing trend until about the end of World War II. Since that time the trend of both has been decidedly downward. Consumption of veal amounted to only 3 lb per person in 1970, and lamb and mutton consumption was about the same. Thus, the gain in total meat consumption since the early 1950's has been virtually all in beef.

While by far the bulk of meat consumed is in the fresh form, Ives (1966) has pointed out that the share of toal meat represented by sausage and canned meats has risen more than the overall trend.

Meat Consumption Patterns—Regional and Type of Household

By Specie.—Consumption data are reported on a regular annual basis for the United States as a whole, but regional or state information is available only from special studies which are not made at regularly scheduled intervals. During the spring of 1965, the USDA carried out a nationwide survey[1] during one week which provides some information on regional meat consumption characteristics by type of household and income level (Rizek and Rockwell 1970). A comparable study was made 10 yr earlier which provides a basis for determining temporal changes. The 1965 study showed that meat was the most important item in the food budget—accounting for 30.2¢ of each dollar spent for food at home. This was up from 29.5¢ in 1955. Approximately 88% of the meat expenditures were for red meat and the remaining 12% for poultry. Fruits and vegetables ranked second to meat, taking 19¢ of the food dollar.

For purposes of analysis, the United States was divided into four regions—North Central, Northeast, South and West. During the week of the study, "Consumers (Rizek and Rockwell 1970) in the North Central region used the most red meat—3.6 lb per person . . . Those in the West consumed 3.4 lb of red meat; the Northeast, 3.3 lb; while those in the South averaged 3.1 lb" (Table 5.7). These differences may appear to be minor, but on this basis consumption in the North Central would be 17% greater than in the South.

[1] This section draws heavily on a USDA national survey of household consumption of meat and poultry (Rizek and Rockwell 1970).

TABLE 5.7

USE (POUNDS) OF MEAT PER PERSON, FARM AND NONFARM HOUSEHOLDS,
FOR ONE WEEK IN THE SPRINGS OF 1955 and 1965, BY REGIONS

Region and Household Group	All Meat[1]		Beef		Pork		Veal		Lamb and Mutton		Variety Meats[1]		Luncheon Meats	
	1955	1965	1955	1965	1955	1965	1955	1965	1955	1965	1955	1965	1955	1965
United States														
All	3.02	3.35	1.25	1.65	1.14	1.10	0.08	0.05	0.09	0.06	0.10	0.07	0.36	0.43
Urban	3.17	3.43	1.34	1.69	1.13	1.09	0.10	0.06	0.12	0.07	0.11	0.08	0.36	0.43
Rural nonfarm	2.80	3.10	1.10	1.51	1.15	1.06	0.05	0.02	0.03	0.02	0.08	0.05	0.39	0.44
Farm	2.82	3.44	1.18	1.73	1.21	1.25	0.02	0.01	0.02	0.01	0.07	0.05	0.32	0.39
Northeast														
All	3.07	3.34	1.29	1.63	0.98	0.98	0.12	0.10	0.19	0.11	0.13	0.08	0.37	0.44
Urban	3.10	3.42	1.29	1.64	0.95	1.02	0.15	0.11	0.23	0.13	0.14	0.09	0.35	0.43
Rural nonfarm	2.92	3.09	1.23	1.60	1.01	0.88	0.06	0.05	0.09	0.05	0.10	0.04	0.43	0.48
Farm	3.30	3.35	1.54	1.87	1.15	0.95	0.05	0.04	0.07	0.00	0.09	0.06	0.39	0.43
North Central														
All	3.37	3.60	1.51	1.81	1.23	1.17	0.07	0.04	0.05	0.02	0.09	0.06	0.42	0.50
Urban	3.42	3.59	1.52	1.77	1.22	1.18	0.10	0.05	0.08	0.03	0.09	0.06	0.42	0.50
Rural nonfarm	3.17	3.46	1.43	1.76	1.17	1.11	0.05	0.02	0.01	0.01	0.08	0.06	0.43	0.51
Farm	3.45	3.91	1.61	2.16	1.34	1.24	0.02	0.01	0.01	0.01	0.06	0.06	0.40	0.44
South														
All	2.57	3.10	0.85	1.43	1.26	1.18	0.04	0.03	0.02	0.02	0.09	0.06	0.30	0.38
Urban	2.93	3.26	1.09	1.56	1.33	1.16	0.06	0.04	0.03	0.03	0.12	0.08	0.30	0.39
Rural nonfarm	2.32	2.88	0.64	1.27	1.22	1.14	0.03	0.02	0.02	0.02	0.06	0.05	0.34	0.38
Farm	2.18	2.89	0.68	1.17	1.18	1.34	0.01	0.01	0.01	0.01	0.06	0.05	0.23	0.32
West														
All	3.31	3.41	1.62	1.86	1.00	0.95	0.07	0.02	0.13	0.10	0.11	0.08	0.37	0.39
Urban	3.25	3.43	1.52	1.85	1.00	0.95	0.07	0.03	0.17	0.11	0.12	0.09	0.38	0.39
Rural nonfarm	3.58	2.99	1.89	1.66	1.05	0.90	0.12	0.00	0.04	0.02	0.09	0.02	0.38	0.38
Farm	3.15	4.26	1.73	2.60	0.89	1.12	0.03	0.02	0.10	0.02	0.08	0.07	0.31	0.42

Source: Rizek and Rockwell (1970).
[1] Excludes game.

Farm families were the biggest consumers of red meats, however farm consumption also varied considerably among regions. Western farm households ate 47% more red meat than did Southern farm households.

Beef consumption was highest in the Western region, with the North Central a close second. The South was lowest in beef consumption, but highest in pork consumption. The Northeast and West were relatively low in pork consumption, but exceeded the South and North Central in lamb and mutton consumption. It is worth noting that luncheon meats accounted for 13% of total consumption for the United States as a whole.

Per capita consumption of red meat increased 1/3 lb per week between the 1955 and 1965 surveys, with the largest increase occurring in the South.

Beef consumption in the survey week increased from 1.25 pounds per capita in 1955 to 1.65 pounds in 1965 (Rizek and Rockwell 1970). Pork consumption by farm families increased slightly from 1955 to 1965, but this was more than offset by declines in other households, resulting in a net decline for total pork consumption. In this connection it is noted that pork production was 7% higher in 1965 than in 1955, but population increased more than 7% so per capita production was lower in 1965 than in 1955. The per capita consumption of veal and also of lamb and mutton declined from 1955 to 1965.

For the United States as a whole, beef accounted for about 1/2 of all meat, but was considerably higher in the West (54%) than in the South (46%). However, the sharpest increase in beef consumption between 1955 and 1965 was in the South (see Table 5.8). Pork comprised 1/3 of the red meat consumed nationwide. In 1955, pork accounted for 49% of the red meat consumed in the South versus only 33% for beef. By 1965, the positions of pork and beef were just about reversed (Rizek and Rockwell 1970).

By Cut of Meat.—When meat was shipped to retail outlets in carcass form, sales and consumption of the various cuts were in about the same ratio throughout the various regions. This generally was the case with beef in 1955.

TABLE 5.8

BEEF, PORK, AND OTHER MEATS, AS A PERCENTAGE OF TOTAL RED MEAT CONSUMPTION, ALL HOUSEHOLDS BY REGIONS, FOR ONE WEEK IN THE SPRINGS OF 1955 AND 1965

Regions	Beef		Pork		Other Meats[1]	
	1955 (%)	1965 (%)	1955 (%)	1965 (%)	1955 (%)	1965 (%)
United States	41	49	38	33	21	18
Northeast	42	49	32	29	26	22
North Central	45	50	36	32	19	18
South	33	46	49	38	18	16
West	49	54	30	28	21	18

Source: Rizek and Rockwell (1970).
[1] Veal, lamb, variety meats, and luncheon meats.

By 1965 an increase had occurred in shipment of primal-wholesale cuts of beef. As a result, consumption of different cuts varied considerably by region and by type of household. For the United States as a whole, steaks comprised a larger percentage of total beef consumption in 1965 than in 1955—41% compared to 31%. Ground beef was a smaller percentage of total beef consumption—25% compared to 30% (Rizek and Rockwell 1970).[2]

Consumption of steak increased markedly (as a percentage of total beef consumption) in all regions and among all types of households (Table 5.9). The increase was greater in the Northeast and West than the North Central and Southern regions. While the consumption of ground beef increased in absolute terms during this interval (from 0.38 lb in 1955 to 0.41 lb in 1965) it decreased in relative terms, i.e., as a percentage of the total. Exceptions were in the farm households of the Northeast, North Central and South. Relative declines also occurred in all regions for roasts and "other" beef cuts.

TABLE 5.9

PERCENTAGE OF BEEF CONSUMED AS VARIOUS CUTS, BY REGION AND TYPE OF HOUSEHOLD, FOR ONE WEEK IN THE SPRINGS OF 1955 AND 1965[1]

Region and Household Group	Steaks 1955 (%)	Steaks 1965 (%)	Roasts 1955 (%)	Roasts 1965 (%)	Ground 1955 (%)	Ground 1965 (%)	Other[2] 1955 (%)	Other[2] 1965 (%)
United States								
All	31	41	28	26	30	25	11	8
Urban	32	44	28	27	29	22	11	7
Rural nonfarm	28	36	26	25	34	31	12	8
Farm	32	36	29	25	27	31	12	8
Northeast								
All	31	48	28	27	30	17	11	8
Urban	33	51	28	27	28	14	11	8
Rural nonfarm	24	43	27	25	36	26	13	6
Farm	27	29	29	28	31	34	13	9
North Central								
All	31	36	29	27	30	30	10	7
Urban	32	37	30	28	29	28	9	7
Rural nonfarm	29	33	27	25	35	35	9	7
Farm	32	34	29	26	29	33	10	7
South								
All	31	39	25	25	30	27	14	9
Urban	31	41	26	26	30	25	13	8
Rural nonfarm	30	36	21	24	34	31	15	9
Farm	33	37	27	22	23	30	17	11
West								
All	32	44	29	26	29	21	10	9
Urban	31	46	30	25	29	20	10	9
Rural nonfarm	34	27	26	31	29	33	11	9
Farm	33	44	28	24	27	26	12	6

Source: Rizek and Rockwell (1970).
[1] Excludes quantities of those meats consumed as luncheon meats.
[2] Corned, chipped dried, stewing and canned beef.

Changes in consumption of various pork cuts by regions and type of household are shown in Table 5.10. Here, wide differences are noted among

[2] Part of this change was attributed to possible changes in retailing practices and survey reporting procedures.

TABLE 5.10

PERCENTAGE OF PORK CONSUMED AS VARIOUS CUTS, BY HOUSEHOLD GROUP AND REGION, FOR ONE WEEK IN THE SPRINGS OF 1955 AND 1965[1]

Region and Household Group	Loin and Chops 1955 (%)	Loin and Chops 1965 (%)	Ham[2] 1955 (%)	Ham[2] 1965 (%)	Sausage 1955 (%)	Sausage 1965 (%)	Bacon 1955 (%)	Bacon 1965 (%)	Salt Pork 1955 (%)	Salt Pork 1965 (%)	Other 1955 (%)	Other 1965 (%)
United States												
All	23	21	26	25	8	9	22	22	5	2	16	21
Urban	25	23	27	25	7	9	21	21	3	1	17	21
Rural nonfarm	22	18	25	25	9	11	23	25	6	3	15	18
Farm	19	15	24	26	10	10	24	22	8	5	15	22
Northeast												
All	27	26	32	28	5	9	17	17	1	1	18	19
Urban	27	27	32	27	5	9	18	16	1	1	17	20
Rural nonfarm	27	24	36	32	6	8	17	21	1	1	13	14
Farm	22	16	30	36	9	10	18	20	2	1	19	17
North Central												
All	28	22	26	26	8	9	21	21	1	1	16	21
Urban	29	24	28	24	7	8	20	21	1	[3]	15	23
Rural nonfarm	30	19	24	31	8	10	23	23	[3]	1	15	16
Farm	27	17	25	29	10	8	20	21	1	2	17	23
South												
All	16	17	22	22	10	11	25	26	11	4	16	20
Urban	18	19	24	24	9	10	24	26	8	3	17	18
Rural nonfarm	15	14	21	19	11	13	24	28	14	6	15	20
Farm	11	14	21	22	11	11	27	22	17	9	13	22
West												
All	24	21	23	23	7	8	27	25	1	1	18	22
Urban	23	21	24	23	6	8	27	25	1	1	19	22
Rural nonfarm	27	21	20	20	10	10	27	28	2	1	14	20
Farm	18	16	23	22	10	14	30	27	2	[3]	17	21

Source: Rizek and Rockwell (1970).
[1] Excludes quantities consumed as luncheon meats.
[2] Fresh and cured. About 9/10 is cured.
[3] Less than 0.5%.

regions in both 1955 and 1965. Changes between the two time periods appear rather minor. Consumption of pork chops was particularly low in the South, as was bacon in the Northeast. Consumption of ham was relatively low in the South and West. Consumption of salt pork was far higher in the South than in any other region, but in this region a marked decline occurred between 1955 and 1965.

Factors Related to Meat Consumption

Many factors are related to the quantity of meat consumed and to the amount of money spent for meat. In previous sections attention was called to differences in consumption among nations and among regions within the United States. These differences largely are reflections of more basic factors, of which the more important are price of the product, level of family income, and prices of competing products. Other factors are ethnic background, type of occupation, religious beliefs, personal tastes and preferences, diets, and food fads. In terms of total consumption, the number of people obviously is an important factor. The relationship involved between number of people and meat consumption needs little analysis. Other things being equal, a 1% increase in the number of people will result in about 1% increase in quantity of meat consumed. Our concern primarily is with factors which affect the quantity consumed per person, and emphasis is placed on product prices, incomes, and prices of competing products.

Price of the Product.—The relationship between consumption and price of the product is explained by theories of demand. It is quite obvious to the housewife with a limited budget that she can, and will, buy more meat at lower prices than at higher prices, and vice versa. Prices, of course, are established at various levels throughout the marketing system. An examination of the price-quantity relationship at the retail and farm levels follows.

Retail Demand.—The relationship between prices and quantity consumed involves the notion of price elasticity of demand which was discussed in Chap. 3. A considerable amount of research has been done on price elasticity for various products. The results are not identical, but reasonably consistent. Differences in research results on this problem can arise from differences in the time period upon which the study is based, and differences in research methodology.

Two general conclusions are: (1) demand is less elastic at the farm level than at retail, and (2) demand is less elastic for aggregates of food than for individual items. In an exhaustive study Brandow (1961) found retail price elasticities as follows: beef −0.95, veal −1.60, pork −0.75, and lamb and mutton −2.35. These coefficients are shown in the diagonal position in Table 5.11 (the other data in Table 5.11 are cross-elasticities and will be discussed later).

Interpretation of the elasticity coefficients, taking beef as an example, is that a 1% increase in retail beef prices will result in a decrease in quantity purchased of 0.95 of 1% (or vice versa for price decrease). This can be classed as slightly inelastic. In an earlier pioneering study, Working (1954) reported that the demand for beef was more price elastic in the long-run (5 or 10 yr) than in the short-run (1 yr). His calculation of short-run price elasticity was −0.90 which is reasonably close to Brandow's figure. Working determined the long-run price elasticity for beef to be −1.401-N−1.50. At this level demand definitely would be elastic. No one disagrees with the proposition that the long-run price elasticity for beef to be − 1.401 − 1.50. At this level demand researchers agree that Working's analysis proved the point. From the standpoint of market control, the degree of elasticity is an important consideration. Supply reduction programs are based on the supposition that demand is price inelastic (that a reduction in quantity would result in a more than proportionate increase in price). This would mean an increase in total revenue and (unless costs increased) presumably an increase in net revenue. But if the demand is elastic, supply reduction would decrease rather than increase revenue. Whatever the degree of price elasticity, the beef cattle industry, through the spokesmanship of its national organization, has never condoned a mandatory supply control program. The opposition to such an approach has never been based on possible negative revenue effects as a result of an elastic demand. It is not known whether industry actions are the reflection of an intuitive feeling that revenue would decline, simply a reflection of rugged individualism, or some other aspect. While the question of degree of price elasticity in the long-run is not settled, there is general agreement that the short-run elasticity of demand for beef is less than unity. As mentioned, Brandow reported −0.95, Working, −0.90. Others (Breimyer 1961; Hassler 1962) have reported somewhat lower elasticities and there is some evidence that the degree of elasticity is decreasing with the passing of time.

The elasticity of demand for veal is −1.60, and for lamb and mutton −2.35 (Table 5.11). In the latter it can be assumed that the coefficient represents primarily the demand for lamb, rather than mutton. Consumers are more sensitive (i.e., respond by adjusting purchases) to price changes of veal and lamb than to price changes of beef or pork.

Pork has the lowest degree of price elasticity of any meat, according to Brandow's calculations. Table 5.11 shows the coefficient of elasticity to be −0.75. Results of other studies range both higher and lower than this, but most studies put the elasticity of pork less than unity and slightly below that for beef.

Price elasticity coefficients for chicken (−1.16) and turkey (−1.40) also are shown in Table 5.11. Both are relatively elastic, meaning quantity purchased is relatively responsive to price change. Thus, it is seen that at retail the two major meats (beef and pork) have a relatively inelastic demand—the others

TABLE 5.11

PRICE ELASTICITIES OF DEMAND AT RETAIL; PERCENTAGE CHANGES
IN QUANTITIES DEMANDED RESULTING FROM
1% CHANGE IN PRICES, 1955-1957

Quantities Demanded of:	Retail Prices of:					
	Beef	Veal	Pork	Lamb and Mutton	Chicken	Turkey
Beef	−0.95	0.06	0.10	0.04	0.07	0.01
Veal	0.38	−1.60	0.19	0.07	0.14	0.01
Pork	0.13	0.04	−0.75	0.03	0.07	0.01
Lamb and mutton	0.62	0.17	0.41	−2.35	0.22	0.02
Chicken	0.23	0.06	0.16	0.04	−1.16	0.12
Turkey	0.10	0.03	0.07	0.02	0.50	−1.40

Source: Brandow (1961).

(veal, lamb and mutton, chicken and turkey) have a relatively elastic demand.

Farm Level Demand.–Producers generally are more concerned with price-quantity relationships at the farm level. Most realize that demand for their products is derived from retail demand, but lags and market imperfections often screen the direct relationships. So far, we have discussed elasticity of demand in terms of the effect on quantity purchased of variations in price. This is the viewpoint of a merchandiser. The same situation viewed in the inverse may be put in the form of a question. What is the effect upon price of variations in quantity? This is more in line with the viewpoint of producers. There is evidence that more and more producers are becoming concerned. Various farm organizations have undertaken programs designed to gain some control over variations in quantity marketed, both in terms of total quantities and cyclical and seasonal variations. If price elasticity is known, this question can be answered by calculating its reciprocal—which gives an approximation of the "price flexibility" coefficient. It follows that price flexibility increases as elasticity decreases. In other words, the more inelastic the demand, the greater effect a given change in quantity will have upon price received. The following discussion of farm level demand for livestock will be in terms of price elasticity. The implications to price flexibility are obvious.

Farm level price elasticity coefficients from Brandow's (1961) study are as follows: cattle −0.68, calves −1.08, hogs −0.46, and sheep and lambs −1.78 (Table 5.12). In all cases elasticity is less at the farm level than at retail. This follows from the fact that marketing charges remain relatively fixed when prices vary. A price change at retail will be passed back through marketing channels to farmers in almost its entirety. Since farm prices are lower than retail (by the amount of marketing charges), a given price change has a greater percentage effect on farm price (which is a lower absolute amount than retail price) than on retail price. An example will make this clear. Assume retail price is $1.00 per lb and marketing charges are 40¢ per lb. Farm price equivalent would be 60¢ per lb (i.e., $1.00 − 0.40 = $0.60). Suppose retail prices decrease 10¢ per lb. At the retail level the change amounts to 10%. If the entire 10¢ decrease is taken from the farm price, the change amounts to almost 17% of the farm price. If it is assumed that the percentage change in quantity marketed was the same at both levels, this translates to a lower degree of elasticity at the farm than at retail. This situation appears to be verified by the evidence presented.

TABLE 5.12

ELASTICITY OF TOTAL FARM LEVEL DEMAND
FOR FARM PRODUCTS, 1955-1957

Quantities Demanded	Cattle	Calves	Hogs	Farm Prices of: Sheep and Lambs	Chicken	Turkey
Cattle	−0.68	0.04	0.06	0.03	0.05	0.01
Calves	0.26	−1.08	0.11	0.06	0.09	0.01
Hogs	0.09	0.02	−0.46	0.03	0.04	[1]
Sheep and lambs	0.42	0.12	0.25	−1.78	0.14	0.01
Chickens	0.16	0.04	0.09	0.03	−0.73	0.08
Turkeys	0.07	0.02	0.04	0.01	0.32	−0.92

Source: Brandow (1961).
[1] Less than 0.01

The relatively low price elasticity at the farm level for most agricultural products is at the root of the comparatively violent price fluctuations that accompany production variations, e.g., seasonal and cyclical variations in livestock and weather-induced variations in crop production.

A knowledge of price elasticities, coupled with good estimates of impending changes in quantities available for market, provides one basis for forecasting price changes. Take the case of hogs as an example. The coefficient of price elasticity is −0.46 and its reciprocal is $\frac{1}{0.46} = -2.17$. This is interpreted to mean that a 1% change in the quantity of hogs marketed will result in change in price at the farm level (in the opposite direction) of 2.17%. Thus, if one had a good estimate that hog marketing will increase 10% next year he can predict that, other things being equal, prices will decline about 22%.

This type of information also can be used as a criterion for determining market strategy or market policy. An organization (or public agency) charged with developing a market program would be interested in knowing the effect upon price of reducing supplies some specified percentage. A knowledge of price elasticities is essential in such a situation. It might be noted in this connection, that an organization or agency will be interested not only in the immediate price and income effect but also in the longer period situation. This involves the possibility and probability of competitors coming in with alternate products which may be domestically-produced substitutes or the same product imported from other countries.

The price elasticity of "all meats" taken as an aggregate is less than that of most individual meats. This arises from the reaction of consumers in general that "meat," in some form, virtually is a necessity. Price elasticity is lower on necessities than on luxuries. It is recognized, of course, that such foods as eggs, fish, cheese, etc., can replace meat to a degree, but to a smaller degree than one meat item can replace another. In addition, the quantity of total meat consumers will purchase is somewhat limited by the capacity of the human stomach. Once a person's stomach is reasonably full it takes substantial price reductions to induce that person to purchase additional quantities. He will, however, substitute one meat for another as relative prices change.

Price of Competing Products.—The quantity of a product consumed during a given time is affected by prices of competing products. Competing products are defined as goods that can be used as substitutes for the product in question. Most people prefer some change in the meat dish from day to day simply for the sake of variety and enjoyment. Here, however, we are concerned with the degree of response that purchasers will make in substituting one meat for another as a result of price changes. If the price of pork rises, consumers will purchase larger quantities of beef, lamb, chicken, etc.—assuming prices of the competing products remain unchanged. How much effect will a 1% increase in pork prices have upon the consumption of beef? This information is obtained from a determination of cross elasticities.

A summary of coefficients of cross-elasticities is shown in Table 5.11. It will be recalled that the negative numbers in the diagonal of Table 5.11 are price elasticities. The remaining numbers are cross elasticities and all are positive. Under the column headed "beef" one finds 0.38 on the row titled "veal." This is interpreted as follows: a 1% increase in beef prices will result in an increase of 0.38 of 1% in the quantity of veal purchased by consumers—or, as it often is stated, a 10% increase in beef prices will result in an increase of 3.8% in the quantity of veal purchased.

The reaction of consumers in purchasing pork in response to a change in beef prices is relatively low. The coefficient is 0.13. It is noted that the reaction in purchasing beef in response to a change in pork prices is about the same (0.10). A change in pork prices has a greater effect on purchase of veal, lamb, and chicken than it does on purchases of beef. Among the red meats, it appears that lamb is substituted more readily than other meats. This may be questioned. However, when one considers the difference in absolute level of lamb consumption compared to beef, pork, or chicken, the lamb cross elasticity coefficients appear more plausible. The consumption of lamb is so low that, for example, a 0.62% increase amounts to a considerably smaller absolute quantity than a 0.13% increase in pork consumption.

In general, the cross elasticities between poultry and red meats are low. This appears to belie a rather common assumption that a lowering of poultry prices will result in a drastic switch from red meat. Over the years, a long-term declining trend in poultry prices has been associated with a long-term increasing trend in poultry consumption. It has been presumed this was at the expense of red meat. The low degree of cross elasticity shown in Table 5.11 might cast some doubt on this presumption. However, over a long period of years even a relatively low cross elasticity could have a considerable cumulative effect. It might also be possible that the degree of cross elasticity declined as consumption of poultry reached higher and higher levels. If this were the case, competition from poultry could taper off in the future.

Cross elasticities also have implications when viewed from the standpoint of the effect that a change in quantity of one meat will have on the price of another—or the effect that a change in quantity marketed on one species of live animals will have upon the price of another. The latter ordinarily is more generally the concern of producers. During the fall of 1970 it was predicted that hog production would expand in 1971 by 10%. What effect would this have upon beef cattle prices? Two things are obvious: (1) increased hog production will result in lower hog prices and lower beef cattle prices (assuming no change in other factors), and (2) the lower the cross elasticity (i.e., the lower the degree of substitutibility) the less will be the effect on beef cattle prices. As may be observed in Table 5.12, the cross elasticities between hogs and cattle are among the lowest of the red meat animals. These data indicate that a 1% increase in hogs marketed will result in less than 0.1 of 1% decline in cattle prices. It should be noted here, however, that the cattle price used in this study is an aggregate of all cattle. The effect on slaughter steers and heifers likely would be somewhat greater than the effect on a composite average price for all cattle.

Income.—The relationship of income changes to meat purchases can be expressed as (1) changes in quantity purchased, (2) changes in expenditures (or value), (3) changes in prices paid. A number of studies have developed this type of information. We will draw primarily from just two: (1) a USDA analysis which relied on cross-sectional data obtained from a national household survey (Rizek and Rockwell 1970), and (2) Brandow's (1961) analysis mentioned earlier which was derived from time-series data.

The USDA study shows graphic income-consumption relationships for all meat, for beef, and for pork by regions (Fig. 5.2) and veal, lamb and mutton, luncheon meats, and variety meats for the United States as a whole (Fig. 5.3). Data for both of these figures are plotted on double-logrithmic scale. Therefore, the slope of the curves allows a direct indication of relative (or percentage) change regardless of the level of consumption.

It may be observed in Fig. 5.2 that the consumption of all meat increases as income increases, although this tendency is less pronounced in the North Central region than in the others. It also is apparent that the negative relationship between income and pork consumption in the North Central

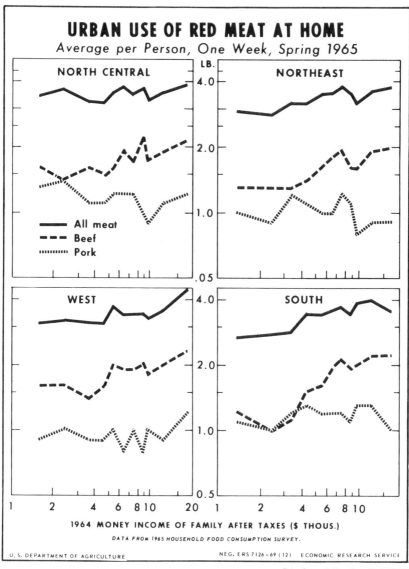

Rizek and Rockwell (1970)

FIG. 5.2. RELATION OF ALL MEAT, BEEF, AND PORK CONSUMPTION TO INCOME

region is the factor that holds down "all meat" consumption in upper income brackets. Beef consumption has a pronounced positive relationship with income in that region. Beef consumption and income are positively related in all four regions. There appears to be a tendency for pork consumption to increase with income at lower income levels, but then decline at upper income levels in both the Northeast and South. Pork consumption overall in the West appears to remain fairly constant with increasing income.

Figure 5.3 shows a positive relationship between income and veal consumption, and also with lamb and mutton consumption, but a negative relationship exists between income and variety meat consumption. Luncheon meat consumption increases with increasing incomes at lower income levels, then decreases with increasing incomes at upper income levels.

URBAN USE OF SECONDARY MEATS
Average at Home per Person, One Week, Spring 1965

1964 MONEY INCOME OF FAMILY AFTER TAXES ($ THOUS.)

DATA FROM 1965 HOUSEHOLD FOOD CONSUMPTION SURVEY.

U.S. DEPARTMENT OF AGRICULTURE   NEG. ERS 7125-69 (12)   ECONOMIC RESEARCH SERVICE

Rizek and Rockwell (1970)

FIG. 5.3. RELATION OF THE CONSUMPTION OF LAMB AND MUTTON, VEAL, AND LUNCHEON MEATS TO INCOME

Table 5.13 shows that a positive relationship exists between income changes and (1) quantity of beef consumed, (2) value per person (expenditures for beef), and (3) value per pound (price paid for beef). Other studies (Breimyer 1961) have shown a positive correlation between time and beef consumption. In a statistical sense, time is a rough indicator of change in personal tastes and preferences. These factors—income, tastes and preferences—go a long way in explaining the increased demand for beef in recent decades. Table 5.14 (the Brandow analysis) shows beef with an income elasticity of 0.47 and veal with 0.58. This is somewhat higher than the coefficients indicated by the USDA study (Table 5.13). The time periods are different and the methodological approaches are different.

TABLE 5.13

PERCENTAGE DIFFERENCE IN QUANTITY, PRICE, AND VALUE OF MEAT
CONSUMED PER PERSON FOR EACH 10% DIFFERENCE IN FAMILY INCOME,
FOR ONE WEEK IN SPRING OF 1965[1]

Region and Household Group	All Meat (%)	Beef (%)	Pork (%)	Veal (%)	Lamb and Mutton (%)
Quantity per person					
All households	1.3	2.3	−0.1	4.5	5.6
Urban-all regions	1.0	2.0	−0.3	3.7	3.6
Northeast	1.1	2.0	−0.7	5.1	3.2
North Central	0.1	1.0	−0.8	6.6	−0.4
West	0.6	1.7	−0.2	−5.1	1.1
South	1.5	2.9	0.3	1.2	0.7
Rural nonfarm	1.7	2.8	0.4	3.0	1.2
Farm	1.5	2.7	−0.2	5.3	6.2
Value per person					
All households	2.5	3.4	1.1	5.3	6.0
Urban-all regions	2.1	3.1	0.9	4.4	3.8
Northeast	2.1	2.8	0.6	5.7	3.7
North Central	1.3	2.2	0.2	7.0	0.8
West	1.6	2.9	0.7	−3.8	1.0
South	2.6	3.8	1.3	1.3	0.7
Rural nonfarm	2.8	3.6	1.6	4.3	1.2
Farm	2.0	3.1	0.3	6.0	5.2
Value per pound[2]					
All households	1.2	1.1	1.2	0.9	0.3
Urban-all regions	1.2	1.1	1.2	0.7	0.1
Northeast	1.0	0.8	1.2	0.6	0.4
North Central	1.2	1.2	1.0	0.5	1.3
West	1.0	1.2	0.9	1.4	−0.1
South	1.1	0.9	1.0	0.1	[3]
Rural nonfarm	1.1	0.8	1.2	0.2	0.1
Farm	0.5	0.4	0.5	0.6	−1.1

Source: Rizek and Rockwell (1970).
[1] Not all results will meet tests of significance—primarily veal and lamb and mutton.
[2] Differences in price per pound reflect differences in price paid for each cut or product, quality, plus differences in kinds of meat eaten.
[3] Less than 0.05%.

Data in Table 5.13 show that pork consumption does not bear the same relationship to income as does beef. Incomes and quantity of pork consumed are negatively related in all except in urban Southern households and rural nonfarm households for the United States as a whole. It should be pointed out that this analysis applies at average incomes and average pork consumption. The coefficient has not been calculated at lower levels of income. There is reason to believe it may be different (may be positive) at lower incomes than at the average or higher incomes. In any event, the negative relationship, at the average income, has serious implications for the pork industry. This means that as average incomes increase, consumers will cut back on the quantity of pork they purchase. Increasing average income is taken to be a symbol of economic progress. Average incomes have been increasing over the years and national economic policy is designed to continue the trend. Other studies (Breimyer 1961) have shown that a negative relationship also exists between time and per capita pork consumption. Thus, the demand for pork has been on a declining trend. The industry has been supported primarily by an increasing population. There is reason to doubt that the industry can continue to rely on this factor indefinitely. A major key in the solution of the pork consumption problem seems to be in the quality of pork. In earlier years, pork developed an image of excess fat, which industry has worked hard at overcoming. Much progress has been made in improving the lean:fat ratio of pork as well as improving the quality of the lean meat. This will be discussed in some detail in a later chapter. As mentioned earlier, there is some evidence that consumer reaction to pork may have changed in recent years.

Table 5.13 shows a positive relationship between income and value per pound (price) for pork and also a positive relationship between income and value per person (expenditures) for pork in all regions. Brandow's (1961) analysis agrees, as do other studies. The income elasticity coefficient of 0.32 (Table 5.14) for pork while positive is substantially less than that of any other red meat.

TABLE 5.14

INCOME ELASTICITIES OF DEMAND AT RETAIL;
PERCENTAGE CHANGES IN QUANTITIES
DEMANDED RESULTING FROM 1% CHANGES
IN INCOMES, 1955-1957

Quantities Demanded of:	Income[1] Elasticities
Beef	0.47
Veal	0.58
Pork	0.32
Lamb and mutton	0.65
Chicken	0.37
Turkey	0.49

Source: Brandow (1961).
[1] The food income elasticities satisfy the homogeniety condition but may be too high.

Consumer purchases of veal and lamb are considerably more sensitive to income changes than in the case of pork or beef. This is indicated by the higher coefficients shown in Table 5.13 and the higher income elasticities in Table 5.14.

The persistent decline in lamb consumption appears to be a direct reflection of reduction in the available supply. Lamb ranks relatively high in both price and income elasticity. Consumers who eat any lamb, generally have a distinct preference for it. There is a presumption that consumers who previously ate lamb when it was available, lose their preference when it is unavailable and will not again purchase lamb. Evidence is lacking on this point, but it is a reasonable hypothesis. It is known that lamb consumption is highest on the

East and West Coasts, and extremely light in the heartland of the country.

Veal consumption has declined as the demand for feeder cattle has strengthened relative to the veal slaughter market. The demand for beef is strong enough to hold this position. Currently most vealers are grown out for feedlot finishing. Consumption will continue to decline, but most of the possible shift already has been accomplished.

Income-chicken consumption relationships fall in about the same patterns as that of pork, i.e., negative with relation to quantity, but positive with relation to value of purchases and price paid (see Table 5.15). In the case of turkey, the relationships are positive and at a higher level than for chicken (Table 5.15).

Other Factors.—In addition to income, meat prices, and prices of competing products, meat consumption is influenced by type of occupation, ethnic background, religious beliefs, diets and food fads, and perhaps other factors.

TABLE 5.15

PERCENTAGE DIFFERENCE IN QUANTITY, VALUE, AND PRICE OF POULTRY CONSUMED PER PERSON FOR EACH 10% DIFFERENCE IN FAMILY INCOME, BY HOUSEHOLDS, FOR ONE WEEK IN SPRING OF 1965[1]

Item	All Poultry (%)	Chicken (%)	Turkey (%)
Quantity per person			
All households	0.1	−0.2	6.5
Northeast	0.1	−0.4	9.6
North Central	0.4	0.4	−0.9
South	0.5	0.2	4.4
West	−0.8	−1.0	−1.1
Urban	−0.2	−0.5	6.0
Rural nonfarm	[2]	−0.3	6.6
Farm	−0.3	−0.5	2.4
Value per person			
All households	1.0	0.6	8.0
Northeast	0.9	0.4	7.3
North Central	1.1	0.9	0.6
South	1.2	0.7	6.6
West	0.2	−0.2	1.4
Urban	0.6	0.2	7.0
Rural nonfarm	0.9	0.5	7.0
Farm	0.2	[2]	3.4
Value per pound[3]			
All households	1.1	0.8	1.5
Northeast	0.8	0.8	−2.3
North Central	0.6	0.6	1.5
South	0.7	0.5	2.2
West	0.9	0.8	2.5
Urban	0.9	0.7	1.0
Rural nonfarm	0.9	0.8	0.4
Farm	0.5	0.4	1.0

Source: Rizek and Rockwell (1970).
[1] Not all results will meet tests of significance.
[2] Less than 0.05%.
[3] Differences in price per pound reflects differences in price paid for product, plus differences in kind and quality purchased.

Mechanization and automation not only have influenced type of occupation but also have reduced the amount of heavy, physical labor involved in given occupations. These factors were, and still are, instrumental in shifting large numbers of people from farm residencies and farm occupations to cities and, in many cases, less strenuous occupations. Farm households typically consume more pork than do urban or rural nonfarm households. The only exception to this in the 1965 household consumption survey was in the Northeastern region (see Table 5.7). This factor undoubtedly contributed to the decline in pork consumption experienced in recent decades.

Farm households also tend to eat more beef than do urban and rural nonfarm households. This was the case in all regions except the South (Table 5.7).

Ethnic background shows up particularly in food habits of immigrants. For example, people from the Mediterranean and the Near East areas have a much higher preference for lamb and mutton than many other peoples. These preferences are especially strong during the lifetime of the immigrants. They carry over to a considerable extent to their children, but gradually dissipate with succeeding generations. This phenomenon is considered to be a factor, though not a controlling one, in the decline in lamb consumption in the United States. People from certain areas in Europe, and especially eastern Europe, have a decided preference for rather highly seasoned sausages. This shows up not only as an ethnic characteristic, but also as a geographic characteristic due to the tendency of immigrants to settle near relatives and friends, thus developing geographic concentrations of certain nationalities in the United States. An area south of the Great Lakes at one time was known as the "dry sausage belt" largely for this reason.

Religious beliefs can influence meat consumption. Jewish and Moslem restrictions on pork consumption obviously reduce the average consumption of pork and enhance the consumption of beef, veal and mutton, and undoubtedly other foods. It is estimated that Orthodox Jews consume 40–50% more beef per capita than the national average (Anon. 1953).[3] Jewish kosher[4] as applied to meat necessitates the purchase of more pounds per person to get the same net pounds of beef as nonkosher meats. Only the forequarters are used for the kosher trade, and forequarters contain more waste in the form of bone and fat than do hindquarters. Prior to 1966, Roman Catholics were restricted in the consumption of meat on Fridays and during Lent. The lifting of this ban probably resulted in a small increase in meat consumption, but tradition still induces a considerable restraint on Friday meat consumption.

---

[3] An analysis of meat consumption in the Northeast, however, indicated no significant difference in beef consumption among members of Jewish, Catholic, and Protestant faiths.

[4] Kosher is a Hebrew word meaning clean or fit to eat according to Jewish dietary laws.

Widespread publicity and pronouncements from the medical profession on possible linkage of obesity and overweight to diseases of the heart and blood vessels have resulted in some shifting away from fatter to more lean cuts of meat and probably to some extent away from animal fats to vegetable fats. The question of animal fats versus vegetable fats is not resolved. Nevertheless, it has an impact on meat consumption. Pork consumption probably has sustained the greatest adverse effect due to public image of pork as a relatively fat meat.

BIBLIOGRAPHY

ANON. 1953. Armour's Analysis. Armour's Livestock Bur., Chicago. Apr.-May.

BRANDOW, G. E. 1961. Interrelations among demands for farm products and implications for control of market supply. Penn. Agr. Expt. Sta. Bull. *680*.

BREIMYER, H. F. 1961. Demand and prices for meat. USDA Econ. Res. Serv. Tech. Bull. *1253*.

Federal Reserve Bank of Kansas City. 1970. Economic growth and the beef industry. Monthly Rev., Febr.

FOLWELL, R. J., and GIFFORD, J. C. 1969. Consumption and supply of beef and pork in Washington. Wash. Agr. Expt. Sta. Circ. *500*.

FOOTE, R. J. 1956. Price elasticities of demand for nondurable goods, with emphasis on food. USDA Agr. Marketing Serv. *96*.

GOODWIN, J. W. *et al*. 1968. The irreversible demand function for beef. Oklahoma Agr. Expt. Sta. Tech. Bull. *T-127*.

HASSLER, J. B. 1962. The U.S. feed concentrate-livestock economy's demand structure, 1949-59 (with projections for 1960-70). Nebraska Res. Bull. *203*. Also North Central Regional Publ. *138*.

HEIMSTRA, S. J. 1970. Food consumption, prices, expenditures supplement for 1968. USDA Econ. Res. Serv., Agr. Econ. Rept. *138*.

IVES, J. R. 1966. The Livestock and Meat Economy of the United States. American Meat Institute, Chicago.

MCDONALD, R. F. 1966. Influence of selected socio-economic factors on red meat consumption patterns in the Northeast Region. Maryland Agr. Expt. Sta. Bull. *477*.

RIZEK, R. L., and ROCKWELL, G. R. 1970. Household consumption patterns for meat and poultry, spring 1965. USDA Econ. Res. Serv., Agr. Econ. Rept. *173*.

STANTON, B. F. 1961. Seasonal demand for beef, pork and broilers. USDA Agr. Econ. Res., Agr. Marketing Serv. *ARS XIII*, No. 1.

USDA. 1969. World meat consumption. USDA Foreign Agr. Serv. Circ. *FLM 12-69*.

WORKING, E. J. 1954. Demand for Meat. Inst. Meat Packing, Univ. Chicago.

CHAPTER 6

Types of Livestock Markets and Marketing

This chapter is devoted to market arrangements concerned primarily with the buying and selling of livestock. As pointed out in Chapt. 2, the entire marketing process involves the performance of many functions, such as transporting, grading, financing, storing, market news reporting, risk bearing, as well as buying and selling. All are important and from time to time serious problems have been encountered with each. There is considerable interrelationship among them. Certain aspects of other functions will be discussed in later chapters. In terms of producer problems, doubts, frustrations and confusion, buying and selling stand out from all others. It is probable that this, at least partially, explains the multiplicity of market arrangements designed to facilitate the buying and selling of livestock.

TYPES OF LIVESTOCK MARKETS

Producers in most sections of the United States have access to several alternative types of markets. From the standpoint of competition among markets this is a desirable situation. On the other hand, some researchers have pointed out the operational inefficiencies of duplicative, small-scale markets in certain parts of the country (Broadbent 1970). These are aspects of market organization that also have implications for pricing efficiency.

Newberg (1959) distinguished 13 types of livestock markets as follows:

(1) "Terminal Public Markets. These markets are referred to as public stockyards, central public markets, or terminal markets. Livestock is consigned to commission firms for selling at these markets. Two or more commission firms must operate on such a market. A stockyard company owns and maintains the physical facilities, such as yards, alleys, scales, loading and unloading docks, office buildings, and facilities for feeding and watering livestock. Individuals, partnerships, corporations, and cooperative associations operate as commission agencies on terminal public markets.

(2) "Auctions. Auctions also may be called sale barns, community auctions. Livestock auctions receive livestock and sell to buyers on an auction basis. Bidding and selling are open to the public. They may be owned privately by individuals, partnerships, corporations, or cooperative associations.

(3) "Local Markets, Concentration Yards. These may be referred to as local stockyards, union stockyards, etc. At such markets livestock is purchased from farmers on a lot or graded basis, and usually is resorted and sold to slaughterers, order buyers, or to other markets. All have fixed facilities, such as chutes, pens, etc., for handling livestock. Livestock is purchased directly from the farmer at these fixed facilities. Individuals, partnerships, corporations, or cooperative associations may own and operate these markets.

(4) "Country Dealers, These are independent operators who buy and sell

livestock. They may resell the livestock to any of the outlets used by farmers. Country dealers may also be referred to as local dealers, truck buyers, traveling buyers, traders, or in some areas as scalpers or pinhookers. Most of their dealing is with farmers. Trading usually is done at the farmer's home. Local markets differ from dealers primarily in the place of purchase. Dealers purchase primarily at the farm, while local markets buy mostly at their own yards.

(5) "Packer Buyers. Packer buyers are employed by slaughterers. They travel in the country and buy livestock from the farmer, usually in his own feedlot. The farmer's check for the stock is drawn on a packing company. If the buyer issues his own pay check, he is assumed to be acting as a country dealer.

(6) "Packing Plants and Packer Buying Station. Livestock may be sold by a farmer to the slaughtering plant or to yards owned and operated some distance away from the slaughtering plant. The farmer gets the check from the packing company. These outlets are called packing plants or packer buying stations. In some states, packer buying stations are called concentration yards.

(7) "Order Buyers. Order Buyers act as agents of livestock buyers in procurement of livestock. Most commonly they buy through terminal markets or auctions or from dealers and local markets. However, they also occasionally act as agents of the buyer in purchase of livestock directly from farmers. In procuring livestock, order buyers sometimes are authorized to execute a draft on the funds of the purchaser.

(8) "Other Farmers. One farmer may sell breeding or feeding stock to another farmer or to members of calf clubs. This includes auction sales which a farmer may hold when liquidating all his livestock and other farm assets when he is going out of business or for similar reasons.

(9) "Locker Plants and Retailers. Occasionally, farmers sell a few head of livestock to a local locker plant, or to a store which retails the meat itself.

(10) "Pools. In some areas lambs from many farmers are pooled by grades and sold by grades to slaughterers. The farmers then share the receipts from the sales on the basis of each grade they supplied. This type of selling is referred to as a lamb pool.

(11) "Special Type Auctions. Special auctions are held primarily for feeder calves and cattle. Generally, these sales are held at infrequent intervals.

(12) "Cooperative Shipping Associations. These organizations, which are owned and operated by farmers, assemble livestock from farmers, load the livestock and ship cooperatively by rail or truck to a market, usually where the selling function is performed by commission-men. The primary function of cooperative shipping associations is assembling and forwarding livestock.

(13) "Cooperative Selling Associations. These are cooperatives which operate much like the cooperative shipping associations, but generally they perform more services in obtaining bids on livestock, selecting outlets for livestock, and providing information for the farmers. The precise functions they perform vary from one area to another. Where a cooperative actually takes title to the livestock, it is defined as a 'local market,' not a cooperative shipping association. Where the cooperative may only act as a cooperative commission firm, as at a terminal, it is not a cooperative selling association as defined here.

In many cases cooperatives operated auction markets on a certain day or days of the week, purchased livestock directly from farmers outside the ring all week, and also may have handled farmers' livestock essentially as a commission agent selling the livestock to other agencies. Many independently-owned auction markets also regularly purchased livestock directly on non-auction days or outside the ring on auction days."

Commercial feedlot operations, country commission-men, and producers' bargaining associations can be added to this list.

There is no satisfactory nomenclature of market types that serves all purposes. Some would object to ambiguity and duplication in the above list. For example, order buyers operate at terminal public markets and auctions as well as carrying out free lance country operations. Some terminal public markets have incorporated auctions in their operations. Packer buyers operate at terminal public markets and auctions, and buy directly from feeders in the country.

TYPES OF MARKETING

In addition to classifying markets, there is merit in a two-way classification of marketing. The differentiation rests on whether the principals to the transaction (sellers and buyers) utilize the services of a professional intermediary, i.e., a market agency, or middleman. From the producer's standpoint, public terminal markets, auctions, country commission-men, bargaining associations on the selling side, and order buyers on the buying side, all are clearly in the class of markets providing or utilizing intermediaries. Other types of markets ordinarily do not use professional intermediaries. In essence, this differentiation of the market process involves the issue of direct versus indirect marketing (although the term indirect is not commonly used in marketing literature). This has been a controversial issue for decades. It involves the question of whether a livestock producer engages the services of a professional to make the sale or purchase transaction, or does the job himself. The issue revolves around the question of whether a professional marketer can obtain a net return for the producer over and above what the producer himself could get, that will at least pay for the services of the marketer—and, hopefully, something in excess of that. In deciding whether to engage such services, the producer must weigh additional costs against additional revenue. The additional costs may include commission, shrinkage, trucking, yardage, feed, insurance, etc.

Trends in the use of various channels over the years reflect a combination of forces, such as changes in technology (communication, transportation, refrigeration) that spurred decentralization of the packing industry, and producer dissatisfaction with existing market channels.

MARKET CHANNELS

Market channels for live animals are defined as the routes, or paths, in the marketing system through which livestock pass as they move from farm or ranch to slaughter. The typical process of finished livestock production consists of three production stages or phases which are followed by slaughter. The phases are: (1) the basic cow-herd, sow-herd and ewe flock operations from which arise increases in livestock numbers and the initial growth that takes place prior to weaning, (2) a growing phase—a period during which the chief objective is growth involving liberal use of roughages and grass, and sometimes limited quantities of grain, (3) a finishing phase—a period of relatively heavy grain feeding during which the chief objective is finishing or fattening, and (4) the slaughtering of the animals. It is recognized that the first three stages are not entirely separate and distinct in all production programs. For example, young animals may be creep fed prior to weaning. This is the normal process of producing spring lambs and baby beef. Hog production often is a more or less continuous full-feeding process from weaning to slaughter. Cattle sometimes are grain fed while on grass. Lambs and cattle may go directly to slaughter off wheat pasture. Lambs often go to slaughter upon weaning at the end of the grazing season. Formerly it was normal to slaughter large numbers of grass-fat cattle directly off native pasture, but this largely is a thing of the past.

Cull livestock normally are not put through a finishing stage. However, as Fowler (1961) reports, feeders in the Beet Belt (western Nebraska, through northern Colorado, Wyoming, and Montana) follow a practice of buying broken mouth ewes and fattening them. Also, cull cows sometimes are fattened on wheat pasture or in feedlots.

While the above list of exceptions and modifications may appear to be large, the bulk of meat produced from each of the three species is finished. A relatively large proportion of cattle and lambs change ownership during the production process, while a large proportion of hogs are grown out and finished without a change of ownership.

Change in ownership as livestock moves through successive production phases necessitates the use of markets. Figure 6.1 is a simplified diagram of marketing channels. The least complicated channel arises in the case where the original herd or flock owner grows out and finishes his own output, and then sells the finished animals directly to a packer. In many cases the channels are more complicated than any combination shown. This may arise where livestock pass through ownership of several dealers, for example, moving from one phase to another. There also may be a change of ownership while livestock are within a given phase of production. Nevertheless, the diagram gives a general picture of types of markets and a number of connecting linkages that together portray the bulk of channels used. It also shows the links where professional intermediaries ordinarily are used. In this discussion, use of the latter will be referred to as indirect marketing.

INDIRECT MARKETING

Public Terminal Markets

For brevity, public terminal markets will be referred to simply as terminal markets. Key elements in the definition indicate this is a public market. Anyone

FIG. 6.1. SCHEMATIC DIAGRAM OF LIVESTOCK MARKET CHANNELS

Wide arrows are channels in which professional marketing assistance is used by livestock producers.

has the privilege of buying or selling on a terminal market. Shippers consign their livestock to a commission agency for selling. Physical facilities are owned by a stockyard company.

A brief sketch of the evolution of terminal markets was given in Chapt. 2. They were a logical outgrowth of the pattern of railroad transportation and the concentration of packing plants at rail terminal points.

In 1970 there were 55 terminal livestock markets in operation. Terminals are located primarily in the North Central states, although some are found in other areas, particularly Southern Plains and Mountain States. Decentralization of the packing industry and technological developments in communication and transportation have had an adverse effect on terminals. The impacts still are being felt and undoubtedly will be felt for some time to come. The most notable recent development was the closing of the Chicago Union Stockyards. After more than a century of operation this landmark stopped marketing hogs in May 1970, and in August 1971 it was closed for all livestock. For decades Chicago had been the prime example of terminal marketing. Its organization and operation were cited in textbooks, research publications, and popular articles as the pattern for terminals. The Chicago market is now closed, but this does not necessarily mark the end of terminal marketing. Receipts had been declining at Chicago for a number of years. The yards were located on relatively high-priced land—land that had other, and more lucrative, alternative uses. Some other terminals are in this same situation and may in time succumb to declining receipts.

Powers and Bendt (1968A) make the following observation: "Technological changes have made obsolete the idea that space is an important element in the definition of a market. Today, widely scattered buyers and sellers can be in instant communication with each other via telephone, radio, and television. Transportation facilities are such that supplies can be quickly and easily distributed to areas of greatest demand. In short, there is less need for large centralized markets to serve as collection points for livestock and there is less need for buyers and sellers to be in close physical proximity to have keen competition in a market system . . .

". . . the terminals must now adjust to the new realities, the new demands of a changed marketing system operated by new participants with new technologies and new demands."

The trend in receipts of livestock at terminal markets is shown in Fig. 6.2. Recent data are shown in Table 6.1. The decline in terminal hog marketings has been greater than for other species in both absolute numbers and in percentage of total marketings. Numbers of calves and sheep have dropped, but total numbers slaughtered also have dropped. The number of head of cattle marketed through terminals held fairly constant until recent years (Table 6.1). However, the total number slaughtered has been on an inclining trend so the percentage of total slaughter cattle moving through terminal markets has steadily declined.

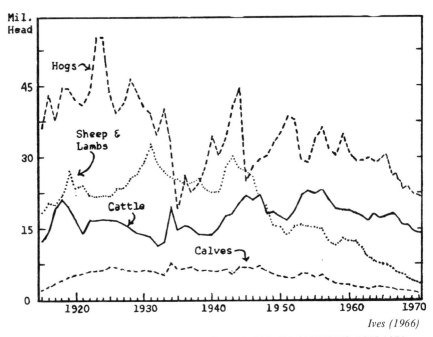

Ives (1966)

FIG. 6.2. TOTAL LIVESTOCK RECEIPTS AT TERMINAL MARKETS, 1915-1970
1965-1970 added from USDA data.

There is no question of the declining relative importance of terminals as a class. However, there is a considerable difference among the remaining markets, as some are holding their own very well and will be in the picture for the foreseeable future.

Organizational Arrangements.—The organizational setup at all terminals is similar but not identical. As indicated in the definition above, physical facilities are owned by a stockyards company—usually a corporation. The stockyards company does not engage in buying and selling of livestock. Its remuneration is derived from charges for use of the yards, sale of feed, office rental, and charges for various services such as branding, castrating, dehorning, vaccinating, and dipping livestock.

The yards physically are divided into divisions by species, cattle, hogs, and sheep. The stockyards company assigns certain pens to specific commission firms for their exclusive use. Scales are owned by the stockyards company and operated by its employees. The scales, however, are inspected and tested from time to time and are under the supervision of government personnel from the Packers and Stockyards Administration of the USDA—commonly called P&S.

While buying and selling is open to the public, the selling of patrons' livestock is done almost exclusively by personnel of commission firms. Buying is done by a wide range of types of buyers: packer buyers, order buyers, yard dealers,

TABLE 6.1

TERMINAL MARKET PURCHASES BY PACKERS, 1960-1969

Year	Cattle (1000 Hd)	(%)	Calves (1000 Hd)	(%)	Hogs (1000 Hd)	(%)	Sheep (1000 Hd)	(%)
1960	9,987	45.8	1,538	25.4	23,356	30.3	5,020	35.4
1961	9,677	42.3	1,470	23.1	21,012	29.2	6,037	36.8
1962	10,030	42.6	1,436	23.3	22,304	29.3	5,504	35.4
1963	9,546	39.1	1,042	18.2	21,136	26.6	4,561	30.0
1964	10,124	36.5	1,231	18.8	19,608	23.8	4,180	28.6
1965	10,162	34.0	1,127	16.5	17,375	23.4	3,321	25.5
1966	9,434	31.0	976	15.7	15,246	22.1	2,803	21.9
1967	8,746	28.7	796	14.4	14,540	18.8	2,457	19.0
1968	7,738	24.7	706	14.0	15,421	19.3	2,084	18.6
1969	6,856	21.2	606	12.9	15,380	18.9	1,669	16.1

Source: Compiled from USDA, P&S Admin. Reports.

wholesale provisioners, local butchers, farmers, ranchers, and feedlot operators.

Packer buyers are employed by a particular packing firm (usually located in relatively close proximity to the market) and receive a salary from the employer.

Order buyers are not salaried. They buy livestock which normally is shipped to some more or less distant point. Order buyers usually specialize in a particular class of livestock and have clientele who phone them orders for livestock that meet certain specifications—both slaughter and feeder livestock. Order buyers do not take title (ownership) to the livestock they purchase. They simply act as agents in filling the orders. Their remuneration is a commission received from the parties who place the orders.

Yard dealers (also known as yard traders, speculators, and scalpers) buy livestock with the objective of reselling at a higher price. The term "yard trader" has, for some people at some times, carried a derogatory connotation. To a large extent, this is a misunderstanding. Yard dealers perform a function of always being in the market. At certain times other buyers may be relatively scarce or inactive, particularly on odd lots. In the absence of yard dealers these odds and ends might be in distress situations. Yard dealers often can accumulate enough livestock through a number of such transactions to form larger lots of uniform quality. Such lots then are attractive to buyers and the enhanced price for the larger, more uniform lot provides a profit incentive for yard dealers.

Wholesale provisioners often like to go into the yards to personally select slaughter livestock for a specific trade. They have the livestock slaughtered on a custom basis. Local butchers, who may operate a retail store or locker plant, buy limited numbers of slaughter livestock. Farmers, ranchers, and feedlot operators do some buying at terminals, but most purchasing for this group is done through their order buyers.

From an organizational standpoint, sellers and buyers (including primarily commission firms, order buyers, and packer buyers, and sometimes yard dealers) usually form a "livestock exchange." In some cases yard dealers form a separate "dealers exchange." The livestock exchange serves as a self-regulatory organization. It also makes recommendations on changes in commission rate charges, promotes various public relations activities, and cooperates with conservation organizations in the interest of reducing loss from bruising, crippling, disease, and death.

An original distinction of terminal markets was the transacting of business by "private treaty." Private treaty simply means that price is arrived at by buyer and seller bargaining in privacy. The outcome (price or other terms of the transaction) is known only to the participants. This is in contrast to an auction where bidding is done by public outcry and terms of the transaction are known to everyone in attendance. With the introduction of auction selling at a number of terminals, private treaty no longer is a singular distinction. Most terminals which have introduced auctions also maintain use of the private treaty method.

The Denver market is an exception in that it has moved exclusively to the auction method.

Operational Features.–Terminals ordinarily transact business Monday through Saturday, although activity is light late in the week (Cramer 1958). The markets are open seven days a week to receive livestock. Hog receipts are relatively uniform Monday through Friday, although some markets deviate from this pattern. Cattle receipts at terminals traditionally have been concentrated early in the week–with more than 40% of the week's receipts on Monday and about 20% on Tuesday. From an operational standpoint this is an inefficient, under-utilization of physical facilities and manpower during the latter part of the week. Among factors associated with early week concentrations on terminals are more active buying by packers and order buyers, influence of truckers, and tendency on some markets for prices to be higher early in the week (Cramer 1958).

Many Commission agents are not opposed to early receipts since they like to spend the latter part of the week in the country visiting patrons and soliciting business. By holding an auction late in the week, some terminals have attempted to spread out receipts of feeder cattle. In the operation of its auction, the Wichita market is somewhat of an exception in that it operates the auction Monday through Thursday–handling slaughter cattle as well as feeder cattle. Slaughter cattle receipts still are heaviest early in the week. The Wichita yards are also open for private treaty sales throughout the week.

A producer who wishes to sell livestock at a terminal market must consign his livestock to a commission firm. Most producers who patronize terminals have such acquaintanceship. Anyone who has not established a contact probably should visit the market for this expressed purpose prior to shipping livestock. Most commission firms send their personnel to the country several days a week to solicit business and advise with patrons about the condition of their livestock, the market situation, and the probable value of their livestock.

The number of commission firms varies with the size of market. Most terminals have enough firms so that shippers have some choice. Competition among commission firms for producer patronage is the major force that makes a market go. Likewise, competition among markets makes the market system effective.

Some commission firms specialize in certain species. Others handle all species, and larger firms have specialists who devote their time exclusively to a single class of a given specie.

A shipper ordinarily notifies the commission firm in advance of his intentions to ship–giving approximate time of arrival. He also should give any special instructions he may have regarding feeding or handling of the livestock at the market. Upon loading of the livestock at the feedlot, farm, or ranch, the trucker is given the name of the commission firm. The name of this firm, together with a count and description of the livestock, is entered on a ticket by the trucker. This serves several purposes. Upon arrival at the market, it indicates the commission firm to which the cattle are to be delivered. It also provides a check on the count and description, and it provides the commission firm with the name of the trucker. When the livestock is sold, trucking charges are deducted from the proceeds and remitted directly to the trucker by the commission firm.

In this process the shipper of the livestock "consigns" his livestock to the specified commission firm. He, in effect, authorizes personnel of that commission firm to act as his agent in selling the livestock. For this service the firm charges a fee or "commission." Each market has its specified schedule of charges for selling and buying livestock. These schedules are known as "tariffs." There can be differences in selling and buying charges among terminal markets, but there is no difference in charges among commission firms at a given market. This is enforced by federal government regulation. The logic of this arrangement is that competition among firms at a given market must be on the basis of services performed rather than on the amount of commission charged. It is presumed this enhances the services received by producers.

Terminal market commission charges are on a per head basis rather than a percentage of the proceeds. From time to time it has been argued that logically a difference should exist in the commission on, say, a choice slaughter steer selling for $350 and a canner cow selling for $160. While there are points pro and con, the basic rationale has been decided on the proposition that the time, effort, and knowledge required to handle the various classes is reasonably equivalent, and a charge by the head again keeps competition on the basis of service performed.

Upon notification by a customer of an impending shipment, the commission agent issues a feeding order to stockyard company personnel in accordance with instructions received from the consignor (shipper). In the absence of instructions, the commission agent issues feeding instructions in accordance with his own judgment.

Livestock delivered before opening of the market is sorted for uniformity in weight, grade, color, etc., by the commission agent, if, in his judgment, that will enhance their sale. When the market opens the commission agent stays at his pens, shows the livestock to prospective buyers, offers them for sale, and attempts to sell them at the most advantageous terms from the standpoint of the seller. This involves considerable bargaining over a single price for the entire lot versus sale of the majority at an agreed price with the privilege of cutting back specified animals at a lower price.

The skill and expertise of a commission agent comes in knowing when he has the best possible offer for a pen of livestock on that particular day. If he is unable to obtain a reasonable offer, he may hold the livestock over for the following day's market, but this involves some expense and risk and is not common operating procedure.

It is possible for a shipper to specify that the agent notify him of bids before consumating a sale. However, this ordinarily is not done. It tends to severely restrict the actions of the commission agent unless the shipper has accompanied his livestock and is at the pen when the bargaining takes place. A bid by a prospective buyer is good only at the time it is made. Once the bidder leaves the pen, his bid, so to speak, "goes with him." An owner who has specified that the commission agent must call him for an approval on bids, could lose a sale from a bidder who will not wait for the commission agent to place a long-distance call.

Upon completion of sale, the livestock are weighed and delivered to pens of the buyer, or holding pens, pending shipping instructions. Title of ownership passes to the buyer upon the weighing.

Details of the transaction (price, weight, and name of buyer) are transmitted to the commission firm's office. An "account of sale" is prepared for the shipper giving the information and calculation of gross proceeds, itemized charges, and net proceeds. This, along with a check for the net proceeds, is transmitted to the shipper. Itemized charges include the trucking charge (which, as mentioned earlier, is forwarded directly to the trucker), commission charges which are retained by the commission firm for its selling services, a small deduction per head which is transmitted to the National Livestock and Meat Board and used for industry promotional purposes, brand inspection (applicable in some states), a small charge for transit insurance, and charges assessed by the stockyards company. Included in the latter are yardage, feed, and insurance applicable at the yards. The deduction for the National Livestock and Meat Board will be refunded to a consignor upon request, otherwise it is forwarded to the Board's central office in Chicago. All commission firms are required by federal regulation to carry bond which helps assure a shipper that he will receive payment.

A shipper who prefers to have his livestock sold by auction at a terminal would consign the livestock to a commission firm in the manner described above (for private treaty), but would specify he wanted them sold at auction. The commission agent again would sort and shape up lots which in his judgment would enhance the sale. At most terminal auctions a member of each commission firm provides the starting price for livestock consigned to that firm. Some terminals assess a "ring fee" in addition to yardage on livestock sold through the auction.

An individual who wishes to purchase livestock at a terminal may, if he chooses, deal directly with a commission agent by private treaty or by personal bidding at the auction. On the other hand, if he wishes to engage the services of an order buyer he simply conveys to the order buyer specifications of the particular class of livestock he desires, including price constraints. In addition to firms and individuals who limit their activities exclusively to order buying, most commission firms also act as order buyers in filling requests of their patrons.

Types of Receipts.–Three different types of livestock receipts are handled at terminal stockyards: (1) saleable, (2) direct, and (3) through receipts. "Saleable receipts" are livestock delivered to the market for sale at that market. "Direct receipts" are livestock which have been purchased elsewhere by a local packing plant which does not have sufficient holding pen space. They are delivered to the terminal yards for temporary holding prior to slaughter. A yardage fee, somewhat smaller than the regular charge, is assessed for direct receipts. "Through receipts" are livestock which are unloaded for feed, water, and rest, then reloaded for further shipment. Ordinarily, "throughs" are not assessed yardage, but are charged for feed.

Regulation and Supervision.—Terminal markets are subject to regulation at two levels: (1) self-regulation imposed by rules of livestock (and dealers) exchanges, and (2) federal regulations—specified by the Packers and Stockyards Act of 1921 and amendments.

Rules and regulations of livestock exchanges are drawn up voluntarily by members in accordance with the constitution and by-laws of the exchanges. The overall objective is a matter of self-interest in maintaining a viable and progressive market. Rules are designed to maintain a high level of ethical business activity and provide a mechanism for settling controversies.

Prior to 1958, only stockyards involved in interstate trade and having 20,000 or more square feet of pen space came under jurisdiction of P&S. The P&S Act was amended in 1958 to include all persons and firms engaged in marketing and meat packing in interstate or foreign commerce. This amendment substantially expanded the number of markets covered. The Act prescribes rules of fair competition and fair trade practices. Terminal markets (and auctions) are "posted," which means that a notice is posted in three conspicuous places at the market by P&S personnel giving notice that this is a posted market and setting forth a schedule of charges for services performed. Posting gives P&S jurisdiction over the following: (1) Changes in charges and fees of agencies operating at that market. (This applies to commission charges, yardage, etc. To change the established rates, agencies concerned must file recommended changes in writing with P&S at least 10 days before the change is to be effective, and present evidence substantiating reasons for the change.) (2) Trade practices which may be construed as fraudulent or unfair competition. (3) Maintenance of reasonable and adequate facilities. (4) Testing of scales to the capacity used, at least twice a year. (5) The requirement that individuals and agencies operating on the market carry a prescribed minimum bond and report annually all transactions of livestock and payments as well as all other operating accounts.

Auctions

Although the auction method of selling livestock has a long history, it was not until the 1920's and 1930's that auction marketing really caught on. As illustrated in Fig. 6.3, growth during the 1930's was especially pronounced. Expansion continued through the 1940's and early 1950's, though the rate of increase gradually tapered off. A peak in numbers (about 2500) was reached in 1952 followed by a slight decline. However, the volume of livestock handled continued to increase.

FIG. 6.3. LIVESTOCK AUCTION MARKETS

Annual data are not available on a national basis for recent years, but the data shown for Kansas in Table 6.2 probably are typical. This shows a continuing slight decline in number of auctions with a tendency toward stability in animal units handled.

Auction markets are distributed fairly uniformly throughout the United States

TABLE 6.2

NUMBER OF KANSAS AUCTIONS AND VOLUME OF LIVESTOCK HANDLED AT 5-YR INTERVALS (AND INCLUDING PEAK YEARS) DURING A 20-YR PERIOD (JULY 1, 1947-JUNE 30, 1967)

Fiscal Year	No. of Licensed Auctions	No. of Cattle	No. of Hogs	No. of Sheep and Goats	No. of Horses and Mules	No. of Animal Units
1947-48	160	1,081,636	551,077	20,547	32,490	1,253,350
1949-50[1]	165					
1951-52[1]			1,001,378			
1952-53	153	1,448,960	583,668	26,228	13,519	1,611,019
1957-58	132	1,887,191	557,344	38,976	3,428	2,033,853
1962-63	128	2,871,930	935,904	68,939	11,380	3,124,180
1964-65[2]	114	2,848,072	856,927	50,061	13,796	3,081,106
1965-66[1]		3,098,541				3,307,311
1967-68	109	2,754,184	995,377	44,140	14,328	3,021,770

Source: Beaton and McCoy (1970) whose tabular material was based on annual reports of
    public livestock markets in Kansas, State Livestock Sanitary Commissioner, Topeka.
[1] Peak year.
[2] Study based on data from 87 of the auctions operating in 1964-1965.

relative to the density of livestock production (Fig. 6.4). However, the proportion of livestock handled by auctions varies considerably by region, as shown in Table 6.3. Auctions are used to a much higher degree for all species in southern regions than elsewhere. With the exception of swine, auctions are used less in Pacific States than in other regions. The West North Central States (particularly the Dakotas, Nebraska, and Kansas) utilize auctions to a relatively low degree in marketing swine.

FIG. 6.4. GEOGRAPHICAL CONCENTRATION OF LIVESTOCK AUCTION MARKETS, 1955

Organization.—From a business standpoint, auctions may be organized as corporations, partnerships, or individual proprietorship (Newberg 1959). A limited number are organized as cooperatives. Most of the larger ones are corporations and many small ones are owned and operated by individuals. In contrast to terminals, where ownership and operation of yards, scales, building, etc., are separate from the selling agencies, the ownership of physical facilities and the selling function of auctions are all under the same management.

Auction markets are used primarily, but not exclusively, for feeder livestock and cull animals. While not a major avenue for slaughter livestock sales, packers nevertheless obtain substantial numbers through auctions. Table 6.4 shows packer purchases through auctions in recent years. These purchases in 1969

TABLE 6.3

LIVESTOCK SOLD BY FARMERS THROUGH DIFFERENT MARKET OUTLETS, BY GEOGRAPHIC REGIONS, 1955[1]

Kind of Livestock and Region	No. Marketed[2] (1000)	Percentage Sold Through Market Outlets						
		Terminal Public Markets	Auctions	Direct to Packers[3]	Country Sales		Total Country Sales	All Others
					Local Dealers	Farmers		
Cattle								
Northeast	1,302	21	36	3	22	15	40	3
East North Central	5,478	49	20	9	12	8	29	2
West North Central	12,952	56	23	11	4	5	20	1
South Atlantic	2,576	4	68	8	13	6	27	1
East South Central	1,916	22	45	4	12	16	32	1
West South Central	3,109	13	46	7	11	20	38	3
Mountain	3,402	39	22	11	10	10	31	8
Pacific	2,807	17	8	39	16	17	72	3
United States	33,542	38	29	12	9	10	31	2
Calves under 1 yr								
Northeast	1,915	13	48	5	26	6	37	2
East North Central	3,214	28	27	12	25	7	44	1
West North Central	3,775	31	50	5	5	8	18	1
South Atlantic	1,247	3	69	3	5	15	23	5
East South Central	1,984	19	56	9	8	7	24	1
West South Central	3,489	25	47	4	11	11	26	2
Mountain	1,626	17	22	2	21	24	47	14
Pacific	1,139	8	21	26	20	14	60	11
United States	18,389	22	43	8	14	10	32	3
Hogs and Pigs								
Northeast	1,251	24	13	7	21	29	57	6
East North Central	24,585	35	10	20	32	2	54	1
West North Central	37,702	32	9	28	27	3	58	1
South Atlantic	5,831	1	73	9	8	8	25	1
East South Central	4,325	39	33	6	4	15	54	3
West South Central	2,066	8	36	14	20	20	54	2
Mountain	535	8	33	27	18	12	57	2
Pacific	1,217	57	17	7	8	9	24	2
United States	77,512	31	16	22	25	5	52	1

TABLE 6.3 (continued)

LIVESTOCK SOLD BY FARMERS THROUGH DIFFERENT MARKET OUTLETS, BY GEOGRAPHIC REGIONS, 1955[1]

Kind of Livestock and Region	No. Marketed[2] (1000)	Percentage Sold Through Market Outlets						
		Terminal Public Markets	Auctions	Direct to Packers[3]	Country Sales			All Others
					Local Dealers	Farmers	Total Country Sales	
Sheep and lambs								
Northeast	379	23	46	8	11	4	23	8
East North Central	3,625	29	18	27	9	17	53	—
West North Central	4,447	60	9	19	2	7	28	3
South Atlantic	751	8	71	—	17	2	19	2
East South Central	406	36	55	8	—	1	9	—
West South Central	2,062	11	18	3	44	23	70	1
Mountain	6,881	36	6	32	13	9	54	4
Pacific	2,554	24	9	12	28	20	60	7
United States	21,105	35	14	21	15	12	48	3

Source: Phillips and Engelman (1958).
[1] Data for subdivisions have less statistical reliability than estimates for larger regions.
[2] Estimated from Survey of Farmers' Expenditures, 1955.
[3] Includes local butchers.

TABLE 6.4
AUCTION MARKET PURCHASES BY PACKERS, 1960-1969

Year	Cattle (1000 Hd)	(%)	Calves (1000 Hd)	(%)	Hogs (1000 Hd)	(%)	Sheep (1000 Hd)	(%)
1960	3,393	15.6	1,940	32.1	6,695	8.7	1,493	10.6
1961	4,511	19.7	2,502	39.4	8,025	11.2	1,799	10.9
1962	4,428	18.8	2,823	45.7	8,461	11.1	2,356	15.2
1963	4,343	17.8	2,663	46.4	10,125	12.7	2,118	14.0
1964	5,244	18.9	3,242	49.5	10,801	13.1	2,007	13.7
1965	6,235	20.9	3,373	49.2	10,151	13.7	1,571	12.1
1966	6,028	19.8	3,153	50.6	10,458	15.2	1,722	13.5
1967	5,559	18.2	2,880	52.2	12,019	15.5	2,099	16.2
1968	5,755	18.3	2,631	52.2	11,284	14.1	1,682	15.0
1969	5,492	17.0	2,427	51.9	11,155	13.7	1,363	13.1

Source: Compiled from USDA, P&S Admin. Reports.

amounted to approximately 17% of the cattle, slightly more than 1/2 the calves, 14% of the hogs, and 13% of the sheep slaughtered by packers.

Operation.—Auctions are distinguished by public bidding in response to an auctioneer's chant—with final sale to the highest bidder. Most auctions sell livestock just 1 day per week, however a few operate 2 or more days per week.

A livestock owner consigns his livestock to an auction in a manner similar to that described for terminals. Though not a requirement, it is good business practice for an owner to contact the auction manager several days prior to sale day and notify him of intentions to deliver. It is a common practice for auction managers or their representative to visit patrons on request, inspect their livestock and advise the patron regarding condition of the livestock, market conditions, and probable value of the livestock.

Upon delivery, the livestock are penned or marked in a way to maintain identity for each individual owner. Operators usually follow a consistent order in sale by species. That is, hogs may be sold first, followed by sheep, and then cattle. Within a given specie, most auctions follow the practice of presenting livestock for sale in the order in which they are received. Some auctions, however, have a considerably greater lag in time from delivery to sale than do other auctions, which can be a factor in weight shrinkage.

Auction operators usually sort an owner's livestock for size, grade, or other characteristics to obtain uniformity as the animals are presented in the sale ring. This is intended to enhance sale of the entire lot. As the animals arrive in the ring it is common practice for the manager, or his representative, to provide a starting bid. This is not done in all parts of the United States, but does speed up movement through the ring. The starter attempts to put the initial price just slightly below what he thinks the livestock will sell for. To the extent he is able to judge this value, the procedure obviates the necessity of needless bidding. Following the auctioneer's chant, bidding progresses to higher levels until no one is willing to advance the bid. The livestock is sold to the highest bidder.

Depending upon local custom and/or class of livestock involved, the selling may be done on a per head basis or by weight.

Several different procedures are followed in obtaining sale weight. Probably the most common is to weigh the livestock immediately upon leaving the sale ring. Some markets, however, locate the scales on the "in" side of the sale ring and the livestock are weighed prior to entering the ring. In this case the weight can be announced or flashed on a lighted sign. This eliminates the need for buyers estimating weight. It is not uncommon, however, where the scale is located on the "out" side, for the operator to "catch" the weight of a draft of animals or a part of a draft prior to final sale so bidders will have an estimate of average weight while bidding. However, in this case the official weight is taken after sale. At some markets, weights are taken as livestock is unloaded at delivery to the auction, although this is not common practice in the midwest.

After the livestock is sold they are penned for loading out. Large volume buyers who wish their purchases penned by sex, weight, grade or other characteristics, may specify as the livestock leaves the sale ring, how they wish each draft penned.

Packers and Stockyard Act regulations allow auction operators to purchase livestock that otherwise would sell at a price below what would be considered a competitively established level for that particular class, grade, and weight of animal at that time. This is known as "market support," and is designed to provide a degree of price protection to sellers at times when buying activity is slack. A Kansas study (Beaton and McCoy 1970) based on 1965 data indicated that market support was carried out on only 3.7% of the livestock handled. This study showed that auctions averaged a loss on livestock bought in their market support activities. The losses ranged from approximately 12¢ per animal unit in smaller auctions to 7¢ in the larger auctions when the losses were spread over all livestock handled.

Other means of price protection also are available to consignors. One method is to set up a reservation price with the auction operator prior to sale. This price may be noted on the ticket which accompanies the livestock into the sale ring. A reservation price means that if bids do not reach that price the livestock are not sold. Another method is for the consignor to declare "no sale" at the time the auctioneer has received the last bid. This necessitates the consignor or his representative being present during the sale. A third alternative, one which definitely is frowned upon, is for the consignor to bid on his own livestock, or arrange for a cohort to do the bidding. This is known as "by-bidding." Charges assessed for "no-sale" livestock vary, depending upon the policy of particular auction operators (Abel and Broadbent 1952).

Costs of marketing at an auction fall in essentially the same categories as at a terminal, although there are slight differences among states. The major items are commission and yardage. Lesser deductions may be made for such items as insurance, feed, state inspection, state fee, National Livestock and Meat Board, and brand inspection depending upon the particular state. A considerable variation exists among auctions in the determination of commission charges. Some auctions assess commission on a per head basis, others on a percentage of the proceeds, and some on a combination of the two.

An innovation in auction marketing is the Tel-O-Auction. This consists of an interlocking system of telephone communications whereby bidders in geographically separated locations can bid on livestock. This system is used to a limited extent in Virginia. A hog marketing installation is located in Wisconsin. In the Wisconsin setup producers deliver their hogs to a designated point. Here the hogs are identified by owner, weighed, and graded by recognized experts. They are then comingled and sold in lots of uniform weight and grade. Each lot is described over the communication system by number of hogs, their weight, and grade. Bidding can be done by ringside buyers as well as by telephone participants. Farmers pay a fixed fee per head for the selling service. The Wisconsin Tel-O-Auction is part of a larger program, the Modern Merit Market, in which an attempt is made to establish a market outlet that recognizes top-quality hogs and rewards farmers for producing them. In addition, it is anticipated that packer procurement costs will be reduced.

The Missouri Farmers Association (MFA), a cooperative marketing organization, has operated a successful Tel-O-Auction for feeder pigs since December 1965. In January, 1968, MFA initiated Tel-O-Auction sales for slaughter hogs. The slaughter hog Tel-O-Auction is operated in conjunction with their already existing (since 1958) dealer operations in slaughter hogs (producers are given the option of selling their hogs outright to MFA's dealer operations or consigning them for sale through the Tel-O-Auction). Partial success has been achieved, but additional time will be required to determine whether farmers will patronize the Tel-O-Auction in preference to alternative outlets.

Practically all auctions in the United States operate on ascending bids. An auctioneer calls for higher and higher bids until no one is willing to raise the last bid. There is another approach known as the Dutch (or Danish) auction. In a Dutch auction the starting price is slightly above the price at which a sale is expected. The price then is lowered in predetermined increments at regular intervals until a buyer accepts. This system is used in some western European countries. It has been used in Canada's Ontario hog market under a teletype auction arrangement since 1961 and in several additional Canadian province hog markets for lesser periods. The Dutch auction requires that someone provide a starting price, but that is about the only way it resembles a regular auction. Once the starting price is provided, the incremental lowering can be done mechanically, or electronically, as well if not better than by human means. A starting price and a series of lower prices can be prepunched on a tape for an electronic display. As the tape is activated, prices can be made to show up on a lighted board or printed out on a receiving tape. Prospective buyers can be provided with a button to push when the price reaches an acceptable point. The first person who presses a button is the buyer. This system can be carried out without an auctioneer and in so doing can avoid human error in taking bids, but does not have the flexibility of auctioneering in such things as cutting certain animals from a lot (Eckert 1965).

Regulation and Supervision.—Auctions which handle livestock that move interstate are considered to be public markets. They are posted and are under the jurisdiction of the Packers and Stockyards Act. The applicable provisions are those discussed previously under terminal markets. Marketing charges, once established, cannot be changed without following procedures set out by P&S. Scales must be tested twice a year. The auction must (1) refrain from trade practices that limit or restrict competition, (2) must carry bond to help assure payment to patrons, and (3) report annually all transactions and payments.

Auctions not regulated and supervised under P&S may be regulated under state provisions. Many states require bonding to help assure payment to consignors. Many states require health inspection by qualified veterinarians; however, few auctions assume any responsibility or grant any warranty regarding health or condition of livestock sold. Many auctions plainly display a sign disclaiming guarantees of any kind. In addition, it is common in case of an animal in doubtful condition, for the auctioneer to declare that the animal is being sold "as is."

Country Commission-man

The term "country commission-man" is not well established in marketing literature, but such agents do exist. A country commission-man simply is a commission agent who operates in the country rather than at an established market. He represents producers in the sale of their livestock. This may be a case of the proposition that "if producers will not take their livestock to the commission-man, then the commission-man will go to the producer." It also probably is a recognition on the part of some producers that selling is a specialized function, and some would rather specialize in other aspects of production than attempt to be a jack-of-all-trades.

These commission-men tend to operate in areas of highly concentrated production as are found in the cattle feeding areas of the Milo Belt, Colorado, Arizona, and California. They travel with packer buyers to the feedlots. Final transactions may be made at the feedlot or elsewhere.

This movement has not been underway long enough to know if it will develop into significant proportions. It would appear to have merit for producers, large and small, who need the service. On the other hand, it is of doubtful feasibility where production is widely scattered.

Order Buyers

Order buyers act as agents or intermediaries for purchasers. They buy livestock of certain specifications to fill orders which they have received from clients. The specifications normally detail weight and grade. Some orders specify maximum price–others leave price to the discretion of the order buyer. But, good order buyers attempt to fill their orders at the lowest price possible consistent with getting that order filled. This, of course, is what keeps an order buyer in business. He works in the interest of the purchaser.

Order buyers operate at terminal markets and at auctions. They also will buy from dealers, from local markets, and directly from farmers and ranchers in the country. Many buyers are specialists in a particular class and many operate at only one type of market. Specialists in buying slaughter cattle, slaughter hogs, and slaughter lambs are found at most terminals purchasing for packers located at distant points. Feeder cattle order buying specialists also operate at terminals and, as mentioned earlier, commission agents at terminals act as order buyers when requested by patrons. Commercial feedlots utilize the services of order buyers at all types of markets. The demand for feeder cattle to stock the rapidly expanding feedlot industry has created problems in filling these orders.

Many slaughter lambs are bought by order buyers for forwarding to packers. The number of packers who slaughter lambs has gradually declined, so buying has become more scattered and lambs must be shipped longer distances. Many hogs are bought on order at midwestern markets for shipment to the west coast and other points.

The true order buyer does not take title to the livestock he handles, but instead merely acts as agent for the purchaser. The order buyer typically is authorized by the purchaser to draw a draft on the purchaser's bank in payment for the livestock. His reimbursement is a fee for the service performed. In most cases the fee is a flat rate per head, which varies by class of animal. Some order buyers mix dealer operations with their order buying (i.e., they sometimes buy livestock outright, take title, and attempt to sell at a higher price for a profit). There are no regulations to prevent an individual or a firm from engaging in both activities simultaneously. There are no regulations to prevent the filling of an order with personally-owned livestock. However, most purchasers prefer to deal with order buyers who stick strictly to order buying. The mixing of dealer and order buying activities tends to diminish the confidence of purchasers. Experience has shown that one of the biggest problems of livestock growers and finishers is the purchase of stocker and feeder animals. Order buyers of feeder livestock, with widely accepted reputation, are much in demand.

Bargaining Associations

Bargaining associations are organizations set up with the express purpose of bargaining for producers in the sale of their products or purchase of inputs. Bargaining often covers terms of trade in addition to price. For a number of years, milk producers in Federal Order Milk Markets have had an organization for bargaining with milk handlers and processors. These are set up under federal market orders and agreements. The federal enabling act specifies application only to certain commodities. Livestock, meat, and wool are not included in the federal act.

Some states have statutes authorizing market orders and agreements for specified commodities. But again, most states do not include livestock, meat or wool. Colorado authorized a marketing order for lambs in 1969 but it was discontinued in 1970.

Bargaining associations are not limited to governmentally sponsored organizations. There also are privately organized bargaining associations. Probably the best known example at this time which includes livestock in its operations is the National Farmers Organization—commonly known as NFO, organized in 1955. The NFO is a farmer organization which bargains with packers in the sale of members' slaughter livestock. This organization operates as a cooperative under provisions of the Capper-Volstead Act which authorizes farmers to organize and bargain collectively. Members pay an annual membership fee and agree to turn over to the organization the job of bargaining for price and other considerations.

The NFO gained wide attention and some notoriety during several "withholding" actions. These were attempts to use withholding tactics as a leverage in negotiating contracts with packers. Early attempts were not successful in forcing the signing of contracts. Subsequently, it has been reported that contracts have been signed, but the organization has not revealed the extent of its contracts nor the terms.

It is generally held among economists that the withholding approach used by NFO (the withholding of a perishable or at least semiperishable product like finished livestock, after the livestock are produced and ready for market) does not give the leverage needed for effective bargaining power. Withholding at this point results in even greater tonnages to be marketed at the end of the withholding since additional weight is gained during withholding.

It is possible, however, that some packers are willing to enter into a contract if, in return, the association guarantees scheduled delivery of uniform weight and grade of livestock. Such a contract would reduce the packer's procurement costs which would make possible a higher paying price. Effective withholding, however, necessitates the power to control production. Private, voluntarily organized, bargaining associations have problems in maintaining the necessary discipline to gain production control. If some members abide by an organization's production control plan, a powerful incentive develops for individuals to drop out of the association and increase production. It is difficult for a private organization to enforce stringent enough penalties to prevent this. Nevertheless, the desire and enthusiasm for bargaining power among producers has gained considerable momentum in recent years. This is an area that will attract increasing attention. It is a complex problem. The trend toward fewer and bigger farm operators enhances the possibility of forming bargaining associations, from an organizational standpoint. The number of livestock producers, however, still is relatively large. Production is widely dispersed and producers have not exhibited a complete unanimity of interests.

Recent antitrust decisions indicate a recognition that farmers legally have the power to form collective bargaining associations (Clodius 1962). At the same time, these decisions make it fairly clear that undue enhancement of prices would be construed as a violation of antitrust laws. Even if a bargaining association legally gained sufficient control to raise prices above otherwise prevailing levels, economic limits still would exist on the extent to which this power could be exercised long term. Unduly high prices would tend to encourage consumers to switch to substitute products.

DIRECT MARKETING

As used in this discussion, direct marketing is the marketing of livestock without the services of an intermediary (commission agents, order buyers, auctioneers, or personnel of a bargaining association).

Historically, direct marketing has been defined as the use of any channel, or channels, which by-pass terminal markets. This definition is too restrictive for many purposes. The range of markets that would be included in the nonterminal classification still would require subclassification to differentiate markets within that group. From the producer's standpoint it appears that the chief point of distinction is whether he himself performs the functions of selling and buying or whether he engages the services of someone else.

Live Versus Carcass Grade and Weight Direct Marketing

Two major arrangements are practiced in direct marketing of slaughter livestock: (1) sale on live grade and weight, and (2) sale on carcass grade and weight. The latter is also commonly known as rail grade and weight. Live grade and weight is the historical arrangement whereby price is negotiated on the basis of live animals. Whatever grading is done is an estimated grade from inspection of the live animals. Weight and carcass yield are estimated on live animals. Weight is estimated at the time price bargaining is taking place. However, where sale is made on weight instead of by the head, the pay weight is a scale weight (sometimes reduced by a pencil shrink which is discussed later).

In sharp contrast, under sale by carcass grade and weight the price is not finally determined until the animals are slaughtered. Pay weight is taken from the carcass weight as it hangs on the rail. The carcass is graded either by a packing plant employee or a government grader. Fill is no factor since weight is based on the carcass. Price is established from a predetermined scale of prices based on weight and grade. This method requires that each carcass be identified as to producer ownership. Hog carcass identity can be maintained rather successfully by tattooing. Cattle and sheep carcasses can be tagged, but there is some risk of tags becoming lost. Either procedure necessitates a cost not incurred in live selling. Additional record keeping for settlement purposes also adds to cost. Grading by packing plant employees has raised the question of possible bias, as has weighing on packing plant scales by plant employees. Objections also have been raised due to delayed payment since final settlement cannot be made until the livestock is slaughtered, weighed, and graded. Some firms, however, give an advance payment upon delivery of the animals. It is obvious in carcass grade and weight selling that practically no opportunity exists for bargaining after the livestock has been delivered and slaughtered. Bargaining must precede delivery.

Due to lack of uniformity among packers in carcass grade and weight buying procedures, the USDA in 1968 established regulations as follows: (1) packers must divulge to sellers, either orally or in writing, terms of the purchase contract prior to sale; (2) identity of each carcass must be maintained; (3) sufficient records must be maintained to verify settlement with producers; (4) purchase and payment must be made on the basis of carcass prices; (5) weight must be established on the hot carcass (not chilled); (6) all hooks, rollers, gambels, and other equipment must be uniform in weight for each species and only this weight be deducted as tare; (7) payment may be made on USDA grades or other grades, but if the latter, the seller must furnish written specifications, and (8) carcasses must be graded no later than the close of the second business day following slaughter. These regulations, although somewhat obnoxious to many packers, have established some needed uniformity among packers which permits better comparison of carcass price offers than formerly was the case.

Research results, although not completely unanimous, have indicated that this method has the potential for improving pricing efficiency (Engelman et al. 1954; USDA 1954). If the price applied to various grades and weights truly reflects market value, each producer would receive true value for his livestock. Each animal would be valued separately (not an average grade and weight for an entire lot). Thus, a producer would receive a differential for the more desirable grade and weight animals. Presumably, such a differential would encourage production of the more desirable animals and discourage production of those less desirable.

It is possible, of course, to sort live animals and apply price differentials according to grade and weight. This is done to some extent in all types of direct and indirect markets. Commission agents and auction operators normally do some sorting. It is standard procedure for buyers to cut, or attempt to cut, less desirable animals from a lot and apply a price discount. Two restrictions, however, limit the extent of sorting on a live basis. First, it generally is agreed that grading of carcasses is more precise than grading on the hoof (Naive et. al. 1957). Second, market agents and buyers are reluctant to make extensive sorts. A common argument is that sorting, while possibly resulting in higher prices for some animals, will at the same time necessitate lower prices for others, so the average price may be no better than selling unsorted. This ignores the issue of pricing efficiency. While the arguments pro and con go on, producers have shown a tendency to increase direct marketing. Table 6.5 shows the number and percentage of packer purchases by carcass grade and weight in recent years. The most significant increase occurred in cattle. In 1963 only 8% of the cattle were purchased by this arrangement. By 1969 the proportion had increased to slightly more than 20%. Smaller increases are shown in carcass grade and weight purchases of calves, hogs and sheep.

Controversial Issues in Direct Marketing

It is impossible to state unequivocally whether a producer should use direct marketing. It is possible, however, to state some criteria upon which producers can make a decision. As mentioned earlier, the critical consideration is net return. Net return is gross return less marketing costs. Involved here are livestock prices, out-of-pocket costs, and noncash costs. Out-of-pocket costs such as commission, yardage, trucking, etc., are relatively easy to determine. In direct marketing, commission, yardage and other marketing costs, as enumerated on published market "tariffs," are avoided. Trucking may be less in direct marketing or it may be more depending upon the specified delivery point and upon whether seller or buyer provides the trucking service.

Shrinkage is a major noncash marketing cost. What is needed is the difference in shrinkage that would be incurred under direct marketing as compared to the indirect method. Some shrinkage is incurred regardless of the method of marketing. As will be seen in a later chapter, shrinkage is affected by a number of variables. Some research is available that provides guidelines, but research application is not precise to a given farm situation. Producers with an adequate set of scales on the premises can, over a period of several shipments, develop applicable shrinkage standards for their particular operation.

The question of price level under direct versus indirect marketing is an unresolved controversy. Terminal market personnel and auction operators who see direct marketing as a threat to their existence have opposed this method, contending that producers will not get full price due to lack of competition when a producer deals directly with professional market personnel, such as packer buyers, order buyers, dealers and local market operators.

Lack of Competition.—The contention that competition is lacking in direct marketing appears to rest upon the assumption that sellers, buyers, and the livestock must be physically present to have effective competition. Economic theory, however, does not substantiate this argument. What is needed are well-informed buyers and sellers with an adequate communication system. It may be assumed that most buyers are well informed. Whether a producer is well informed is largely up to him. Market news reports are available from both public and private sources. The decline in receipts at some terminal markets

TABLE 6.5

LIVESTOCK PURCHASED ON CARCASS GRADE AND WEIGHT BY TYPE OF PACKER, 1963-1969[1]

Type of Packer and Year	Cattle Total Purchases (1000 Hd)	Cattle Grade and Weight Purchases (1000 Hd)	Cattle Grade and Weight Purchases (% of Tot)	Calves Total Purchases (1000 Hd)	Calves Grade and Weight Purchases (1000 Hd)	Calves Grade and Weight Purchases (% of Tot)	Hogs Total Purchases (1000 Hd)	Hogs Grade and Weight Purchases (1000 Hd)	Hogs Grade and Weight Purchases (% of Tot)	Sheep and Lambs Total Purchases (1000 Hd)	Sheep and Lambs Grade and Weight Purchases (1000 Hd)	Sheep and Lambs Grade and Weight Purchases (% of Tot)
10 Major packers												
1963	8,122	667	8.2	1990	94	4.7	43,845	1529	3.5	9,362	590	6.3
1964	9,257	984	10.6	2236	123	5.5	44,927	1368	3.0	9,058	489	5.4
1965	9,668	1240	12.8	2359	186	7.9	39,877	1453	3.6	8,169	379	4.6
1966	9,804	1261	12.9	1969	124	6.3	36,243	1473	4.1	7,992	533	6.7
1967	10,267	1680	16.4	1626	96	5.9	39,316	1332	3.4	7,650	571	7.5
1968	10,106	2057	20.4	1393	76	5.5	40,651	2159	5.3	6,595	679	10.3
1969	11,028	3235	29.3	1137	50	4.4	42,326	2313	5.5	6,387	299	4.7
Other packers												
1963	16,285	1254	7.7	3746	49	1.3	35,770	538	1.5	5,810	199	3.4
1964	18,474	1786	9.7	4318	300	6.9	37,446	394	1.1	5,559	224	4.0
1965	20,184	2143	10.6	4492	128	2.8	34,262	489	1.4	4,850	277	5.7
1966	20,652	2364	11.4	4255	96	2.3	32,716	693	2.1	4,807	249	5.2
1967	20,214	2705	13.4	3894	82	2.1	38,191	1164	3.0	5,283	288	5.5
1968	21,293	3328	15.6	3651	105	2.9	39,232	904	2.3	4,622	322	7.0
1969	21,292	3104	14.6	3543	132	3.7	39,115	1154	3.0	4,014	386	9.6
All packers (No. of firms)												
1963 (295)	24,407	1921	7.9	5736	143	2.5	79,615	2067	2.6	15,172	789	5.2
1964 (324)	27,731	2770	10.0	6554	423	6.5	82,373	1762	2.1	14,617	713	4.9
1965 (339)	29,852	3383	11.3	6851	314	4.6	74,139	1942	2.6	13,019	656	5.0
1966 (353)	30,456	3625	11.9	6224	220	3.5	68,959	2166	3.1	12,799	782	6.1
1967 (355)	30,481	4385	14.4	5520	178	3.2	77,507	2496	3.2	12,933	859	6.6
1968 (395)	31,399	5385	17.2	5044	181	3.6	79,883	3063	3.8	11,217	1001	8.9
1969 (383)	32,320	6339	19.6	4680	182	3.9	81,441	3467	4.3	10,401	685	6.6

Source: USDA (1970).
[1] Summarized from annual reports of packers filed with the Packers and Stockyards Administration, USDA.
Note: Data includes livestock where the amount of settlement was determined after slaughter on basis of carcass grade, carcass weight, or carcass grade and weight.

makes quotations from those sources less reliable than formerly. The USDA Market News Service has extended coverage to some auctions and interior markets. Some of these offices have up-to-date market information taped on an automatic telephone hookup. With direct dialing anyone can easily call, either locally or long distance, and obtain current information almost instantly. Further changes may be necessary in the future to obtain adequate information from both producers and packers on terms of direct sales.

Producers' organizations may play a greater part in the future in developing market intelligence. The American National Cattlemen's Association recently organized a market information gathering system under the name CATTLE-FAX. With this system producers furnish information which is summarized and interpreted in a central office, then disseminated to subscriber members. The National Farmers Organization has an organizational arrangement which funnels market information to its central office. These types of market news services are beyond the capability of any one individual, but where such information can be obtained on a subscription basis (as with CATTLE-FAX) a producer can be well-informed. Reasonably adequate communications systems are available in radio, television, telephone, teletype, etc. Improvements in electronic processing and in communications are constantly improving the availability of information. Nevertheless, it probably is true that many producers are ill-informed either through neglect or in ignorance of the availability of information. If so, they are not in position to be competitive in direct marketing. However, operators of most commercial type feedyards and many progressive farm feeders probably are as well informed as the buyers.

Research studies have not verified the contention that direct marketing has lowered prices received by producers (USDA 1935; Stout and Feltner 1962).

Producers often claim a stronger competitive position in direct marketing at their premises, in that they know what the terms of the transaction are before committing themselves to a sale. Producers who have delivered their livestock to a market any substantial distance from home are just about committed to sell. Technically they may have a reservation price and may take the stock back, or to another market if dissatisfied, but from a practical standpoint this usually is not feasible. It may be more feasible at local auctions, but even there it is not a common practice.

Lower Quality at Terminals.—On occasion, opponents of direct marketing have argued that direct buyers take higher quality stock, leaving the lower quality to be marketed at terminals, and since direct purchase prices are based on terminal prices, lower quality animals are setting the standards. No recent studies are available to test this statement. It was tested in 1935 (USDA 1935). The results of the study showed no evidence of a difference in quality of hogs marketed at public (terminal) markets and interior markets. The latter represented direct markets. The same study found no difference in quality of hogs marketed at the Chicago terminal and hogs sold direct to packers.

While information is not available on the current situation, past studies have shown that producers generally tend to be relatively firmly opinionated in regard to market preferences. A 1956 study (Newberg 1959) covering the entire North Central Region revealed that "four fifths of the farmers interviewed indicated that in selling livestock they had only one outlet where they sold all their major class."

Noncash Marketing Costs.–Out-of-pocket marketing costs are less in direct marketing than in the indirect methods since no commission and yardage are charged. Opponents of direct marketing claim, however, that producers overlook the importance, particularly, of shrinkage concessions. Most producers would argue that shrinkage is less in direct sales, but this issue has several ramifications. It is not uncommon for buyers to attempt to get a concession that the livestock be kept off feed and water for a period, usually overnight, and in addition apply a "pencil shrink." Pencil shrink is an agreed-upon percentage reduction from the scale weight in arriving at a pay weight. If the scales happen to be located some distance from the producer's premises the actual shrink (from an overnight stand, loading, hauling, unloading, and weighing) can be considerable. Then, if a pencil shrink is applied, the combined shrinkage concession may be more than producers realize. Only by the installation of adequate scales on the premises will a producer know the shrinkage.

Many producers of slaughter livestock apparently have not been convinced that direct marketing is detrimental to their interests as the number and proportion of cattle and hogs marketed direct continues to increase. Table 6.6 shows direct packer purchases for recent years. The number of sheep purchased direct by packers has not changed substantially in recent years, but the proportion has increased as numbers purchased at terminals has declined (Table 6.1) and numbers purchased at auctions has not changed greatly (Table 6.4).

TABLE 6.6
DIRECT PURCHASES BY PACKERS, INCLUDING ALL EXCEPT TERMINAL
MARKET AND AUCTION PURCHASES, 1960-1969

Year	Cattle (1000 Hd)	(%)	Calves (1000 Hd)	(%)	Hogs (1000 Hd)	(%)	Sheep (1000 Hd)	(%)
1960	8,420	38.6	2,572	42.5	47,104	61.0	7,654	54.0
1961	8,714	38.0	2,384	37.5	42,791	59.6	8,591	52.3
1962	9,086	38.6	1,914	31.0	42,269	59.6	7,681	56.0
1963	10,518	43.1	2,031	35.4	48,354	60.7	8,493	56.0
1964	12,363	44.6	2,081	31.7	51,964	63.1	8,430	57.7
1965	13,455	45.1	2,351	34.3	46,613	62.9	8,127	62.4
1966	14,994	49.2	2,095	33.7	43,255	62.7	8,274	64.6
1967	16,176	53.1	1,844	33.4	50,948	65.7	8,377	64.8
1968	17,906	57.0	1,707	33.8	53,178	66.6	7,451	66.4
1969	19,976	61.8	1,647	35.2	54,906	67.4	7,369	70.8

Source: Compiled from USDA, P&S Admin. Reports.

It is not the intent here to pass judgment on whether producers should do their own selling and buying. The operator of a commercial cattle feedlot who is buying and selling cattle every day undoubtedly is in a different situation than many farmer feeders who buy one lot of feeder cattle a year. Yet even in the latter case, much depends upon the qualifications of the individual.

The qualifications of a livestock marketer, whether he be a commission agent, an order buyer, a packer buyer, or a producer doing his own selling and buying, include three major attributes: (1) He must have the ability to judge livestock. In this he must be able to evaluate all the characteristics which affect price–grade (including both quality grade and yield grade), carcass yield (including fill and shrinkage factors), and weight. (2) He must know the market value of the particular class, grade, and weight of livestock under consideration–at that particular time. In other words, he must be up-to-date on the market situation. (3) He must have the ability to bargain. In the bargaining process it is imperative to know livestock and the current market situation, but that is not enough. Bargaining involves personality traits, attitude toward the other party, knowledge of trade language, persuasiveness without antagonizing the other party, and ability to leave the impression that the other party obtained full value in the bargain.

In developing the attributes of a livestock marketer, training can be important but does not completely substitute for experience. Market evaluation of quality characteristics changes over time. Demand and supply factors change. To stay abreast of the changing situation requires continuous attention. Many professional marketers upon returning from a vacation will spend time up-dating themselves to the current situation before attempting to carry out transactions.

Analogies seldom portray a situation perfectly. However, producers in day-to-day problems find themselves faced with many decisions about whether to hire a professional or to do the job themselves. Few producers hesitate to make routine carpenter, plumbing, electrical, and mechanical repairs. On the matter of personal health and legal problems, operators almost invariably utilize services of doctors and lawyers. It would be possible under many circumstances for an individual to handle his own legal case, but few attempt it, and few would consider attempting to doctor themselves. The question of doing one's own marketing probably lies somewhere in between these extremes. Just as some individuals can do better than others in carpentering and plumbing, and some can come closer to handling their own legal problems than others, some livestock producers have the knowledge and ability to do their own marketing. Others undoubtedly would be ahead financially by hiring the services of professionals.

Outlets Used in Direct Marketing

For those who desire to use direct marketing, a number of alternative channels are available in both feeder livestock and slaughter livestock. The types of markets within this group can be subclassified into two categories. On the one hand, operators deliver livestock to an established place of business where the price is generally on a "take it or leave it" basis. This includes direct sale to packing plants, packer buying stations and local markets (the latter includes concentration yards and locally-owned and -operated stockyards). Only limited opportunities are available for bargaining over price at these markets. On the other hand there are outlets where the operators do not have an established place of business. Country packer buyers, country dealers, and order buyers circulate among producers (usually in a given area), visit their premises, view the livestock, and transact business on the premises or elsewhere. Here price is negotiated. Weighing conditions and delivery time are negotiated. If delivery is delayed, written contracts often are drawn up specifying terms of the trade. One producer may deal with another producer in a direct marketing transaction. This often is the case with breeding stock and is a common occurrence with feeder livestock.

These market outlets were defined earlier. At this point a brief commentary is presented on characteristics of those outlets in most prevalent use.

Direct to Packing Plant.—This is a situation where producers haul their livestock to a packing plant, and sale is made upon arrival. The sale may be live grade and weight, or carcass grade and weight. Most packing plants are prepared to buy livestock on a live basis upon delivery. The price is established basically by the plant management. Producers, of course, may call or visit the plant to ascertain paying prices, but bargaining is limited.

Packer Buying Stations.—Packer buying stations simply are outlying yards owned and operated by packing firms as assembly points. Buying stations are competitive devices designed to attract receipts since they are more convenient for producers located in the vicinity of the station. Trucking expense and shrinkage usually are less for short distance hauling. Pricing arrangements at buying stations are similar to those of plant purchases, although discounts may be applied to offset the firm's absorption of trucking and shrinkage, and possible feed expense—depending upon the degree of competition encountered with other packers.

Local Markets.—Local markets include locally-owned stockyards and concentration yards. Historically, a difference existed in that concentration yards were granted certain privileges by railroads in assembling and forwarding hogs by rail.

Concentration yards developed primarily in the Corn Belt, but with the advent of truck transportation, the importance of concentration yards has declined. It is worth noting, however, that the granting of through-rail rates on livestock which are unloaded at a point, sorted, reloaded and forwarded to another point can on occasion be an important consideration. In transportation parlance this is known as "transit privilege" or feed-in-transit privilege. It is applied also to products other than livestock. Grain may be unloaded, stored for a time, and/or milled into various products, the products reloaded and shipped to another destination at an additional charge which is the balance of the through-rate. Through-rate is that which would have applied had the grain moved directly from point of original loading directly to the final destination. Without the transit privilege the sum of the two rates (from origin to point of unloading and from this point to final destination) invariably is greater than the through-rate. Transit privilege is applicable to cattle, which may be unloaded for grazing, reloaded at the end of the grazing season and forwarded to another point (Riley *et al.* 1952). In this case the balance of the through-rate applies just to the original weight. Gain added from grazing must pay the applicable flat rate from point of reloading to final destination. While its use is not as prevalent as in former years, this can amount to important saving in freight charges where applicable.

Locally-operated stockyards apparently are more prevalent in southern, southeastern, and eastern states than elsewhere. However, many auctions in other parts of the country act as local markets on off-auction days. For example, a day or two of the week may be specified for the purchasing of hogs. The hogs are bought outright by the auction operator upon delivery. The auction operator may or may not have a standing agreement for sale to a packer. If he has such an agreement, he is performing the function of a packer buying station. A Kansas study (Beaton and McCoy 1970) showed that local market (and dealer) operations of auction firms were just about a break-even proposition from a profit standpoint.

Country Packer Buyers.–Many, and perhaps most, of the larger packers employ buyers who travel designated areas buying livestock directly from farms and commercial feedlots. Some larger packers have well organized and equipped buying systems. Some have two-way radio communication with a head buyer's office so that instant instructions may be relayed regarding current market conditions, plant needs, relative availability of livestock as observed by various buyers and other contacts, and pricing instructions. Such a system permits a high degree of coordination in procurement objectives within a firm.

The development and growth of commercial feedlots provide a concentration of livestock which attracts packer buyers. Small producers are at a relative disadvantage not only in the reluctance of country packer buyers to visit their yards, but with only a few head their bargaining power is less than that of large operators.

Country Dealers.–Country dealers usually are one-man operations, although a few are regional and even inter-regional in scope. Livestock are bought outright, the dealer taking title and attempting to resell at a profit. Smaller dealers operate in a relatively local area without an established place of business; however, holding and sorting pens are typical. Dealers are found in all parts of the United States. In various parts of the country localized terminology may label them as truck buyers, traveling buyers, traders, speculators, scalpers, or pinhookers. In spite of the somewhat derogatory connotation to some of these labels, country dealers have survived all the changes that have occurred in the development of the U.S. marketing system. Dealers serve the function of assembling livestock—bringing together of odd head and small lots into larger, more uniform, more marketable lots. The larger regional and inter-regional operators, of course, deal in numbers by the carlot.

In early U.S. history, relatively large lots were needed for droving. With the development of railroads, larger lots (carlots) could be shipped at lower rates than less-than-carlots. Dealers thrived in these circumstances. In a countermove, producers formed shipping associations whereby several producers could ship together in carlots and qualify for the lower rates. Development of truck transportation quickly changed this situation. Shipping associations waned. Dealers, however, simply changed with the times. Many purchased trucks and either went into strictly hauling operations or a combination dealer and hauling operation. With the expansion of auction markets, local dealers added auction buying and selling to their country operations. As is the case with terminal market dealers, these country dealers provide a market at all times. They tend to keep geographically separated markets in line by arbitrage operations. Dealers constantly are looking for opportunities to buy in one market and resell in another. One market will not remain out-of-line long before dealers start buying in the low-priced market and reselling in the high-priced market.

Dealers handle all classes of livestock, but their activity is substantially greater in feeder livestock (particularly feeder cattle and feeder lambs) than in slaughter livestock. All types of markets are used by dealers in disposing of their purchases. They sell in the market which appears most advantageous whether it be a producer, order buyer, local market, auction, terminal, or packer.

Many studies have been made by researchers in various states on dealer operations. Unfortunately, no comprehensive national studies have been made and most of the state reports are out-of-date. A regional study covering the North Central Region in 1956 (Newberg 1963A) provides the latest information on dealer activities in the midwest. At that time there were 5401 dealers in the North Central Region—down from 9880 in 1940. This study showed that " . . . most dealers had volumes below 2000 animal units per year and half of them had volumes of less than 1000 animal units per year" (Newberg and Hart 1963).

Many dealers carry on some order buying along with their dealer activities and those with facilities mix some local market operations in the business. Newberg and Hart (1963) showed that dealers commonly had other occupational interests with farming the most common, trucking second, and auctioneering third.

Livestock dealers who handle livestock which moves in interstate trade are under regulations by the Packers and Stockyards Act. They must register with the USDA and file bond when dealing on their own account. Dealers who maintain scales for livestock which moves interstate must operate those scales and have them tested as any other market under P&S. In addition, dealers are prohibited by P&S regulations from using unfair, discriminatory, or deceptive trade practices and they must maintain records of transactions carried on for their own account (USDA 1963).

Order Buyers.—Order buyers buy livestock but do not take title. They merely act as agents in buying for another party and receive reimbursement in the form of a fee (or commission). Order buyers, therefore, provide an outlet for direct sales by producers.

Data are not available on the extent of producer sales to order buyers. In former years it probably was almost nil in slaughter livestock. In feeder cattle and feeder lambs order buyers have long played an important role in furnishing a connecting link in market channels. With the recent expansion in commercial cattle feedlots and a similar, but less extensive, trend in hog feeding, it is probable that order buyers are buying directly from these operators just as are packer buyers. The trend in size of feeding units and the tendency for these operators to market direct indicates that order buyers will of necessity go directly to producers to fill their orders.

Feeder cattle and feeder lamb order buyers for years have dealt directly with producers, especially in the range states. While data are not available on the extent of this activity, the increasing demand for feeder cattle will tend to expand the use of this outlet by producers in the future.

Other Producers.—On a local basis, direct sales among producers have always been common practice. In former years it was not a customary practice for farm cattle feeders to go beyond their local area in buying replacement stock, although some larger operators did travel to range areas and deal directly with ranchers. The increased demand for feeder cattle resulting from commercial feedlot expansion has precipitated changes in feeder cattle procurement by both commercial feedlot operators and farm feeders. Commercial feedlot operators attempt to buy directly from producers as well as through other channels. Most farm feeders depend upon order buyers, but some significant moves are under way.

The American Farm Bureau in 1960 established an affiliate—the American Agricultural Marketing Association. Then individual states at their option set up state marketing associations. The purpose is " ... to assist producers of agricultural commodities to organize their market power, when the need and desire exists. The American Farm Bureau Federation established this affiliate because it recognizes that the marketing of farm products by negotiating contracts with the buyer of the agricultural products will be a dominant factor in the future" (Shuman 1963). Early efforts of this organization were directed at fruits and vegetables. As experience was gained it moved into some areas of livestock marketing. It is not known to have effected contracts in livestock marketing at this time, but it has organized a feeder cattle marketing program. For example, the Kansas Agricultural Marketing Association, through contracts with affiliates in southeastern states, buys and transports feeder cattle to Kansas for its members. This type of activity, and other modifications, are likely to increase as the trend toward direct marketing increases.

COOPERATIVE LIVESTOCK MARKETING

Cooperative marketing associations are recognized as a special form of business organization whereby producers own and operate the business for their mutual benefit. Two factors have been largely responsible for the development of cooperatives: dissatisfaction with services available from existing market agencies, and dissatisfaction with marketing charges of existing agencies. In 1922, the U.S. legislature enacted the Capper-Volstead Act in recognition of farm producers' disadvantage with other sectors of the economy in the marketing process. Among other things, this Act made it clear that farm producers had the right to organize cooperative marketing associations without violating existing antitrust laws.[1] A number of states also have statutes recognizing cooperatives as a special form of business activity. Cooperatives may be incorporated or nonincorporated as is the case with other businesses. In a cooperative, however, the profits (referred to by co-ops as savings) ordinarily are distributed back to the members on the basis of patronage. This is in contrast to other forms of business which distribute profits on the basis of ownership or investment.

Long before enactment of the statutes authorizing cooperatives, farmers had banded together in cooperative ventures, including several forms of livestock marketing cooperatives. In colonial days, co-ops were formed for importation of purebred cattle. Droving often involved informal cooperation.

Shipping Associations

The first cooperative shipping associations were formed during the early 1880's to counteract excessive margins taken by local dealers, and as a means of assembling livestock in lots large enough to gain the advantage of carlot rail freight rates. By combining shipments, scattered local producers could qualify for carlot rates. In addition, this allowed them to send their livestock to the more competitive terminal markets. This proved to be a sound educational process as producers became aware of market conditions beyond their immediate locality.

The formation of shipping associations spread throughout the heavy producing region of midwestern states, reaching a peak during the 1920's. For the most part they were concerned with assembly and forwarding stock to terminal markets. They were not engaged in buying and selling. Livestock in the shipments was consigned to established private commission firms for sale at the

[1] Clodius (1962) and Nourse (1962) point out that the mere fact of being a cooperative does not protect an association from antitrust laws if the association unduly enhances price by trade restraint activities.

terminals. Opposition was encountered at some terminals as sorting and maintenance of identity for individual shippers presented some problems. But this was not a controlling factor. The movement was reversed by technological developments which largely removed the need. Truck transportation and road improvements opened the way for smaller shipments. Improved communications permitted wider and more accurate dissemination of market news. Development of artificial refrigeration and improved transportation were instrumental in decentralization of the packing industry.

Now, only a few shipping associations remain. Several lamb shipping associations operate in Kansas. One such association, under auspices of the Kansas Farm Bureau, is more than a shipping association. It acts also as a selling agency in direct sales to eastern packers. Another ships lambs to terminal markets where the selling is done by commission firms. Both of these associations sort the lambs by grade and weight and comingle lambs of different producers in a pooling arrangement. In this way larger lots of uniform lambs are made available and are more attractive to buyers than are small, uneven lots.

Terminal Market Commission Firms

One of the greatest achievements in cooperative livestock marketing was the formation of terminal commission firms. Part of the stimulus came from the resistance of established agencies to shipping association activity. In addition, there was dissatisfaction with commission charges and distrust of commission firm allegiance. With shipping associations as a source of shipments, it was logical for producers to carry integration an additional step and organize their own terminal commission agency.

Initially, the opposition was intense and several early attempts failed. Established commission firms opposed cooperatives due to fear of losing business. Yard dealers objected because the cooperatives formed stocker and feeder divisions which completed movement of one producer's stock back to another producer without movement through a dealer. Feelings were high enough that many packer and order buyers boycotted the early cooperative commission firms.

Some success had been attained by World War I. The Equity Cooperative Exchange had been established at South St. Paul and the Farmers Union at several markets, but the breakthrough occurred during the 1920's. A conference called by the American Farm Bureau Federation in 1921 resulted in a marketing strategy which, among other things, called for the establishment of terminal market commission firms with stocker and feeder divisions, shipping associations, and a national livestock producers' organization. An outgrowth of this was formation of the National Live Stock Producers Association. Affiliated commission agencies with stocker and feeder divisions were organized at a number of terminals. Some mergers have occurred among the affiliates and some have ceased operation, but most still are in operation. Other cooperative commission firms also are in operation. While opposition has not entirely disappeared, the cooperatives generally are accepted and in many cases are the most enthusiastic advocates of terminal markets. The number of co-op commission firms reached a peak in the early 1930's. In some instances, the terminal agencies have branched out into local operations. An example of this is the Producers Livestock Marketing Association, a merged association of terminal commission firms in St. Joseph, Mo., and Omaha, Neb., which also operates an auction market in central Nebraska. Another such example is the Producers Live Stock Association of Columbus, Ohio, which represents a merger of three terminal commission firms and has a number of country branches operating auctions and local markets.

Meat Packing

From time to time cooperatives have ventured into meat packing. Fox (1957) reported that of 17 attempts between 1914 and 1920 all failed. Failures were attributed to " . . . lack of operating capital and member support, poor facilities, inadequate volume of livestock, inexperienced and unskilled management, keen competition and unsatisfactory sales outlets." The subsequent record, although hardly an example of outstanding success, indicates some lessons were learned from earlier experiences. While a number of later attempts have failed, in 1970 five cooperative packing plants were in operation. One of these has operated since 1936.

Other Cooperative Activities

Cooperatives are attempting other innovations in livestock marketing. In 1963 the California Farm Bureau Marketing Association experimented with a Dutch auction type of installation for marketing slaughter cattle and feeder cattle. By an interconnected wire system, packers could bid on slaughter cattle as the number, location, and description came over the wire system. Feedlot operators could bid on feeder cattle in a like manner. This attempt was abandoned after a trial of less than 1 yr, due to lack of participation. Buyers and sellers apparently were not willing to transact business on the basis of description. Nevertheless, the experience gained in this venture may be valuable in the future.

As explained earlier, the American Farm Bureau Federation, through its state affiliates, is engaged in feeder cattle procurement for its members. Cooperatives also are engaged in cattle feedlot operations. Two yards were opened in Kansas in 1969 and another has been in operation for several years. Cooperative feedlots are operating in Oklahoma, Wyoming, and other states.

National Farmers Organization operations, already noted as a bargaining association, is another example of cooperative livestock marketing.

An area of growth in cooperative livestock marketing in recent years has been specialized feeder cattle and feeder pig sales. All parts of the country have experienced growth in this area, but southeastern states have been particularly active. In 1967, 200 southeastern auctions were engaged in cooperative livestock activities. The principal activities of 182 were marketing livestock, and 138 of these were devoted exclusively to specialized feeder cattle and feeder pig sales (Hass 1970).

Most specialized feeder livestock sales use the auction method where livestock is pooled and ownership is comingled. In pooling, animals are sorted by weight, grade, and other physical characteristics. This makes possible the sale of larger lots of uniform quality. Producers are paid for the weight of their particular animals from the pooled price received for the entire lot.

The Future for Cooperative Livestock Marketing

Cooperatives never have attained a dominant status (except in localized areas) in the marketing of livestock. Their influence, however, has been felt and the effect has been beneficial to producers. Early shipping associations enhanced the bargaining position of isolated producers in relation to local dealers and local market operators. At the same time they provided some relief in transportation costs. Upon passage of the Packers and Stockyards Act (1921) terminal market commission firms supported enforcement of provisions which alleviated unfair and discriminatory practices. These same agencies were instrumental in providing production and marketing credit, fostering improvements in market news services and grade standards, sponsoring research, and in carrying out various educational activities designed to improve quantity and quality of livestock produced.

From the standpoint of marketing efficiency, cooperatives have the dual objective of improving both operational and pricing efficiency. Results of improved operational efficiency are easier to measure and appear to have been the chief pursuit of most cooperative endeavors. This has been in the form of reduced marketing costs—coming back to producers as patronage refunds. Mehren (1965) has stated that "probably the three keys to co-op success have proved to be: keen sensitivity to changing needs of the market; willingness of members to unite in a common front and commit themselves to a common program of action; aggressive, alert, efficient farmer leadership and professional management." Neither cooperatives nor any other form of market organization will succeed by clinging to methods of the past. Marketing is highly dynamic. Success in the future will depend upon how well changes are anticipated and how well action programs are implemented which benefit producer members.

BIBLIOGRAPHY

ABEL, H., and BROADBENT, D. A. 1952. Trade in western livestock at auctions. Utah Agr. Expt. Sta. Bull. *352.*
BEATON, N. J., and McCOY, J. H. 1970. Economic characteristics of Kansas livestock auctions. Kansas Agr. Expt. Sta. Bull. *537.*

BROADBENT, E. R. 1970. Are we willing to adjust? *In* Long-Run Adjustments in the Livestock and Meat Industry: Implications and Alternatives, T. Stout (Editor). Ohio Agr. Res. Develop. Center, Res. Bull. *1037*. Also North Central Regional Publ. *199*.

CLIFTON, E. 1954. Pricing accuracy of slaughter cattle, veal calves, and lambs. Indiana Agr. Expt. Sta. Bull. *611*. Also North Central Regional Publ. *53*.

CLODIUS, R. L. 1962. Lesson from recent anti-trust decisions. J. Farm Econ. Dec., 1603-1610.

CRAMER, C. L. 1958. Why the early week market? Missouri Agr. Expt. Sta. Bull. *712*. Also North Central Regional Publ. *91*.

DOWELL, A. A., and BJORKA, K. 1941. Livestock Marketing. McGraw-Hill Book Co., New York.

ECKERT, A. R. 1965. Prices, motivations and efficiency in price determination in Nebraska livestock auction markets. Univ. Nebraska Dept. Agr. Econ. Rept. *40*.

ENGELMAN, G. *et al.* 1953. Relative accuracy of pricing butcher hogs on foot and by carcass weight and grade. Minn. Agr. Expt. Sta. Tech. Bull. *208*.

FOWLER, S. H. 1961. The Marketing of Livestock and Meat, 2nd Edition. Interstate Printers & Publishers, Danville, Ill.

FOX, R. L. 1957. Farmers' meat packing enterprises in the United States. USDA Farmers Coop. Serv. Gen. Rept. *29*.

FOX, R. L. 1965. Livestock and wool cooperatives. *In* Farmer Cooperatives in the United States. USDA Farmer Coop. Serv. Bull. *1*.

HAAS, J. T. 1970. Livestock cooperatives in the southeast. USDA Farmer Coop. Serv. Res. Rept. *13*.

McPHERSON, W. K. 1958. How well do auctions discover the price of cattle? J. Farm Econ. Febr., 30-43.

MEHREN, G. L. 1965. Potential for cooperatives in livestock. Proc. Stockholders' and Directors' Meeting Natl. Live Stock Producers Assoc., Chicago, March.

NAIVE, J. J. *et al.* 1957. Accuracy of estimating live grades and dressing percentages of slaughter hogs. Indiana Agr. Expt. Sta. Bull, *650*.

NEWBERG, R. R. 1959. Livestock marketing in the North Central Region. I. Where farmers and ranchers buy and sell. Ohio Agr. Expt. Sta. Res. Bull. *846*. Also North Central Regional Publ. *104*.

NEWBERG, R. R. 1963A. Livestock marketing in the North Central Region. II. Channels through which livestock moves from farm to final destination. Ohio Agr. Expt. Sta. Res. Bull. *932*. Also North Central Regional Publ. *141*.

NEWBERG, R. R. 1963B. Livestock marketing in the North Central Region. III. Auction markets. Ohio Agr. Expt. Sta. Res. Bull. *961*. Also North Central Regional Publ. *149*.

NEWBERG, R. R., and HART, S. P. 1963. Livestock marketing in the North Central Region. IV. Livestock dealers and local markets. Ohio Agr. Expt. Sta. Res. Bull. *962*. Also North Central Regional Publ. *150*.

NOURSE, E. 1962. Lessons from recent anti-trust decisions. J. Farm Econ. Dec., 1614-1623.

PHILLIPS, V. B., and ENGELMAN, G. 1958. Market outlets for livestock producers. USDA Agr. Marketing Serv., Marketing Res. Rept. *216*.

POWERS, M. J., and BENDT, D. R. 1968A. Livestock marketing in the Upper Missouri River Basin. II. The Sioux City Stockyards–facilities and costs of operation. S. Dakota Agr. Expt. Sta. Bull. *548*. Also North Central Regional Publ. *188*.

POWERS, M. J., and BENDT, D. R. 1968B. Livestock marketing in the Upper Missouri River Basin. III. Cost-volume relationships of commission firms. S. Dakota Agr. Expt. Sta. Bull. *549*. Also North Central Regional Publ. *189*.

RANDELL, C. G. 1955. Cooperative livestock marketing came early. USDA Farmers Coop. Serv. Bull. *1*.

RILEY, H. M. *et al.* 1952. Feed-in-transit privilege in marketing livestock. Kansas Agr. Expt. Sta. Circ. *288*.

SHUMAN, C. B. 1963. Best interest of farmers lies in working to form own supply-management program. *In* Selected Papers on Marketing. Am. Meat Inst., Chicago.

STOUT, T. T., and FELTNER, R. L. 1962. A note on spatial pricing accuracy and price relationships in the market for slaughter hogs. J. Farm Econ. *44*, Febr., 213-219.

USDA. 1935. The direct marketing of hogs. USDA Bur. Agr. Econ. Misc. Publ. *222*.

USDA. 1963. The Packers and Stockyard Act as it applies to livestock dealers. USDA, P&S Admin., Agr. Marketing Serv. *319*, Revised June 1963.

USDA. 1970. Packers and stockyards resume. USDA, P&S Admin. *8*, No. 13, Dec.

UVACEK, E., and WILSON, D. L. 1959. Livestock terminal markets in the United States. USDA Agr. Marketing Serv. Res. Rept. *299*.

WILLIAMS, W. F., and STOUT, T. T. 1964. Economics of the Livestock-Meat Industry. Macmillian Co., New York.

Meat Packing and Processing[1]

EARLY DEVELOPMENT

Chapter 2 reviewed briefly some developments that helped shape the structure of the meat packing industry. Among the more important were development of railroads and refrigeration. The railroad system made possible the assembly of large concentrations of livestock at terminal markets. It was logical that packing plants should also locate at these points. Refrigeration and use of refrigerated rail cars opened the way for year-round slaughtering and distribution.

Two additional early developments are worthy of note: (1) development of mechanical power, and (2) public assent to the corporate type of business organization. Mechanical power gave firms the mechanics of large-scale operation, while the corporate business structure gave them the economic power to organize, finance, and perpetuate large-scale operations.

Thus, it is not surprising that in the development period meat packing evolved as a highly concentrated industry. Many other early American industries developed along essentially the same pattern. The "captains of industry" were adept in both technological and economic innovations. Among the latter were trusts, combinations, mergers, pools, and holding companies. While the basic U.S. business and legal philosophies were oriented toward a highly competitive free enterprise economy, individual interests were directed toward developing imperfections in the competitive model. Individual objectives centered on gaining an advantage over competitors, i.e., to compete the competitors out of existence. This was (and still is) construed by the general public as a trend toward monopoly, and hence, as inherently undesirable. A considerable body of literature exists on these early developments and public reaction as expressed by laws, regulations, and various "movements" (Dewey 1959; Dirlam and Kahn 1954; Kaysen and Turner 1959; Watkins 1927; Wilcox 1960). Among the more important public enactments were the Interstate Commerce Act, 1887; Sherman Antitrust Act, 1890; Clayton Act, 1914; Federal Trade Commission Act, 1914; Packers and Stockyards Act, 1921; Robinson-Patman Act, 1936, and others.

The meat packing industry was subjected to criticism and investigation along with others. The U.S. Senate in 1888 authorized a study to determine possible monopolistic elements in the transportation, production, and distribution of meat. This investigation confirmed alleged collusion and other monopolistic practices. However, no direct corrective action was taken. In 1904, Congress authorized an investigation to determine whether monopolistic practices were holding cattle prices down relative to beef prices. In general, the results of this study indicated no undue profits accruing to packers. No action was taken in antimonopoly aspects, but a by-product of this investigation was the revelation

[1] Material in parts of this chapter draw heavily on information in National Commission on Food Marketing (1966).

that unsanitary conditions existed in some packer operations. As a result, Congress enacted the Federal Meat Inspection Act in 1906.[2]

With the onset of World War I, food prices rose relative to livestock prices, and packer profits increased. Dissatisfaction was intense on the part of both consumers and livestock producers. President Wilson authorized the Federal Trade Commission in 1917 to investigate the food industry, including meat packing. The report revealed that the so-called "big five" packers (Armour, Cudahy, Morris, Swift, and Wilson) slaughtered 70% of the livestock that entered interstate trade. By specie and class this broke down to 61% of the hogs, 82% of the cattle, 77% of the calves, and 86% of the sheep. This was construed by the Commission to be prima facie evidence of monopolization of the industry. The Commission recommended that the monopoly be broken up, and proposed various steps for doing this.

As a result of this study, the U.S. Department of Justice in 1919 began proceedings for prosecution of the "big five" under provisions of the Sherman Act. While the Department of Justice was preparing the case, the packers, in conference with the Attorney General, settled the case out of court in 1920 in what is known as the Packers Consent Decree. In arriving at the consent decree, the packers did not admit guilt to monopolistic practices but, nevertheless, agreed to certain provisions designed to prevent monopolistic control of packing and distribution of meat. The provisions were comprehensive and restrictive, including, among other things, that these packers would: (1) divest themselves of physical facilities in public stockyards, stockyard railroads, market newspapers, and public cold storage facilities; (2) not engage in the retailing of meat and a large number of additional specified commodities; and (3) submit to perpetual jurisdiction of the U.S. District Court whereby the court could add provisions, if necessary, to carry out the intent of the decree in abolishing monopolistic control of these packers.

Another outgrowth of the investigation was enactment by Congress of the Packers and Stockyards Act in 1921. Subsequently the packers have, from time to time, sought relief from consent decree provisions. Minor relief was initiated in 1971 when the Department of Justice granted freedom from restrictions on manufacturing and wholesaling certain items previously prohibited.

CLASSIFICATION AND NUMBER
OF MEAT PACKING AND PROCESSING PLANTS

Classification

Meat packing and processing plants are classified in a number of ways. For some purposes they are classified as "Federally inspected" (FI), or "non Federally inspected" (non-FI). Non-FI packing plants are further subclassified according to size as large, medium or small. Livestock slaughtered by farmers is

---

[2] This was not the first indication of public interest in sanitation in the meat industry. The Meat Inspection Act of 1890 provided for inspection of meat products entering export trade but was inadequate for comprehensive inspection.

classed as "farm slaughter." All other is classed as "commercial." Packers also are classified, for some purposes, on the geographical extent of plant location. National packers are firms with plants located generally throughout the country or at least in several regions. Regional packers are those with plants generally in a given region. Thus, it is obvious that all classifications are not mutually exclusive. National packers may also be large *and* FI. Commercial slaughter includes FI *and* large, medium, and small FI plants. Prior to 1966 custom slaughtering done for farmers was included in farm slaughter; since 1966 it is classed as commercial slaughter.

Type of Inspection.—Federally inspected plants are those at which federal employees make various checks and tests designed to provide the consuming public with wholesome meat and meat products. In the interests of general welfare, the U.S. Congress, in 1906, enacted the Meat Inspection Act providing for federal inspection.[3] All packers who ship meat in interstate or international trade must be under federal inspection. All meat purchased by the federal government for military personnel and for welfare programs must be from FI plants. Non-FI plants are limited in meat shipments to trade within the borders of the state where located. Individual states are responsible for inspection of meat moving in intrastate trade. Some municipalities have separate inspection.

Under provisions of the U.S. Wholesome Meat Act of December 1967 each state was required to either set up inspection specifications equivalent to federal standards or submit all plants to federal inspection. Prior to this act, a considerable variation existed in state inspection standards and their enforcement among states. When states comply with provisions of the 1967 act, classification by type of inspection will not carry the connotation of variation in inspection standards that prevailed previously.

Data on FI plants have always been more complete and uniform than on non-FI plants due to centralized assembly (in Washington D.C.) of required reports. This probably will continue to be the case. However, the new law will necessitate more complete information on state inspected plants than formerly.

Subclassification by Size.—Most FI plants are relatively large, but a substantial variation exists in size of non-FI plants. Subclassification of non-FI plants by size is based on an arbitrarily selected set of size intervals, or ranges, of total live weight slaughtered annually. The intervals are as follows: more than 2,000,000 lb—large; 300,000 to 2,000,000 lb—medium; less than 300,000 lb—small.

Information currently available on small plants is less complete than for the others. While small plants constitute 1/2 of all plants in number, they slaughter only 1% of the livestock. Many of them are locker plants.

In previous years the term "wholesale" packer was used where "large" packer now is used, and "local" packer was used where "medium" packer now is used. The term "small" has been used consistently for a number of years.

[3] The first Meat Inspection Act was passed in 1890. It was aimed primarily at meat for export and did not compare in effectiveness with the Act of 1906.

Number of Slaughter Plants

Table 7.1 is a tabulation of the number of slaughter plants in the United States in 1965 and 1970. In this 5-yr period the total number of plants (FI plus non-FI) remained virtually unchanged, but substantial changes occurred within classes. FI plants generally are large and may be compared with the large non-FI plants. As shown in Table 7.1, FI plants increased more than 1/4, while large non-FI plants declined by 1/3. It is likely that at least part of this change resulted from large non-FI plants switching to federal inspection following enactment of the U.S. Wholesome Meat Act of December 1967. This Act, among other things, tended to tighten inspection standards on non-FI plants. It may be noted also that the number of medium size non-FI plants increased by 2/3, while the number of small non-FI plants declined by nearly 1/5. Thus, in the aggregate, increases in FI plants and medium size non-FI plants were just about equal to declines in large and small non-FI plants.

TABLE 7.1

NUMBER OF U.S. SLAUGHTER PLANTS BY TYPE OF INSPECTION AND SIZE
(Mar. 1, 1965-Mar. 1, 1970)

| Year | Federally Inspected | Non-Federally Inspected | | | Total Non-Federally Inspected | All Plants |
		Large	Medium	Small		
1965	571	855	1552	4750	7157	7728
1970	726	567	2596	3845	7008	7734
Change 1965 to 1970 in number	155	−288	1044	−905	−149	6
Change 1965 to 1970 in percentage	27.1	−33.9	67.3	−19.0	−2.1	0.1

Source: Data from USDA (1970A).

Location of Slaughter Plants

The location of FI plants is shown in Fig. 7.1. When Fig. 7.1 is compared to Fig. 4.1 and 4.2 (in Chap. 4) it is apparent that FI plants are distributed roughly in proportion to density of livestock production. The same observation holds for medium size non-FI plants (Fig. 7.2). Large non-FI plants (Fig. 7.3) are less concentrated in areas of heavy production but show a more general distribution, particularly in the eastern half of the country.

Volume of Livestock Slaughtered

Tables 7.2 and 7.3 give the number of head slaughtered of various species. At this point attention is called to the substantial increase (amounting to 34%) only

FIG. 7.1. NUMBER AND LOCATION OF FEDERALLY INSPECTED SLAUGHTER PLANTS (EXCLUDING HORSE SLAUGHTERING PLANTS), MAR. 1, 1970

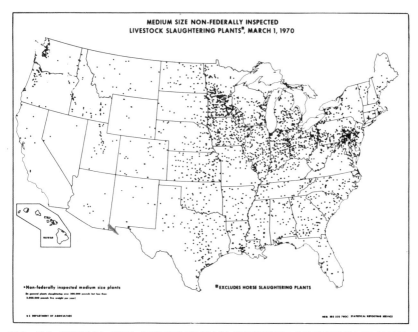

FIG. 7.2. MEDIUM SIZE NONFEDERALLY INSPECTED LIVESTOCK SLAUGH-
TERING PLANTS (EXCLUDING HORSE SLAUGHTERING PLANTS), MAR. 1, 1970

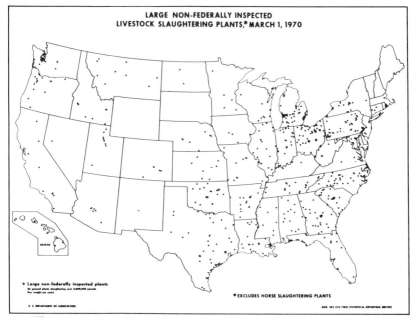

FIG. 7.3. LARGE NONFEDERALLY INSPECTED LIVESTOCK SLAUGHTERING
PLANTS (EXCLUDING HORSE SLAUGHTERING PLANTS), MAR. 1, 1970

TABLE 7.2

CATTLE AND CALF SLAUGHTER: NUMBER BY CLASS OF SLAUGHTER, 48 STATES, 1961 TO DATE

	Cattle					Calves				
	Commercial					Commercial				
	FI	Other Non-FI	Total [1] [2]	Farm [2]	Total	FI	Other Non-FI	Total [1] [2]	Farm [2]	Total
Year	(1000 Head)	(1000 Head)	(1000 Head)	(1000 Head)	(1000 Head)	(1000 Head)	(1000 Head)	(1000 Head)	(1000 Head)	(1000 Head)
1961	19,968	5666	25,635	836	26,471	5005	2696	7701	379	8080
1962	20,339	5745	26,083	828	26,911	4980	2515	7494	363	7857
1963	21,662	5570	27,232	838	28,070	4535	2298	6833	371	7204
1964	25,133	5685	30,818	860	31,678	4820	2434	7254	378	7632
1965	26,614	5733	32,347	824	33,171	5076	2344	7420	368	7788
1966	27,319	6408	33,727	444	34,171	4432	2215	6647	214	6861
1967	27,780	6089	33,869	426	34,295	4002	1917	5919	188	6107
1968	29,592	5434	35,026	388	35,414	3876	1567	5443	170	5613
1969	30,537	4700	35,237	339	35,576	3637	1226	4863	146	5009
1970	30,793	4232	35,025	329	35,354	3024	1048	4072	132	4204

Source: USDA (1971).
[1] Total based on unrounded data.
[2] Data after 1965 not comparable with earlier years due to change in definition to include custom slaughtering in plants for farmers as part of commercial slaughter. Prior to 1966 custom slaughter for farmers is included as part of farm slaughter.

TABLE 7.3

HOG AND SHEEP AND LAMB SLAUGHTER: NUMBER BY CLASS OF SLAUGHTER, 48 STATES, 1961 TO DATE

	Hogs					Sheep and Lambs				
	Commercial					Commercial				
	FI	Other Non-FI	Total [1] [2]	Farm [2]	Total	FI	Other Non-FI	Total [1] [2]	Farm [2]	Total
Year	(1000 Head)	(1000 Head)	(1000 Head)	(1000 Head)	(1000 Head)	(1000 Head)	(1000 Head)	(1000 Head)	(1000 Head)	(1000 Head)
1961	65,632	11,702	77,335	4635	81,970	15,036	2154	17,190	347	17,537
1962	67,770	11,564	79,334	4090	83,424	14,692	2145	16,837	331	17,168
1963	71,577	11,747	83,324	3793	87,117	13,955	1867	15,822	325	16,147
1964	71,667	11,352	83,018	3266	86,284	12,947	1647	14,595	300	14,895
1965	63,708	10,076	73,784	2610	76,394	11,710	1297	13,006	294	13,300
1966	63,729	10,282	74,011	1314	75,325	11,553	1184	12,737	267	13,003
1967	70,915	11,209	82,124	1297	83,421	11,516	1275	12,791	244	13,034
1968	74,789	10,371	85,160	1241	86,401	10,888	996	11,884	235	12,119
1969	75,682	8,156	83,838	1120	84,958	10,070	621	10,691	232	10,923
1970	78,187	7,630	85,817	1145	86,962	10,010	542	10,552	250	10,802

Source: USDA (1971).
[1] Total based on unrounded data.
[2] Data after 1965 not comparable with earlier years due to change in definition to include custom slaughtering in plants for farmers as part of commercial slaughter. Prior to 1966 custom slaughter for farmers is included as part of farm slaughter.

in cattle slaughter and the decline in slaughter of calves, sheep and lambs, and a relatively even trend in hog slaughter.

Table 7.4 shows that FI packers' slaughter was 89% of all livestock slaughtered for the commercial trade in 1969. Federally inspected slaughter would approach this proportion even if farm slaughter were excluded since in 1969 the latter amounted to only 1.35% of total slaughter. In the 5-yr interval, the proportion of all species slaughtered in FI plants increased from 84 to 89%. The percentage of calves slaughtered in FI plants (63%) is considerably less than other species—cattle 88%, hogs 91%, and sheep and lambs 95%. However, veal constituted less than 2% of total red meat production in 1969. Data on FI slaughter (since it includes nearly 9/10 of all livestock slaughtered), give a fairly adequate picture of the total slaughter industry for many aspects of market analysis. Due to mandatory reporting requirements and collection of the data in a central office, this information becomes available to market analysts earlier than data on non-FI plants.

TABLE 7.4

SLAUGHTER BY CLASS OF PLANT AS PERCENTAGE OF TOTAL COMMERCIAL
SLAUGHTER, BY SPECIES, 48 STATES, 1964 AND 1969

Species	FI Plants 1964 (%)	FI Plants 1969 (%)	Large and Medium Non-FI 1964 (%)	Large and Medium Non-FI 1969 (%)	Total FI plus Large and Medium Non-FI 1964 (%)	Total FI plus Large and Medium Non-FI 1969 (%)	Small Non-FI 1964 (%)	Small Non-FI 1969 (%)	Total Commercial 1964 (%)	Total Commercial 1969 (%)
Cattle	83	88	16	11	99	99	1	1	100	100
Calves	59	63	37	31	96	94	4	6	100	100
Hogs	87	91	12	8	99	99	1	1	100	100
Sheep and lambs	89	95	11	5	100	100	0	0	100	100
All species	84	89	15	10	99	99	1	1	100	100

Source: USDA (1970A) with data added by author.

DECENTRALIZATION AND DECLINE IN CONCENTRATION

Following World War II a series of developments commenced which led to an alteration of the structural organization of the meat packing industry. A reversal began in the degree of concentration. Simultaneously, a trend began in decentralization. Decentralization and lessening of concentration has taken place by a gradual, but not uniform, dilution of the position held by the big five. The total number of firms (and plants) increased in a roughly cyclical pattern. Most of the increase was by firms other than the big five—leading to a lessening of concentration.

Reasons for Decrease in Concentration

It is possible that the consent decree had some effect on the lessening of concentration. The big five became the big four in 1923 when Armour acquired Morris. But the big four probably became less aggressive in further expansion.
Development of the motor truck and construction of all-weather highways probably were the greatest factors in decentralization of the packing industry.

As mentioned in earlier chapters, livestock producers became skeptical of marketing practices at terminals during hard times of the 1920's and especially during the depression years of the 1930's. Packers found that many producers were willing to market direct under these circumstances and with packing plants reasonably close, trucks provided the means of delivery where railroads were previously the only feasible transportation.

Other factors also influenced packers to construct plants at interior points. Approximately 1/3 of the live weight is dropped during slaughtering. Thus, total transportation costs can be reduced by slaughtering close to areas of production. Some other costs also can be reduced. Labor wage rates typically are lower in the more rural areas than in large cities. Eventual unionization usually raises wages at interior points, but until that occurs a plant may realize a labor cost advantage over competitors. Property taxes and utility costs often are less in smaller towns than in large cities, and cost of living often is less for plant employees.

The acceptance of federal grades, especially for fresh beef, has tended to encourage smaller firms which located at interior points. Since branding of fresh meat has not been accomplished to any material extent, smaller new packers were able to compete favorably with larger established firms. Fresh beef is traded largely on U.S. federal grades. Fresh pork is seldom sold on U.S. grades. However, a substantial portion of fresh pork is sold by interior packers to processors located close to consumption areas.

From the standpoint of packing plant technology, the new, smaller plants could compete very well with older, larger plants. Many of the latter were approaching obsolescence, but the big companies were reluctant to modernize. A modern large cattle slaughter plant has some economies of size as compared with a modern small plant, primarily in labor utilization (Logan 1966), but these economies are relatively small beyond a capacity of around 100 head per hour. In actual operation they might be offset by less than optimum achievement in other costs.

Measures of Concentration Trends

As derived from census data, the 4 largest packers, by 1947, accounted for 41% of the value added by all meat packing firms (see Table 7.5). This 41% is not exactly comparable to the 70% determined by the FTC for the big five in the 1918 study (based on 1916 data). Nevertheless, it is close enough in concept to indicate a substantial reduction in concentration.[4]

Table 7.5 shows a continued decline in the degree of concentration since 1947. This holds whether one considers the 4 largest, the 8 largest, or the 20 largest firms. The fraction of value added by the 4 largest packers declined from

[4] The FTC study determined percentages on number of livestock, while data in Table 7.5 are percentages of value added in the slaughtering process. Obviously, the two sets of data would be closely correlated.

TABLE 7.5

CENSUS CONCENTRATION RATIOS FOR MEAT SLAUGHTERING AND
PROCESSING FIRMS, INDUSTRY BASIS,[1] 1947, 1954, 1958, AND 1963

Year	No. of Firms	No. of Establishments	Value Added by Manufacture (Million Dollars)	1-4	1-8	1-20	All Firms
					Percentage of Value Added by Manufacture — Firms Ranking		
Meatpacking (SIC 2011)							
1947	1999	2154	977	41	54	63	100
1954	2228	2367	1397	39	51	60	100
1958	2646	2810	1749	34	46	57	100
1963	2833	2992	1908	31	42	54	100
1967	2529	2697	2220	26	38	50	100
Meat Processing (SIC 2013)[2]							
1954	1254	1316	334	16	24	35	100
1958	1430	1494	442	17	25	36	100
1963	1273	1341	563	16	23	35	100
1967	1294	1374	742	15	22	31	100

Source: Data for 1963 from special tabulation of the Bureau of the Census; "industry basis"
for 1947, 1954, and 1958 from Table 2 of *Concentration Ratios in Manufacturing
Industry, 1958*, Part I, report prepared by the Bureau of the Census for the
Subcommittee on Antitrust and Monopoly, Committee on the Judiciary, U.S.
Senate, 87th Congress, 2d sess.
  Reproduced from National Commission on Food Marketing (1966A) with data from 1967
added from "1967 Census-Concentration Ratios" and "1967 Census of Manufactures, Meat
Products," U.S. Dept. Commerce.
[1] All sales of plants assigned to primary industry even though secondary products and
  miscellaneous receipts may be included.
[2] Industry definition comparable only for 1954 and 1958.

41% in 1947 to 26% in 1967. During this period the number of firms engaged in
meat packing increased from 1999 to 2833 in 1963, then declined to 2529.
Some firms operate more than 1 establishment (or plant) as can be deduced by
comparing column 1 with column 2 in Table 7.5. For the years for which data
are available, the trend in number of establishments roughly parallels that of
number of firms.

    Little change occurred in the degree of concentration in meat processing
between 1954 and 1967 (see Table 7.5). "Meat processors" by census definition
include firms primarily engaged in the manufacturing of processed meat from
purchased meat. These firms do little slaughtering. The 4 largest processors
accounted for 16% of value added in 1947 and 15% in 1967. This, by most
standards, would be classified as a relatively low degree of concentration. When
the 20 largest processors are grouped, a tendency toward lessening of
concentration is indicated.

    Data presented in Table 7.6 show the trend in degree of concentration in the
meat packing industry by specie of livestock handled. "The declining trend in
concentration has been most striking for cattle slaughtering. The largest 4 firms
(ranked according to red meat sales in 1963) produced 35% of commercial beef
and veal in 1947 and 24% in 1964. The next group of 4 held their relatively
small 4%-share throughout the period.

TABLE 7.6

PERCENTAGE OF U.S. COMMERCIAL MEAT PRODUCTION ACCOUNTED FOR
BY LARGEST COMPANIES IN 1963,[1] 1947-1964

	Beef and Veal		Pork, Including Lard		Lamb and Mutton		Total Red Meat	
	Percentage of U.S. Commercial Production by Companies Ranking							
Year	1–4	5–8	1–4	5–8	1–4	5–8	1–4	5–8
1947	35.0	3.9	41.0	10.1	63.3	7.2	38.7	6.9
1948	32.4	4.0	39.4	10.2	60.9	5.9	36.8	7.1
1949	35.1	3.9	40.6	10.4	64.6	7.2	38.7	7.2
1950	33.5	3.5	40.6	10.6	64.9	6.9	37.9	7.2
1951	30.8	3.5	39.1	10.6	62.2	6.7	36.2	7.5
1952	32.1	3.7	40.2	11.3	61.7	6.3	37.3	7.9
1953	32.8	4.5	40.6	14.8	84.9	6.7	37.7	9.1
1954	32.9	4.7	37.8	14.9	63.5	6.2	35.8	9.1
1955	31.4	4.7	38.2	15.0	61.4	6.6	35.2	9.3
1956	30.7	4.7	38.8	15.4	62.5	7.1	35.1	9.5
1957	29.9	4.6	38.7	15.7	60.1	7.1	34.4	9.4
1958	27.9	4.2	35.3	15.2	56.5	6.5	31.9	9.2
1959	25.1	4.2	32.3	14.4	53.9	6.6	29.3	9.2
1960	24.2	4.2	33.7	15.8	54.1	7.0	29.3	9.5
1961	24.4	4.0	33.4	14.5	53.9	6.1	29.2	8.7
1962	24.2	4.2	33.7	14.1	54.0	4.4	29.3	8.6
1963	23.1	4.0	33.2	13.9	53.1	4.4	28.3	8.4
1964	23.7	4.2	34.1	14.2	55.8	4.3	28.7	8.4

Source: Data for companies from survey by National Commission on Food Marketing:
commercial meat production from *Livestock and Meat Statistics*, Statist. Reporting
Serv. Bull. *333*, July 1963 and Suppl. for 1964, September 1965, USDA.
Reproduced from National Commission on Food Marketing (1966A).
[1] Ranked according to red meat sales in 1963. Largest 4 companies include Armour, Morrell,
Swift, and Wilson. Companies in second group of 4 include Hormel, Hygrade, Oscar Mayer,
and Rath.

"A different pattern emerged in hog slaughtering. While the share of the largest 4 firms declined from 41 to 34%, that of the next 4 as a group rose from 10 to 14%. As a consequence, pork produced by the top 8 firms declined only slightly, from 51% of commercial production in 1947 to 48% in 1964.

"Concentration in lamb and mutton production has historically run higher than in beef or pork. The top 4 firms produced nearly 2/3 of the total in 1947 and 56% in 1964. The share held by the second 4 firms decreased from 7 to 4%" (Natl. Comm. Food Marketing 1966A).

As is noted in the footnote to Table 7.6, Cudahy was replaced by Morrell in the big four. Furthermore, Cudahy dropped out of the top eight largest packers, based on 1963 red meat sales. Iowa Beef Packers Inc. has grown rapidly since these tabulations were made and is now well up on the size scale. Unofficial reports indicate that Iowa Beef is now the leading beef packer in the United States. However, it is doubtful that its growth would significantly change the overall degree of concentration in the industry.

The evidence clearly indicates a decrease in concentration in the meat packing industry. While antitrust laws may have had an influence on this trend, it appears that economic forces were dominant. The same laws that apply to meat packing also apply to other industries and there is little evidence of a comparable trend in concentration in most other major industries.

SPECIALIZATION[5]

There are two aspects to packing plant specialization: horizontal specialization refers to the number of different species slaughtered in a plant, while vertical specialization refers to the extent to which meat is processed in the plant where slaughtering takes place. A plant in which only one specie is slaughtered is considered highly specialized horizontally. If no processing is done, the plant is considered to be highly specialized vertically. A plant which slaughters only hogs and sells the pork only in carcass form is highly specialized in both ways—this is the so-called "kill and chill" pork packing plant.

TABLE 7.7

NUMBER OF FI PLANTS IN UNITED STATES SLAUGHTERING GIVEN COMBINATIONS OF LIVESTOCK SPECIES, 1950, 1954, 1958, 1962

| Year | Number of Species Slaughtered and Percentage of Change | | | | Total |
	1 Species	2 Species	3 Species	4 Species	
1950	73	81	128	175	457
1954	109	98	129	143	479
1958	145	112	127	127	511
1962	193	154	136	84	567
Percentage of change 1950-1962	164	90	6	−52	24

Source: From data in Anthony (1966).

Horizontal Specialization

In a study of FI slaughter plants covering the period 1950-1962, Anthony (1966) reported that "Horizontal specialization of FI slaughter plants is increasing." Data in Table 7.7, derived from that study, show that the number of single specie plants increased from 73 to 193 (a 164% increase). Two specie plants increased 90%, while 3 specie plants increased only 6%, and plants slaughtering all 4 species declined 52%. Data (USDA 1970) for a later interval, 1965-1970, while not based on an indentical breakdown by species, also indicate increasing specialization in hog and sheep plants (see Table 7.8). However, in this later period, the number of cattle and calf slaughter plants increased by a smaller amount (15%) than did total plant numbers (27%), or full line plants slaughtering all species (32%), and cattle, calf and hog plants (46%). This appears to indicate a change (a reduction in rate of change) from that shown in the Anthony (1966) study for 1950-1962 where it was stated that "the greatest portion of the increase in single species plants can be attributed to the increase in number of plants slaughtering cattle only." Data in Table 7.9 for all large and

[5] Material in this section is largely from Anthony (1966).

TABLE 7.8

NUMBER OF FI LIVESTOCK SLAUGHTER PLANTS IN UNITED STATES BY SPECIES SLAUGHTERED, 1965 and 1970

Year	Cattle and Calves, Hogs, and Sheep and Lambs	Cattle and Calves and Hogs	Cattle and Calves and Sheep and Lambs	Hogs, and Sheep and Lambs	Cattle and Calves Only	Hogs Only	Sheep and Lambs Only	Total
1965[1]	108	87	72	3	234	64	3	571
1970[2]	143	127	75	2	269	99	11	726
Percentage of change 1965-1970	32	46	4	-33	15	55	267	27

Source: Data from USDA (1970A).
[1] Classified as to species in 1964.
[2] Classified as to species in 1969.

TABLE 7.9

NUMBER OF ALL LARGE AND MEDIUM SIZE LIVESTOCK SLAUGHTER PLANTS[1] IN UNITED STATES BY SPECIES SLAUGHTERED, 1965 AND 1970

Year	Cattle and Calves, Hogs, and Sheep and Lambs	Cattle and Calves and Hogs	Cattle and Calves, and Sheep and Lambs	Hogs, and Sheep and Lambs	Cattle and Calves Only	Hogs Only	Sheep and Lambs Only	Total
1965[2]	873	1,150	221	3	530	183	18	2,978
1970[3]	1,477	1,557	206	2	465	169	13	3,889
Percentage of change 1965-1970	69	35	-7	-33	-12	-8	-28	31

Source: Data from USDA (1970A).
[1] Includes all Federally inspected plants plus all plants not under Federal inspection with an output of 300,000 pounds or more live weight annually.
[2] Classified as to species in 1964.
[3] Classified as to species in 1969.

medium sized slaughter plants, both FI and non-FI, indicate a reversal of the former trend toward horizontal specialization. Table 7.9 shows a decline in number of single specie plants while the total number of plants increased (31%), the number of full line plants increased (69%), and the number of plants slaughtering cattle, calves, and hogs increased (35%). Contrary to what these data show for the United States as a whole, unofficial reports indicate a continued trend toward horizontal specialization in new plant construction in the Corn Belt and Milo Belt.

Vertical Specialization

The concept of vertical specialization is similar to that of vertical integration—-i.e., the control by ownership or contract over successive stages of production or marketing. Slaughtering and processing are successive stages in meat production. Meat can be processed by a firm in the plant where slaughtering takes place, it can be shipped to a specialized processing plant owned by the same firm, or it can be sold to another firm for processing. The less processing done by a plant, the more specialized is that plant.

Empirical analysis of vertical specialization is limited. Table 7.10 presents data for 1961 for FI plants. Of the 570 primarily slaughter plants only 49, or 9%, were doing no processing, and these plants represented only 4% of FI slaughter. This indicates a low degree of vertical specialization. However, it has been pointed out by Anthony and Egertson (1966) that "a rather high proportion of the slaughter plants were doing only a limited amount of processing. Half of the slaughter plants which engage in meat processing activities processed only an average of 14% of their slaughter production. These limited processing activities tended to consist of some boning, carcass breaking, and other fresh meat operations. Specialization in meat processing, which includes curing, smoking, fabricating, etc., appears to be greater than in slaughtering—65% of the processing plants performed no slaughtering."[6]

Of the 1483 plants classed as primarily processing plants, 65% did no slaughtering at all. This is a considerably higher degree of specialization than was shown in slaughter plants (9%). The combination slaughter-processing plants were placed in 3 classifications—those that processed less that 50% of their slaughter, those that processed 50–100% of slaughter, and those that processed more than 100% of their slaughter. The latter obviously purchased meat for processing. "Fifty percent of the plants processed less than 1/2 of their slaughter output. Ten percent of the slaughter plants processed 50–100% of output. A fairly large number of FI slaughter plants (32%) processed more

---

[6] This quotation illustrates some difficulties encountered in definitions. For purposes used here, processing includes boning, carcass breaking, and other fresh meat operations. For other purposes, processed meat is defined to include only such meat as bologna, luncheon meats, sausages, cured meat, smoked meat, etc., and, in addition, ground (hamburger) and comminuted meat—with only ground and comminuted being in the fresh state. A more explicit comment is given on the definitions of processed meat and processing in Chap. 8.

TABLE 7.10

VERTICAL (SLAUGHTER-PROCESSING) PLANT SPECIALIZATION
FOR NINE REGIONS AND UNITED STATES, 1961

Item	New England	Mid-Atlantic	South Atlantic	Southeast	Regions East North Central	West North Central	South Central	Mountain	West Coast	United States
Slaughter plants										
Total number	14	94	33	28	116	116	41	44	84	570
Number not processing	3	12	1	...	10	16	...	1	6	49
Percentage of plants not processing	21	13	3	...	9	14	...	2	7	9
Percentage of slaughter in spec. plants	15	13	0.02	...	3	4	...	0.02	3	4
Slaughter-processing plants										
Processing under 50% of slaughter										
Number	5	42	12	10	61	50	22	25	56	283
Percentage of plants	36	45	36	36	53	43	54	57	67	50
Average percentage processed	5	14	15	24	13	8	22	16	2	14
Processing 50-100% of slaughter										
Number	1	9	3	...	7	15	7	8	7	57
Percentage of plants	7	10	9	...	6	13	17	18	8	10
Average percentage processed	78	69	69	...	65	80	71	81	66	73
Processing over 100% of slaughter										
Number	5	31	17	18	38	35	12	10	15	181
Percentage of plants	36	33	52	64	33	30	29	23	18	32
Average percentage processed	199	864	172	209	188	323	168	240	195	333
Processing plants										
Total number	135	340	96	60	286	183	100	76	207	1483
Number not slaughtering	124	258	64	32	180	83	59	33	129	962
Percentage not slaughtering	92	76	67	53	63	45	59	43	62	65

Source: Anthony (1966).

than they slaughtered; that is, they acquired meat for processing from other plants. The average processing of these plants was 333% of their slaughter" (Anthony 1966).

Specialization was greatest in slaughter plants in New England, Mid Atlantic and in the two North Central regions. Specialization was greatest in processing plants in the New England and Mid Atlantic regions.

Studies are not available showing the trend in specialization over a period of time. However, there are economies to be gained in breaking, fabricating, and boning at point of slaughter. For this reason processing of fresh meat in connection with slaughter operations is expected to increase, which will tend to reduce specialization in slaughter plants. There appear to be no economies, however, in manufacturing processes (or prepared meats such as cured, bologna, sausages, etc.) at point of slaughter. This aspect of processing probably will continue to be oriented to locations near heavy consumption areas and will tend to foster a higher degree so specialization in that aspect of processing which we call manufacturing (as contrasted to cutting, breaking, and fabricating of fresh meat).

DIFFERENTIATION OF PRODUCT

Branding and differentiating fresh meat presents a difficult problem. Only limited success has been achieved in this area. Some packers have established cutting and trimming characteristics in wholesale cuts as a basis for differentiating their product. Swift has an enzimatic tenderizing process which it promotes under the Proten trademark. However, the widespread use of federal grades in wholesaling and retailing fresh beef and lamb has largely forestalled the differentiation of these products by individual firms. During 1969, 64% of carcass beef and 69% of lamb in commercial slaughter was officially grade marked. Federal grades are virtually unused in marketing pork. Only a relatively small proportion of pork is retailed in the fresh state, and at the wholesale level individual specifications are used in preference to U.S. grades.

A different situation exists with processed meats. Here, processors have been able to develop individualized characteristics such as flavor, color, texture, brand-name, and packaging. By advertising and other promotional efforts processors have succeeded in differentiating their products.

Table 7.11 presents data from the National Commission on Food Marketing (1966A) study on the extent of branding by packers. The report stated, "Processed items—such as bacon, hams, sausage, and luncheon meats—are labeled with the packer or retailer name. A number of variations exist in product composition, packaging and branding, and these frequently differ among firms. Some packers have promoted their brands enough to influence consumers. As a result, in some sections of the country highly advertised brands sell at higher prices than unadvertised brands.

" . . . Two thirds or more of fresh beef, veal, lamb and pork was sold

TABLE 7.11

PROPORTIONS OF SPECIFIED MEAT ITEMS SOLD BY
TYPE OF BRAND, 1954–1965[1]

Firm Group	Seller's Brand	Customer's Brand	Un- branded	Not Indicated
Beef and veal				
4 largest meat packing companies[2]	26.6	3.8	69.6	. . .
Second 4 largest meat packing companies[3]	34.6	3.2	62.2	. . .
All other firms reporting (131 firms)	17.8	2.1	69.1	11.0
Lamb and mutton				
4 largest meat packing companies[2]	28.6	. . .	71.4	. . .
Second 4 largest meat packing companies[3]	5.6	. . .	94.4	. . .
All other firms reporting (19 firms)	6.8	. . .	93.2	. . .
Fresh and frozen pork				
4 largest meat packing companies[2]	. . .	. . .	100.0	. . .
Second 4 largest meat packing companies[3]	34.7	. . .	65.3	. . .
All other firms reporting (75 firms)	13.3	. . .	64.9	21.8
Cured hams, picnics, and bacon				
4 largest meat packing companies[2]	86.4	4.9	8.7	. . .
Second 4 largest meat packing companies[3]	76.2	10.9	12.9	. . .
All other firms reporting (62 firms)	75.1	11.8	10.1	3.0
Other processed meats				
4 largest meat packing companies[2]	85.8	4.8	9.4	. . .
Second 4 largest meat packing companies[3]	81.2	9.8	9.0	. . .
All other firms reporting (77 firms)	77.7	9.0	4.5	8.8

Source: National Commission on Food Marketing (1966A).
[1] Firms were requested to report total sales by customer class and brand type for a period of at least 2 months between Nov. 1, 1964, and Apr. 30, 1965. Data furnished were converted to monthly averages. Percentages were computed from totals of firm groups.
[2] Armour, Morrell, Swift, and Wilson.
[3] Hormel, Hygrade, Oscar Mayer, and Rath.

unbranded by packers. But less than 10% of cured pork items and processed meats was sold unbranded by most groups of packers.

"On branded items, the packers' brands predominated. Less than 5% of the cured and processed meat sold by the largest 4 packers carried the customers' labels. However, the second largest 4 packers and other reporting packers sold around 10% of their cured and processed meats under custom labels. Customer branded meats were sold chiefly to large retail chains."

CONDITIONS OF ENTRY INTO THE MEAT PACKING AND PROCESSING INDUSTRY

Entry into an industry is defined as the initiation of operations by a new firm. Exit from an industry is the discontinuance of operations by an established firm. Firms already established and operating in an industry which is difficult to enter (has high barriers to entry), are hypothesized to behave differently (to have some degree of control over prices and profits) than firms in an industry which is easy to enter. High barriers to entry do not in themselves furnish proof of adverse economic behavior. However, if an industry (meat packing or processing) has high barriers to entry, this would at least provide some grounds for further investigation of behavior and performance of firms in that industry. Livestock producers and consumers both have a stake in this issue just as they do in any other structural characteristic which affects relative bargaining power, prices of livestock, and retail prices of meat.

Anthony (1966) analyzed entry and exit of firms in the meat packing industry for the 1950-1962 period. The National Commission on Food Marketing (1966A) made a similar study for a shorter, but later, and partially overlapping period, 1958-1964 (see Table 7.12). During this period, 84 of an original 389 firms exited while 155 new firms entered. Thus, the rate of both exit and entry (i.e., number per year) increased in the latter period. Both of these studies show a relatively high rate of entry—indicating relative ease of entry. Even casual observation of numerous new plant constructions in heavy livestock areas in recent years seems to confirm this ease of entry.

TABLE 7.12

CHANGES IN NUMBER OF FI MEAT PACKING AND PROCESSING FIRMS THROUGH ENTRY AND EXIT, 1958—1964

| | | | Number of Firms | | |
| | | | Change Between 1958—1964 | | |
Type of Firm	1958	1964	Entries	Exits	Net
Slaughter					
Cattle	347	391	126	82	+44
Calves	222	217	83	88	−5
Lambs	160	148	66	78	−12
Hogs	180	199	78	59	+19
All slaughter	389	460	155	84	+71
Meat processing[1]	735	730	21	26	−5

Source: Derived from Meat Inspection Div. data assembled by the Marketing Econ. Div., USDA.
Reproduced from National Commission on Food Marketing (1966B).
[1] Beginning year was 1961 rather than 1958.

Table 7.12 also presents data on entry and exit in the meat processing industry for the period 1961-1964 as is noted in a footnote to that table. In 1958 there were nearly twice as many processors as slaughterers—735 compared to 389. However, only 21 new firms entered the industry and just 26 exited. This averaged out to be about 4 new entries per year compared to 31 for the slaughter industry.[7] These data indicate that entry into processing is

[7] These results differ from those of a study made by Anthony (1968). Anthony, using the same time period, reported 1155 processors at the beginning and 1322 at the end,

not as easy as entry into meat packing. There are several possible explanations. Processors have been able to brand and differentiate their products more successfully than packers have differentiated fresh meat. A newcomer in processing, therefore, has the problem of winning customers who may have preferences for a particular brand. Another possible factor is that processors in general have a more stable geographic orientation. Many of them are located near areas of heavy consumption which have been relatively stable. Livestock production, on the other hand, and particularly finished cattle production, has shifted considerably and new packing plants have tended to follow.

It should be noted that these analyses included only inspected plants. As was apparent in an earlier section on packing plant classification, the FI plants are a distinct minority in numbers, but they are considerably larger in average size and slaughter a substantially larger percentage of livestock than do the non-FI plants. In commenting on possible implications of results to the entire industry, Anthony (1966) states, "Far more complete data are available for meat packers operating under federal inspection than for those not receiving this service. As a result, most evidence presented in this report pertains directly to this sector of the meat packing industry and only indirectly to the industry as a whole as it is represented by the federally inspected sector. Because of the importance of the federally inspected sector, the necessary assumption that it is representative is not especially damaging. Nevertheless, the conclusions possible from the evidence presented are limited." A comparable qualification is appropriate for conclusions regarding the meat processing industry.

INTEGRATION IN THE PACKING INDUSTRY

Horizontal Integration by Packers

A number of packers are integrated, both horizontally and vertically. National packers and many regional packers have a number of establishments (plants) at different locations. This is horizontal integration. The 4 largest slaughtering firms owned or controlled 87 establishments in 1964 (Table 7.13). These four firms undoubtedly were large, national packers. The 4 largest meat processors owned or controlled 112 establishments. The next 4 slaughtering firms in size had 22 establishments—an average of slightly more than 5 each—and the next 4 largest meat processors had 50 establishments. Empirical evidence is lacking on reasons why firms expanded horizontally, but possible motives are (1) attempts to gain economies in purchasing supplies or in selling products, (2) possible forestalling of competitors from gaining a

---

with 270 entries and 103 exits. Apparently, processors were not defined identically in the two studies. Neither report was explicit in the definition used.

TABLE 7.13

NUMBER OF ESTABLISHMENTS OWNED OR CONTROLLED BY LARGEST
EIGHT FIRMS ENGAGED IN THE MEAT TRADE, DEC. 31, 1964

Type of Establishment	Establishments Owned or Controlled by Firms Ranking:	
	1–4	5–8
Livestock slaughtering	87	22
Meat processing	112	50
Meat distribution	374	28
Chicken slaughtering	37	...
Turkey processing	35	...
Egg processing	11	...
Total	656	100

Source: National Commission on Food Marketing (1966A).

foothold in particular locations, and (3) attempts to increase total profits by increasing volume of meat handled.

The public has been concerned in previous times with the amount of horizontal integration, to the extent that it was related to concentration in the industry. With the decline in concentration, as discussed in a previous section, concern with horizontal integration has abated. However, horizontal integration can expand while concentration in the industry is decreasing. Data reported by the National Commission on Food Marketing from 200 responding firms indicated that horizontal type acquisitions by meat packing firms exceeded horizontal type disposals during the period 1947-1964 (Table 7.14). More acquisitions were made by the 4 largest firms than any other 1 size of group, but total acquisitions by other (smaller) size firms exceeded that of the largest 4.

TABLE 7.14

HORIZONTAL TYPE ACQUISITIONS AND DISPOSALS BY MEAT PACKERS
IN SPECIFIED SIZE GROUPS, 1947 TO 1964

Size of Firm (1964 Sales in Million $)	No. of Firms	No. of Acquisitions[1]	No. of Disposals[1]
Under 10	94	5	1
10 to 24.9	48	7 (3)	3 (1)
25 to 49.9	32	14 (2)	3
50 to 99.9	13	13 (2)	8 (2)
100 to 499.9	9	38 (2)	13 (1)
500 and over	4	46 (7)	11 (5)
All reporting firms	200	126 (16)	39 (9)

Source: Data from National Commission on Food Marketing (1966A).
[1] Numbers in parentheses indicate number of acquisitions and disposals by lease. This number is included in acquisitions and disposals.

Conglomerate Integration

Conglomeration in business means the collection of diverse business endeavors under one firm's management. During the recent decade conglomerates expanded at a rapid rate. Some ran into financial difficulties in 1970 and the pace of development changed rather abruptly.

During the period of rapid development, however, meat packing firms were involved in conglomerate mergers which might be called conglomerate integration. Ostensibly, this has been an involuntary development on the part of packers. Controlling interests allegedly were obtained in securities market activities. Other examples could be cited, but one of the most widely publicized conglomerate mergers was the take-over of Wilson & Company by Ling Tempco Vaught—a conglomerate with many diverse interests.

It should be noted that several of the national packers (e.g., Swift, Wilson, and Armour), over the years, voluntarily diversified into a number of lines unrelated to meat packing. In a sense they expanded into conglomerage ventures. However, these generally were by purchase rather than by merger and did not attract the attention which accompanied recent conglomerate merger activity.

Vertical Integration by Packers

As mentioned earlier, the carrying out of processing activities by slaughterers involves integration of successive stages in meat production. This has never been a matter of serious public concern. Processing is considered to be in the domain of packers. However, concern has been voiced in recent years by segments of the cattle industry over packer and food chain backward vertical integration into cattle feeding. From time to time, public concern also has been expressed over lamb and hog feeding by packers. Federal legislation has been proposed to curb cattle feeding by packers but has not been enacted.

Data are not available on packer feeding prior to 1954, however since 1954 the Packers and Stockyards Administration of the USDA has reported livestock feeding activities of meat packers and retail food chains. The National Commission on Food Marketing also investigated certain aspects of vertical integration by packers.

Table 7.15 shows that major packers are expanding in cattle and hog feeding but, with the exception of 1966, their activities in sheep and lambs have been somewhat erratic but indicate an increasing trend. Packers other than the ten major packers are increasing the volume of cattle, calves, and sheep and lambs fed, but show a decline in hog feeding. Retailers are only lightly involved in cattle feeding.

Two special studies conducted by USDA in 1961 and 1965 show that packer associated interests (such as packing plant owners, directors, officers, employees, nonreporting subsidiaries, and affiliates) feed additional cattle which are not included in the regular annual report. This is shown in Table 7.16. It also may be seen in Table 7.16 that the rate of increase in feeding by packers has been at about the same rate at which total fed cattle marketings

TABLE 7.15
LIVESTOCK FEEDING ACTIVITIES OF MEAT PACKERS, 1962–1969[1]

Type of Packer and Year	Cattle		Calves		Hogs		Sheep and Lambs	
	No. of Firms	1000 Head	No. of Firms	1000 Head	No. of Firms	1000 Head	No. of Firms	1000 Head
10 Major packers								
1962	8	296.4	2	19.8	1	1.1	6	510.4
1963	9	377.6	2	36.5	2	4.5	7	581.2
1964	9	375.4	2	34.7	2	2.9	6	709.9
1965	8	308.6	1	30.8	2	4.0	6	676.9
1966	8	410.1	1	26.1	1	0.9	6	1136.4
1967	7	510.2	1	25.3	2	6.1	5	714.7
1968	7	389.6	2	14.8	2	22.5	5	745.0
1969	7	517.7	2	12.0	3	24.1	5	856.0
1970	8	503.0	1	7.0	2	43.4	5	827.1
Retail food chains								
1962	2	25.5	—	—	—	—	—	—
1963	4	53.8	1	1.0	1	—	1	0.1
1964	3	36.2	—	—	1	0.1	1	0.2
1965	3	58.8	—	—	—	—	—	—
1966	3	51.8	—	[2]	—	—	—	—
1967	3	49.3	1	—	—	—	—	—
1968	3	45.9	—	—	—	—	—	—
1969	3	42.6	—	—	—	—	1	4.6
1970	3	38.0	—	—	—	—	1	8.9
Other packers								
1962	197	614.4	47	25.3	42	26.3	20	40.3
1963	189	652.4	42	54.3	35	40.0	21	60.9
1964	170	640.4	43	40.0	28	30.2	22	157.0
1965	184	862.1	41	31.1	21	39.1	14	149.0
1966	178	922.2	41	63.5	18	31.9	11	159.1
1967	167	912.4	36	50.6	22	20.2	7	210.9
1968	155	876.1	32	70.8	14	19.4	11	207.3
1969	144	1001.3	23	59.2	14	19.0	9	411.7
1970	118	837.6	25	68.9	15	21.7	7	397.5
Total								
1962	207	936.3	49	45.1	43	27.4	26	550.7
1963	202	1083.8	45	91.8	37	44.5	29	642.2
1964	182	1052.0	45	74.8	31	33.2	29	867.1

TABLE 7.15 (Continued)

LIVESTOCK FEEDING ACTIVITIES OF MEAT PACKERS, 1962–1969[1]

Type of Packer and Year	Cattle		Calves		Hogs		Sheep and Lambs	
	No. of Firms	1000 Head	No. of Firms	1000 Head	No. of Firms	1000 Head	No. of Firms	1000 Head
1965	195	1229.5	42	61.9	23	43.1	20	825.9
1966	189	1384.1	42	89.6	19	32.8	17	1295.5
1967	177	1471.9	38	75.9	24	26.3	12	925.6
1968	165	1311.6	34	85.6	16	41.9	16	952.3
1969	154	1561.6	25	71.2	17	43.1	15	1272.9
1970	129	1378.6	26	75.9	17	65.1	13	1233.5

Source: USDA *Packers and Stockyards Resume* Nov. 29, 1971 and previous issues.
[1] Summarized from annual reports of packers filed with Admin. USDA. Includes livestock fed by or for meat packers and removed from feedlot for slaughter or sale during the reporting period. Separate feeding activities by owners, officers, or employees of meat packers or nonreporting subsidiaries or affiliates are not included.
[2] Less than 100 head.

TABLE 7.16

NUMBER OF PACKERS FEEDING CATTLE AND NUMBER OF HEAD FED
COMPARED WITH TOTAL FED MARKETINGS OF CATTLE
IN 39 STATES, 1954-1969

Year	No. of Packers Feeding	No. of Cattle Fed by Packers[1] (1000 head)	Fed Cattle Marketings in 39 States[2] (1000 head)	Packer Feeding as Percentage of Fed Marketings (%)
1954	165	564.9	9,482	6.0
1955	161	545.8	10,762	5.1
1956	157	520.8	11,331	4.6
1957	151	557.6	11,285	4.9
1958	176	729.1	11,787	6.2
1959	157	617.0	12,843	4.8
1960	165	856.7	13,621	6.3
1961[3]	206	919.2 (1251.2)	14,561	6.3 (8.8)
1962	215	981.4	15,434	6.4
1963	211	1175.6	16,808	7.0
1964	190	1126.8	18,319	6.2
1965[3]	204	1291.4 (2059.2)	18,936	6.8 (11.5)
1966	202	1473.7	20,597	7.2
1967	198	1547.8	21,920	7.1
1968	174	1397.3	23,286	6.0
1969	154	1632.8	24,930	6.6
1970	140	1454.5	25,830	5.6

Source: USDA *Packers and Stockyards Resume* Nov. 29, 1971.
[1] The number of cattle (including calves) fed by meat packers was summarized from annual reports of packers filed with the Packers and Stockyards Administration, USDA. Feeding by packer-associated interests is not included. Most packer feeding is reported on a fiscal year basis.
[2] USDA Econ. Res. Serv. *Livestock and Meat Situation*, May 1967 and October 1965 issues and *Livestock and Meat Statistics*. Estimates for 39 States are on a calendar year basis and account for most fed cattle (and calf) marketings in the United States. The figure for 1954 was based on earlier data from Breimyer (1961).
[3] Numbers and percentages enclosed by brackets include feeding by packer-associated interests. Data not available for other years.

increased during the past 10 yr. Packer feeding has been 6–7% of fed cattle marketing since about 1960–if feeding by packer-associated interests are excluded. When feeding by associated interests is included, the proportion was 8.8% in 1961 and 11.5% in 1965. Integration into feeding by packers is accomplished by ownership of feedlots, ownership of cattle which are fed on a custom basis, contractual arrangements for feeding, or various combinations of these alternatives.

Aspelin and Engelman (1966) investigated the effect on prices of packer feeding by one slaughterer at a leading terminal market in 1962. They concluded that "packer feeding was about 3% of cattle slaughter by packers located near the market. The primary packer-feeder in the area fed about 10% of its cattle slaughter. Data on movement of cattle by weeks throughout the year did not show evidence that shipments of packer-fed cattle consistently offset fluctuations in the receipts of cattle on the local (terminal) market. Apparently, packer-fed shipments did not serve to stabilize the market supply to any great extent.

"The statistical analysis indicated that packer feeding had significant depressive effects on weekly average prices at the teminal market, relative to prices at other terminals. Price effects were within the range of $0.25–$0.50 per cwt on the weekly average price for choice steers at the market. According to the mathematical analysis, a given increase in packer-fed supplies transferred to plant had more than ten times as much effect upon the local price for choice steers as did the same increase in market supplies of choice steers."

A major criticism leveled at this study was the limited sample upon which it was based, i.e., 1 packer at 1 market. Nevertheless, it called attention to a public concern over the expansion in packer feeding. While this was the only attempt at quantitative analysis of the effect on prices of packer feeding, it was followed by a number of articles of a subjective nature. The following summary draws heavily from one such article.

Various motives undoubtedly exist for packer feeding. Farris (1967) suggests the following:

(1) A more even supply of cattle may increase plant operating efficiency. Receipts fluctuate from seasonal factors and erratically from day to day and week to week. If livestock are not available, plants are shut down. This is an expensive proposition due to high fixed costs in plant and equipment. Packers can reduce fixed cost per unit of output by continuous operation. Labor also has a minimum fixed cost in that unions are guaranteed a minimum week's pay whether livestock is available or not.

(2) Livestock procurement costs may be lowered. Fewer livestock buyers are needed and transportation costs can be reduced if cattle are fed near the plant by the packer.

(3) Risks may be reduced. The packer can control not only numbers, but also quality of livestock and thereby meet specifications of meat purchasers. In addition, price risk may be reduced by strengthening the packer's bargaining position in buying livestock—especially during periods when supplies of particular grades are scarce.

(4) New organizational and technological innovations may be discovered. By being actively engaged in feeding, a packer may increase his knowledge of that aspect of the industry and participate in development of new technology.

(5) Implementation of new developments may occur rapidly. Access to funds may permit packers to implement new developments more rapidly than farmers or commercial feeders.

(6) Public policy generally sanctions freedom of enterprise. Livestock producers have integrated forward into meat packing, even though the extent is limited. This in itself could be grounds for arguing the case for packer backward integration. There is merit in consistency in public policy.

Farris (1967) also recognizes some potential problems associated with packer feeding:

(1) Market price manipulation may be possible. Vertical integration may provide a means of altering the market structure and in turn allow a business conduct not possible under purely competitive conditions. A packing firm able to dominate purchases at a particular location could exercise some control over prices. According to Farris (1967), "The packer practice of negotiating for large numbers of cattle several days in advance of shipment from the feedlot may also give packers opportunities to use such cattle in affecting paying prices."

(2) The pricing process may be affected by reduced proportion of cattle bought and sold in the marketing channel. Prices in established markets are widely publicized and used. Reduction in transactions at these markets erodes the base upon which they are established.

(3) The organizational structure of agricultural production may be adversely affected. Since packer feeding generally is large scale, its expansion may adversely affect family farm type feeding operations. The same observation can be made on large-scale commercial feedlots in general.

(4) Packer feeding may bring unfair competition to specialized producers. This is an extension of (3) above. Since packers have earnings from other interests which could be used to cover losses in feeding operations, it has been suggested that losses could be sustained for extended periods in a given area, to the detriment of specialized feeders. It also has been suggested that packers could destabilize supplies and enhance price swings. This point, as well as several others mentioned above, prompted the National Commission on Food Marketing to propose the public reporting of activities of large, diverse firms engaged in feeding.

(5) The total volume of cattle fed may be higher if packers feed—leading to depressed producer prices. Historically, variations in production have been associated with profit levels. It seems likely this will continue to be the case, whether feeding is done by packers or others.

In summing up public policy considerations Farris (1967) commented, "In considering policy alternatives toward packer feeding, it may be possible to adopt a course which would avoid the undesirable possibilities associated with the practice, yet preserve its efficiency, flexibility, and potential for technological gain. One alternative would be to permit packers to feed or have custom fed for them a certain proportion of their slaughter capacity. Analysis of various considerations would be necessary to ascertain what prohibition would best minimize adverse side effects while retaining efficiency advantages of packer feeding. Without better factual knowledge, it may be desirable to place increased emphasis on supervising market practices of integrated firms more closely, while determining whether it would be in the public interest to restrict vertical integration.

EARNINGS IN THE PACKING INDUSTRY

Historically, the meat packing industry has been noted for low earning rates compared to other U.S. industries. This is apparent in Fig. 7.4, 7.5 and 7.6 where net income after taxes as a percentage of net worth is plotted for a number of industries. Meat packing is the lowest of any shown. These figures represent the average performance for the entire industry. Undoubtedly, variation exists in earnings among firms within the industry, but this information is not available. Table 7.17, however, shows earnings over the period 1947-1964 for the 4 largest and the 4 next largest meat packers. Earnings for the largest 4 ranged from 3.3 to 15.5% of net worth with an average of 6% for the period. Earnings for the second largest 4 firms were higher, averaging 9.5%. Earnings as a percentage of sales are notoriously low—running less than 1¢ on the dollar in most years; but this statistic is not very revealing of firm and industry profits without also citing sales volume.

Earnings of specialized cattle slaughtering firms at 16.0% and specialized meat processing firms at 13.1% were considerably higher (see Table 7.18) than average industry rates or earnings of the largest firms. Specialized hog slaughtering firms earned about 1/2 the rate of cattle slaughterers, but still were above the industry average.

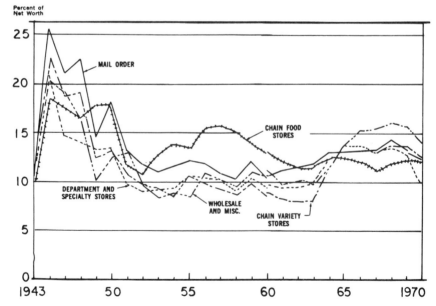

National Commission on Food Marketing (1966B) and
First National City Bank of New York

FIG. 7.4. NET INCOME AFTER TAXES AS A PERCENTAGE OF NET WORTH, 1945-1970

National Commission on Food Marketing (1966B) and
First National City Bank of New York

FIG. 7.5. NET INCOME AFTER TAXES AS A PERCENTAGE OF NET WORTH,
1945-1970

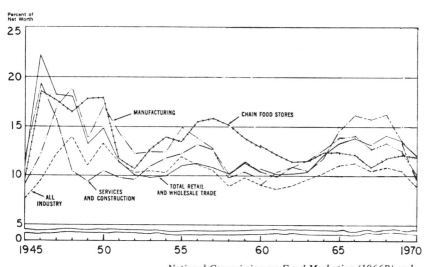

National Commission on Food Marketing (1966B) and
First National City Bank of New York

FIG. 7.6. AVERAGE ANNUAL RATES OF RETURN—NET INCOME AFTER TAXES
AS A PERCENTAGE OF NET WORTH, 1945-1970

TABLE 7.17

EARNING RATES FOR LARGE MEAT PACKING COMPANIES, 1947-1964[1]

| | Total Sales | | Net Income after Taxes as Percentage of:
Total Assets | | Net Worth | |
| | | | Firms Ranking | | | |
Year	1-4 (%)	5-8 (%)	1-4 (%)	5-8 (%)	1-4 (%)	5-8 (%)
1947	1.70	1.12	10.2	9.2	15.5	14.9
1948	0.68	1.21	3.6	10.2	6.0	15.7
1949	0.63	0.52	2.7	3.5	5.0	5.4
1950	0.80	0.99	3.6	6.3	6.3	10.4
1951	0.58	0.87	3.0	6.1	5.1	10.6
1952	0.56	0.68	2.7	4.4	4.8	8.0
1953	0.84	0.62	4.0	4.3	7.0	7.7
1954	0.44	0.60	2.0	4.3	3.4	7.5
1955	0.75	1.17	3.5	7.6	5.6	13.7
1956	0.70	1.43	3.2	8.5	5.6	15.4
1957	0.42	0.80	1.9	4.7	3.3	-8.2
1958	0.46	0.71	2.2	4.4	3.6	7.4
1959	0.90	1.23	4.1	7.5	6.8	12.3
1960	0.76	1.05	3.4	5.8	5.7	9.8
1961	0.64	0.43	3.0	2.4	4.9	3.8
1962	0.73	0.51	3.3	2.9	5.7	4.5
1963	0.77	0.78	3.4	4.4	5.8	6.6
1964	1.10	1.16	5.0	6.5	8.6	9.9
Avg 1947-1964	...	...	...	...	6.0	9.5

Source: National Commission on Food Marketing (1966A).
[1] Ranked according to red meat sales in 1963. Largest 4 companies include Armour, Morrell, Swift, and Wilson. Companies in second group of 4 include Hormel, Hygrade, Oscar Mayer, and Rath. The data are for fiscal years ending approximately Oct. 31.

Relatively low earnings in the meat packing industry probably result from a combination of factors. To some degree it reflects the highly competitive nature of the industry. Also, it probably is at least partially due to operational inefficiencies. The variation in receipts due to cyclical and seasonal factors has resulted in a chronic overcapacity and unused facilities at times other than peak receipts. This tends to increase average costs and reduce profits. Under historical supply conditions, overcapacity has been virtually inherent in the industry. During cyclical and seasonal downswings in receipts, packers compete with each other for available livestock in an attempt to maintain volume. This tends to increase procurement costs and reduce profits. As has been noted earlier, structural changes are taking place which are leading to a greater degree of stability in supply. Both cyclical and seasonal trends are becoming less pronounced.

Although empirical evidence is unavailable on the subject, specialization in slaughtering probably improves operational efficiency and enhances profits. Many of the newer, specialized plants have incorporated technologically-improved equipment, more efficient layouts, and sophisticated management techniques, all of which enhance operational efficiency.

TABLE 7.18

EARNING RATES FOR MEAT PACKERS BY TYPE OF 1964 OPERATION,[1] 1947-1964

	Meat packers slaughtering cattle but no hogs in 1964 Net Income after Taxes as Percentage of:				Meat packers slaughtering hogs but no cattle in 1964 Net Income after Taxes as Percentage of:				Meat packers at least slaughtering cattle and hogs in 1964[2] Net Income after Taxes as Percentage of:				Meat processor in 1964 (no slaughter) Net Income after Taxes as Percentage of:			
Year	No. of Firms	Sales (%)	Assets (%)	Net Worth (%)	No. of Firms	Sales (%)	Assets (%)	Net Worth (%)	No. of Firms	Sales (%)	Assets (%)	Net Worth (%)	No. of Firms	Sales (%)	Assets (%)	Net Worth (%)
1947	14	1.2	29	58	4	1.4	11	16	42	1.5	10	17	12	2.8	20	27
1948	16	1.4	20	33	5	2.0	10	17	45	0.4	2	5	13	1.7	12	17
1949	18	0.9	10	16	5	0.8	5	7	45	0.2	1	2	14	2.6	17	22
1950	19	0.9	11	16	5	1.4	9	14	48	0.9	5	9	15	2.2	14	20
1951	21	0.8	11	18	5	1.1	7	11	51	0.7	4	7	15	1.3	8	12
1952	22	0.7	7	13	6	0.5	3	4	52	0.2	1	2	15	1.4	8	13
1953	23	0.9	8	13	6	0.1	1	1	54	0.5	3	5	15	1.4	8	12
1954	27	0.9	9	12	7	0.5	3	5	56	0.2	1	1	17	1.6	9	13
1955	30	0.8	6	12	9	1.1	6	10	60	0.9	4	8	19	2.0	11	13
1956	32	1.0	9	13	9	1.1	6	9	62	1.1	5	11	20	1.6	9	16
1957	33	0.9	8	13	13	0.8	5	9	64	0.5	3	5	22	1.0	7	13
1958	36	0.6	6	11	13	0.5	4	6	67	0.6	3	6	24	0.6	5	9
1959	38	0.6	7	12	13	0.9	6	9	71	1.1	6	10	26	1.1	8	6
1960	42	0.5	6	11	16	0.4	3	4	71	0.9	5	8	31	1.0	7	12
1961	53	0.3	4	7	17	0.5	3	5	76	0.7	3	6	37	0.3	2	10
1962	58	0.3	6	9	18	0.6	4	7	79	0.7	4	6	35	0.8	5	4
1963	67	0.2	2	4	22	0.5	4	6	95	0.8	4	7	42	0.9	6	8
1964	67	0.7	8	17	22	1.1	7	12	96	1.2	6	10	43	1.2	7	10
Avg 1947-1964	...	...	...	16.0	...	...	...	8.4	...	...	...	6.9	...	...	...	13.1

Source: National Commission on Food Marketing (1966A) with 1947-1964 averages added by author.
[1] Each firm was classified according to its operation in 1964. Minor quantities were ignored in classifying firms. Earning rates were weighted by total dollars; therefore, small firms had little influence on the ratios. Fiscal years of reporting packers were not all identical, although most ended either around Dec. 31 or Oct. 31.
[2] Excluding meat packers with poultry operations.

BIBLIOGRAPHY

ANTHONY, W. E. 1966. Structural changes in the federally inspected livestock slaughter industry 1950-62. USDA Econ. Res. Serv., Agr. Econ. Rept. *83*, Revised Febr.

ANTHONY, W. E. 1968. Structural changes in the federally inspected meat processing industry 1961-64. USDA Econ. Res. Serv., Agr. Econ. Rept. *128*.

ANTHONY, W. E. 1969. Patterns of firm growth in livestock slaughtering. Minn. Agr. Expt. Sta. Tech. Bull. *261*.

ANTHONY, W. E., and EGERTSON, K. E. 1966. Decentralization in the livestock slaughter industry. USDA Econ. Res. Serv., Suppl. Agr. Econ. Rept. *83*.

ASPELIN, A., and ENGELMAN, G. 1966. Packer feeding of cattle, its volume and significance. USDA, C&MS Marketing Res. Rept. *776*.

BREIMYER, H. F. 1961. Demand and prices for meat. USDA Econ. Res. Serv. Tech. Bull. *1253*.

BUTZ, D. E., and BAKER, G. L. 1960. The Changing Structure of the Meat Economy. Harvard Univ. Graduate School Business Admin., Boston.

COX, R. W., and TAYLOR, F. R. 1965. Feasibility of cooperatively owned slaughter plants. N. Dakota Agr. Expt. Sta. Agr. Econ. Rept. *39*.

DEWEY, D. Monopoly in Economics and Law. Rand McNally & Co., Chicago.

DIETRICH, R. A. *et al*. 1963. The Texas-Oklahoma meat industry, structure and marketing practices. USDA Econ. Res. Serv., Agr. Econ. Rept. *39*.

DIRLAM, J. B., and KAHN, A. E. 1954. Fair Competition. Cornell University Press, Ithaca, N.Y.

DUDDY, E. A., and REVZAN, D. A. 1938. The Changing Relative Importance of the Central Livestock Market. University of Chicago Press, Chicago.

FARRIS, P. L. 1967. Economic evaluation of cattle feeding by meat packers. Econ. Marketing Inform. Indiana Farmers, May 4-5.

FOWLER, S. H. 1961. The Marketing of Livestock and Meat, 2nd Edition. Interstate Printers & Publishers, Danville, Ill.

IVES, J. R. 1966. The Livestock and Meat Economy of the United States. Am. Meat Inst., Chicago.

KAYSEN, C., and TURNER, D. F. 1959. Antitrust Policy: A Legal and Economic Analysis. Harvard University Press, Boston.

LOGAN, S. H. 1966. Economies of scale in cattle slaughter plants. Natl. Comm. Food Marketing Tech. Study *1*, Suppl. *2*.

LOGAN, S. H., and KING, G. A. 1962. Economies of scale in beef slaughter plants. Calif. Agr. Expt. Sta., Gianni Found. Res. Rept. *260*.

NATIONAL COMMISSION ON FOOD MARKETING. 1966A. Organization and competition in the livestock and meat industry. Natl. Comm. Food Marketing Tech. Study *1*.

NATIONAL COMMISSION ON FOOD MARKETING. 1966B. Organization and competition in food retailing. Natl. Comm. Food Marketing Tech. Study *7*.

SCHNAKE, L. D. *et al*. 1968. Economies of size in non-slaughtering meat plants. Oklahoma Agr. Expt. Sta. Tech. Bull. *T-125*.

TROTTER, C. E., and McINTOSH, K. D. 1965. Procurement costs of independent slaughter plants in the northeast. Penn. Agr. Expt. Sta. Bull. *729*.

USDA. 1970A. Number of livestock slaughter plants, March 1, 1970. USDA Statist. Reporting Serv. *SRS-8* (Revised).

USDA. 1971. Livestock and meat statistics. USDA Econ. Res. Serv. Statist. Bull. *333*, Suppl. for 1970.

U.S. Dept. Commerce. 1970. 1967 census of manufacturers, meat products. U.S. Dept. Com. Bur. Census Oct.

WATKINS, M. W. 1927. Industry Combinations and Public Policies. Houghton Mifflin Co., Boston.

WILCOX, C. 1960. Public Policies Toward Business. Richard İrwin, Homewood, Ill.

WILLIAMS, W. F., and STOUT, T. T. 1964. Economics of the Livestock-Meat Industry. Macmillan Co., New York.

CHAPTER 8

Meat Marketing-Wholesale

The previous chapters examined routes and means by which live animals are moved to the point of slaughter. But meat in the packing plant must reach the ultimate user to attain its full economic value. Between the packing house and the consumer lies a vast and complex system of market channels. Three things complicate the situation: (1) the quantities involved are enormous, (2) the distances of movement are great, and (3) the products have a relatively high degree of perishability.

U.S. consumers in 1970 ate approximately 36 billion pounds (carcass weight) of red meat—185.5 lb for every man, woman, and child. But, the bulk of meat is not produced in close proximity to areas of heavy population concentration. Consumers are concentrated on the east coast, around the Great Lakes, and on the west coast, while meat production is concentrated in the Corn Belt and in Central and Southern Plains states. This situation is becoming more pronounced as beef production becomes more concentrated in the Milo Belt and the packing industry follows.

Under present economic conditions and with the present state of technology, fresh meat is not stored for an appreciable length of time. It is moved rapidly through market channels into the hands of consumers. While great strides have been made in meat preservation (refrigeration revolutionized the distribution and merchandizing of meat), refrigerated meat must be moved into consumption in a matter of days. Freezing, freeze drying, drying, and various methods of curing increase the storability of meat in varying degrees. For certain cuts of pork (hams, bellies and shoulders) freezing and curing are used extensively—partly to take advantage of seasonal price trends. But in terms of total meat production, and particularly with beef and lamb, storage is not a major factor. Market channels move the relatively perishable product from packers, to processors, to retailers and food service outlets. Significant changes have occurred and are occurring, in this system.

Refrigeration and transportation improvements probably would have to be classed as the two major factors affecting meat distribution. But of more recent origin are the development of chain supermarkets and structural changes within the packing industry, i.e., a fragmentation of the industry into an increased number of smaller firms scattered throughout the producing area. The big chain retailers purchase wholesale meat by the carlot, often directly from packers: the smaller neighborhood type retailer, of necessity, purchases smaller lots from a more local wholesale type of distributor. Smaller packers often have problems making contact with purchasers in distant markets. They find an increasing need for intermediaries, independent wholesalers, brokers,

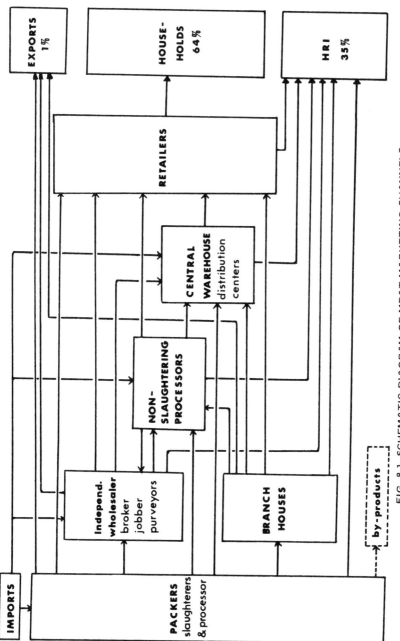

FIG. 8.1. SCHEMATIC DIAGRAM OF MEAT MARKETING CHANNELS

and jobbers. A tremendously increasing hotel, restaurant, and institution (HRI) trade (often referred to as the food service industry) has been another recent development of importance in meat marketing.

Fig. 8.1 is a generalized diagram of the major channels of meat distribution. A cell is shown for by-products simply to call attention to the fact that the output of a packing plant consists of more than meat. The actual distribution of meat is considerably more complex than indicated. For example, the cell labeled independent wholesalers, brokers, etc., does not do justice to the many types of wholesalers nor to the functions they perform. Involved here is the handling of fresh, cured, and processed meat; the handling of carcasses, primal, subprimal and portion control cuts; boning; buying outright versus simply acting as agent; peddling; etc. Some retail establishments (and some restaurant chains) also operate slaughtering and processing facilities, while some packers also operate retail establishments. There is trade among packers and among processors which goes through agents. Sometimes more than one agent may handle a given lot of meat (either physically or by title) as it is transferred from one point in the distribution system to another.

In general, the transfer of title, i.e., the buying and selling, can be classified as either a wholesale or retail operation. To a large extent the cuts of meat involved in these transfers also can be classified as wholesale and retail, but this distinction gradually is losing the universality it once had. Where, at one time, all of the cutting into retail cuts was done in the retail store, a strong trend is underway to move that function to earlier points in market channels. This will be discussed in greater detail in a later section. Here it will only be mentioned that a major factor preventing its movement all the way back to the packer and processor level is lack of an acceptable method of preservation for the retail cut. A limited quantity of retail cuts already is moving, primarily as frozen meat, through wholesale channels.

WHOLESALING DEFINED

Wholesaling operations are defined here as movements from point of slaughter (packer) to retail outlets, HRI outlets, and export. Under some circumstances, the definition of a wholesaler or wholesaling is made contingent upon the breaking of a carcass into wholesale cuts. In this sense some difficulty is encountered in differentiating between manufacturing and wholesaling. In the above definition it makes no difference who does the breaking or the extent of breaking; any movement through distribution channels to retail, HRI, or export points is classed as wholesaling.

Products included are processed meats[1] as well as fresh meat. The National

---

[1] Processed meat includes such items as bologna, luncheon meats, sausages, cured meat, smoked meat, and ground and comminuted meats even though the latter may be in the fresh state. The term sausage carries a double meaning. It is used to indicate fresh ground pork, but also is used as a general term to include all prepared meats of the bologna,

Livestock and Meat Board has prepared charts of wholesale (and retail) cuts of beef (Fig. 8.2), veal (Fig. 8.3), pork (Fig. 8.4), and lamb (Fig. 8.5). These wholesale cuts correspond generally to primal cuts, in trade terminology. However, standardized cutting has not been accepted nationwide. Wholesale trade also is carried on in sides and quarters of beef, and in entire carcasses (unsplit) of veal and lamb. Wholesale shipments of carcass pork may be either "packer style" (jowls attached, head and leaf fat removed, and carcass divided into halves) or "shipper style" (head and leaf fat attached and carcass not split). The latter constitute only a minor fraction of pork shipments. A considerable quantity of portion control cuts is traded on a wholesale basis to the HRI trade and, to a limited extent, retail cuts are being wholesaled to retailers. This type of activity is carried on by wholesalers who specialize in breaking down to portion cuts and retail cuts.

In earlier days, larger packers built "full line" plants—plants in which all species and classes of livestock were slaughtered. Many also had a "sausage kitchen" in the same establishment where smoking, curing, and manufacturing of processed meats were done. Others did nothing but slaughtering. For some years the trend has been away from full line plants and away from combination slaughtering and manufacturing of processed meats. Now, many simply are kill-and-chill plants with shipment of sides or quarters, although, as mentioned, a trend also is apparent to move more breaking and cutting back toward the packer.

Figure 8.1 indicates wholesale movement from packers (who may process as well as slaughter) to the following: branch houses, independent wholesalers and brokers, processors, HRI trade, export, and direct to retail outlets. Many additional linkages are indicated and some are not shown, as mentioned before. No attempt is made in this discussion to give a completely detailed description of the wholesaling of meat. Those who are interested will find more detail by consulting Fowler (1961), Ives (1966), and Williams and Stout (1964).

What goes on in this complex network of marketing may seem rather remote to the average livestock producer. In terms of distance, many of the things which happen are far removed from the feedlot scene. Nevertheless, they are vitally important. It is in this framework that wholesale prices are generated. What the packer gets at wholesale largely determines what he can

---

luncheon meat types, cured and smoked sausage, etc. The word "processing," when used in the term "central processing unit," also has another meaning from that which might be implied in the above definition of processed meat. A central processing unit is one in which meat is broken down by a central unit of a larger operating unit, e.g., of a chain of retail stores or restaurants. To make the situation even more confusing, wholesalers who engage in the breaking down of carcasses to wholesale cuts or retail cuts are known as "fabricators." This is a misnomer, as the word fabricate ordinarily refers to an assembly process whereas the cutting of meat is disassembly. However, there is no confusion in the meat trade where these terms are commonly used and well understood.

WHOLESALE CUTS OF BEEF AND THEIR BONE STRUCTURE

CHUCK   RIB   SHORT LOIN   SIRLOIN   ROUND

FORE SHANK   BRISKET   SHORT PLATE   FLANK

APPROXIMATE YIELDS*

	PERCENT
FOREQUARTER	
Chuck (5 ribs)	26
Rib (7 ribs)	9
Shank	4
Brisket	5
Short Plate	8
	52
HINDQUARTER	
Round	23
Sirloin	9
Short Loin	8
Flank	5
Kidney, Suet and Hanging Tender	3
	48
Total	100

*No allowance for cutting shrink

RETAIL CUTS OF BEEF AND WHERE THEY COME FROM

① Standing Rump   ① Rolled Rump

① Round Steak   ③ Top Round Steak

③ Outside (Bottom) Round Steak or Pot-roast

④ Heel of Round

③ Eye of Round

① Pin Bone Sirloin Steak   ② Flat Bone Sirloin Steak   ③ Wedge Bone Sirloin Steak   ①②③ Boneless Sirloin Steak

① Club Steak   ② T-Bone Steak   ③ Porterhouse Steak   ①②③ Top Loin Steak   ②③ Filet Mignon Tenderloin Steak (also from Sirloin 1, 2, 3)

② Standing Rib Roast   ② Rib Steak   ② Rib Steak, Boneless   ②→ Delmonico (Rib Eye) Roast or Steak

⑤⑥ Chuck Short Ribs   ③ Petite Steaks   ④⑤ Arm Pot-roast or Steak   ⑥ English (Boston) Cut

②③ Inside Chuck Roll   ② Chuck Tender   ②③ Blade Pot-roast or Steak   ⑤ Boneless Shoulder Pot-roast or Steak

Courtesy of National Live Stock and Meat Board

FIG. 8.2. WHOLESALE AND RETAIL CUTS OF BEEF

WHOLESALE CUTS OF VEAL AND THEIR BONE STRUCTURE

APPROXIMATE YIELDS *

	PERCENT
FORESADDLE	
Shoulders (5 ribs)	26
Hotel Rack (7 ribs)	9
Shanks	5
Breasts	10
	50
HINDSADDLE	
Legs (Sirloin on)	39
Loin, trimmed	7
Flanks	2
Kidneys and Suet	2
	50
Total	100

*No allowance for cutting shrink

RETAIL CUTS OF VEAL AND WHERE THEY COME FROM

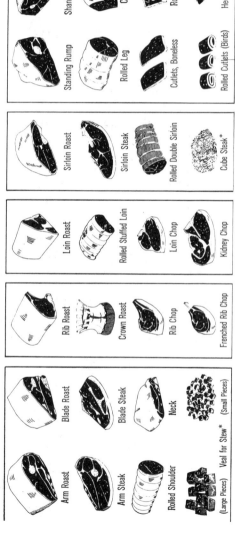

Shank Half of Leg   Center Leg   Round Steak   Heel of Round

Standing Rump   Rolled Leg   Cutlets, Boneless   Rolled Cutlets (Birds)

Sirloin Roast   Sirloin Steak   Rolled Double Sirloin   Cube Steak*

Loin Roast   Rolled Stuffed Loin   Loin Chop   Kidney Chop

Rib Roast   Crown Roast   Rib Chop   Frenched Rib Chop

Blade Roast   Blade Steak   Neck   (Small Pieces)

Arm Roast   Arm Steak   Rolled Shoulder   Veal for Stew*   (Large Pieces)

SHOULDER   HOTEL RACK   LOIN TRIMMED   LEG

FORE SHANK   BREAST   FLANK

FIG. 8.3. WHOLESALE AND RETAIL CUTS OF VEAL

WHOLESALE CUTS OF PORK AND THEIR BONE STRUCTURE

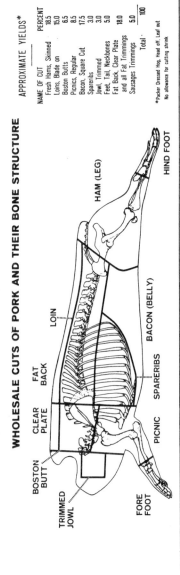

APPROXIMATE YIELDS*

NAME OF CUT	PERCENT
Fresh Hams, Skinned	18.5
Loins, Blade on	15.0
Boston Butts	6.5
Picnics, Regular	8.5
Bacon, Square Cut	17.5
Spareribs	3.0
Jowl, Trimmed	3.0
Feet, Tail, Neckbones	5.0
Fat Back, Clear Plate and all Fat Trimmings	18.0
Sausages Trimmings	5.0
Total	100

*Packer Dressed Hog. Head off. Leaf out
No allowance for cutting shrink

BOSTON BUTT — CLEAR PLATE — FAT BACK — LOIN — HAM (LEG) — HIND FOOT — BACON (BELLY) — SPARERIBS — PICNIC — FORE FOOT — TRIMMED JOWL

RETAIL CUTS OF PORK AND WHERE THEY COME FROM

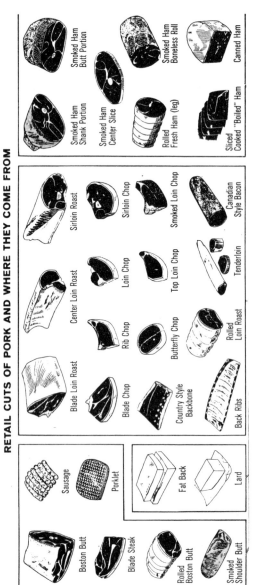

Smoked Ham Shank Portion — Smoked Ham Butt Portion — Smoked Ham Center Slice — Smoked Ham Boneless Roll — Rolled Fresh Ham (leg) — Canned Ham — Sliced Cooked "Boiled" Ham

Blade Loin Roast — Center Loin Roast — Sirloin Roast — Blade Chop — Rib Chop — Loin Chop — Sirloin Chop — Country Style Backbone — Butterfly Chop — Top Loin Chop — Smoked Loin Chop — Rolled Loin Roast — Tenderloin — Canadian Style Bacon — Back Ribs

Boston Butt — Blade Steak — Rolled Boston Butt — Smoked Shoulder Butt — Sausage — Porklet — Fat Back — Lard

FIG. 8.4. WHOLESALE AND RETAIL CUTS OF PORK

Courtesy of National Live Stock and Meat Board

WHOLESALE CUTS OF LAMB AND THEIR BONE STRUCTURE

RETAIL CUTS OF LAMB AND WHERE THEY COME FROM

APPROXIMATE YIELDS*

	PERCENT
FORESADDLE	
Shoulders (4 ribs)	24
Hotel Rack (8 ribs)	12
Shanks	4
Breasts	10
	50
HINDSADDLE	
Legs (Sirloin on)	33
Loin, trimmed	11
Flanks	3
Kidneys and Suet	3
	50
Total	100

*No allowance for cutting shrink

FIG. 8.5. WHOLESALE AND RETAIL CUTS OF LAMB

pay for slaughter livestock. The producer who intends to do his own marketing must have an acquaintance with the wholesale market—its methods and procedures, changes that are occurring, and sources of price quotations. Livestock sales which are made on the carcass grade and weight method are related directly to wholesale carcass prices. Sales made on live grade and weight basis are only one step removed from the wholesale carcass market.

PACKER BRANCH HOUSES

Packer branch houses are satellite warehouse-processing-distribution centers owned and operated by a parent packing firm, and located in relatively large population centers away from the packing plant(s). Basically, the branch house is a sales and distribution activity with a considerable amount of carcass breaking, processing, smoking, and curing. In the hey-day of big packers (before decentralization of the packing industry got underway in the 1920's and 1930's), this was the major channel of distribution to larger cities. Meat was moved from packing plants to branch houses in car and truck lots, then from branch houses to retailers, independent wholesalers, hotels and restaurants, processors, and minor quantities to export.

The U.S. Census of Manufactures (1967) provides the latest data available on branch house, jobber, and broker operations.

The number of branch houses, according to U.S. census reports, dropped from 1157 in 1929 to 522 in 1958. A slight increase has occurred since then (Table 8.1). In dollar amount, shipments and sales were higher in 1967 than in 1929, but have remained relatively constant in recent years. Higher meat prices have held up the dollar volume. The National Commission of Food Marketing (1966) reported that "only about 14% of meat was handled by branch houses in 1963, compared with 30% in 1939." The decline in branch house use is attributed largely to increases in direct sales by packers to large chain retailers. These large operators by-pass intermediate steps between packer and retailer. The greater adaptability and flexibility of truck transportation makes direct deliveries more feasible and economical. Increasing operational costs, particularly labor, in large cities also have been factors in the decline of branch houses.

PACKER DIRECT SALES

Concurrent with the decline in branch house operations has been an increase in wholesale selling at the packing plant level. Part of this is due to the desire and ability of large retail chains to deal directly with sources of supply of wholesale meat, part is due to packers' desire to cut out costly branch house operations, and part is due to increased use of federal grades and specification buying which facilitates buying by telephone. In regard to the latter point, some large buyers still buy by inspection (rather than description) in order to

TABLE 8.1

MEAT SLAUGHTERING PLANTS, PROCESSING PLANTS, PACKER SALES
BRANCHES, MEAT MERCHANT WHOLESALERS, MERCHANDISE AGENTS;
NUMBER OF ESTABLISHMENTS AND DOLLAR VOLUME OF SHIPMENTS
AND SALES, CENSUS YEARS 1929-1967

Census Years	Meat Packing Plants	Processing Plants[1]	Packer Sales Branch Offices	Meat Merchant Wholesalers (Jobbers)	Merchandise Agents (Brokers)
		No. of Establishments			
1929	1277	. . .	1157	2225	. . .
1939	1392	. . .	940	2552	. . .
1948	2154[2]	. . .	756	3200	. . .
1954	2367	. . .	664	4357	. . .
1958	2810	1494	522	4482	154
1963	2992	1341	577	5170	134
1967	2697	1374	616	5041	163
		Shipments and Sales (Million $)			
1929	3,435[3]	. . .	1923	690	. . .
1939	2,540[3]	. . .	1091	520	. . .
1948	8,970[2]	. . .	2810	1977	. . .
1954	10,265	. . .	2697	2866	. . .
1958	11,972	2066	2263	3891	609
1963	12,436	2130	2446	5371	810
1967	15,576	3008	2811	7395	853

Source: U.S. Dept. Commerce adapted from Ives (1966).
[1] In census publication called *Sausages and Other Prepared Meats*.
[2] Meat packing figures are for 1947.
[3] "Value of production" rather than "value of shipments" used prior to 1947.

take advantage of certain specifications not pinpointed by federal grade standards.

Direct plant sales are accomplished by plant sales departments, car and truck routes, and the maintenance of sales offices in cities away from the location of packing plants.

Plant Sales

Practically every large packer and many medium sized ones maintain a carlot sales department, and, in addition, practically all handle less than carlot sales. Carlot sales departments deal directly with large buyers—primarily retail chains. The shipments move by refrigerated boxcar or truck directly to the buyer's warehouse or processing center. Local sales of less than carlot quantities are handled either by buyers visiting the plant to make selection or salesmen taking local orders.

Car and Truck Routes

In that range of territory outside of local sales and not covered by either branch houses or sales offices away from the plant, less than carlot sales are handled by car and truck routes branching out from the plant. Usually orders are taken by route salesmen who make rounds of retail stores, restaurants, hotels, and institutions. Orders are relayed back to the plant and delivery made periodically—possibly several times a week by truck or rail. Trucks have the decided advantage of store door delivery. Trucks and refrigerated cars are loaded so that the last order in will be the first to come out, and so on around the route. The optimization of routing a fleet of trucks in a manner to minimize delivery costs is a problem that lends itself well to mathematical programming. Significant savings often can be made by access to solutions of this type.

Packer Sales Offices

Many packers are too small to maintain branch houses. Some larger ones prefer not to operate branch houses. At the same time some in both categories want to handle sales without going through an intermediary. One way of doing this is to establish sales offices in cities away from the plant. These offices take orders and solicit orders, catering primarily to larger customers. They perform the selling function of branch houses, but do not physically handle the meat. Orders are relayed back to the plant, and shipments are made directly from packing plant to purchaser.

INDEPENDENT WHOLESALERS

Many packers by choice or necessity engage the services of an intermediary in selling their products. Small independent packers located in production areas great distances from high consumption areas often do not have the connections or facilities for direct sales. Others prefer to emphasize plant production aspects and hire experts, so-to-speak, to do the marketing associated with the buying and selling of carcasses and wholesale cuts. A multitude of other activities is performed by independent operators who function in channels between the packers and retailers, HRI buyers, and the export trade. Among these activities are breaking (or fabricating), boning, freezing, processing, etc.

A major distinction can be made within this group of intermediaries on whether the intermediary buys the meat outright (takes title) or simply acts as an agent on a commission basis. By following a strict definition, the former can be classified as jobbers and the latter as brokers. In the meat trade, the term jobber ordinarily is used in a narrower sense; however, there is some ambiguity in its meaning. In general, the term jobber is used to indicate the type of outlet of the wholesaler rather than method of operation. In this discussion, jobber will be used in the broader sense—i.e. independent wholesalers who buy (take title) and resell, hopefully at a profit. Within this general classification, reference will be made to various specialities which are related to the activities performed. By the same token, it is possible to indicate specialities, or subclassifications, within the broker class.

Wholesaling operations have grown substantially in recent years, as shown in Table 8.1. The number of meat wholesalers more than doubled between 1929 and 1967. During the same time the value of shipments and sales by wholesalers increased more than 19 times. This was a period of relatively rapid fragmentation of the packing industry and rapid expansion in both chain retail operations and the food service trade (HRI). The latter is directly related to enormous growth in franchised motel and restaurant chains. Important also has been the growth in institutional feeding, e.g., educational dormitories, other state institutions, and factory and store cafeterias. These types of buyers not only purchase large quantities, but want regular delivery of uniform quality meat. Many of them are discriminating buyers with substantial bargaining power.

A continuation of cold and hot wars since World War II has necessitated large meat purchases for military installations. Military purchases generally are on contract bids as are governmental school lunch and welfare purchases.

Under these circumstances many packers find it advantageous either to sell their meat to a jobber and let him take it from there, or employ the services of a broker who acts as their agent for a fee. The expansion in independent wholesaling activities in recent years seems to attest to the fact that wholesaling is a complicated, competitive aspect of the meat business and that there is a place for specialists in the performance of wholesaling functions.

Jobbers

As mentioned, the term jobber is used here to mean a meat wholesaler who takes title (he buys the products and resells) hoping to make a profit. Mention already has been made that some of these operators deal in carcass meat, some in wholesale cuts, and some in retail and HRI cuts. Some specialize in breaking (fabricating), others in boning, freezing, etc. One type of specialist within this group deserving of particular mention is the "purveyor." This term generally is restricted to meat wholesalers who deal rather exclusively with the food service industry. Particular purveyors often limit their clientele to a specific segment of that industry. For example, some handle only the very highest quality meat and deal exclusively with high class hotels, night clubs, and steamship lines. Others cater to franchised motel chains, etc. Purveyors with long-established reputations are among the most discriminating buyers. Ives (1966) reports that "this specialized type of wholesaling has had its greatest growth during and since World War II, coincident with the growth of food service establishments in these years."

Boners specialize in the preparation of boneless meat. This, primarily, is lower grade beef. This meat moves on through channels to processors, the military, and retailers.

The meat "peddler" is another independent wholesaler. Other terms used for this operator are "wagon or truck jobber" and "truck distributor." The peddler is a small operator, often consisting of only one man who does the buying, selling, and delivering. The importance of peddlers has declined along with the decline in neighborhood meat retailers and neighborhood grocery stores.

Brokers

The meat broker and live cattle broker perform similar functions at different levels in the marketing system. By definition a broker acts as agent for the principals to a transaction. He facilitates transfer of title by bringing the seller and buyer together on terms of trade, but does not take title in his own name. His reimbursement is a fee (a commission) usually paid by the seller.

Some packers without direct sales organizations prefer the use of brokers rather than selling to jobbers. Under any type of wholesaling arrangement, it is not unusual for shifting demand and supply conditions to leave packers and processors in distress situations at times. In such cases brokers may be called upon to assist in moving the meat.

While brokers are not involved in the movement of a major fraction of the total meat supply (see Table 8.1 and 8.2), they are an important link in the

TABLE 8.2

USE OF BROKERS AND BROKERAGE RATES PAID
BY TYPE OF PRODUCT AND FIRM, 1964

Type of Product and Type of Firm	No. of Firms Reporting Use of Brokers	Avg Percentage of Sales Handled by Brokers[1] (%)	Avg Brokerage Rate[1] (¢/Cwt)
Carcass and primal beef			
Slaughterer of cattle and hogs	15	16	17
Slaughterer of cattle only	21	16	18
Processor (no slaughter)	4	9	25
Boned beef			
Slaughterer of cattle and hogs	4	12	19
Slaughterer of cattle only	3	22	17
Processor (no slaughter)	5	15	25
Other beef			
Slaughterer of cattle and hogs	5	14	17
Slaughterer of cattle only	4	10	. . .
Processor (no slaughter)	6	27	40
Fresh and frozen pork			
Slaughterer of cattle and hogs	18	16	19
Slaughterer of cattle only	6	20	20
Processor (no slaughter)	4	25	20
All variety meats			
Slaughterer of cattle and hogs	15	19	24
Slaughterer of cattle only	6	9	17
Slaughterer of hogs only	4	27	21
Processor (no slaughter)	4	20	21

Source: National Commission on Food Marketing (1966).
[1] Simple average for firms using brokers.

system for certain packers, and under certain conditions. Motts (1959) reported that brokers and packer agents handle less than 5% of the total meat supply. The National Commission on Food Marketing (1966), in a sample of packers and processors, found a range from 9 to 27%, depending upon type of product and type of firm (see Table 8.2).

WHOLESALE PRICING[2]

Meat pricing at the wholesale level long has been somewhat of a mystery to producers. Unlike live animal markets, where the producer is on more or less familiar ground, there are no public markets for wholesale meat[3] such as auctions or terminals where transactions can be observed. Public and private sources have published quotations of wholesale prices for some time, but the quotations themselves give no insight into the pricing mechanism, and many smaller producers are not even aware of the sources of such quotations.

Basically, pricing at wholesale is done either by formula or negotiation. There are, of course, variations in both of these approaches.

Negotiated Prices

This simply is private bargaining between seller and buyer. It is analogous to private treaty in live animal marketing in that principals to the transaction rely on knowledge of the product, familiarity with current market conditions, and expertise in bargaining. The negotiation may take place by telephone based on stipulated specifications, or purchasers (or their representatives) may personally inspect and select meat in the wholesaler's cooler.

The prices retailers are willing to pay for wholesale meat is a reflection of consumer demand. In other words, retailer demand is a derived demand—derived from consumer demand. The prices at which wholesalers are willing to sell is a reflection of the costs they have incurred in obtaining the meat. In the case of a packer-wholesaler this is reflected in the cost of live animals and is a derived supply. Under competitive conditions, trading prices are expected to tend toward an equilibrium of the supply-demand situation. It is not surprising that stable equilibrium conditions are not found in the real world as supply and demand conditions are constantly changing and assumptions of a perfectly competitive market are constantly upset.

The crux of this approach to pricing is well-informed buyers and sellers with at least approximate equality in bargaining power.

[2] This section is based largely on National Commission of Food Marketing (1966) and Williams (1970).

[3] In early days there were public markets; e.g., Faneuil Hall was erected in Boston in 1742 for trading in provisions. Other large cities followed with provisions markets. Even when operating, however, quotations from these markets were largely unavailable to producers. In those days packers were concerned primarily with packing operations and left merchandising of meat up to wholesalers. As the packers established branch houses, public meat markets largely disappeared.

Prior to the 1920's and 1930's, the packing industry was highly concentrated in the hands of a relatively few big packers, while meat retailing was highly decentralized in a large number of relatively small firms. Under these conditions there is little question but what the balance of bargaining power was with the packer-wholesalers. That situation has changed. Development of large retail chains and cooperative and voluntary wholesale buying arrangements among independent retailers has shifted the balance of bargaining power. There has been a great deal of conjecture about the implications of the present situation, but a study by the National Commission on Food Marketing in reports issued in 1966 failed to develop evidence of undue market power of any sector in the food economy.

One variation of negotiated pricing that usually merits special attention is "offer and acceptance pricing." Large volume buyers under this arrangement invite wholesalers (packers, independent wholesalers, processors, etc.) to make offers on orders in which the purchaser sets forth rather rigid specifications. Specifications include such things as grade (may be both quality and yield), sex, weight (range per cut), and terms of delivery. Sales by specification normally carry the agreement or understanding that any product which does not meet the specifications, upon delivery, may be rejected by the purchaser. This can leave the supplier in a serious situation. However, unofficial reports indicate that only a small fraction of shipments is rejected.

Upon receipt of offers from several prospective suppliers the purchaser compares offering prices. Other things being equal, the lowest price will be accepted. Some would argue that such an arrangement can scarcely be classed as negotiation. This undoubtedly is the case at times. However, often there is discussion and some negotiation, particularly on deviations from the specifications.

Offer and acceptance pricing ranks high in operational efficiency. Very little cost is involved in a transaction. When buying is accomplished on specification the transaction can be consummated by telephone. Salary and travel expense of personnel who otherwise would personally select carcasses or cuts is averted. Sellers are relieved of some expense in attending these buyers.

From the standpoint of the mechanics of operation, this method also has the potential for a high degree of pricing efficiency. Specifications can be quite rigid. The crucial point is how well price differentials among meats of various specifications reflect the real differences to final users. Sellers whose offers are rejected are left somewhat in the dark in not knowing by how much their offer exceeded the acceptance price. For the system to work effectively over a period of time sellers need to have either invitations from alternative buyers, or alternative outlets. The degree of competition in this respect has a direct bearing on price level of offers made. If enough time is allowed in delivery of the product, suppliers conceivably could push equivalent acceptance prices back to live animal prices. This, of course, could work either way on the level of livestock prices.

Formula Pricing

In formula pricing the transaction price is determined by applying a formula to some predetermined base price for the particular product being traded. The base prices most generally used are from *The National Provisioner's Daily Market and News Service*—commonly called the "Yellow Sheet." The National Provisioner is a Chicago-based, privately-operated firm which assembles and publishes, on a subscription fee basis, daily Chicago closing prices for wholesale meat and meat products. Prices are obtained by telephone from sellers, buyers, and brokers in the meat trade. National Provisioner claims that only freely competitive transactions are used in the quotations and that each is verified.

Using the Chicago price as the base, traders adjust by formula to arrive at prices applicable to, say, New York, Boston, Omaha, Kansas City, Denver, etc. A typical example of formula pricing would be the case of a Kansas City packer agreeing to deliver a carlot of carcass beef (meeting certain specifications) to Boston at a price equal to the Chicago Yellow Sheet carlot price (for beef of those specifications) on a given day, plus transportation cost from Chicago to Boston. Presumably, the equivalent Kansas City price could be determined by subtracting the Kansas City to Chicago transport cost from the Chicago Yellow Sheet quotation.

Williams (1970) states that "The formula works fairly well within the territory under the influence of the northeastern market." He further indicates that "Numerous other examples could be presented, however, in which the implied Chicago price is $0.50–$1.00 higher or lower when based on delivered prices as compared with FOB prices or on alternative delivery point prices. The implied price at Chicago on a shipment from Denver to Atlanta often is $0.75 under the Chicago price of the same or a similar shipment to New York . . . The practice of adjusting prices at other markets to a Chicago base price leads to other problems. For example, the transportation cost employed does not include all transfer costs. Then, too, there is the question of which transportation cost shall be employed. The truck load rate from Chicago to New York usually is quoted as $1.50, but this is an average figure. The piggyback rate is $1.25. Which should be used in adjusting New York prices? Transportation costs often are not the same in both directions between two markets. It is also well to remember that while the system may operate satisfactorily within the trading area defined, the Yellow Sheet is used by all sectors of the trade everywhere."

Formula pricing is widely used. The National Commission on Food Marketing found in a 1965 survey that of the meat packers and processors responding, 41% of beef and veal, 24% of lamb and mutton, 41% of fresh and frozen pork, 29% of cured hams, picnics and bacon, and 20% of other processed meat transactions (with most important customers) were determined by formula pricing. "In nearly all cases the quotation source was the Yellow Sheet" (National Commission of Food Marketing 1966). Stout *et al.* (1968), in an Ohio study, found that, "All 24 firms employed formula prices in purchasing some or all of their fresh meats." Williams (1970) questions whether formula pricing is used as extensively as is indicated in either the Stout or the Food Commission study. While there may be some question on the precise quantity of meat moving under formula pricing, there is little question that it is an important method used in the wholesale trade. The Food Commission concluded that use of formula pricing was increasing, but noted that it rarely was used by two of the largest U.S. retail food chains. These two (unnamed) chains purchased by negotiation. The Food Commission also mentioned several important implications of formula pricing. These include: (1) whether formula pricing tends to perpetuate geographic price patterns unrepresentative of changing supply and demand conditions, (2) whether prices used as base prices are subject to manipulation by trade interests, and (3) whether base prices accurately reflect equilibrium supply-demand conditions.

Does Formula Pricing Perpetuate Geographic Patterns?.—The reasoning here is that if prices today are based on yesterday's closing prices, and if yesterday's prices had been based on the previous day's closing prices, and so on—it is conceivable that the pattern of prices would remain fixed over an area even though supply and demand conditions changed. The reasoning is logical. Furthermore, it would appear that the price level would remain fixed under these circumstances. The record shows, however, that geographic price relationships have not remained fixed and price level has varied. There are several apparent explanations. Not all meat is traded on a formula basis. Some of the prices collected in assembling Yellow Sheet quotations undoubtedly come from negotiated sales. Furthermore, some negotiation takes place even where the base price may be used as a point at which bargaining starts. There is no evidence at this time that formula pricing has perpetuated geographic patterns, although this cannot be ruled out as a possibility if greater use were made of it on a strict formula basis.

Can Formula Pricing Be Manipulated?.—In a discussion of the beef marketing system, DeGraff (1960) stated "no one organization involved in processing or distributing beef is big enough or powerful enough to dominate the market or to dictate prices in the market. The reasons why this is true center on two points. First, beef, like any major food, has a nationwide market. Prices among the regions and localities of the country are closely tied together by competitive forces, by highly developed transportation, and by effective market news services, both public and private . . .

"Second, in order to control such a market, or prices in such a market, it would be necessary to accomplish what is impossible for any food industry firm, or indeed any group of firms. It would be necessary to have a large measure of control over the following: (a) the wants and preferences of consumers; (b) the availability and price of substitute products; (c) the level and distribution of consumer incomes; and (d) a substantial part of the supply of the product involved . . .

"There are, of course, always possibilities of monopoly attempts or of collusion in any one market area. They seldom get far or last long . . . "

Comments by Williams (1970) indicate that the Yellow Sheet is vulnerable to manipulation. He states that the National Provisioner's " . . . sample of open trades selected as closing necessarily is smaller than the total number of trades for a given weight and grade. In short, closing prices require more judgment and are more vulnerable to effects of a few 'planted' sales . . .

"Several brokers have stated in informal interviews that they had, and within limits could, manipulate the Yellow Sheet. It seems that techniques have been developed which induce Yellow Sheet editors to use price reports of 'private sales' which cannot be checked . . .

"To the extent that it exists, the practice of formula pricing on a fixed forward basis increases incentives for manipulating Yellow Sheet prices. In some degree USDA reports, as well as the Yellow Sheet, are vulnerable. It must be nearly impossible to fully verify even a high percentage of the eligible trades in an area which includes more than half of the nation."

While some conditions and incentives may exist for manipulation, there apparently is a lack of any clear-cut evidence that is has been done. The extent to which the Yellow Sheet is used seems to indicate a substantial degree of confidence in its reliability.

Do Formula-Generated Prices Accurately Reflect Equilibrium Prices?.—As long as base prices are derived from prices determined in a freely competitive market, and as long as the price reporting agency, whether it be private or public, obtains an adequate sample of prices, then they could be said to reflect equilibrium prices. Both the National Provisioner and USDA contend that a sufficient volume of competitively determined sales are made to accurately reflect the market (Williams 1970). Current trends in market structure, however, indicate that the number and volume of trades meeting the requirements indicated above, is becoming smaller. If this trend continues, and there is reason to believe that it will, it is probable that this approach will not represent an equilibrium situation and may not adequately reflect the major movement of meat in wholesale channels.

BIBLIOGRAPHY

ARMSTRONG, J. H. 1968. Cattle and beef buying, selling and pricing handbook. Indiana Coop. Ext. Serv. May.

BUTZ, D. E., and BAKER, G. L. 1960. The changing structure of the meat economy. Res. Div. Harvard Business School.

DEGRAFF, H. 1960. Beef Production and Distribution. University of Oklahoma Press, Norman.

DIETRICH, R. A., and WILLIAMS, W. F. 1959. Meat distribution in the Los Angeles Area. USDA Agr. Marketing Res. Rept. *347*.

FOWLER, S. H. 1961. The Marketing of Livestock and Meat, 2nd Edition. Interstate Printers & Publishers, Danville, Ill.

IVES, J. R. 1966. The Livestock and Meat Economy of the United States. Am. Meat Inst., Chicago.

KOLMER, L. *et al.* 1959. Consumer marketing handbook. I. Meat. Iowa Coop. Ext. Serv. Nov.

MOTTS, G. N. 1959. Marketing handbook for Michigan livestock, meat and wool. Mich. Agr. Expt. Sta. Spec. Bull. *426*.

NATIONAL COMMISSION ON FOOD MARKETING. 1966. Organization and competition in the livestock and meat industry. Natl. Comm. Food Marketing Tech. Study *1*. Govt. Printing Office, Washington, D.C.

PRICE, J. F., and SNELL, J. G. 1965. Meat processing handbook. Mich. Coop. Ext. Serv. Sept.

STOUT, T. T., and HAWKINS, M. H. 1968. Implications of changes in the methods of wholesaling meat products. Am. J. Agr. Econ. *50*, 660-675.

STOUT, T. T., HAWKINS, M. H., and MARION, B. W. 1968. Meat procurement and distribution by Ohio grocery chains and affiliated wholesalers. Ohio Agr. Res. Develop. Center Res. Bull. *1014*.

USDA. 1969. Feasibility of a physical distribution system model for evaluating improvements in the cattle and fresh beef industry. USDA Agr. Res. Serv. *52-36*.

WILLIAMS, W. F. 1958. Structural changes in the meat wholesaling industry. J. Farm Econ. *40*, 315-329.

WILLIAMS, W. F. 1970. Implications of developments in the pricing structure of the livestock-meat economy. *In* Long-Run Adjustments in the Livestock and Meat Industry: Implications and Alternatives. Ohio Agr. Res. Develop. Center Res. Bull. *1037*. Also North Central Regional Publ. *199*.

WILLIAMS, W. F., and STOUT, T. T. 1964. Economics of the Livestock-Meat Industry. Macmillan Co., New York.

CHAPTER 9

Meat Marketing-Retail

The final step in food production and marketing is getting the food into possession of consumers. In the United States, 99% of all red meat production is consumed domestically—the remaining 1% is exported (National Commission on Food Marketing 1966B). The major share of domestically-consumed meat is obtained through retail outlets, although it should be noted that a significant fraction is obtained through HRI outlets. HRI trade amounted to 35% in 1963 (the latest available data) and undoubtedly is higher now as the trend has been upward for a number of years. Some smaller units in the HRI trade, however, obtain supplies through retail stores. The National Commission on Food Marketing (1966B) showed that retailers supplied slightly more than 1/4 of HRI purchases. Farm slaughter, once an important source of meat, now amounts to less than 5% of the total. Meat is the highest dollar volume food product carried by retailers, comprising approximately 25% of gross sales.

DEVELOPMENTS IN FOOD RETAILING

Significant changes have occurred in food retailing during the past 60 yr, and particularly since the 1930's. Two major developments are closely associated with these changes—development of the chain system,[1] and development of the supermarket. These were not simultaneous. The chain system came first, resulting in a rapid increase in number of stores. This was followed by development of the supermarket, which resulted in consolidation and reduction in store numbers. The total volume of business expanded greatly during this period. Table 9.1 illustrates the trends in number of stores and sales for the period 1929 to 1963.

Retail Chains

The origin of corporate retail chains dates back to 1859 with organization of the A&P Tea Company (DeGraff 1960). Early development of chains was almost entirely a matter of horizontal integration; and the emphasis was on number of stores rather than size of individual units. "Between 1910 and 1930, chains grew from 2000 to 45,000 stores and encompassed 1/3 of one of the nation's largest industries. The speed and scope of this development was alarming to businessmen as well as the public" (National Commission on Food Marketing 1966B).

Early chain activity also centered on the economics of obtaining supplies. Primarily, it was one of integrating wholesaling operations and retailing under one management. This was vertical integration—the control of successive stages in production and marketing channels. Some chains rather quickly went one

---

[1] Chains are defined as firms with 11 or more stores.

TABLE 9.1

GROCERY STORE¹ SALES, NUMBER OF STORES, AND AVERAGE SALES PER STORE BY ANNUAL SALES SIZE, CENSUS YEARS 1929 TO 1963

	Total			Less Than $50,000 Annual Sales			$50 to $299 Thousand Annual Sales		
Year	No. of Stores	Sales (Million $)	Avg Sales per Store (1000 $)	No. of Stores	Sales (Million $)	Avg Sales per Store (1000 $)	No. of Stores	Sales (Million $)	Avg Sales per Store (1000 $)
1929	307,425	7,352.8	23.9	267,786	3,893.8	14.5	39,150	3,172.8	81.0
1933	303,910	5,004.3	16.5	283,461	3,216.8	11.3	20,157	1,634.2	81.1
1935	354,971	6,352.4	17.9	327,665	3,884.1	11.9	26,827	2,221.2	82.8
1939	387,337	7,721.8²	19.9	354,284	4,135.3	11.7	31,606	2,876.1	91.0
1948⁵	299,016	23,126.3	77.3	188,410	4,270.9	22.7	97,138	10,027.6	103.2
1954	266,738	32,898.7	123.3	149,787	3,523.3	23.5	95,491	10,380.9	108.7
1958	242,796	41,182.5	169.6	130,035	3,091.3	23.7	84,968	9,662.5	113.7
1963	222,442	50,062.5	224.9	103,823	2,453.3	23.5	83,889	9,643.0	114.9

	$300 to $999 Thousand Annual Sales			$1,000,000 and More Annual Sales		
Year	No. of Stores	Sales (Million $)	Avg Sales per Store (1000 $)	No. of Stores	Sales (Million $)	Avg Sales per Store (1000 $)
1929	442	196.5	444.5	47	89.7	1,907.7
1933	274	122.8	448.2	18	30.5	1,693.5
1935	449	200.1	445.7	30	47.0	1,566.0
1939	1,388	613.2³	446.6	59	85.4⁴	1,499.1
1948⁵	11,557	6,971.0	525.3	1,911	2,756.8	1,442.6
1954	15,218	8,271.8	543.6	6,242	10,722.7	1,717.8
1958	17,461	9,572.0	553.9	10,332	18,756.7	1,815.4
1963	20,266	11,561.0	570.5	14,464	26,405.3	1,825.6

Source: National Commission on Food Marketing (1966B) as compiled from Bureau of Census.
¹ Grocery stores defined as grocery stores with and without fresh meat. The data for 1929 to 1939 include stores operated part of the year. In 1948, 1954, 1958, and 1963 only stores operated the entire year are included.
² Includes sales of 17 stores whose sales (by sales size) were withheld to avoid disclosure.
³ Sales of 15 stores of the 1,388 were withheld to avoid disclosure. Average sales per store in this size group for 1,373 stores.
⁴ Sales of 2 stores of the 59 were withheld to avoid disclosure. Average sales per store in this size group for 57 stores.
⁵ In 1954 the Bureau of the Census estimated that, had the 1954 minimum sales criterion to qualify as a retail trade establishment been applied in 1948, 27,185 fewer grocery stores, having sales of $40,406,000 would have been enumerated. These adjustments are reflected here in the totals given for all sales-size groups and in those for the "less than $50,000" group.

step farther and brought processing operations under their management.[2] Thus, significant gains were made in operational efficiency which were reflected in prices below competing nonchain stores. Management was able to standardize, coordinate, and control activities that previously were under widely scattered, independent operations. However, operational efficiency was not the only source of economic strength. Perhaps of even greater significance was the gain in bargaining power that came with mass purchasing. This enabled the chains to obtain price concessions from suppliers that small, independent operators could not obtain. Chain purchasing departments dealt directly with packers for meat supplies, by-passing entirely established wholesale agencies.

Rapid expansion of chain activity placed small, independent meat markets and grocery stores under severe competition. The situation was aggravated by widespread economic depression during the 1930's. Many were absorbed by the chains. The small business operators did not give up without a struggle. They agitated for, and obtained, legislation designed to thwart unfair competition. The Robinson-Patman Act passed in 1936 reflected the failure of the earlier Clayton Act in restraining discriminatory practices. The Robinson-Patman Act contained provisions aimed at prevention of price concession to some (the large) buyers and not to others, and other discriminatory trade practices which allegedly gave advantages to large purchasers. Many states also imposed taxes and regulatory strictures on chain operations. Nevertheless, expansion of chains continued.

Supermarkets

While early chain activity centered on economies in procuring supplies, it soon became apparent to grocers that economies also were available by possible changes in selling. A major development here was the supermarket. The supermarket idea—large volume, low cost, and mass retailing—actually originated among independent operators, but is was adopted almost immediately by the chains. Where previously the emphasis was on number of outlets, a shift began during the 1930's to fewer and larger outlets. The emphasis shifted to volume—not just for volume per se, but for economies of scale that came with volume. In addition, such innovations as self-service, cash-and-carry, and standardized accounting and operating procedures came into prominence.

Economies in both purchasing and sales allowed large volume operators to reduce margins. The small, independent specialized meat markets, as well as grocery stores, were at a serious competitive disadvantage, and numbers declined sharply. The small independent meat market all but vanished. However, independent grocers (including meat departments) did not give up.

To counteract corporate chains, the independents made two major adaptions: (1) independent wholesalers sponsored the development of voluntary

[2] As will be noted later, meat processing by retailers has been on only a limited scale. Most extensive processing is in dairy products, fruits, vegetables, and bakery products.

chain arrangements which gave independent retailers advantages of large-scale purchasing and many associated services, and (2) retailers formed cooperative wholesale purchasing and servicing organizations. In the former, a large wholesaler takes on many of the purchasing and servicing functions of the centralized purchasing department of a corporate chain. This may include many kinds of assistance for its members in operation and management of retail stores. The cooperative chain differs in that the independent retailers organize, own, and operate the wholesale agency for the benefit of its members. It would be a mistake to visualize all independent retailers as small operations. Many of them are large supermarkets—just as large as corporate supermarkets but with fewer stores. Many of the independents, however, own and operate more than one supermarket. There also are many superettes in the independent system, both voluntary and cooperative. In marketing terminology, supermarkets are defined as stores with annual sales of $500,000 or more. Superettes are stores with annual sales $150,000 to $500,000. Those with annual sales below $150,000 are classed small stores.

Development of chain operations and expansion of supermarkets were restricted during World War II. However, immediately upon termination of the war, expansion continued at an accelerated rate. "The rapid postwar adoption of the supermarket came at the expense of many thousands of small grocery stores. The number of grocery stores operated by single-store firms dropped by more than 130,000 between 1948 and 1963. Stores with annual sales less than $5000 dropped 86%" (National Commission on Food Marketing 1966B).

Recent developments in food retailing which are relevant to the meat industry are (1) the discount store, (2) the convenience store, (3) central cutting and packaging, and (4) "fast foods."

Discount Houses

The discount house in a sense is a throw-back to the notion of early supermarket operation. Basically they feature high volume, limited service, low cost, and low price merchandising. They usually carry a wide variety of goods. Some carry no food at all. Some carry food but only a limited selection of meat items, while others carry a full line of meat. Many discounters are organized as corporate chains.

Perhaps the best evidence that discounting has made inroads on established food retailers is found in the fact that established firms responded by adopting discount tactics themselves. It was reported that in 1969, 47% of the chain grocery stores and 27% of independent grocery stores were discounting—and further, that the meat departments in 19% of the supermarkets and 22% of the superettes were discount pricing meat. (Anon. 1970).

During recent years operating costs have been increasing. Whether the strictly discount house can command an advantage over established food chains remains to be seen. *Progressive Grocer* indicated that the practice of discounting increased sales 15– 30% (Anon. 1970). This may be plausible for early discounters when they comprised a relatively small segment of the industry. Wide adoption of discounting, if that were possible, probably would defeat its purpose. The price elasticity of demand for food in total is relatively low—as indicated in an earlier chapter.

Discounting is not limited to retailing. In 1969, it was reported that 33% of all grocery wholesalers discounted prices (Anon. 1970). The data did not reveal the extent of wholesale discounting in meats.

Convenience Stores

Convenience stores are relatively small installations in carefully selected locations with potential for a large volume of traffic. They feature long hours of operation and a reasonably wide range of items with a limited number of lines of a particular item. Attempts are made to hold operating costs as low as possible, but prices generally run higher than in discount or supermarket operation. The emphasis is on convenience in location, service, and items carried.

The neighborhood grocery stores that survived the chain-supermarket revolution are, in essence, convenience stores. However, the recent movement is not a revival of neighborhood stores. Some are independently owned and operated, but corporate chain systems dominate the field.

The sharp growth in convenience stores is shown in Table 9.2. In a little over 10 yr the movement has grown from virtually nothing to 13,613 stores with 3.0% of all grocery sales. There appears to be no doubt of continued growth. The extent of growth probably will be closely associated with trends in affluence of consumers. Additional convenience stores will be built if patronage is forthcoming. Capital investments per unit are small compared to supermarkets.

TABLE 9.2
CONVENIENCE STORE GROWTH

Year	No. of Stores	Share of U.S. Total Grocery Sales (%)
1957	500	0.2
1960	2,500	0.7
1962	3,500	0.9
1965	5,000	1.1
1967	8,000	1.7
1968	9,600	2.1
1969	11,620	2.6
1970	13,613	3.0

Source: Anon. (1971A)

In 1970, processed meat was handled by 97% of convenience stores and fresh meat by 20%. However, the selection of cuts was limited. Under present methods of operation, convenience stores are not major outlets for meat, when considered on a per store basis. Nevertheless, with continued expansion in number of stores, the aggregate quantity of meat can become increasingly important. Current research underway at Kansas State University in the technology of production and marketing of frozen fresh meat is particularly relevant to convenience stores. Wider consumer acceptance of frozen meat would enhance convenience store sales.

Central Cutting and Packaging

Central cutting and packing is the use of a central unit consisting of cold storage, cutting, packaging, and delivery facilities for the servicing of a number of retail outlets. Centralized warehousing and breaking has been customary for many years for large chain metropolitan operations. The extension to retail cutting and wrapping is of more recent origin. Centralized cutting and packaging for retail appears to be increasing, but at this time there are several factors retarding its acceptance. Under present packaging techniques it is difficult to maintain the bloom of fresh beef. The irregular sizes of packaged cuts are difficult to pack and handle without breaking the packages— necessitating some rewrapping. Lack of standardization in cutting is a bottleneck to extensive centralization. This is not a problem in a given metropolitan area, but is a problem as the area under consideration widens. Certain areas have become accustomed to particular methods of cutting and to the use of names for particular cuts that would not readily move in other areas. Centralized cutting permits a greater degree of specialization in use of labor and more efficient techniques that reduce labor costs. Widespread adoption probably would result in a decrease in the number of meat cutters needed for a given volume of meat, resulting in labor union reluctance.

The farther centralized cutting and wrapping can be carried back in meat marketing channels, the greater are the savings in transportation. Elimination of bone and waste fat would reduce the tonnage of shipments by some 20–25%, and hence, an approximately equivalent reduction in freight costs.

As noted in the previous section, the freezing of fresh meat appears also to be particularly adapted to centralized cutting and packaging—if techniques can be perfected to maintain the bloom and acceptable appearance in the packaged meat. The Kansas State University research project mentioned earlier indicates this can be done.

Centralized cutting and wrapping has been used successfully by some retailers for a number of years. Yet its use has not expanded significantly. Apparently a break-through will be required in some of the restraining factors if its growth is to be stimulated.

Fast Foods

"Fast foods" is one of the latest developments in food retailing that appears to have major possibilities. Fast foods are fully prepared, carry-out foods ready for consumption without additional preparation. For years larger grocery stores have operated delicatessen departments in which such meat items as luncheon meats, bacon and canned hams are carried. In some instances the delicatessen may feature ribs and chicken cooked in the store and sold warm. However, generally it remains for the consumer to cut, serve, and furnish accessory items.

Retail food operators recently have noted, with some envy, the acceptance and expansion of franchised, chain carry-out, ready-to-eat food establishments (such as Kentucky Fried Chicken, McDonalds, etc). Currently there is discussion and some experimentation with adapting this type of outlet to retail grocery stores, possibly as a separate department. No data are available on the volume of meat moving through current franchised establishments, but there is no question that it is significant. It appears likely that retail grocers will attempt to capture some of this market. If this happens, it will put the retailers more directly into the HRI trade, but is not likely to change meat marketing channels or methods. Added outlets with promotional activity, however, could increase the demand for meat.

STRUCTURAL CHARACTERISTICS

In previous sections it was noted that food retailing changed from an industry of predominantly small, independent operators to one typified by chain operations with large supermarkets during the past 50–60 yr. Mergers, purchases, and extensive new construction were used by chains in their expansion activities. Integration, both horizontal and vertical, was used extensively in expansion and market control. Many firms developed their own brand names and through advertising and promotion attempted to differentiate their products from those of competitors. Capital requirements for establishing a new store rose to heights that could not be attained by small firms.

There are characteristics associated with the structure of an industry which are presumed to have some effect on the conduct or behavior of firms in setting price and product policies. These, in turn, are presumed to bear some relationship to the performance of firms and the industry. In other words, under structural conditions which permit the attainment of a relatively high degree of bargaining power it might be hypothesized that firms would be able to buy inputs at prices relatively low compared to more competitively determined prices—and relatively low compared to costs of production. If the same conditions existed in the selling arena, selling prices might be set relatively high in comparison to costs. Under these circumstances, the resulting performance would be profits in excess of those under more highly competitive conditions.

As evidenced by legislation designed to restrict monopolistic tendencies and unfair and discriminatory practices (e.g., Sherman Act, Clayton Act, Robinson-Patman Act) and investigations by such bodies as the Federal Trade Commission and Justice Department, the trend in these characteristics of the food industry was a matter of serious social concern. This concern extended not only to small, independent retailers but also to farmers and ranchers and to consumers in general. There was a growing feeling that the large chains were in position to exercise undue market power. As a result, the U.S. Congress in 1964 provided for a National Commission on Food Marketing to investigate conditions in the food industry. The remainder of this section draws heavily on findings of that commission.

Degree of Concentration in Food Retailing

The degree of concentration in an industry is indicated by the size distribution of firms in that industry. One measurement of concentration is the market share. This is determined by calculating the percentage of an industry's business done by the 4 (or 8, or 12, or ?) largest firms. The larger the proportion of business done by a given number of firms, the greater is the degree of concentration in that industry. And it generally is hypothesized that the greater the degree of concentration, the greater is the possibility of firms enhancing their economic or market power. Industries dominated by a relatively few firms (e.g., U.S. automobile or steel manufacturers) presumably have a greater degree of control over price policy than an industry of many firms with none large enough to claim any dominance (e.g., farming). It may be noted that the mere existence of a high degree of concentration does not in itself provide proof that firms in fact utilize the economic power they may have, but the calculation of market shares usually is a first step in structural analysis. If it can be shown that concentration is relatively low, then this factor generally can be eliminated as a source of undue market power.

Earlier discussion in this chapter indicated a tendency toward concentration in the food retailing industry. It was pointed out that due to the chain and supermarket movements the trend was toward fewer and bigger firms. "The rate of expansion of the chain store movement reached its peak in the early 1930's when stores belonging to chains totaled about 80,000. By this time the chain organizations had encompassed 1/3 of the nation's retail food business" (National Commission on Food Marketing 1966B). Chain store movement was followed by expansion in supermarkets. "Between the late 1940's and the late 1950's, retail chain organizations and groups of affiliated independents expanded rapidly . . . The supermarket movement progressed from 28% of the grocery store business going to supermarkets in 1948, to 69% in 1963 (see Table

TABLE 9.3

SHARE OF U.S. GROCERY STORE BUSINESS ACCOUNTED FOR
BY SUPERMARKETS
(Sales in million $)

Size of Store in Annual Sales	1948	1954	1958	1963
$1,000,000 or more				
Sales	2,757	10,723	18,757	26,405
Share of grocery store sales	11.9	32.6	45.5	52.7
Increase in grocery store				
sales over 1948 (%)	. . .	174	282	343
$500,000 or more				
Sales	6,437	16,017	25,202	34,460
Share of grocery store sales	27.8	48.7	61.2	68.8
Increase in grocery store				
sales over 1948 (%)	. . .	75	120	147

Source: National Commission on Food Marketing (1966B) as compiled from Bureau of Census.

TABLE 9.4

NUMBER OF U.S. GROCERY STORES AND
AVERAGE SALES PER STORE,
1960-1969

Year	No. of Stores	Avg Sales per Store ($)
1960	260,000	202,000
1961	248,000	218,000
1962	235,000	229,000
1963	231,000	254,000
1964	228,000	272,000
1965	227,000	290,000
1966	227,000	311,000
1967	226,000	328,000
1968	227,000	342,000
1969	219,000	375,000
1970	208,300	424,000

Source: Anon. (1971B)

9.3) . . . (National Commission on Food Marketing 1966B).

"The late 1950's and early 1960's marked a change in behavior and growth patterns in most markets in the United States. The replacement of small stores by supermarkets in most areas slowed considerably . . . Thus on the whole, a saturation point was reached, with supermarkets doing 2/3 of the grocery business. The other 1/3 went through convenience stores and other small stores" (National Commission on Food Marketing 1966B). The number of convenience stores has expanded rapidly in recent years, this has slowed considerably the rate of decline in total store numbers. Table 9.4 indicates that the number of stores was virtually stabilized from 1964 to 1968, but a further decline is indicated in 1969 and 1970.

Fig. 9.1 shows that the growth of affiliated independent grocers (affiliated in wholesale purchasing under either voluntary or cooperative arrangements) has roughly paralleled that of the chains since 1948. This, together with expansion of convenience stores, has tended to neutralize the impact of growth in established chains.

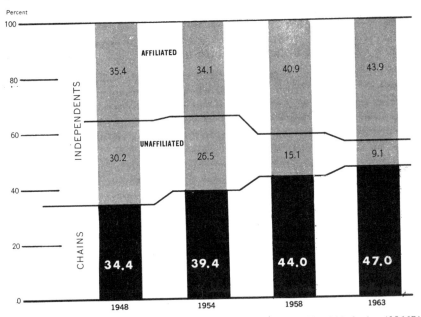

National Commission on Food Marketing (1966B)

FIG. 9.1. SHARE OF TOTAL GROCERY STORE SALES BY CHAINS, AFFILIATED INDEPENDENTS, AND UNAFFILIATED INDEPENDENTS

The extent of concentration in grocery chain sales on a national basis is shown in Table 9.5. "During the postwar expansion, the market position of the largest 4, the largest 8, and the largest 20 food retailers in the nation increased. From 1948 through 1958, the largest 20 increased their market position by more than 7% of the U.S. grocery store business.

"Between 1958 and 1963, growth patterns were somewhat different. The market position of the largest 4 retail chains declined approximately 1.7%, while the market share of the largest 8 combined, declined about 1%. The market share of the largest 20 companies remained constant. These data again illustrate the more rapid growth of smaller firms when compared to the largest food retailers" (National Commission on Food Marketing 1966B).

There are no absolute standards for evaluating whether, for example, the concentration of 20% of the grocery chain business in the 4 largest firms is excessive. However, generally it is agreed that in the retail trade, concentration in local market areas is a more relevant consideration than the national

TABLE 9.5

MARKET SHARE OF 20 LEADING GROCERY CHAINS
(PERCENTAGE OF TOTAL GROCERY STORE SALES)

	1948		1954		1958		1963	
	Group Total (%)	Cumulative (%)	Group Total (%)	Cumulative (%)	Group Total (%)	Cumulative (%)	Group Total (%)	Cumulative (%)
1st to 4th largest	20.1	20.1	20.9	20.9	21.7	21.7	20.0	20.0
A&P	10.7	. . .	11.3	. . .	11.1	. . .	9.4	. . .
2d to 4th largest	. . .	9.4	. . .	9.6	. . .	10.6	. . .	10.6
5th to 8th largest	3.6	. . .	4.5	. . .	5.8	. . .	6.6	. . .
1st to 8th largest	. . .	23.7	. . .	25.4	. . .	27.5	. . .	26.6
2d to 8th largest	. . .	13.0	. . .	14.1	. . .	16.4	. . .	17.2
9th to 20th largest	3.2	. . .	4.5	. . .	6.6	. . .	7.4	. . .
1st to 20th largest	. . .	26.9	. . .	29.9	. . .	34.1	. . .	34.0
2d to 20th largest	. . .	16.2	. . .	18.7	. . .	23.0	. . .	24.6

Source: Table prepared by Federal Trade Commission, and reproduced from National
Commission on Food Marketing (1966B).

market. "The primary influence which level of concentration will have upon
the performance of food retailers as sellers, however, will develop from the
level of concentration in local markets" (National Commission on Food
Marketing 1966B). The Food Commission analyzed market shares of the 4, 8,
and 20 largest grocery companies in 218 Standard Metropolitan Statistical
Areas (SMSA)[3] to provide an indication of concentration in local areas. Data
for the individual SMSA's are not reproduced here, but Table 9.6 shows the
averages for the 218 areas. It is readily apparent that level of concentration is
substantially higher in many local areas than for the country as a whole.

TABLE 9.6

AVERAGE MARKET SHARE OF THE LOCALLY LARGEST 4, 8, AND 20
GROCERY COMPANIES IN 218 STANDARD METROPOLITAN STATISTICAL
AREAS, 1954, 1958, AND 1963

	Top 4 Grocery Store Companies			Top 8 Grocery Store Companies			Top 20 Grocery Store Companies		
Year	1954	1958	1963	1954	1958	1963	1954	1958	1963
Market share (%)	45.4	49.3	50.1	54.4	59.5	62.0	64.5	71.0	74.3

Source: Adapted from National Commission on Food Marketing (1966B).

The Food Commission analyses contained further breakdowns which led to
the concluion that, "Market concentration increased substantially both at the
national level and locally during the postwar growth period until the late
1950's. During the early 1960's, the postwar building period was replaced by
market saturation throughout most markets of the nation. Concentration of
retail sales has declined slightly on a national level during this period of
saturation.

[3] Standard metropolitan statistical areas are areas including major cities and, in some
cases, the immediately surrounding area (depending upon political boundaries) to obtain a
cohesive economic area.

"While the largest national firms' position in local markets on the average has been declining over the last few years, the rapid growth of local and regional firms has contributed to slight average increases in local market concentration during the early 1960's" (National Commission on Food Marketing 1966B).

Vertical Integration

Vertical integration is the control of successive stages of production or marketing—usually by ownership or contracts. Vertical integration in meat marketing by retailers would be classed as backward integration. Successive backward stages, if carried all the way, would include wholesaling, processing, slaughtering, feedlot finishing, growing, and primary cow-calf operations. It is not known whether any major retail chain is fully integrated vertically. However, the Food Commission reported that, "The number of food chains slaughtering livestock declined from 10 in 1950 to 6 in 1964. Four major chains slaughtered livestock in the early 1950's: Acme, Food Fair, National Tea, and Safeway. The major chains accounted for over 90% of livestock slaughtered by food chains. In 1957, Safeway ceased slaughtering operations, but the other three chains have continued." The Commission also reported that 3 food chains operated meat processing plants; processing activities of the 3 chains amounted to 60% of their processed meat sales.

Table 9.7 shows that cattle slaughter by major chains increased from 1.2% of commercial slaughter in 1950 to 2.3% in 1964. Slaughtering by the 3 chains amounted to 4.2% of fed cattle marketings in 1964. Slaughter of calves and sheep by food chains also is increasing.

Table 9.8 shows, "The number of cattle fed by the 3 chains has shown a gradual rising trend, amounting to 64,000 head in 1964. This was 8.5% of beef and veal production by these chains, 0.2% of U.S. commercial beef and veal production, and 0.4% of fed cattle marketings in 39 states" (National Commission on Food Marketing 1966B).

The Food Commission, however, investigated only integration by ownership. It did not attempt to determine contractual arrangements. Although not classed as vertical integration, it may be noted that direct transactions between retailer buyers and packers (and processors) in effect integrate the wholesaling stage by eliminating it.

It is apparent that the extent of vertical integration in meats by retailers via ownership of successive stages is minor at this time. However, it is likely that integration will expand in the future. Among the motives for backward integration is the possiblity of establishing a brand name and thereby effecting product differentiation. This, of course, is possible in processed meats, but to date, has extremely limited application to fresh meat. As will be noted in a later section, contracting for production under "private label," in effect, is

TABLE 9.7

PURCHASES OF LIVESTOCK FOR SLAUGHTER BY MAJOR RETAIL
FOOD CHAINS[1] AND PERCENTAGE OF COMMERCIAL
SLAUGHTER, 1950-1964

| Year | No. of Cattle (1000) | No. of Calves (1000) | No. of Hogs (1000) | No. of Sheep (1000) | Fed Cattle Marketings (%) | Percentage of Commercial Slaughter | | | |
						Cattle (%)	Calves (%)	Hogs (%)	Sheep (%)
1950	206	19	68	162	. . .	1.2	0.2	0.1	1.3
1951	204	11	57	148	. . .	1.3	0.1	0.1	1.3
1952	194	16	73	133	. . .	1.1	0.2	0.1	1.0
1953	234	16	62	171	. . .	1.0	0.1	0.1	1.1
1954	290	14	50	88	. . .	1.2	0.1	0.1	0.6
1955	339	15	72	316	3.1	1.3	0.1	0.1	2.0
1956	347	40	81	301	3.1	1.3	0.3	0.1	1.9
1957	331	50	139	379	2.9	1.3	0.4	0.2	2.5
1958	387	64	159	465	3.3	1.6	0.7	0.2	3.3
1959	422	114	194	422	3.3	1.8	1.5	0.2	2.8
1960	495	154	193	531	3.7	2.0	1.9	0.2	3.3
1961	611	165	230	523	4.3	2.4	2.1	0.3	3.0
1962	635	164	220	526	4.3	2.4	2.2	0.3	3.1
1963	655	173	217	534	4.1	2.4	2.5	0.3	3.4
1964	719	185	223	514	4.2	2.3	2.6	0.3	3.5

Source: National Commission on Food Marketing (1966A).
[1] Includes National Tea, Food Fair, and Acme markets for all years, and Safeway prior to 1958.

TABLE 9.8

CATTLE FED BY CHAIN FOOD STORES FOR MORE THAN 30 DAYS
OR PURCHASED 11 TO 30 DAYS IN ADVANCE OF DELIVERY, 1957-1964

| Year | Cattle Owned More Than 10 Days in Advance of Slaughter by 3 Major Food Chains[1] | | Beef Produced from Cattle Owned in Advance[3] as Percentage of: | |
	(1000 Hd)	Fed Cattle Marketings in 39 States[2] (%)	Total Commercial Beef and Veal Production (%)	Beef and Veal Production by 3 Food Chains (%)
1957	25	0.2	0.1	6.3
1958	35	0.3	0.2	7.7
1959	38	0.3	0.2	7.1
1960	35	0.3	0.2	5.5
1961	37	0.3	0.2	5.6
1962	40	0.3	0.2	5.9
1963	42	0.3	0.2	5.7
1964	64	0.4	0.2	8.5

Source: National Commission on Food Marketing (1966A).
[1] Acme, Food Fair, and National Tea.
[2] Source of fed cattle marketings in 39 States: USDA Econ. Res. Serv., *Livestock and Meat Situation*, Oct. 1965.
[3] Computed by assuming the average weight of packer fed cattle was the same as for all U.S. fed cattle in the years indicated and that dressed weight of slaughter equaled 59% of the live weight.

vertical integration. Other motives (National Commission on Food Marketing 1966A) such as reduced procurement costs, control over quality, and control over availability of supplies are important incentives.

Differentiation of Product

In a perfectly competitive market situation it is impossible for firms to establish and capitalize on brand names. This is an axiom of competitive theory. That corporate chains and affiliated independents have been able to establish brand names attests to the fact that competition is something less than the competitive norm.

Food retailers, as in many other industries, have several major options in distributing branded products. For example: (1) They can own outright the manufacturing and processing facilities which enable them to establish their own brand names, manufacture to their own specifications, and carry out their own advertising and promotional activities: (2) They can contract with an established manufacturer for production under their (the retailer's) own "private label." In this case the retailer lays out the specifications of the product and carries out the advertising and promotion: (3) They can handle products manufactured and branded by an independent manufacturer or processor. Larger, well-established manufacturers carry out extensive promotional and advertising activities. Retailers, ordinarily, simply handle these products without advertising. (4) A fourth category is the same as (3) above, except the manufacturer does no advertising, and ordinarily neither does the retailer.

Table 9.9 shows the extent of use of private labels compared to advertised and unadvertised brands. Advertised brands in this table are defined as "a manufacturer's or producer's brand of merchandise having wide distribution and supported by heavy advertising and/or promotion regionally or nationally to the public. Advertising is paid for by the manufacturer." This corresponds to (3) above. "Unadvertised labels refer to 'manufacturer's or producer's brand not usually advertised to the public by the manufacturer.' The latter is called a packer's label" and is (4) above (National Commission on Food Marketing 1966B).

It was shown in the previous section that retailers own only a limited amount of meat packing and meat processing facilities. Although the Food Commission report was not specific on this point, it is presumed that wholesale value of products shown in Table 9.9 under private label included both (1) and (2) as defined above.

It may be seen in Table 9.9 that privately-labeled weiners amounted to 1/3 of the wholesale value of all weiners handled by retail (corporate) chains. Privately-labeled bacon amounted to 44.8% of the bacon handled by this category of retailers. Affiliated groups (voluntary and cooperative) utilized

TABLE 9.9

EXTENT OF PRIVATE LABEL COMPARED WITH ADVERTISED AND
UNADVERTISED BRANDS FOR 9 PRODUCT GROUPS:
RETAIL CHAINS, VOLUNTARY GROUPS, COOPERATIVE GROUPS,
AND INDEPENDENT WHOLESALERS, 1964

Product Group and Label	Retail Chains Wholesale value ($1000)	(%)	Voluntary Groups Wholesale value ($1000)	(%)	Cooperative Group Wholesale value ($1000)	(%)	Independent Wholesalers Wholesale value ($1000)	(%)
Canned vegetables								
Advertised	247,950	66.1	93,651	67.2	59,535	72.1	39,010	61.3
Unadvertised	28,651	7.7	11,927	8.6	7,607	9.2	5,062	8.0
Private label	98,389	26.2	33,797	24.2	15,456	18.7	19,516	30.7
Canned fruit								
Advertised	181,882	65.3	60,137	72.0	31,836	71.2	26,389	63.8
Unadvertised	12,852	4.6	4,139	5.0	2,260	5.0	2,519	6.1
Private Label	83,753	30.1	19,259	23.0	10,634	23.8	12,480	30.1
Frozen Vegetables								
Advertised	74,024	46.8	17,503	60.5	17,149	63.0	3,802	50.2
Unadvertised	6,761	4.3	2,394	8.3	2,599	9.5	1,478	19.5
Private label	77,386	48.9	9,025	31.2	7,485	27.5	2,293	30.3
Frozen fruit juice								
Advertised	66,970	47.1	12,488	54.8	12,107	64.2	3,979	72.7
Unadvertised	4,565	3.2	2,165	9.5	1,682	8.9	635	11.6
Private label	70,592	49.7	8,129	35.7	5,082	26.9	859	15.7
Bakery products								
Advertised	415,839	45.3	12,128	48.5	675	10.0	825	42.5
Unadvertised	7,189	0.8	2,427	9.7	45	0.7	618	31.8
Private label	495,649	53.9	10,471	41.8	6,057	89.3	498	25.7
Dairy products								
Advertised	729,572	47.5	85,859	67.3	53,837	73.6	17,671	74.6
Unadvertised	35,523	2.3	4,055	3.2	3,472	4.7	1,315	5.5
Private label	772,104	50.2	37,711	29.5	15,838	21.7	4,719	19.9
Coffee								
Advertised	349,721	63.7	92,672	90.2	75,813	94.2	37,084	85.4
Unadvertised	2,745	0.5	315	0.3	372	0.5	81	0.2
Private label	196,547	35.8	9,709	9.5	4,281	5.3	6,248	14.4
Bacon								
Advertised	112,957	48.2	11,537	60.8	3,599	53.6	1,534	76.2
Unadvertised	16,378	7.0	1,543	8.1	868	12.9	5	0.2
Private label	104,888	44.8	5,906	31.1	2,252	33.5	475	23.6
Wieners								
Advertised	86,571	63.2	7,800	77.8	2,169	65.6	692	91.2
Unadvertised	4,911	3.6	997	9.9	90	2.7	5	0.7
Private label	45,457	33.2	1,237	12.3	1,049	31.7	62	8.1

Source: National Commission on Food Marketing (1966B, C).

private labeling to a lesser degree than corporate chains, although in the case of bacon, private labels amounted to about 1/3 of the bacon. Almost 1/3 of the weiners handled by the cooperative group were privately labeled. Private labeling was used on only 8% of the weiners and 23.6% of the bacon handled by independent wholesalers. It is not surprising that fresh meat does not show up on Table 9.9. As mentioned previously, fresh meat is not well adapted to private branding. Swift & Co. has succeeded in identifying its Proten Beef[4] for a number of years, but data are not available on the degree to which it is

[4] Trademark of Swift & Co.

differentiated in the eyes of consumers. Considerable effort and funds are expended, however, in attempts to differentiate processed meats. A number of additional meat products could have been included in Table 9.9, for example, ham and various sausages.

Barriers to Entry

Market structure theory holds that established firms in an industry which has relatively high barriers to the entry of new firms may behave differently (in price and product policies) from firms in an industry with low barriers to entry. Technically, barrier to entry is defined as price or cost advantage held by established firms in an industry relative to potential new entrants. (Bain 1956).

Prior to chain and supermarket developments, food retailing was considered an industry with relatively low barriers to entry. This accounted for the numerous neighborhood "pa and ma" grocery stores. The Food Commission states, "There are strong indications, however, that post-World War II developments in food retailing have brought about a significant change in entry conditions. First, there have been dramatic organizational changes in food retailing, which themselves suggest alterations in the condition of entry. Second, various parts of this study have developed evidence which sheds light directly on the changing conditions of entry."

Organizational changes have resulted in the reduction in number of stores, increasing average size of stores, increasing capital requirements for starting new stores, and declining profits for small volume stores relative to supermarkets. Small retailers are at a disadvantage in obtaining desirable locations in competition with chains and affiliated groups. Most of the desirable locations are in shopping centers, and developers give preference to established firms. Advertising rates favor large-scale operators and trading stamp companies prefer to have exclusive agreements with larger retailers. As already discussed, the concentration associated with corporate chain and affiliated groups gives them more bargaining power and price concessions in their buying programs. Vertically integrated buying arrangements and advantages gained in conglomerate aspects of geographically large coverage of chain operations give large-scale operators advantages which are, in effect, barriers to entry by new firms.

The National Commission on Food Marketing (1966B) comments on barrier to entry are summarized as follows: "This inquiry has dealt with only a suggestive, not an exhaustive list of barriers to entry in food retailing. It should be stressed, moreover, that not only does the height of each of the barriers vary, but the height of some barriers (e.g., advertising) varies from one market to another. Thus, no effort has been made to determine the combined height of barriers to entry. Nonetheless, it is clear that today significant barriers to entry do exist. Some of these (e.g., vertical integration and firm conglomeration) can only be achieved by very large firms. Other barriers appear to result solely in private advantages of size, such as those associated with price discrimination, rather than real economies of scale resulting in lower costs to society.

"Countervailing efforts of organizations such as cooperative and voluntary groups may assist new competitors in overcoming some barriers to entry. But none of these groups appears to aid small retailers in overcoming some of the more formidable entry barriers (e.g., vertical integration and firm conglomeration).

"In sum, it is quite apparent that today's entry barriers are substantial, and that rather than causing erosion of existing levels of concentration, the conditions of entry may well contribute to further increases."

The relevance of indicated barriers to entry in food retailing is the same for meats as most other food products. Relatively high barriers to entry give firms in large chain operations the ability to exercise some control over pricing the product. Retail meat prices are considerably more rigid than either wholesale meat prices or live animal prices. The points discussed in this section on structural characteristics (degree of concentration, vertical integration, differentiation of products, and barriers to entry) at least partially explain the basis upon which retailers derive the market power to exercise price control. These actions affect marketing margins and profit rates of large retailers.

RETAIL PRICING

Retailers have one common problem, whether they be chain or independent operator, supermarket or small store. Each has operating expenses which must be covered to stay in business. In addition, retailers hope to make a profit.

The pricing of processed meats differs little from nonmeat merchandise—the product sold can be identified with the one bought at wholesale. A predetermined margin can be applied to the wholesale cost to determine a target retail selling price. In practice, this is not as simple as it may appear if the price of each item is to cover expenses to particular items, or even to particular departments within a store.

The pricing of fresh meat, however, is considerably more complicated than that of processed meat. Most fresh meat is bought in wholesale cuts which must be fabricated (broken down) into retail cuts. In this process some shrinkage (weight loss) inevitably occurs. This may be called "cutting shrinkage." In addition, a so-called "store shrinkage" must be expected due to weight loss in rewrapping damaged packages, pilferage, spoilage, and returns by dissatisfied customers. These shrinkages are costs that must be covered, and it makes little difference whether they are included in operating expenses or listed separately.

In the cutting process, bone may be removed and fat may be trimmed away. The salvage value of bone and fat is negligible.

Figures 8.2, 8.3, 8.4, and 8.5 show the numerous retail cuts derived from various wholesale cuts. Retailers may buy sides, quarters, primal or subprimal wholesale cuts. The extent of fabrication by the retailer, the extent of cutting shrinkage, and the amount of salvage will vary with the type of wholesale cut. But, probably of greater importance, is the variation in quantity of saleable meat from carcass to carcass.

Thus, in retailing fresh meat, the individual items (cuts) sold at retail are different from the item purchased at wholesale and the quantity sold at retail is different from the quantity purchased at wholesale.

It is well known that some retail cuts are more preferred than other. Yet all must move into consumption at a fairly uniform rate. This means that individual cuts must be priced at differential rates per pound—the more desirable cuts at higher prices than less desirable cuts. The aggregate weighted average price per pound for *all* retail cuts derived from the wholesale cut must cover all expenses (including shrinkage) and yield a profit, if a profit is to be attained.

Table 9.10 illustrates several aspects of the retailer's problem in merchandising meat. It should be immediately apparent that the total value of the carcass to the retailer is dependent, not only upon retail price per pound, but also upon the cut-out. Cut-out is defined as the quantity of saleable meat obtained from a wholesale cut. In this example, the wholesale cut is an entire carcass. Cut-out long has been recognized as an extremely important factor in meat marketing. Two carcasses of identical weight and quality grade can yield significantly different quantities of saleable meat. This characteristic prompted the adoption of official USDA yield grades in June, 1965. Other things being equal, carcasses with higher cut-out have higher value. The example shown in Table 9.10 should not be construed as representative for all 600-lb choice steer carcasses.[5] Among the variables which affect cut-out are: conformation of the animal, degree of finish, weight of the carcass, sex, method of cutting, and degree of trim. By rigid specifications, careful selection of wholesale cuts, and standardization of cutting procedures, a retailer can narrow the range of cut-out obtained. But under present conditions he cannot hold this factor completely constant.

Table 9.10 also illustrates differential pricing among various cuts. Prices are shown to range from 36¢ to $1.39 per lb. The average retail price per pound of meat purchased by this retailer was ($383.38 ÷ 600) 63.9¢. His wholesale cost was 49¢ per lb. In this case, the gross margin was $89.38 which amounted to ($89.38 ÷ 383.38) 100=23.3% of the retail value. Data were not available to determine whether the $89.38 yielded the expected profit rate above expenses. The percentage gross margin shown is about the national

[5] Actually, a carcass can, and usually does, yield a greater variety of retail cuts than shown in Table 9.10, which makes the pricing problem more complicated than indicated.

TABLE 9.10

CUT-OUT, RETAIL PRICES AND RETAIL VALUE
OF CHOICE 600-LB STEER CARCASS

	Cut-out per 600-Lb Carcass (Lb)	Retail price ($)	Retail value ($)
Steak			
Sirloin	34	1.29	43.86
Porterhouse	11	1.39	15.29
T-bone	13	1.29	16.77
Club	9	1.29	11.61
Round	37	1.09	40.33
Flank	2	0.98	1.96
Roasts			
Standing rib	29	1.19	34.51
Rolled rib	10	1.09	10.90
Rump roast	28	1.09	30.52
Arm chuck	29	0.73	21.17
Blade chuck	72	0.69	49.68
Boston pot roast	16	0.79	12.64
Heel of round	16	0.79	12.64
Other			
Brisket	11	0.89	9.79
Short ribs	15	0.48	7.20
Plate	20	0.36	7.20
Boneless neck	15	0.79	11.85
Stew meat	12	0.79	9.48
Shank	7	0.49	3.43
Hamburger	60	0.69	41.40
Kidney	2	0.39	0.78
Total retail wt, avg price, and retail value	448	0.88	393.01
Salvage (bone and fat)	130	0.025	3.25
Cutting shrink	22	. . .	. . .
Total weight and value	600	. . .	396.26
Store shrink (3.25%)			12.88
Realized gross			383.38
Cost (wholesale)			294.00
Gross margin			89.38
Percentage gross margin			23.3

Source: Data derived by author from large supermarket, Tucson, Ariz., Dec. 1970.

average for retail meat departments, although better managers are reported to set a target at 25% (Anon. 1969).

If detailed research information were available on the demand for each retail cut, retailers would be able to adjust prices in a manner to maximize profits. Since this information is not available, retailers have had to discover market clearing prices through trial and error pricing.

Retailers, operating on a continuous basis, can observe those cuts which move slowly and adjust prices downward to speed up the movement before spoilage occurs or before those cuts have to be converted to a different form. Steaks and roasts can be converted to ground beef, for example, but this is not the way to stay in business. If certain cuts move out rapidly, this is a signal that prices can be raised.

Retailers to some extent are constrained in pricing policies by their competitors' actions. This applies particularly to price raises, but also to a lesser degree to price cuts. A retailer who raises prices above those of his competitors on cuts of a given quality is likely to lose customers. A retailer who cuts prices may expect retaliation by competitors and his actions could precipitate a price war. The latter is not likely, however, in the normal course of price adjustments designed merely to keep the usual volume of meat moving into consumption.

Approaches to Retail Pricing

Several different approaches are used by retailers in establishing selling prices. (1) A method used by many large operators is "percentage gross margin."[6] Here the retailer calculates an average weighted selling price such that the gross margin over wholesale cost is some predetermined percentage of the selling price. In the example provided in Table 9.10, the gross margin was 23.3%. As mentioned earlier, the retailer may set up a target gross margin of, say, 25% but the margin actually realized will depend upon the cut-out and prices obtained for the various cuts.

(2) Some retailers use a "percentage mark-up" over wholesale cost. One study indicated this to be the most widely used method among retailers in the North Central States (Forstad 1955). The National Commission on Food Marketing (1966B) stated that "of the many operating measures utilized in food retailing, (percentage) gross margin is probably the most frequently used." It is obvious that any given absolute gross margin would comprise a higher percentage of wholesale cost than of retail value.

(3) A third approach to retail pricing is "cents-per-pound mark-up" over wholesale cost. A *Food Topics* report indicated a trend toward this method with a further comment that 25% gross margin works out to be about 10–12¢ per lb on the costs-per-pound approach. (Anon. 1969).

(4) Smaller retailers sometimes simply used a prepared "retail meat pricing chart." These charts are available from various agencies. The format generally is similar. The chart is a Table set up in such a way that the retailer locates a column corresponding to his wholesale cost (per side of beef, for example) or he may use a column corresponding to his average desired selling price. The retailer then simply follows down that column to successive rows which show him suggested retail prices for the various retail cuts that may be derived from the side. The suggested retail prices are such that their weighted average will

---

[6] Percentage gross margin is synonymous with percentage gross profit. It also follows that absolute gross margin is synonymous with absolute gross profit. Absolute gross margin or absolute gross profit is expressed in cents per pound rather than as a percentage.

equal either the average wholesale cost or average desired selling price as selected at the column heading. Such charts are based on a standardized cut-out of the various cuts of meat. Earlier comments indicate the weakness of accepting an average cut-out without knowing specifications of the carcass and the cutting and trimming specifications. Even established retailers who work hard at maintaining such specifications periodically run cut-out tests to keep their operations in line. The chart prices, while possibly appropriate for a particular area at a particular time, may not agree with consumer preferences in another location or at a different time. In spite of the weaknesses, price charts may serve as guides and if up-dated and made specific to particular locations, may be very helpful.

(5) A fifth approach, one which cannot be ignored by any retailer, is to be guided by the prices of competitors. As with the pricing chart, this method ignores possible differences in cut-out resulting from differences in specifications of wholesale cuts ordered by competitors, differences in cutting methods, and in trimming specifications. Undoubtedly most retailers take note of prices charged by their competitors. Stout *et al.* (1968), in a study restricted to a sample of Ohio retailers, reported, "Product pricing procedures reflected the intensely competitive nature of meat retailing. All firms, with costs and margin goals firmly in mind, priced products within the restrictive framework permitted by competitors' prices. Although net profit goals, product mix, cut-out test results, volume and turnover, brand loyalty, and other factors entered into the pricing decisions, competitors' prices were the dominant consideration."

Meat Price Specials

The complications of retail meat pricing are further compounded by the use of "special" sales—short-term (week-end or early week) substantial price reductions, usually accompanied by intensive advertising and in-store promotion. Price cuts in a "special" may amount to 20% off regular prices (Tongue 1963). The evidence indicates that consumers do in fact respond to specials. William Tongue (1963) presented data showing that a beef special raised the tonnage of beef from about 20% of weekly store meat sales to 60–65%, smoked meats from about 1% to 41% and poultry from about 9% to 29%. DeGraff (1960) reported data from the National Association of Food Chains which indicated a smaller but nevertheless significant response. The retailer knows that a price reduction will cut his gross returns per unit, but as long as the margin still yields a positive profit he hopes the increased volume will maintain, if not improve, his net earnings.

Livestock producers have questioned the effect of meat price specials on livestock prices. No definitive research studies are available on this subject. Tongue (1963) and DeGraff (1960) both attempt to show that, logically, meat price specials may be expected to benefit the livestock industry. The reasoning, in part, is that specials result in increased volume of sales. This necessitates larger purchases at wholesale, which, in turn, would be expected to add strength to the wholesale market. Somewhat contrary to this line of reasoning is an opinion that packers, eager to obtain the large volume meat sales that go with a large chain special, may be willing to grant price concessions rather than hold for higher prices. Neither of these hypotheses has been verified by empirical analysis.

FROZEN FOOD LOCKERS AND PROVISIONERS

Sales by frozen food purveyors and the use of lockers, including home freezers, are classed as retail activity in that patrons and owners are final consumers. The widespread use of home freezers is an important stimulant to the demand for meat.

The commercial frozen food locker industry, including combination slaughter-locker plants, began in the early 1900's, had its greatest period of growth during the 1930's and 1940's, and reached a peak during the early 1950's. Numbers have declined since that time, coincident with an increase in use of home freezers. Most refrigerators currently on the market have a freezing compartment which adds greatly to total home freezing capacity. Many households also have a separate freezer unit. The availability of home freezers is closely associated with consumer response to meat price specials. Housewives often stock-up on specials, using home freezers for storage.

As noted above, many small locker plants have gone out of business since the early 1950's. It is reported that many of those remaining are experiencing difficulties in complying with the U.S. Wholesome Meat Act of 1967 and associated state requirements. As a result, an acceleration is expected in the rate of decline of this class of frozen food locker plant.

Of relatively recent origin is the freezer provisioner—a specialized food service firm which contracts with households to supply frozen foods, including meat. This type of operator is oriented directly toward supplying owners of home freezers. Some firms handle freezers as well as frozen food, while others handle only food. Various services are provided including cutting, wrapping, sharp freezing, house delivery, and financing. At present, only a relatively small fraction of total meat consumed is obtained in this manner. Future growth in this segment of the meat industry will depend largely on the degree to which the quality of meat delivered conforms to expectations of consumers and the level of prices as compared to supermarket prices.

BIBLIOGRAPHY

ANON. 1969. Meat marketing trends and practices. Food Topics Jan., 64-67.
ANON. 1971A. The convenience store study. Progressive Grocer Sept. 226.
ANON. 1971B. Grocery business annual report—1971. Progressive Grocer Apr., 68.

BAIN, J. S. 1956. Barriers to New Competition. Harvard University Press, Cambridge, Mass.

BUTZ, D., and BAKER, G. L. 1960. The changing structure of the meat economy. Harvard Univ., Graduate School Business Admin., Div. Res.

DeGRAFF, H. 1960. Beef Production and Distribution. University of Oklahoma Press, Norman.

DeLOACH, D. P. 1960. Changes in food retailing. Washington Agr. Expt. Sta. Bull. *619*.

DIETRICH, R. A., and WILLIAMS, W. F. 1959. Meat distribution in the Los Angeles area. USDA Agr. Marketing Serv., Marketing Res. Rept. *347*.

EZZEL, A. B., and RILEY, H. M. 1959. Estimated costs of retailing frozen meats as compared to fresh meats. Mich. Agr. Expt. Sta. Quart. Bull. *41*, No. 3, 41-72.

FEDERAL TRADE COMMISSION. 1960. Economic inquiry into food marketing. I. Concentration and integration in retailing. Federal Trade Comm. Staff Rept. U.S. Govt. Printing Office, Washington, D.C.

FORSTAD, E. C. 1955. Retailing meat in the North Central States. Indiana Agr. Expt. Sta. Bull. *622*.

HARRISON, T. G. 1962. How we developed our meat program. Food Merchandising *38*, Feb.

LEIMAN, M. 1967. Food retailing by discount houses. USDA Agr. Marketing Serv., Marketing Res. Rept. *785*.

LEIMAN, M., and KRIESBERG, M. 1962. Food retailing by discount houses. *In* Marketing and Transportation Situation. USDA Econ. Res. Serv. *MTS-114*.

MUELLER, W. F., and GAROIAN, L. 1960. Changes in market structure of grocery retailing, 1940-58. Wisconsin Agr. Expt. Sta. Res. Rept. *5*.

MUELLER, W. F., and GAROIAN, L. 1961. Changes in Market Structure of Grocery Retailing. University of Wisconsin Press, Madison.

NATIONAL COMMISSION ON FOOD MARKETING. 1966A. Organization and competition in the livestock and meat industry. Natl. Comm. Food Marketing Tech. Study *1*. Govt. Printing Office, Washington, D.C.

NATIONAL COMMISSION ON FOOD MARKETING. 1966B. Organization and competition in food retailing. Natl. Comm. Food Marketing Tech. Study 7. Govt. Printing Office, Washington, D.C.

NATIONAL COMMISSION ON FOOD MARKETING. 1966C. Special studies in food marketing. Natl. Comm. Food Marketing Tech. Study *10*. Govt. Printing Office, Washington, D.C.

STOUT, T. T., HAWKINS, M. H., and MARION, B. W. 1968. Meat procurement and distribution by Ohio grocery chains and affiliated wholesalers. Ohio Agr. Res. Develop. Center Res. Bull. *1014*.

TONGUE, W. W. 1963. Week-end specials pay off at retail level and increase overall consumption of meat. Proc. 58th Annual Meeting Am. Meat Inst., Chicago, Sept. 22-25.

CHAPTER 10

Futures Markets

WHAT IS A FUTURES MARKET?

A futures market is a market in which contracts are bought and sold. These are contracts in which a seller agrees to deliver and a buyer agrees to accept a specified commodity (e.g., live steers) at a future time. Terms of the contract specify the following: (1) commodity being traded, (2) price, (3) quantity, (4) quality, (5) place of delivery, and (6) time of delivery.

Futures trading in livestock and meat is relatively new, but the buying and selling of livestock on contract has been used in the industry for many years. Many examples could be given, but the following is illustrative. It is not unusual for a rancher to enter into agreement with a buyer in the spring in which he sells calves to be delivered in the fall. This contract also would specify the price, time of delivery, place of delivery, etc. Obviously, this is a contract for delivery at a future date. The buyer in this contract may, if he chooses, sell the contract (his obligation to accept) to another buyer. Presumably he would do this only if the second buyer were willing to pay him something above the stated contract price in order to obtain the contract rights. The second buyer might be willing to pay something for the contract if he wanted the cattle and thought the stipulated contract price was a good buy, or if he wanted the privilege of reselling the contract to still another buyer. This can happen on an advancing market. The original seller—the rancher—conceivably could buy back the contract (though he, too, might have to pay a premium to get it) and thus cancel out his obligation to deliver. This illustration involves a contract for future delivery but, technically, it is not a "futures market contract." For the sake of differentiation we shall call this a "cash" contract. Nevertheless, it was this sort of trading in cash contracts for the delivery of grain that prompted the organization more than a century ago of a specialized market to facilitate the trading in cash grain contracts. From this emerged the concept and techniques for trading in futures contracts.

The term "futures market" is reserved for a specialized market in which contracts are bought and sold under formal, and regulated, conditions. Trading is done only by specified people, at a specified place, during specified hours, under specified rules and regulations.

Trades can be made only by members of the organized exchange or employees of a firm which holds membership (owns a seat) in the exchange. Memberships are limited in two ways: (a) only a stated number are made available, and (b) ethical and financial standards must be met. Limitation of membership is no handicap to anyone who wishes to trade. It simply means that a nonmember must have a member make the trade for him, and memberships are held by brokerage firms which are in the business of performing this service for a fee.

Trades can be made only on the "floor" of the designated exchange. Again, this is no handicap to a nonmember .who wishes to trade, as the nonmember can place his trading order through a broker by telephone. Distance from the exchange itself is no factor.

Terms of the contracts are standardized with respect to quantity (per contract), quality, allowable tolerances in delivery of quality other than that specified in the contract, premiums and discounts for delivery of quality other than the specified contract quality, place of delivery, time of delivery, and other factors which affect the value of the commodity. The market exchanges have comprehensive self-regulating safeguards. In addition, they are supervised and regulated by the Commodity Exchange Authority, a branch of the USDA. In other words, a futures market is an "organized" market.

The rancher and cattle buyer used in the illustration could meet anywhere, each act as his own agent, draw up, and sign a contract. This may be satisfactory when only a relatively few contracts are made and when the major objective is actual transfer of the physical commodity (e.g., cattle) from seller to buyer. An active futures market will complete hundreds of trades each day. This type of market facilitates transfer of the physical commodity, but only a minor fraction of futures contracts are fulfilled by actual delivery of the commodity. The futures market serves other functions which will become apparent later.

A number of futures markets are now in operation. Trading is carried on in a large number of commodities including such items as live slaughter cattle, live feeder cattle, live hogs, frozen pork bellies, skinned hams, boneless beef, carcass beef, wool, eggs, iced broilers, most grains, sugar, coffee, onions, potatoes, cocoa, plywood, lumber, propane, silver, copper, mercury, tin, palladium, platinum, and others.

Some markets specialize in only one or a few commodities; others handle trades in a number of commodities. Trading in livestock and/or meat futures is done at just three markets: the Chicago Board of Trade, the Chicago Mercantile Exchange (commonly referred to as CME, the Mercantile Exchange, or simply "the Merc"), and the Minneapolis Grain Exchange which inititated trading in pork bellies in 1971. Each of these markets also handles trades in a number of other commodities.

Like any contract, futures contracts specify a time for delivery (and acceptance)—a time at which the contract matures. However, where many cash contracts specify an exact date of maturity, a futures contract specifies a period within a particular month (contract month) during which delivery may be made. Each exchange, through its organization, determines which months shall be specified as contract months, and the period within the month during which delivery shall be permitted. When the Chicago Mercantile Exchange initiated trading in live cattle in November, 1964 each of the 12 months was designated as a contract month. Traders, however, centered activity primarily in contracts maturing in February, April, June, August, October and December, and trading now is confined to these months. At any given time of the year trades may be made in any one of these contract months. For example, in January of a given year, traders have a choice of making trades in any of the above contract months for that year or in February of the following year.

Trading is done by open, verbal (as well as hand signal) bids and offers between brokers, or their representatives, on the floor of the exchange as these brokers vie with each other to fill their clients' orders to best advantage. At any given time, on an active market, some clients are attempting to sell and others are attempting to buy. Brokers with "buy" orders will, in the interest of their clients, attempt to make purchases at the lowest possible price. Likewise, brokers with "sell" orders will attempt to make sales at the highest possible price. This, with standardized contracts, standardized marketing conditions, and a well-organized system of market information, results in a highly competitive market. Commodity futures markets, along with securities markets, are considered to conform more closely to the perfectly competitive economic model than any other type of market.

In the process of "opening an account" with a broker, a client is required to sign a margin agreement, show evidence of financial responsibility, and deposit prescribed margin funds with his broker. "Margin" is the amount of money a trader is required to put up in order to make a futures transaction. In a sense the margin is equivalent to a down payment or "earnest" money. A trader in the futures market does not put up full value of the contract—only the margin, which amounts to a relatively small fraction of the full value. The same thing is done in many cash contracts upon signing of the contract. Full payment is made upon delivery of title. Similarly in futures trading; if a contract is held until delivery of the commodity, full payment is required.

Minimum initial and maintenance margin requirements are specified by commodity exchanges. Margin requirements normally are higher for speculative accounts than for hedging accounts. If they choose, brokerage firms may require a higher margin than specified by the exchange. If, after having made a trade, the market price moves favorably for a trader, his margin fund simply stays on deposit with the broker and is returned when the trade is closed out. However, if the market price moves unfavorably, the margin is used to cover losses, and before the margin fund is exhausted, the broker will call for additional margin, or if not forthcoming, the account will be closed out by the broker.

A trader never knows who takes the opposite end of his transaction. As indicated above, the transaction is executed by two brokers (or their representatives), one acting as agent for the seller, the other for the buyer. Each commodity exchange has a clearing association (clearing house) which performs a function similar to a bank clearing house. Brokerage firms hold membership in the clearing house and all transactions are cleared through it. For every sale cleared by one broker, an identical purchase is cleared by the broker who took the opposite end of that transaction on the floor of the exchange. A client who has made a trade has an obligation to his broker and the broker has an obligation to the clearing house. This contractual obligation is just as legal and binding as any other type of contract. An important difference, however, is that futures markets are organized in such a way that traders can easily liquidate their original position prior to maturity of the contract. This can be done simply by making an offsetting trade (if the initial trade were a purchase it can be offset by a sale, or vice versa) for the same number of contracts in the same contract month as the original trade.

Traders rarely enter the market with intentions of making or accepting delivery of the actual commodity. They liquidate their position prior to termination of trading in a given contract month. It should be emphasized, nevertheless, that however rarely it may happen, it is possible to make delivery and get delivery on a futures contract. The market would not function properly without this provision.

FUNCTIONS OF FUTURES MARKETS

Futures markets are considered to perform two basic functions: price setting through speculative activity (Tomek and Gray 1970), and hedging (Working 1962). Working and others have shown that the existence of futures markets depends basically upon hedging, which is the use of futures transactions in such a way as to offset the effects of an adverse price change in the cash market.

Any person who owns a commodity automatically assumes risks, one of the most important being that market prices may drop before the commodity is sold. Cattle feeders and hog feeders have seen potential profits vanish as market prices decline. A packer who has a commitment to supply meat to a wholesaler or retail buyer for a stipulated price may see his potential profits vanish as market prices move up. Hedging in the futures market is the transference of such price risks to other parties who usually are speculators.

At any given time prices generated in the futures market represent an aggregate consensus, primarily of speculators' analyses and opinions of future prices based upon current and foreseeable circumstances. As conditions change with the passing of time, the consensus may, and usually does, change. It will be mentioned later in this chapter that historically the futures market has not been an accurate forecaster of future prices, but this does not detract from its performance in hedging and pricesetting.

Speculation in the futures market, as implied above, is the voluntary assumption of price risk. Hedging in the futures market could not adequately be accomplished without speculation. While the interests of the livestock and meat industry primarily are centered in hedging price risk, it is important to understand at least the mechanics of speculation.

Speculation

Speculation in the futures market—the voluntary assumption of price risk—is not done for the fun of it. Speculators hope to make a profit. The concept of speculation in futures is deceptively simple, but consistent and long-run profits are difficult to come by. No attempt is made here to diagnose or prescribe speculative techniques or programs. Only the mechanics of speculation and its relation to hedging will be discussed.

At any given time a speculator may, by whatever means are at his disposal, make a market analysis in which he concludes that during the next "X" days, weeks, or months the futures price for a particular commodity will move up, or down, or remain unchanged. For illustrative purposes, assume that his analysis indicates the price will move up. It is obvious that he could make a profit by buying a futures contract now and reselling it later if the price does in fact rise—providing the selling price exceeded the buying price by more than the amount of charges involved in making the trades. If the speculator's analysis had indicated that the futures market price would move down, it is equally apparent that he could make a profit by selling a futures contract now and buying it back later—again providing the buying price had dropped below the selling price by an amount exceeding the charges involved in making the trades. The futures market provides the mechanism by which speculators can make such trades, but there is nothing inherent in the market which guarantees the speculator a profit. It should be perfectly obvious that if the speculator's analysis is in error—if the market moves in the opposite direction from what his analysis showed—then he would sustain a loss.

A futures market which remains relatively stable over time is of little interest to speculators, since profit potentials arise from price changes. Commodity prices (i.e., livestock, grains, etc.), historically have fluctuated rather sharply. The price of choice 900–1100 lb slaughter steers at Kansas City was $34.00 per cwt during the spring of 1970; by fall of that same year the price was $27.00. During the same period hog prices dropped from $30.00 to $15.00. Grain prices also fluctuate rather sharply, although for a number of years the government price support program has tended to dampen the variations. Over a period of time, futures prices tend to move in the same general direction as market prices for the actual, physical commodity (the latter market is called the "cash" or "spot" market to differentiate it from the futures market).

Following are hypothetical examples of two speculative ventures—one

(Example A) in which prices move in the expected direction, the other (Example B) in which prices move opposite from the expected.

Example A.—Assume a speculator has opened an account with a broker and that on a January 12 his analysis indicates the price of October live cattle futures will rise during the following three months. The speculator on January 12 places an order with his broker to buy two units of CME October cattle "at the market." "At the market" leaves it up to the broker to get the best buy possible at that time.[1] Let us say the order is executed at $29.75 per cwt. At this point (January 12) the speculator is "long" two units of October cattle. Each contract unit, by CME specification, is 40,000 lb liveweight, so the total value would be

$$2 \times \frac{40,000}{100} \times \$29.75 = \$23,800.00$$

Now assume that three months later (April 12) the speculator closes out his position. He will do this by placing an order with his broker to sell two units of CME October cattle. The broker executes the order at, we shall say, $30.50 per cwt. This liquidates the speculator's position in October cattle. The value of the sale would be

$$2 \times \frac{40,000}{100} \times \$30.50 = \$24,400.00$$

Gross profits would be $24,400.00 − $23,800.00 = $600.00. The broker's commission and interest on the margin funds must be deducted from gross profits. CME stipulated commission is $36 per contract unit, 2 × $36 = $72. Minimum margin requirements for speculative accounts are assumed to be $400 per contract unit, or a total of $800. Interest at 8% for 3 months would be $0.08 \times \$800 \times \frac{3}{12} = \$16.00$. Net profits then would amount to $600.00 −$72.00 −$16.00 = $512.00.

Example B.—In this case assume everything identical with Example A up to the point of liquidating the original position. At this point we assume prices have declined so that the liquidation sale of two units of October cattle is made at $29.25 per cwt. Under these conditions the sale value would be

$$2 \times \frac{40,000}{100} \times \$29.25 = \$23,400.00$$

Gross profits would be $23,400.00 − $23,800.00 = −$400.00. Commission charges and interest on margin funds would be the same as in Example A.[2] Net profits therefore would be

$$-\$400.00 - \$72.00 - \$16.00 = -\$488.00$$

[1] Other types of orders are: (1) "Limit order," can be executed only at a specified (or better) price. (2) "Open order," also specifies the price, but the order stands until it is executed or cancelled. (3) "Day order," must be executed on a specified day—or is automatically cancelled. Unless otherwise stated, all orders are considered to be day orders. (4) "Stop (loss) order," stipulates a price, then, if or when the market reaches that price, a market order becomes effective.

[2] Additional margin probably would be required, but this is ignored for simplification.

The speculator under these circumstances would have sustained a loss of $488.00.

There are, of course, many other types of speculative ventures which can be undertaken in futures markets. The type illustrated here is one of the most elementary, but the two assumed outcomes will serve to illustrate the place of speculation as an adjunct to hedging. Without speculation, hedgers at times would have difficulties in placing orders. This will be apparent in the following discussion.

Hedging Price Risk

Hedging price risk in the futures market is the use of futures market transactions in such a way as to offset the effects of adverse price movements in the cash market. Whether a price change is "adverse" depends upon the position one holds in the actual commodity (in the cash market). To the cattle feeder who has a pen of cattle on feed, it is clear that a price decline in cattle would be adverse. To a packer who has an agreement to deliver dressed beef carcasses at a stipulated price, but who has not yet purchased cattle for slaughter, a price rise in cattle would be adverse.

A hedge is accomplished by taking a position in the futures market opposite from the one held in the cash market. The cattle feeder mentioned above has "bought" the cash commodity (actual cattle). His position is said to be "long" the cash market. He would execute a hedge by taking an opposite position (selling) in the futures market. He then is said to be "short" the futures market and in trade terminology this would be called a "short hedge."

The position described for the packer above is said to be "short" the cash market. He would execute a hedge by taking a "long" position (buying) in the futures market. This is called a "long hedge."

How can the hedger be sure that he will be able to take the desired position in the futures market? Here is where speculation comes in. Any transaction requires the participation of two parties. A sale cannot be made in the futures market, or any other market, unless someone else takes the opposite side of the transaction (buys). A purchase cannot be made unless someone else sells. A hedger can never be sure that a speculator stands ready to take the opposite side of a transaction at a particular price the hedger may choose, but in an active, viable market he can be sure that a speculator will take the opposite side at some price. And, if the market has a relatively high volume of hedging and speculative activity, the hedger can be reasonably sure that a trade will be executed near the price level at which other trades are being made at that particular time. Speculators are needed to give markets the flexibility and breadth to absorb hedges without undue price reaction.

Theoretical Cash-Futures Price Relationships.—For the futures market to provide an adequate hedging mechanism, two fundamental cash-futures price relationships must hold: (1) over a period of time cash prices and futures prices for a given commodity must move in the same general direction, and (2) as a futures contract expires (during month of contract maturity) cash price (at par delivery points) and the price of the expiring futures must come reasonably close together.

In the first instance, this means that if one advances, the other must advance; if one declines, the other must decline. Erratic day-to-day, or short-period deviations from this proposition occur and are not particularly damaging, but sustained, unpredictable movements would render the futures market untenable for hedging purposes.

Futures prices, basically, are determined by traders' (primarily speculators) expectations of supply and demand conditions as deduced from current and anticipated conditions.[3] Current cash prices are based upon appraisal of the current supply-demand situation, conditioned by future expectations. Thus, cash and futures prices usually react in the same direction to continuously developing supply and demand factors. Tomek and Gray (1970) state, "The element of expectations is imparted to the whole temporal constellation of price quotations, and futures prices reflect essentially no prophecy that is not reflected in the cash price and is in that sense already fulfilled."

Cash cattle prices declined while futures prices advanced for a period during the fall of 1969. This, however, was an exception to generally observed trends. Records show that, over time, cash prices and futures prices usually move in the same general direction (see Fig. 10.1) though not necessarily at the same rate (Blau 1944-1945).

The tendency for cash prices and futures prices at par delivery points[4] to come reasonably close together at expiration of a futures contract is based upon the fact that any point of time in the future inexorably becomes the present with the passage of time. As mentioned earlier, futures contracts can be liquidated by delivery of the actual commodity (though this seldom is done). The possibility of delivery sets up powerful speculative forces which prevent a wide divergence of prices at termination of futures contracts. To use an exaggerated example, assume that as a June cattle contract approached expiration (during the month of June) the cash price of contract grade cattle in Omaha, Nebr., or Sioux City, Iowa (designated par delivery points for both live slaughter cattle and live feeder cattle CME contracts) was $5.00 per cwt above the futures price. A strong incentive would exist for speculators to buy futures, hold the futures until actual cattle were delivered, then immediately

---

[3] It will be shown later that the futures market has not been an accurate forecaster of cash prices over an extended period, but it was not organized for price forecasting purposes.

[4] Par delivery points are locations specified by futures markets as points where commodities may be delivered to satisfy futures contracts at the contract price. Prior to closing of the Chicago Stock Yards in 1971, Chicago was the par delivery point for live cattle futures contracts.

Price

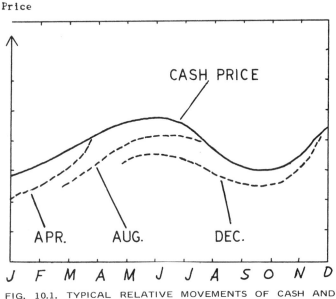

FIG. 10.1. TYPICAL RELATIVE MOVEMENTS OF CASH AND
FUTURES PRICES

sell these cattle on the higher cash market. On the other hand, if cash prices were $5.00 below futures prices as expiration of the futures approached, a strong incentive would exist for speculators to sell futures and when delivery was possible, to buy some actual cattle in the relatively low-priced cash market, then deliver them in satisfaction of the futures obligation. Thus, forces are set in motion which bring cash prices (of the contract grade) and futures prices of an expiring future fairly close together as trading in the contract month terminates. A study by Ehrich (1967) showed that futures prices tended to converge with the average price of 1100–1300-lb choice steer price at Chicago. Of course, there are uncertainties in exact time of delivery, exact quality that might be delivered,[5] and in elapsed time between delivery and resale of the actual commodity so that cash and futures prices are not necessarily identical at contract determination, hence use of the term "reasonably" close.[6]

In futures markets for storable commodities which are produced at one time of the year and stored for use throughout the subsequent period, a logical reason exists for hypothesizing that the futures price for a given contract

[5] Presumably a trader who chooses to deliver actual cattle in fulfillment of a futures contract would deliver the lowest quality which meets contract specifications. However, grading live animals is somewhat subjective.

[6] Occasionally a "squeeze" develops as a contract is being closed out. Traders become anxious to get out before delivery and futures deviate temporarily from cash prices. This, however, is a short-lived phenomenon.

month will be above the cash price, at any particular time by the amount of storage charges that would carry the commodity to termination of the futures contract.[7] Live animals in condition for slaughter are not storable. Some efforts have been made at theoretical explanation of cash-futures price relationship for live cattle. Paul and Wesson (1967), in a theoretical treatment, concluded that the difference between a futures price and the sum of feeder cattle and feed prices on the cash market is the price of feedlot services. However, protracted periods during which futures prices have been below cash prices cast some doubt on this explanation.

The Basis.—"Basis" is defined as the amount by which cash price is above, or below, a specified futures price. The previous section on cash-futures price relationships dealt with certain aspects of the basis because the relationship between cash and futures prices involves the difference between the two. Since the cash price and futures price tend to come together at futures contract maturity, this implies that the basis relative to the "near" futures narrows as the near futures terminates. But which futures market and which cash prices are we concerned with? Any reference to basis should be specific with respect to both points.

There are only three futures markets in which live animal and/or meat futures are traded; two are in Chicago and one is in Minneapolis. Since the bulk of futures trading in these commodities at this time is done in the Chicago Mercantile Exchange, that market will be used in the following discussion as a source of reference for futures price quotations. There are, however, many cash markets for livestock and meat throughout the United States. The earlier comment about cash and futures prices coming reasonably close together at contract maturity specified the cash price at par delivery points. A cattle feeder at Dodge City, Kan., who sells finished cattle to a local packer needs to know the Dodge City basis, i.e., the amount by which Dodge City cash price is below (or above) the CME cattle futures price for a specified contract month. To effectively appraise a potential hedging situation, every feeder needs an understanding of the concept of "basis" and a knowledge of the actual basis of the market in which he sells relative to the futures in which he contemplates placing a hedge. The concept is simple and futures prices are relatively easy to obtain. However, it is difficult to obtain adequate local cash prices at some local points for comparison with the futures prices. Not only are local price quotations by sex, grade, and weight often difficult to obtain, but studies have shown that the basis varies over time. Figure 10.2 shows that the Kansas City basis (relative to Chicago

[7] A considerable body of literature exists on this aspect of cash-futures price relationships. The subject is complicated including consideration of risk premium, and convenience yield, as well as out-of-pocket storage costs. Periods of time when cash grain prices exceeded futures grain prices prompted the development of the theory of "inverse" carrying charges. No effort is made in this text to develop these aspects to livestock and meat futures.

FIG. 10.2. THE KANSAS CITY LIVE CATTLE BASIS (AMOUNT BY WHICH KANSAS CITY CASH PRICE WAS OVER OR UNDER CHICAGO FUTURES PRICE), 1965–1970

Kansas City cash prices from USDA data. Chicago futures prices from Chicago Mercantile Exchange quotations.

futures) varied considerably over the period 1965-1970. Usually, Kansas City cash prices were below Chicago futures, but on occasion the reverse has been the case. There also is an apparent tendency for this basis to narrow during summer months and widen during winter months. Over this period of years the basis averaged about −$1.00, but ranged from −$2.00 to +$0.50.[8]

To this point we have been concerned with the locational basis, i.e., we have assumed that local cash price being compared to futures price was for cattle of identical sex, weight, and grade as specified in the futures contract. On occasion, livestock producers may be interested in a basis which also includes other factors, such as steers of lower or higher grade, heifers (instead of steers), or weights and dressing yield different from those specified in the futures contract.

Very little empirical work is available on the applicable basis for any of these factors at local markets. However, producers often can obtain reasonable estimates from experienced producers and market personnel.

Mechanics of Hedging.—Four steps can be identified in every hedging operation—2 in the cash market and 2 in the futures market. They are: (1) Assumption of original position in cash market. (2) Assumption of original position in futures market. (3) Liquidation of position in cash market. (4) Liquidation of position in futures market.

Steps 1 and 2 usually are carried out at, or about, the same time in a fully hedged operation. At a later date Steps 3 and 4 normally are carried out at,

---

[8] Rules of CME permit delivery of cattle in Guymon, Okla., in fulfillment of a futures contract at $1.00 below the Chicago-based futures contract price, and at Peoria, Ill., and Chicago, Ill., at a premium of $0.50 cwt.

or about, the same time. In the more sophisticated hedging programs, exceptions are made to these generalizations (and also to most other generalizations), but for purposes of this exposition it will be assumed that transactions in Steps 3 and 4 also are executed simultaneously, but at a later date than Steps 1 and 2.

Steps 2 and 4 require the services of a broker. The livestock producer who contemplates hedging should "open an account" with a brokerage firm prior to the time he wishes to place the hedge. The feeder also should acquaint himself with the specifications of the futures contracts. The Chicago Board of Trade, the Chicago Mercantile Exchange and the Minneapolis Grain Exchange publish and distribute free brochures with this information.[9] Most brokerage firms have them for distribution. Among other things, the brochure indicates that the brokerage commission for CME live cattle futures (40,000 lb liveweight) is $36.00 per contract on a round-turn. Round-turn means that the $36.00 covers both assumption of the original position and its liquidation. The brochure may, or may not, indicate the exchange's specified minimum margin requirement. This may be varied by exchange action, but operating policy keeps it relatively stable. Brokerage houses often require a higher margin than the exchange minimum.

In the examples immediately following, none of the transactions is dated. This is to simplify the presentation. It does, however, oversimplify one problem. In executing a hedge in the futures market it is necessary to specify the contract month in which the hedge is to be placed. In general, a hedge is placed in the contract month which coincides with anticipated sale month of the actual commodity, or the contract which matures next after the antici-pated sale date of the actual commodity. For example, if feeder cattle are bought on Sept. 1, to be fed 140 days, the sale date would be Jan. 18. Futures trading is not carried on in a January contract, so a hedge on such cattle usually would be placed in the February contract.

Examples of Hedges.—Assume in the following hypothetical examples that an account has been opened and initial margin requirements deposited with a brokerage firm at the time hedge transactions are initiated.

Example I: "Short" Hedge of Cattle on Feed.—Consider that 600-lb choice feeder steers are purchased, fed 140 days, and sold as 1000-lb choice slaughter steers. At the time feeder cattle are purchased, cash prices are $27 per cwt for choice feeders and $28 for choice slaughter steers at the market used by the cattle feeder.

The conditions set up are elementary. It is assumed that: (1) a short hedge is executed at the same time the feeder cattle are purchased (i.e., today) and the futures position is liquidated by an offsetting transaction at the same time

---

[9] Brochures are available from the Chicago Mercantile Exchange, the Chicago Board of Trade, and the Minneapolis Grain Exchange giving specifications for futures contracts traded in the respective markets.

the cattle are sold (i.e., 140 days after today); (2) cash and futures price movements are exactly parallel; (3) the operation is fully hedged during the entire feeding period; (4) there is no death loss; (5) there are no marketing costs in the cash market; and (6) margin requirements are $250 per contract unit (margin requirements are less on hedge transactions than on speculative transactions) with interest on margin funds at 7%.

Three alternative price movements are considered: downward (Ia), upward (Ib), and no change (Ic).

Tables 10.1, 10.2, and 10.3 summarize hedging results under the three assumed price movements. It will be noted that the indicated net returns are identical ($4986) under each of the three alternatives. This follows from the assumption of identically parallel movements in the cash and futures markets—admittedly an unrealistic assumption, but deliberately chosen to illustrate the point that a hedge tends to offset the effects of price change, whether the change be a decline or an advance.

Results in Table 10.1 show that the hedge provided protection against a cash price decline. This adverse price movement was offset in the futures transaction. The feeding operation would have sustained a loss of $2800 if carried out unhedged. Under hedged conditions (as assumed), the futures market gain ($8000) offset (in fact more than offset) the cash market loss and resulted in a net return of $4986.

It is apparent in Table 10.2 that a hedged feeder will forego windfall profits that otherwise would accrue from a price advance. If the operation were unhedged, a gain of $13,200 would be realized from cash market transactions. But with advancing prices, the futures transactions would sustain a loss of $8000. A hedge "protects" from a favorable price movement just as it does from an adverse price movement.

If prices remain steady (unchanged), nothing is gained from a hedging operation (see Table 10.3). In fact, the commission and interest on funds tied up in margin would reduce net return by those amounts.

In real world hedging operations, the cash and futures markets seldom move in exactly parallel fashion. In a short hedge, if the futures price drops more than the cash price, a hedger will gain more on the futures transaction than he loses on the cash transaction. If the reverse situation occurs, he will gain less on the futures transaction than is lost on the cash transaction.

In the previous examples, the futures price at initiation of the hedge (i.e., $28 per cwt "today") was indicated to be higher than the average total cost per hundredweight of the finished cattle ($50,800 ÷ 2000 cwt = $25.40 per cwt). The latter is known as "break-even" price. This situation was deliberately built into the example. Real world market conditions are not always that accommodating. At times the futures price is less than "break-even" price. When this situation exists, the execution of a hedge usually would result in a net loss. This is illustrated in Table 10.4 where it is assumed that cash

TABLE 10.1

HEDGING EXAMPLE I(a): "SHORT" HEDGE OF CATTLE ON FEED—ASSUMING PRICE DECLINES TO $24 PER CWT DURING FEEDING PERIOD

Cash Market ($)		Futures Market ($)		Results ($)	
Today:		Today:			
(1), Buy 200 feeder steers @	27/cwt	(2) Sell futures contracts, 5 units @			
Cost of feeders	32,400	28/cwt			
Cost of gain @ 23/cwt	18,400	Total value of sale	56,000		
				Loss in cash market	2800
Total cost	50,800			Gain in futures market	8000
				Less commission	180
				Less interest on margin	34
140 days from today:		140 days from today:			
(3) Sell 200 choice slaughter steers @		(4) Buy futures contracts, 5 units @		Net profit	4986
24/cwt		24/cwt			
Total returns	48,000	Total value of purchase	48,000		

TABLE 10.2

HEDGING EXAMPLE I(b): "SHORT" HEDGE OF CATTLE ON FEED—ASSUMING PRICE INCREASES TO $32 PER CWT DURING FEEDING PERIOD

Cash Market ($)		Futures Market ($).		Results ($)	
Today:		Today:			
(1) Buy 200 feeder steers @	27/cwt	(2) Sell futures contracts, 5 units @			
Cost of feeders	32,400	28/cwt			
Cost of gain @ 23/cwt	18,400	Total value of sale	56,000	Gain in cash market	13,200
				Loss in futures market	8,000
Total cost	50,800			Less commission	180
				Less interest on margin	34
140 days from today:		140 days from today:			
(3) Sell 200 choice slaughter steers @		(4) Buy futures contracts, 5 units @		Net return	4,986
32/cwt		32/cwt			
Total returns	64,000	Total value of purchase	64,000		

TABLE 10.3

HEDGING EXAMPLE 1(c): "SHORT" HEDGE OF CATTLE ON FEED—ASSUMING PRICE REMAINS UNCHANGED AT $28 PER CWT DURING FEEDING PERIOD

Cash Market ($)		Futures Market ($)		Results ($)	
Today:		Today:			
(1) Buy 200 feeder steers @	27/cwt	(2) Sell futures contracts, 5 units @			
Cost of feeders	32,400	28/cwt			
Cost of gain	18,400	Total value of sale	56,000		
				Gain in cash market	5200
Total cost	50,800			Gain in futures market	0
				Less commission	180
				Less interest on margin	34
140 days from today:		140 days from today:			
(3) Sell 200 choice slaughter steers @		(4) Buy futures contracts, 5 units @		Net return	4986
28/cwt		28/cwt			
Total returns	56,000	Total value of purchase	56,000		

TABLE 10.4

HEDGING EXAMPLE I(d): "SHORT" HEDGE OF CATTLE ON FEED—ASSUMING FUTURES PRICE AT INITIATION OF HEDGE IS BELOW BREAK-EVEN PRICE

Cash Market ($)	Futures Market ($)	Results ($)
Today:	Today:	
(1) *Buy* 200 feeder steers @ 27/cwt	(2) *Sell* futures contracts, 5 units @ 24/cwt	
Cost of feeders 32,400		
Cost of gain @ 23/cwt 18,400		
Total cost 50,800	Total value of sale 48,000	
Break-even price $\frac{50,800}{2,000 \text{ cwt}} = 25.40/\text{cwt}$		
140 days from today:	140 days from today:	
(3) *Sell* 200 choice slaughter steers @ 22/cwt	(4) *Buy* futures contracts, 5 units @ 22/cwt	
Total returns 44,000	Total value of purchase 44,000	
		Loss in cash market 6800
		Gain in futures market 4000
		Less commission 180
		Less interest on margin 34
		Net loss 3014

prices decline during the feeding period—and the result was a net loss of $3014. It needs to be emphasized that hedging in itself does not guarantee a profit. A hedge only sets the selling price. In this sense, it can be used as a forward pricing device. If that price is above the break-even price, a profit is indicated, but if it is below the break-even price, a loss is to be expected. It will be noticed that in this last sentence the reference to profit and loss is qualified. This is necessary because if cash and futures prices do not move in a parallel manner, i.e., if the basis does not remain constant, then profits (or losses) will vary as mentioned in the paragraph immediately above.

In each of the four examples (Tables 10.1, 10.2, 10.3, and 10.4), it can be seen that the assumed liquidation price of the futures was identical to the cash sale price of the cattle. This conforms to the earlier statement that cash prices and futures prices "tend to come reasonably close together at contract maturity"—the basis tends toward zero. This also needs to be qualified in two respects. (1) This would apply to par delivery point cash prices and futures prices, but the cash price in other markets would not necessarily equal the par delivery point price and in most places would be different. This, however, simply means that prospective hedgers must know the local basis. In evaluating a potential hedge, the basis applicable to the local situation should be used. For example, a feeder using the Kansas City cash market probably would assume Chicago futures to be about $1.00 per cwt above Kansas City cash price for choice slaughter steers. (2) It usually is not possible (and in fact it is not desirable) to attempt to liquidate the hedge during the final days of a terminating contract, at which time cash and futures prices are expected to approach each other. A hedge usually is liquidated as the cattle are sold which may come prior to maturity of the contract month in which the hedge is placed. The basis is less predictable at such times than near contract termination.

The principles and mechanics used by a producer in hedging feeder cattle and hogs on feed are similar to those explained for hedging slaughter cattle. No explicit examples are given. Only one market, the Chicago Mercantile Exchange, exists at this time where live feeder cattle and hog futures are traded.

Example II: "Short" Hedge of Hogs Bought on Contract.—Packers at times buy hogs from producers on cash contract before the hogs are finished out. Terms of the contract call for delivery when the hogs are finished, but the price may be set upon signing the contract.

A primary reason packers enter such contracts is to line up supplies in advance. Producers may be willing to contract to reduce price uncertainty. The producer may prefer such a cash contract in lieu of hedging in the futures market. The packer in this situation may want protection against a price decline. Why? If hog prices decline, this packer's competitors will be able to obtain their kill at prices lower than the contract price to which this packer is committed. In sale of the meat, then, this packer would be at a disadvantage.

By hedging in the futures market the packer can shift this price risk. Upon signing the cash contract the packer assumes a "long" position in the cash market. He can hedge this position by taking an opposite ("short") position in the futures market. Table 10.5 illustrates the results of a hedge in which a contract price was set at $22 per cwt on July 1 but cash price had dropped to $18 per cwt upon delivery Sept. 20. Market sale weight is assumed to be 200 lb per head. A contract unit is 30,000 lb liveweight. Commission is calculated at $35 per unit (round-turn) and margin requirements (for a hedged transaction) at $350 per unit with interest at 7%.

The results in Table 10.5 show that gains in the futures transaction offset declines in the cash market price. The packer's net cost would be $10,881. The cost unhedged would have been $13,200. In this example, the hedge would have offset the $2400 decline in cash value. In a sense the $70 commission and $11 interest on margin could be classed as insurance premium against the price decline in the cash market.

Example III: "Long" Hedge of Forward Beef Sales.—Packers, at times, enter contracts with large retail and wholesaler buyers for the sale of meat of certain specifications—the meat to be delivered at some specified later date—and the price is established at negotiation of the contract. If the packer has livestock already bought, he knows the cost and can price the meat accordingly. On the other hand, if he has not yet bought livestock, he could, if he chose, enter the contract, price the meat, and utilize the futures market to protect himself from an advance in livestock prices.

Unofficial reports indicate this type of hedge is seldom used by packers, but the possibility merits a brief presentation. Flour millers have long used such hedges in contracting for delivery and pricing flour before actually purchasing the wheat from which flour will be milled.

In this example, assume (1) the meat sold under contract is 72,000 lb of USDA choice steer beef carcasses weighing 600 lb each at a stipulated price of $44 per cwt with delivery in 60 days; (2) the packer has not yet bought cattle to fill the contract; and (3) cattle prices advance $1 per cwt by the time cattle are purchased. The price risk of such meat sale conceivably could be hedged in either beef carcass futures or live cattle futures. Futures markets have been established for beef carcasses but have never attracted sufficient volume for effective hedging. However, it is relatively easy to translate carcass requirements into live cattle requirements and a high correlation exists between wholesale carcass prices and live cattle prices. The sale of beef carcasses, therefore, can be hedged in the live cattle futures. Commission and margin costs for live cattle futures hedging transactions are calculated at $36 and $250, respectively, per contract unit.

Table 10.6 illustrates how this contract sale could be hedged by a purchase in the live cattle futures. The $1.00 advance in cash live cattle prices is

TABLE 10.5

HEDGING EXAMPLE II: "SHORT" HEDGE OF HOGS BOUGHT BY PACKER ON CONTRACT—ASSUMING PRICE DECLINES $4 PER CWT IN CASH HOG MARKET

Cash Market ($)		Futures Market ($)		Results ($)	
On July 1:		On July 1:			
(1) Packer contracts 300 hogs for Sept. 20 delivery @ 22/cwt		(2) Packer sells Oct. futures, 2 units @ 22.50/cwt			
Total value of contract	13,200	Total value of sale	13,500	Contract cost of hogs	13,200
				Less gain in futures market	2,400
				Plus commission	70
				Plus interest on margin	11
On Sept. 20:		On Sept. 20:			
(3) Hogs are delivered to packer who pays contract price of 22/cwt, but cash price has dropped to 18/cwt		(4) Packer buys Oct. futures, 2 units @ 18.50/cwt		Net cost to packer	10,881
Total market value	10,800	Total value of purchase	11,100		

TABLE 10.6

HEDGING EXAMPLE III: "LONG" HEDGE OF FORWARD SALE OF BEEF—ASSUMING PRICE ADVANCE
OF $1 PER CWT IN CASH CATTLE MARKET

Cash Market ($)	Futures Market ($)	Results ($)
Today:	Today:	
(1) Sell 72,000 lb choice beef on contract @ 44/cwt equivalent to 120 head of steers (1000 lb each) @ 26.40/cwt[1]	(2) Buy futures contracts, 3 units @ 27.50/cwt	
Total value of sale 31,680	Total value of purchase 33,000	Loss on cash market 1200.00
		Gain on futures market 1200.00
		Less commission 108.00
		Less interest on margin 3.60
25 days from today:	25 days from today:	
(3) Buy 120 choice steers @ 27.40/cwt.	(4) Sell futures contracts, 3 units @ 28.50/cwt	Net cost 111.60
Total cost 32,880	Total value of sale 34,200	

[1] $26.40 per cwt is considered to be liveweight equivalent of dressed cost.

assumed to be matched by an equivalent advance in the futures market, so the additional cost of cattle would be offset by a gain in the futures market. Unhedged, the $1.00 per cwt advance in the cash market would have resulted in an additional cost of $1200 to the packer. This would be offset by the hedge so the only additional cost would be $111.60, the cost of commission and interest on margin. As in the previous example, this can be looked upon as a premium for price risk insurance.

This same type hedge could be used by large retailers in (1) advertising programs where retail prices are announced before wholesale meat purchase contracts have been made, or (2) fixing the purchase price of wholesale meat at a time when their market analysis shows the likelihood of advancing prices. In both instances the price risk is one of advancing prices and the initial step in the futures market would be a long position. This position would be liquidated as actual supplies were purchased in the cash wholesale meat market. There is in actuality little evidence that retailers use such hedges. In most cases retailers are able to obtain a firm agreement on meat prices prior to advertising and as a matter of operating policy retail prices (with the exception of specials) are held relatively steady compared to wholesale meat and live animal prices.

Example IV: Hedging Feed Costs.—Feed cost is a principal component of the total cost of finishing livestock, and the major share is grain cost. A livestock feeder who purchases grain for feeding can, if he chooses, use the futures market to protect himself against a rise in grain prices. Attention is called to an earlier assertion that hedging livestock prices does not in itself guarantee a profit. Likewise, the hedging of feed prices does not in itself guarantee a profit. Hedging grain prices, in effect, sets the price of grain and this can be done at the start of the feeding period (or earlier). Whether or not a feeder chooses to hedge will depend on (a) whether the current grain futures prices permit him to set (lock in) prices which are favorable and (b) the feeder's analysis of whether grain prices are likely to rise. Corn and grain sorghum futures are handled on both the Chicago Board of Trade and the Kansas City Board of Trade. The Chicago Mercantile Exchange initiated trading in grain sorghum futures in 1971.

Explicit step-by-step procedures will not be shown in this case. It is clear that the risk to be avoided is a rise in grain prices. This calls for a long hedge (a purchase of futures) against grain requirements. A feeder would (a) calculate his grain requirements, (b) place a hedge by purchasing futures, then (c) as grain is purchased on the cash grain market he would liquidate an equivalent quantity of futures, hold the remainder until additional grain is purchased, then liquidate more futures.

Soybean meal and some other feed ingredient prices may be hedged in futures markets in a like manner.

Use of a Hedge Worksheet.—It is emphasized, again, that hedging in itself does not guarantee a profit. Each hedging situation should be evaluated by an analysis of estimated costs and estimated returns to labor, management, and profit before a hedge is executed. Profit is defined here as an amount over and above an acceptable return to labor and management. In other words, it is considered that an operator will classify return to his labor and management as a cost to be covered before profits are calculated. Some operators may prefer to place a zero value on labor and management and consider everything over operating costs as profit. This is up to each individual.

Table 10.7 is the author's version of a worksheet designed to evaluate the feasibility of a hedge in terms of profit and returns to labor and management. Even a cursory review of this worksheet reveals two critical components—costs, and basis. Costs are listed as: cost of feeder cattle, cost of gain marketing costs (in cash market), hedging costs, and if an operator chooses to enter it, an "acceptable operator's return to labor and management."

Basis, it will be recalled, is the difference between the applicable cash market price (i.e., the cash market in which the livestock will actually be sold)

TABLE 10.7

HEDGE WORKSHEET FOR CATTLE

Buy _____ lb _____ feeder _____; feed _____ days; sell _____ lb _____ slaughter cattle
       (grade)   (steers or   (grade)
               heifers)

A. Estimated Costs:
    (1) Cost of feeder per head (_____lb @ $_____)......................... $_____
    (2) Cost of gain:
    (3) (a) Feed costs per head...................................... $_____
    (4) (b) Nonfeed costs per head................................ $_____
    (5) (c) Total cost of gain per head [line (3) + line (4)] .... $_____
    (6) Marketing costs per head (in cash market)............................. $_____
    (7) Hedging costs per head... $_____
    (8) Total all costs per head [line (1) + line (5) + line (6) + line (7)].................. $_____
    (9) Acceptable operators return per head for labor and management.............. $_____
    (10) Break-even amount, total per head [line (8) + line (9)]............................ $_____
    (11) Break-even price, per cwt [line (10) ÷ Sale wt] .... $_____

B. Estimated Hedge Selling Price:
    (12) Current Chicago futures price, _____ future, per cwt.......... $_____
                       (month)
    (13) Basis—adj for market location differential per cwt. .... $_____
    (14) Basis—adj for grade differential per cwt.............................. $_____
    (15) Basis—adj for avg. livewt and dressing yield......................... $_____
    (16) Basis—adj for heifer differential per cwt.............................. $_____
    (17) Effective futures hedge price
        [line (12) ± line (13) ± line (14) ± line (15) − line (16)] .... $_____

C. Estimated Profit:
    (18) Est hedged profit per cwt [line (17) − line (11)] .... $_____
    (19) Est hedged profit per head [line (18) × sales wt]..................................... $_____

D. Estimated Hedged Return to Labor, Management, and Profit per Head:
    (20) Line (9) + line (19).. $_____

and the Chicago futures price. As the worksheet shows, this difference can be affected by market location, grade, sex, weight, and dressing yield. If a feeder were located near a par delivery point, feeding choice steers that would weigh 1050-1150 lb with a carcass yield 61%, each of the indicated items of basis adjustment would be zero, for these characteristics meet par specifications of the CME futures contract. However, if the feeder operated near Greeley, Colo., or Lubbock, Texas, he would need to enter a locational differential. If he were feeding cattle of lower grade than choice, he would need to enter a grade differential, and so on for sex, and liveweight and dressing yield.

A question might be raised whether heifers can be hedged in a futures which specifies steers as the base commodity. Obviously, heifers cannot be delivered to satisfy the contract, but delivery is not anticipated. The steer futures could be used, and satisfactorily—providing cash heifer price movements generally parallel the futures price movements, even though they be at different absolute levels. The futures still could be used for hedging on a selective basis (even though cash and futures price movements are not parallel) if they move in a predictable pattern so a determination could be made as to when it is advantageous to hedge and when not to hedge.[10] Records show that slaughter steer and heifer prices for given grade and comparable weights do move in a generally parallel fashion. Deviations from parallel movements occur with variations in relative supplies, but such change occurs at a slow rate.

Worksheet Evaluation of a Cattle Feeding Hedge.—In Table 10.8, an example is shown of a completed cattle hedge work sheet. It is suggested that such an analysis be completed prior to purchasing feeder cattle. Every feeder should have a solid estimate of his cost of gain, including nonfeed costs. It is recognized that cost of gain varies with weather conditions, inherent gainability of cattle, etc., but many factors are controllable. Over a period of time, with the aid of a good set of records and efficient management, cost of gain can be estimated with an acceptable degree of accuracy. Without such an estimate the evaluation of a hedging potential is seriously handicapped.

In calculating basis adjustments, the first prerequisite is a familiarity with futures market contract specifications. Any deviation from those specifications gives rise to variations in the basis. Items listed in lines 13, 14, 15, and 16 of the worksheet (Tables 10.7 and 10.8) indicate the major factors, but not all will apply in every case. Information needed for basis adjustment usually is not available in published form. However, experienced producers and market personnel have satisfactory knowledge of the price effect of such factors.

---

[10]This is precisely what is involved in hedging steers on a local basis. For example, a feeder at Guymon, Okla., does not expect his local price level to equal that at Chicago, but if the Chicago futures is to work satisfactorily as a hedging mechanism, his local cash price movements must generally parallel futures prices or, if not parallel, then move in a predictable relationship.

TABLE 10.8

HYPOTHETICAL EXAMPLE: HEDGE WORKSHEET FOR CATTLE

Buy __700__ lb choice feeder __steers__ ; feed __130__ days; sell __1060__ lb choice slaughter cattle
      (grade)   (steers or   (grade)
                    heifers)

A. Estimated Costs:
    (1) Cost of feeder per head (__700__ lb @ $ 27.00)........................ $__189.00__
    (2) Cost of gain:
    (3) (a) Feed costs per head...................................... $__76.00__
    (4) (b) Nonfeed costs per head............................... $__17.00__
    (5) (c) Total cost of gain per head [line (3) + line (4)] .... $__93.00__
    (6) Marketing costs per head (in cash market)............................. $__4.00__
    (7) Hedging costs per head... $__1.20__
    (8) Total all costs per head [line (1) + line (5) + line (6) + line (7)]................. $__287.20__
    (9) Acceptable operators return per head for labor and management.............. $__15.00__
    (10) Break-even amount, total per head [line (8) + line (9)]............................. $__302.20__
    (11) Break-even price, per cwt [line (10) ÷ Sale wt] .... $__28.50__

B. Estimated Hedge Selling Price:
    (12) Current Chicago futures price, __April__ future, per cwt.......... $__30.25__
                              (month)
    (13) Basis—adj for market location differential per cwt. .... $__– 1.00__
    (14) Basis—adj for grade differential per cwt.................................... $__– 0.50__
    (15) Basis—adj for avg. livewt and dressing yield............................. $____–____
    (16) Basis—adj for heifer differential per cwt.................................. $____–____
    (17) Effective futures hedge price
         [line (12) ± line (13) ± line (14) ± line (15) – line (16)].......................... $__28.75__

C. Estimated Profit:
    (18) Est hedged profit per cwt [line (17) – line (11)] .... $__0.25__
    (19) Est hedged profit per head [line (18) X sales wt]..................................... $__2.65__

D. Estimated Hedged Return to Labor, Management, and Profit per Head:
    (20) Line (9) + line (19)... $__17.65__

In the example of Table 10.8, costs (line 8) are shown to be $287.20. Line 9 provides a space for entering an amount for operator's labor and management. As mentioned ealier, this is a matter for each operator to decide. Most operators hope to obtain some reimbursement for their labor and management. It makes little difference in some respects whether this is set out as a separate item or lumped in with profits. From a business standpoint, however, there is merit in setting an explicit goal for labor and management. In this example, $15.00 per head was entered as an acceptable return for labor and management (line 9). The total amount needed to return all costs ($287.20 plus $15.00 for labor and management), then, is $302.20 (line 10). This amounts to $28.50 per cwt (line 11), referred to as the break-even price. Note that break-even price is calculated from "sale weight." Steers handled in a feeding program as described in this example would have to be fed to a weight of around 1100 lb to realize a sale weight of 1060 lb. This is due to weight shrinkage in marketing—either actual or "pencil" shrink.

The entry in line 12 should be the futures price for the contract month in which the hedge would be placed. The current futures price assumes a hedge could be placed at about the most recently quoted price. This ordinarily would be the case unless the market were actively moving either up or down.

Lines 13, 14, 15, and 16 are for basis adjustments as previously described. In the example (Table 10.8), an adjustment of −$1.00 was indicated for location and −0.50 for grade differential. Nothing was entered in line 15 because the anticipated average weight and dressing yield were assumed to be equivalent to contract specifications. Line 16 does not apply in this case since the example deals with steers. The *effective* futures hedge price (line 17) is line 12 adjusted for basis factors. In this example it is $28.75. This immediately can be compared with the break-even price of $28.50 (line 11). When the effective futures hedge price equals or exceeds the calculated break-even price, a potentially favorable situation is indicated. In this case it is seen in line 19 that the estimated hedged profit is $2.65 per head, and in line 20 this $2.65 is added to line 9 (acceptable operator's return to labor and management) making a total return of $17.65 per head.

Again, this is not a guaranteed return. However, if expected cash-futures price relationships hold and if costs and bases have been accurately estimated, the estimate of line 20 will approximate feeding returns on a hedged operation.

Feeder cattle programs could be hedged in a manner similar to that described above by use of the feeder cattle futures. Feeder cattle growing operations, feedlot finishing, and feed procurement could be tied together in a virtually completely hedged operation by use of the respective futures.

Worksheet Evaluation of a Hog Feeding Hedge.—Table 10.9 illustrates a worksheet evaluation of hedging a hog feeding operation. The format used is similar to the previous example for cattle. In this case, however, the relationships among costs, bases, and futures prices are intentionally set up so the effective futures hedge price ($22.45 on line 16) is less than break-even price ($23.07 on line 11). This situation prevails even though nothing is entered for operator's labor and management (line 9).

In general, an evaluation which shows a negative return to labor, management, and profit (line 19) would be considered a nonhedging situation. Under hedged conditions, the operator would expect to take a loss. However, hedging still might be feasible if, for some reason, an operator (or his banker) preferred to take the indicated loss rather than assume risks of an even greater loss if the feeding operation were carried out unhedged.

The data used in Tables 10.8 and 10.9 are hypothetical. Each feeder should use cost and basis data pertinent to his individual situation.

Worksheet Analysis of Maximum Price to Pay for Feeder Cattle.—The futures market can be used to approximate the maximum price an operator can pay for feeder cattle. This applies to the situation where the operator

TABLE 10.9

HYPOTHETICAL EXAMPLE HEDGE WORKSHEET FOR HOGS

Buy __40__ lb __#2__ feeder __pig__ ; feed __120__ days; sell __220__ lb __#2__ slaughter hog
         (grade)   (grade)

A. Estimated Costs:
   (1) Cost of feeder per head (__40__ lb @ $__0.50__)........................... $____20.00
   (2) Cost of gain:
   (3) (a) Feed costs per head...................................... $____22.50
   (4) (b) Nonfeed costs per head................................ $_____7.50
   (5) (c) Total cost of gain per head [line (3) + line (4)] .... $____30.00
   (6) Marketing costs per head.. $_____0.50
   (7) Hedging costs per head.. $_____0.25
   (8) Total all costs per head [line (1) + line (5) + line (6) + line (7)]................. $____50.75
   (9) Acceptable operators return per head for labor and management.............. $____...
   (10) Break-even amount, total per head [line (8) + line (9)]........................... $____50.75
   (11) Break-even price, per cwt [line (10) ÷ Sale wt] .... $____23.07

B. Estimated Hedge Selling Price:
   (12) Current Chicago futures price, __June__ future, per cwt........... $____22.80
                       (month)
   (13) Basis−adj for market location differential per cwt. .... $____−0.35
   (14) Basis−adj for grade differential per cwt................................... $_____−
   (15) Basis−adj for weight differential per cwt................................. $_____−
   (16) Effective futures hedge price
      [line (12) ± line (13) ± line (14) ± line (15)] .... $____22.45

C. Estimated Profit:
   (17) Est hedged profit per cwt [line (16) − line (11)] .... $____−0.62
   (18) Est hedged profit per head [line (17) × sales wt]..................................... $____−1.36

D. Estimated Hedged Return to Labor, Management, and Profit per Head:
   (19) Line (9) + line (18).. $____−1.36

would follow through with a hedge on the feeding operation. Table 10.10 illustrates an approach to the calculations.

This analysis, like those preceding, necessitates a knowledge of costs and bases. A number of the same items estimated in Table 10.8 are identical for this analysis, but they are used in a different order. The approach used here takes the "effective futures hedge price" (line 6 in Table 10.10) as the estimated selling price of finished cattle, as would be the case if the cattle were hedged. This is in line with earlier discussion where it was shown that selling price can be established by a short hedge in the futures market, providing the appropriate basis is considered.

With selling price established, market value of finished steers would be the product of selling price and sale weight (see line 8, Table 10.10). By deducting all costs except the feeder steer itself (line 17) from market value (line 8) an estimate can be obtained of the maximum amount per head that could be paid for a feeder steer (see line 18). Division of this amount by the weight of a feeder steer gives maximum price per hundredweight (line 19).

The format of Table 10.10 also is readily adaptable for estimating the

TABLE 10.10

HYPOTHETICAL EXAMPLE: HEDGE WORKSHEET—MAXIMUM TO PAY
FOR 650-LB FEEDER STEERS

A. Estimated Hedge Selling Price:
    (1) Current Chicago futures price, <u> Oct. </u> futures, per cwt......... $<u> 29.70</u>
                    (month)
    (2) Basis—adj for market location differential per cwt................... $<u> − 1.50</u>
    (3) Basis—adj for grade differential per cwt................................... $<u> − 0.75</u>
    (4) Basis—adj for avg livewt and dressing yield............................. $<u> . . .</u>
    (5) Basis—adj for heifer differential per cwt.................................. $<u> . . .</u>
    (6) Effective futures hedge price
        [line (1) ± line (2) ± line (3) ± line (4) − line (5)].................. $<u> 27.45</u>

B. Estimated Sale Weight per Head:
    (7) From production records.................(<u> 1060 </u>) lbs

C. Estimated Market Value Finished Cattle, per Head:
    (8) [line (6) × line (7)]... $<u> 290.97</u>

D. Estimated Costs (Exclusive of Feeder Animal):
    (9) Cost of gain:
    (10)   (a) Feed costs per head...................................... $<u> 76.00</u>
    (11)   (b) Nonfeed costs per head................................ $<u> 17.00</u>
    (12)   (c) Total cost of gain per head [line (10) + line (11)] .... $<u> 93.00</u>
    (13) Marketing costs per head.. $<u>   4.00</u>
    (14) Hedging costs per head... $<u>   1.20</u>
    (15) Total costs per head [line (12) + line (13) + line (14)].............. $<u> 98.20</u>
    (16) Acceptable operators return per head for
         labor and management .... $<u> 10.00</u>
    (17) Total of [line (15) + line (16)].. $<u> 108.20</u>

E. Estimated Maximum Amount for Feeders:
    (18) Est amount per head [line (8) − line (17)] .... $<u> 182.77</u>
    (19) Est price per cwt [line (18) ÷ 6.50] [1] .... $<u> 28.12</u>

[1] In general form this term is [line (18) ÷ wt of feeder in hundredweights].

maximum amount a hog feeder could pay for feeder pigs, providing the futures market is used for a short hedge.

It should be noted at this point that the above use of this worksheet is not equivalent to accepting the futures quotation as a forecast of prices. However, by making a sale (a short hedge) in the futures market, an operator can "lock-in" that price—with qualifications as noted earlier regarding possible variation in the basis.

Some Research Findings on Cattle Hedging

A critical question in evaluating the feasibility of hedging is, what effect does it have upon (1) the level of profits and (2) the stability of profits? Other things being equal, most operators would prefer higher profits, but some may prefer more stable profits at somewhat lower average levels to higher average profits if the latter also are highly variable.

McCoy and Johnson (1970) studied the effects of hedging on cattle feeding profits in a simulated feeding program in which profits were calculated for the period Dec. 5, 1964 to Dec. 20, 1969.[11] The beginning date was near inauguration of futures trading in live cattle at the Chicago Mercantile Exchange.

Conditions set up in this study were comparable to continuous operations of a commercial cattle feeding enterprise. It was assumed that feeder steers were purchased every week, fed 17 weeks, then sold as finished steers. In the approximately 5-yr period, the analysis simulated the feeding of 247 separate lots of cattle. Although feeding operations were assumed to start Dec. 5, 1964, the first lot of finished cattle would be marketed in 1965. Profits were dated as of the sale date of each lot of cattle. Throughout the study, calculations were made on a per head basis. Prices of feeder cattle, finished cattle, the futures, feed ingredients, and other items of expense were obtained week by week from published quotations and other sources. These data provided the information needed to generate profits. Four different hedging programs were analyzed: (1) routinely hedging every lot, (2) no hedging, (3) hedging only when the relevant futures quoted price at the beginning of a feeding period was above the break-even price (to be referred to as the "futures-breakeven" method), and (4) hedging only when the relevant futures quoted price at the beginning of a feeding period was above the current cash market price (to be referred to as the "futures-cash" method).

Routine Hedging Versus No Hedging.—The effects on profits of routinely hedging every lot, compared to no hedging, can be seen in Fig. 10.3. A statistical summary is presented in Table 10.11.

It is doubtful that anyone has ever seriously recommended a program of routinely hedging every lot of cattle regardless of feeding costs and cash-futures price relationships. Nevertheless, this is an alternative and was included to round out the study. It is apparent in Fig. 10.3 that routine hedging tended to stabilize profits. Profits from hedged operations were not as high on the positive side nor as low on the negative side when unhedged profits gyrated to the extremes. Profits from hedged operations were relatively stable—except for the pronounced advance in mid-1966 and the rather pronounced swings both up and down during 1969.

It can be seen from Fig. 10.3 that hedging would not automatically convert all losses to profits, though this was indicated on a number of lots from mid-1966 through 1967. It also is apparent that hedging could cause losses in what otherwise would be profits under unhedged operations. This is especially noticeable during the period of 1968 to mid-1969.

While routine hedging would have tended to stablize profits during the period studied, it would have accomplished this at a lower absolute level (and, in fact, at a negative level) than profits from unhedged operations. Table 10.11 shows profits of $-0.49 (a loss) under the routinely hedged program

---

[11]This section is adapted from McCoy and Johnson (1970) and Johnson (1970).

FIG. 10.3. A COMPARISON OF PROFITS PER STEER BETWEEN HEDGED AND UNHEDGED FEEDING OPERATIONS, 247 SIMU-LATED LOTS

Johnson (1970)

TABLE 10.11

SUMMARY OF PROFITS, ROUTINELY HEDGED VERSUS UNHEDGED,
247 LOTS OF CATTLE, 1965—1969

Type of Operation	Average Profit per Head ($)	Range in Profits per Head ($)	Variance of Profits ($)	Financial Outcome by Number of Lots		
				Profit	Loss	Total
Routinely hedged	−0.49	−39.76 @ 41.77	182.95	108	139	247
Unhedged	7.29	−47.95 @ 83.28	555.75	158	89	247

Source: Johnson (1970).

and $7.29 per head under an unhedged program. A lower variance in profits under routine hedging confirms the earlier graphic analysis of greater stability under hedged conditions. It also is noted in Table 10.11 that the number of lots which returned negative profits under routine hedging was 139 compared to 89 unhedged.

Data in Table 10.12 show the effect of hedging upon the 158 lots which returned a profit when unhedged and upon the 89 lots which returned a loss when unhedged. Of the 89 lots which showed an unhedged loss, routine hedging would have improved the profit position of 70 lots or about 80%. In 39 of these, losses would have been converted into profits, and in 31 the loss would have been reduced. However, in 19 cases hedging would have increased losses.

On an unhedged program, 158 lots would have returned profits (Table 10.12). If all these lots had been routinely hedged, profits would have been improved in 14 lots, but the profit situation would have been worsened in the remaining 144 lots. Clearly, the prospects are rather remote that hedging would improve profits in feeding operations which would return positive profits under unhedged conditions. At the same time, it is clear that profits could be improved if a selective hedging program could be developed whereby hedges were executed on those lots which would return losses if unhedged.

This study did not develop criteria for identifying probable loss situations but it did test two hypothesized sets of criteria for selective hedging: (1) the futures-breakeven method, and (2) the futures-cash method.

Selective Hedging—Futures-Breakeven Method.—The futures-breakeven method was based on criteria which specified that a given lot of cattle would be hedged only when the calculated break-even price was equal to or greater than the relevant futures price in which the hedge would be placed. Among the 247 simulated lots, 95 were identified which met the above criteria. Therefore, an analysis was run in which these 95 were considered to be hedged, and the remainder carried unhedged. Average profits under this method of selective hedging at $7.14 per head were virtually unchanged from the $7.29

TABLE 10.12
THE EFFECT OF SIMULATED ROUTINE HEDGING UPON THE
FINANCIAL OUTCOME (PROFIT AND LOSS) OF UNHEDGED
OPERATIONS, 1965—1969

Unhedged		Routinely Hedged		
Financial Outcome	Number of Lots	Effect of Hedging	Number of Lots	
Profit	158	Profits increased	14[1]	
		Profits reduced	55[2]	
		Profits turned into a loss	89[2]	
		Subtotal		158
Loss	89	Losses turned into a profit	39[1]	
		Losses reduced	31[1]	
		Losses increased	19[2]	
		Subtotal		89
Total	247	Total		247

Source: Johnson (1970).
[1] Hedging *increased* returns relative to not hedging.
[2] Hedging *decreased* returns relative to not hedging.

under routine hedging (Table 10.13). Stability of profits, however, would have been improved over unhedged operations as evidenced by a lower variance.

Selective Hedging—Futures-Cash Method.—Under this method a hedge would be executed only when the relevant futures price, at the beginning of a feeding period, was above the current cash market price at that time.[12] During much of the period studied futures prices were below cash prices. There were 86 lots which met the above criteria. A simulation run was made in which these 86 lots were considered hedged and the remainder considered to be fed out unhedged. Results are shown in Table 10.13. This method resulted in substantially improved average profits ($9.63 per head). Variations in profits were slightly higher than under the breakeven method, but less than unhedged.

This study throws considerable light on hedging, although much additional work remains to be done. The period studied contained some ups and downs in the cash cattle market, but the prevailing trend was upward. Therefore, it is not surprising that routine hedging showed lower average profits than no hedging at all. In a period of rising prices hedging would tend to nullify windfall gains. While it is logical that routine hedging would not improve profits relative to unhedged operations under these conditions, the extent of the difference between routinely hedged and unhedged profits is not clear. This aspect needs further investigation. Additional work also is needed to identify those cases of potential feeding loss.

[12] Theoretical reasoning for these criteria are given in Johnson (1970).

TABLE 10.13

PROFITS, VARIANCE AND NUMBER OF LOTS RETURNING NEGATIVE PROFITS, 4 ALTERNATIVE
HEDGING PROGRAMS, 247 LOTS OF CATTLE, 1965—1969

| Hedging Criteria | No. of Lots | | Avg Profit per Head All 247 Lots ($) | Variance of Profits ($) | No. of Lots Returning Negative Profits |
	Hedged	Unhedged			
Routinely hedged	247	0	−0.49	182.95	139
Unhedged	0	247	7.29	555.75	89
Futures—Breakeven method[1]	95	152	7.14	359.91	63
Futures—Cash method[1]	86	161	9.63	434.21	66

Source: Johnson (1970).
[1] Lots were assumed to be produced unhedged if the criteria for hedging were not met.

Do Futures Market Prices Forecast Cash Prices?

It might be argued that traders base their evaluation of futures prices on expected supply-demand conditions and that the price level at any given time represents a consensus of expected prices in the future. Tomek and Gray (1970) state that " ... prices of futures 6 months from maturity, 1 month from maturity, and cash prices are all 'forecasts' or 'nonforecasts' in approximately the same degree ...

"Of course, unforeseen developments occur between futures expiration dates. The new but unpredictable information may indeed change expectations, but this is reflected in the entire constellation of prices. This in no sense implies that the expired future was incorrectly priced before its expiration, nor therefore that the pre-existing price relationship was in error. The range of prices at a point in time is based on the information then available, but new events and information may make the forecast of the previous period incorrect."

If futures prices did not move, there would be little incentive for either speculation or hedging. It is apparent that traders take a position because they believe the price will move. Therefore, it could be said that at any given time the futures price represents a level that neither the long nor the short trader believes is the one that will materialize as the actual price in the future. Regardless of whether one accepts the theory that futures prices represent traders' best estimate of what prices actually will be at a future date, or the opposite—that it represents their judgment of what it will not be—the record clearly shows it has not been an accurate forecaster of prices. This, however, does not negate its usefulness as a hedging mechanism. As long as a market attracts sufficient speculation to absorb hedges without undue price reaction, it can perform the hedging function, which in actuality is a price-setting function. Price forecasting is a responsibility of the personnel who trade on the futures market, and not vice versa.

Does Futures Trading Stabilize Livestock Prices?

While hedging in livestock has been relatively light since initiation of livestock futures, observation of the record would immediately prompt the conclusion that livestock prices have not been stabilized. Price changes are a reflection of changes in supply and demand. If it could be shown that the futures market tends to stabilize supply or demand (or both) then a basis would exist for suggesting that futures trading would tend to stabilize prices. However, there is nothing inherent in the market that would tend to stabilize demand. Factors which affect demand were discussed in Chap. 3, and are beyond the scope of the futures market.

If futures prices were relatively stable and if producers in large volume used the market as a price-setting mechanism (by hedging) then the futures market would impart a degree of stability in prices. Tomek and Gray (1970) state that "for commodities such as potatoes, which lack continuous inventories, prices of distant futures are less variable than cash prices and hence producer-hedging in such markets tends to stabilize revenue." This property is yet to be shown for livestock futures. Livestock futures might continue to exist with somewhat less fluctuation than at present. However, if a futures market became highly stable it probably would disappear. Without price movement there would be no incentive for either speculation or hedging.

While the futures may not be expected to stabilize prices, hedging can contribute to stability of profits. As reported earlier, the McCoy-Johnson study (1970) indicated a reduction in variability of profits under each of the three hedging programs tested as compared to unhedged operations.

Hedging and Livestock Credit

Large-scale feeding operations require large-scale financing. Summers (1967) commented that "not long ago, most cattle loans were to farmers who had feed in their cribs and who seldom asked to borrow more than 20% of their net worth for the purchase of feeders. Today, cattle feeders are more likely to have a modern feedlot, and may have part of the facilities paid for but have a small net worth in relation to the requested loan, yet they ask us to furnish money for the cattle and the feed as well." Grain merchandisers and storage interests long have found bankers more prone to grant credit on hedged than unhedged commodities. With the inauguration of live cattle futures it was anticipated that cattle feeders who hedged would be in better position to obtain credit than formerly. Theoretical considerations link credit availability to the degree of risk, and since hedging is presumed to lessen price risk, it follows that credit would be more readily available to a hedged operator.

Little work has been done to test this hypothesis. In a 1965 survey, Waldner (1965) reported that of the banks he contacted regarding loan policy on hedged cattle, "... no bank had a defined loan policy nor was any bank prepared to alter its customary loan policy to accommodate 'hedged' cattle." This was relatively soon after initiation of futures contracts in live cattle. In a 1968 study of South Dakota lending agencies, Powers (1968) found that hedging and forward contracting (referred to in this text as cash contracting) had little influence on the ability of a producer to obtain a loan. However, if a producer qualified for a loan otherwise, hedging permitted an increase in the size of the loan. He found, also, that hedging had no effect on interest rates. Powers' study is summarized as follows: "The data ... indicate that the average increases in loans on hedged livestock ranged from 12.2 to 17.5% of the value of assets. On contracted livestock the average increases ranged from 11.9 to 18.3%. All of these increases are significantly greater than zero, thus indicating that hedging and forward contracting of livestock assets do aid

armers in obtaining capital by increasing the amount loaned on given
ivestock assets." With respect to interest rate, Powers commented, " ... not a
ingle agency which had made loans on hedged and contracted collateral
educed the interest rates on such loans . . .

"There are probably three major reasons for these results. First, some of the
enders probably believe that hedging and forward contracting do not reduce
their risk . . . Second, a number of the respondents indicated that they based
the interest rate on their cost of money, not on the different amounts of risk
presented by farmers or firms. Third, it is quite likely that the risk reduction
has been fully accounted for by the increase in the size of the loan."

BIBLIOGRAPHY

BAILEY, F., Jr. 1968. The cattle feeder and the futures market. Banking Jan., 57-59.
BAKKEN, H. H. (Editor). 1970. Futures Trading in Livestock—Origins and Concepts.
   Mimir Publishers, Madison, Wisc.
BLAU, G. 1944-1945. Some aspects of the theory of futures trading. Rev. Econ. Studies
   12, 7.
EHRICH, R. L. 1967. Futures trading, direct marketing and efficiency of the cattle
   marketing system. Wyoming Agr. Expt. Sta. Res. Bull. *9*.
EHRICH, R. L. 1969. Cash-futures price relationships for live beef cattle. Am. J. Agr.
   Econ. Febr., 26-40.
FENWICK, R., Jr. 1966. Futures trading in live animals. N. Dakota Coop. Agr. Ext. Serv.
   Circ. *A-502*.
FRAHM, D. G., and SCHRADER, L. F. 1970. An experimental comparison of pricing in
   two auction systems. Am. J. Agr. Econ. *52*, No. 4, 528-534.
FUTRELL, G. A., and SKADBERG, J. M. 1966. The futures market in live beef cattle.
   Iowa Coop. Agr. Ext. Serv. Circ. *M-1021*.
GRAY, R. W. 1961. The search for a risk premium. J. Political Econ. *LXIX*, No. 3,
   250-260.
JOHNSON, D. A. 1970. The use of live steer futures contracts and their effect on cattle
   feeding profits. M.S. Thesis, Kansas State Univ.
KAUFFMAN, R. R. 1956. Recent developments in futures trading under Commodity
   Exchange Act. USDA Commodity Exchange Authority, Agr. Inform. Bull. *155*.
MCCOY, J. H., and JOHNSON, D. A. 1970. Effects of hedging on cattle feeding profits.
   Dept. Econ. Kansas State Univ. Unpublished Data.
MCKINNON, R. I. 1967. Futures markets, buffer stocks and income stability for primary
   producers. J. Political Econ. Dec., 844-861.
PAUL, A. B., and WESSON, W. T. 1967. Pricing feedlot services through cattle futures.
   USDA Agr. Econ. Res. *29*, No. 2, 33-45.
POWERS, M. 1968. Hedging forward contracting and agricultural credit. S. Dakota Agr.
   Expt. Sta. Bull. *545*.
POWERS, M., and JOHNSON, A. C. 1968. The frozen pork belly futures market: An
   analysis of contract specifications and contract viability. Dept. Agr. Econ., Univ.
   Wisconsin Agr. Econ. Bull. *51*.
SCHNEIDAU, R. E. 1967. Hedging on the live hog futures market. Indiana Coop. Agr.
   Ext. Serv. Circ. *EC-312*.
SUMMERS, M. M. 1967. Hedging and how it helps reduce loan risk. Agr. Banking
   Finance May/June 32.
TOMEK, W. G., and GRAY, R. W., 1970. Temporal relationships among prices on
   commodity futures markets: Their allocative and stabilizing roles. Am. J. Agr. Econ.
   52, No. 3, 372-380.

WALDNER, S. C. 1965. Will hedging offer financing advantages? Feedlot Sept. 54.

WIRAK, O. 1970. Hedging feeder cattle in Washington. Wash. Coop. Agr. Ext. Serv. Bull. *601*.

WORKING, H. 1960. Speculation on hedging markets. Food Res. Inst. Studies *1*, No. 2, 185-220.

WORKING, H. 1962. New concepts concerning futures markets and prices. Am. Econ. Review *LII*, No. 3, 434-436.

WORKING, H. 1963. Futures markets under renewed attack. Food Res. Inst. Studies *4*, No. 1, 13-24.

CHAPTER 11

Grades and Grading

Producers, slaughterers, processors and distributors are cognizant of live animal and meat grades. Market news reports utilize federal grade nomenclature in reporting prices, and within the meat trade. both federal and private (brands) grades are used in wholesale transactions. Consumers are exposed to federal grades—though most know little about them (Hutchinson 1970)—and private brands through advertising media and in grocery store shopping. In short, grades and grading are an integral part of livestock and meat marketing.

This chapter is concerned primarily with federal government grades, but private brands which are based on consistent quality specifications are tantamount to private grades.

There is evidence that some consumers confuse inspection with grading (Hutchinson 1970). This point should be clearly understood. Both the USDA inspection mark and USDA grade mark are applied in purple color on meat, but that is the only similarity. Inspection is concerned with the wholesomeness of meat and meat products—such things as diseased animals, sanitation in slaughtering and processing plants, prevention of adulteration, correct labelling, etc. This is a separate and distinct activity from grading. The inspection mark stamped on a carcass is a circle, and if the carcass passed inspection the circle contains the abbreviations "U.S. INSP'D & P'S'D." The grade mark is a shield in which is inscribed the abbreviation USDA and also the grade name or number as the case may be. When viewed side by side the difference is obvious as here shown.

GRADE MARKS

INSPECTION MARK

← Yield grade

← Quality grade

DEFINITION AND PURPOSE

Grading is the segregation of units of a commodity into lots, or groupings which have a relatively high degree of uniformity in certain specified attributes associated with market preferences and valuation.

The relevant attributes differ widely among commodities in number, in range of variability, and in susceptibility to objective measurement. Eight grades are used to cover the range in quality of steer and heifer carcasses, but only three for ready-to-cook poultry. In addition to quality grades, five separate yield, or cutability, grades (i.e., yield of boneless, closely trimmed retail cuts) are used in conjunction with quality grades in beef and lamb. Pork grades incorporate yield and quality considerations without separate quality and yield designations. Poultry grades are based entirely on quality.

Quality grades in beef are determined basically on subjective considerations. "The quality grade of beef carcasses is based on separate evaluations of two general considerations: (1) The quality or the palatability-indicating characteristics of the lean, and (2) the conformation of the carcass" (USDA 1965A). Cutability or yield grades for beef are determined primarily by objective measurements. Pork carcass grades rely heavily on objective measurements to determine expected combined yield of lean cuts, used in conjunction with a subjective determination of "acceptable" or "unacceptable" quality of the lean.

Thus, it can be seen that even though the definition of grading is relatively straightforward, the drawing up of standards or specifications for a system of grades is a complex problem. Some of the attributes upon which grades are based can be evaluated directly, others indirectly, through so-called indicators. For example, the yield of lean cuts of pork is related to (indicated by) backfat thickness, carcass weight, and carcass length. A great amount of research and consultation is involved in developing grade standards.

The purpose of grading is related to whether the grading is a private or public function. Grading is not the sole prerogative of government. Most national packers and many regional packers have private grades and grade standards. The federal government has inaugurated an extensive system of live animal and meat grades.

The objectives of a firm in setting up private grades are only partially compatible with objectives of a public grading system. One primary concern of a private firm is a grading system which adequately describes the quality of the product so that trade can be conducted with a minimum of time, effort, and expense. Grade designations which consistently and fully describe a product do away with the necessity of personal inspection by buyers. Transactions can be made by telephone which lessens the expense of both buyers and sellers. In this respect, private and public grading have a common purpose. Private firms also use grades to differentiate their products from

1ose of competitors. To the extent the products are different, this is an 1formational service which assists buyers and, if the difference commands a igher market price, this is a matter of buyer discretion. On the other hand, if 1e differentiation is spurious, buyers may be misled and the result may be 1dividual and social loss.

From the standpoint of public interest, a profusion of grades and grade :andards is confusing. Without some official supervision of the application of 1ecified standards, doubts and suspicions sometimes arise as to whether roducts meet the standards. The general public also has an interest in the ffect grades have on the efficiency with which the market system allocates :sources among alternative production possibilities.

Producers' interests are associated with the degree to which use of grades ssists them in obtaining equitable prices. Consumers primarily are interested 1 obtaining products commensurate with their preferences and in the prices 1ey pay.

In view of the multiplicity of considerations, it was deemed to be in the ublic interest to inaugurate a system of federal grades and grading. At the ime time individual firms have the privilege of using private (or house) ·ades, either alone or in combination with U.S. grades.

The principal purposes of government grades can be placed under the neral headings of improving (1) pricing efficiency and (2) operational ·ficiency.

;rades and Pricing Efficiency

As indicated in Chap. 1, pricing efficiency is concerned with such things as he accuracy, effectiveness, and speed with which a price system measures roduct values to buyers and reflects these values back through marketing hannels to producers. Involved in this concept are issues of efficiency in llocation of resources among alternative uses, and distribution of income mong producers and others involved in various economic activities of an 1dustry. The uniform application of an appropriate set of grades can ontribute to pricing efficiency. If consumers indicate a willingness and ability o pay more (or less) for a certain quality of meat, that information must be ·ansmitted back to producers before they can react. A market economy epends upon price differentials to relay the message, and grades provide a 1eaningful, common language whereby the price differential can be associated ·ith the desired (or undesired) quality characteristic.[1] It is recognized that, at given time, price differentials among quality levels of a particular product an arise due to variations in relative supplies as well as to variations in emand. Over a period of time, however, the pricing system is presumed to

---

[1] Grades which transmit quality differentials to consumers would enhance total utility en though no price differentials existed.

allocate resources in such a way as to optimize supplies of various qualities of the product. This is implied in pricing efficiency.

The use of grades also has a place in improving efficiency in distribution of products of varying quality among alternative uses. Differential pricing among grades enables wholesalers and retailers to move given supplies into their highest order use at rates which clear the market. Thus Canner and Cutter grades are diverted into processed meats. Prime grade steaks and roasts go to the highest class night club, hotel, restaurant, and steamship trade. Choice and Good grades form the primary retail cuts. As a result, total revenue from the entire supply of meat is enhanced; and increased competition tends to distribute the benefits among all sectors of the livestock and meat industry.

The use of grades can increase the degree of competition in a market by increasing the level of knowledge. Buyers and sellers in a perfectly competitive market are assumed to possess perfect knowledge of market conditions. Grades cannot be expected to impart perfect knowledge, but their use can "enhance" the knowledge of traders. This applies not only to quality aspects but also to yield (cutability) characteristics of meat animal carcasses. The difference in retail sales value between adjacent yield grades, though it varies with relative supply and demand, can easily amount to $3.60 per cwt of choice carcass beef (USDA 1968C). Therefore, a knowledge of yield grades and associated value differentials can strengthen competition between wholesalers and retailers. Uniformity in application of grades which adequately describe a product allows trade by description (as contrasted to inspection) via telephone or wire service. This enhances competition as wholesalers and retailers can shop over wide areas. The use of uniform federal grades permits small packers to compete with large packers in terms of quality of product-if not in volume. This increases the degree of competition and pricing efficiency in the industry.

Grades and Operational Efficiency

Operational efficiency is concerned with costs of performing marketing functions. The concern is not necessarily with reduction in total marketing costs but with reduction in per unit marketing costs. This may be accomplished by marketing a given quantity of goods at lower total costs, an increased quantity at the same total cost, or an increased quantity at a less than proportionate increase in total cost.

In some respects, grading can improve operational efficiency, while in others it may have the opposite effect. Grades permit trading by description, which can result in a reduction in transaction expenses (travel, labor, and associated expense) for both buyer and seller, compared to trading by inspection. Generally, it is assumed this means a reduction in total marketing expense, which probably is correct; however, the statement must be qualified. Grading does not come free. Total marketing costs will be reduced providing the reduction in transactions costs are not exceeded by costs of grading, additional telephone expenses, costs associated with possible misunderstanding, and rejection of shipments which do not meet grade specifications.

Government grading of fresh beef and lamb largely has forestalled the use of private grade advertising of these products. As a result, the total advertising bill undoubtedly is less than it would be otherwise. This reduction in marketing cost can be construed to be a gain in operational efficiency.[2]

Federal grading also has had an impact on decentralization and specialization in the packing and processing industries. Use of federal grades has permitted small packers to compete well with large operations, and smaller independent packers led the way in decentralization. The opening of plants near livestock production centers contributes to cost reduction in a number of ways. Under the prevailing freight rate structure, transportation costs are less for dressed meat than for live animals. Often, operating costs are less at interior points than at terminal locations due to lower wage rates, taxes, utility rates, etc.

Specialization also is enhanced as grading permits more accurate description and identification of products. Specialization in products is complemented by specialization in labor, equipment, plant layout, and work techniques which, in turn, contribute to cost reduction and operational efficiency.

DEVELOPMENT OF LIVESTOCK AND MEAT GRADES

During earlier periods a variety of market terms evolved in particular localities which were more or less descriptive of certain quality characteristics of livestock. Associated with expansion of the large terminal markets of that era was the private publication of market prices using local class and quality terminology. This, of course, was a significant advancement over no published quotations at all; and the reports were useful to livestock interests. However, weaknesses were apparent. There was a lack of uniformity in terminology and standards among markets. A price quotation on "native cattle," for example, has limited meaning when the specifications for "native cattle" vary from one market to the next, or when some markets do not have a classification of "native cattle."

In many cases an accepted term was not used uniformly from person to person, or throughout the year at a given market. These conditions are symptomatic of growing pains in any developing economy. Trade is handicapped to the extent that buyers must physically inspect all lots of animals. Market price quotations cannot serve their full potential of usefulness.

The handicaps of this situation were apparent for many years and some

[2] This is not to be construed as an indictment of all advertising, but brand name advertising designed to alter consumers' preferences to match the characteristics of a product or to develop ficticious differences among products can result in social costs from misallocation of resources (see Farris 1960).

pioneering efforts were made to develop uniform grades and standards. The Agricultural Experiment Station of Illinois was a leader in this area. Between the years 1901 and 1908, a series of investigations were made of actual conditions and ways and means of alleviating the situation. Five Illinois bulletins were issued with following titles: "The Market Classes of Horses," 1901; "Market Classes and Grades of Cattle, with Suggestions for Interpreting Market Quotations," 1902; "Market Classes and Grades of Swine," 1904; "Market Classes and Grades of Horses and Mules," 1908; and "Market Classes and Grades of Sheep," 1908. These studies did not precipitate immediate governmental action, but soon a movement developed for official market news reporting. The ensuing debates over implementation of market reporting could not be separated from consideration of official grades, because the lack of uniformity in local grade names and laxity in local grade specifications rendered them unsatisfactory for market reporting purposes. In response to this need (and for other reasons) the USDA established an Office of Markets in 1913.[3] This office began work in the development of official grades for live animals and meat about 1915 (Dowell and Bjorka 1941). The work done at Illinois provided a starting point, but vested interests in local grades and lack of agreement on grade standards were serious obstacles in obtaining a consensus on uniform grades. Nevertheless, unofficial and unpublished grade specifications were drawn up and used for market reporting of meat prices beginning in 1916.

Derivation of an acceptable and adequate set of grade standards requires an enormous effort. Information must be obtained from all interested parties to determine attributes which impart value to the product. There are differences of opinion on this point among producers, packers, processors, wholesalers, retailers, and consumers. Even when a consensus can be obtained, problems arise in selecting indicators by which the attributes can be measured in live animals and meat. This is especially difficult where only subjective measures are usable. The USDA held many conferences and hearings with all interested parties, including agricultural college personnel. Research was conducted and encouraged at colleges, and a considerable amount of experimentation was carried out using unofficial and tentative standards before grades were officially promulgated. And this work does not stop with establishment of official grade names and standards. Over a period of time, changes occur in quality of the product produced, in consumer preferences, in trade practices, etc. Continuous change requires continuous review of grade standards and revision or amendment as the occasion demands. Figure 11.1 shows the steps and precautionary measures involved in setting up standards.

The application of uniform grades requires some prior classification and

[3] Over the years the federal grading service has been under a succession of different offices resulting from renaming, merging, and reorganizing. Currently, grading is under the Livestock Division, Consumer and Marketing Service, USDA.

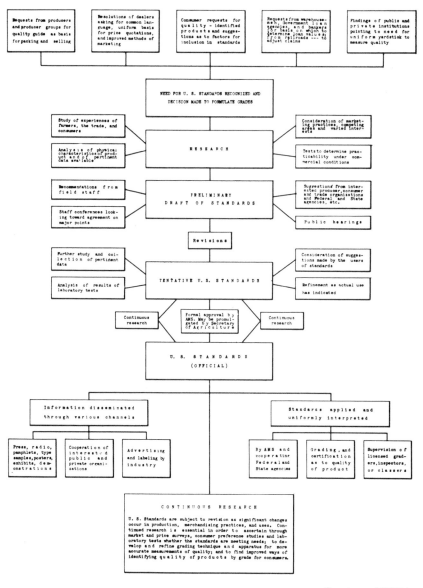

Courtesy of USDA

FIG. 11.1. STEPS IN SETTING UP QUALITY STANDARDS FOR FARM PRODUCTS

subclassification of livestock. An obvious first classification is by specie—cattle, hogs, and sheep. Beyond that, for official grading purposes, livestock are segregated according to use, i.e., slaughter and feeder. Within use categories a further breakdown, referred to officially as *class*, is made on the basis of sex condition, then grades are applied to classes.

Designated classes[4] of the various specie and use categories of livestock are: (A) Slaughter cattle—steers, heifers, cows, bulls, and stags. (B) Feeder cattle—same as slaughter cattle (except bulls and stags are not graded). (C) Slaughter swine—barrows, gilts, sows, boars, and stags (boars and stags are not graded). (D) Feeder pigs—same as slaughter swine (except sows, boars and stags are not graded). (E) Slaughter lambs, yearlings, and sheep—ram, ewe, and wether (these class names are used in conjunction with age groupings, i.e., lambs, yearlings, and sheep). (F) Feeder lambs, yearlings, and sheep—ewe and wether (in the case of feeder sheep, only the ewe class applies).

The first grades to be formulated were for dressed beef in 1916. "They provided the basis for uniformly reporting the dressed beef markets according to grades, which work was inaugurated as a national service early in 1917" (USDA 1965A). These beef grades were used in unofficial, tentative status until 1926, but in the meantime a number of revisions were made as experience and usage dictated. Their use also spread beyond market reporting. "The tentative standards, although designed primarily for meat market reporting purposes, were put to further practical test in numerous ways. During World War I they were used in the selection of beef for the Army, Navy, and Allies. Later they were included in the specifications of the Emergency Fleet Corporation for the purchase of its beef supplies. Soon thereafter they were incorporated in the specifications of many commercial concerns, including steamship lines, restaurants, hotels, dining car services, and hospitals" (USDA 1965A).

Official grades were promulgated for carcass beef on June 3, 1926. The use of federal grades has been on a voluntary basis from the beginning, except during World War II and the Korean Conflict when it was mandatory for all FI plants handling beef, veal, calf, and lamb. The voluntary stamping of graded beef was made available in 1927.[5] For a brief period at the beginning, grading costs were paid by the federal government, but since then costs are paid by the parties who request the service.

Six changes (amendments or revisions) have been made in the official beef grades—1939, 1941, 1949, 1950, 1956 and 1965 (see Table 11.1). The 1965 revision not only changed quality standards, but standards for "cutability" were added. Cutability is the consideration of percentage of trimmed, boneless, major retail cuts which can be derived from a carcass. Cutability has been recognized as an important value-determining characteristic for a number of years, and standards for cutability had been proposed and tested in a 1-yr

---

[4] Some classes are designated and defined, but are not graded.

[5] For a comprehensive analysis of issues involved in early days of grade development and marking of beef see Rhodes (1960). Some opposing views are presented by Williams (1960).

TABLE 11.1
CHANGES IN USDA GRADES FOR SLAUGHTER CATTLE[1]

Tentative				Official		
1918	1925	1928	1939	1950	1956	1966[2]
Adopted for market reporting	Published	Prime	Prime	Prime[3]	Prime[3]	Prime[3]
		Choice	Choice			
		Good	Good	Choice	Choice	Choice
		Medium	Medium	Good	Good	Good
				Commercial	Standard	Standard
					Commercial	Commercial
		Common	Common	Utility	Utility	Utility
		Cutter	Cutter	Cutter	Cutter	Cutter
		Low Cutter	Canner	Canner	Canner	Canner

Source: USDA (1966B).
[1] Area of spaces occupied by grade names is not intended to be proportional to the relative importance of grades.
[2] Reduced marbling requirements in quality grades and added five yield grades (No. 1, 2, 3, 4, and 5) to identify differences in cutability.
[3] Only steers and heifers eligible for Prime grade.

trial period beginning July 1, 1962. With some modifications it was made official in 1965.

The development of other dressed meat grades (veal and calf carcasses; pork carcasses; and lamb, yearling mutton, and mutton carcasses) as well as grades for live slaughter and feeder animals followed a comparable course of formulation, tentative adoption, official promulgation, and subsequent amendment. Comments here are limited to a few major changes. Details may be found elsewhere.[6]

During the period of tentative feeder cattle grades, the grouping was referred to as "Feeder and Stocker Cattle." Although "stocker" is a commonly used term in the cattle trade, it is no longer used in official grade standards. The term "feeder" is intended to include those formerly classed as stockers and feeders. Table 11.2 illustrates changes in feeder cattle grade names which now correspond to slaughter cattle except for the bottom two grades. Grade terminology and changes for vealers and slaughter calves are shown in Table 11.3.

Several major changes have been made in slaughter barrow and gilt grades. In 1952 the former tentative Choice (meat type) was divided into two grades and renamed Choice No. 1 and Choice No. 2; the former Choice (fat type) was renamed Choice No. 3 (Table 11.4). These changes represented a

[6] Details of grade specifications and changes are published in USDA Service and Regulatory Announcements which are issued with each amendment and revision.

TABLE 11.2
CHANGES IN USDA GRADES FOR
FEEDER CATTLE[1]

1925	1934	Tentative 1938	1942	Official 1964
		Fancy	Fancy	Prime[2]
		Choice	Choice	Choice
		Good	Good	Good
		Medium	Medium	Standard
				Commercial
		Plain	Common	Utility
		Inferior	Inferior	Inferior

Source: USDA (1965B).
[1] Area of spaces occupied by grade names is not intended to be proportional to the relative importance of grades.
[2] Only steers and heifers are eligible for Prime grade.

TABLE 11.3
CHANGES IN USDA GRADES FOR VEALERS
AND SLAUGHTER CALVES[1]

Tentative 1926	1928	Official 1951	1956
	Prime	Prime	Prime
	Choice		
	Good	Choice	Choice
	Medium	Good	Good
		Commercial	Standard
	Common	Utility	Utility
	Cull	Cull	Cull

Source: USDA (1957).
[1] Area of spaces occupied by grade names is not intended to be proportional to the relative importance of grades.

significant recognition of preference for leaner, meat-type pork and the importance of yield of lean cuts. Changes in 1968 were designed to reflect improvements in quality which could not be properly evaluated under previous standards. Minimum requirements for backfat thickness were eliminated for U.S. No. 1 grade. A new U.S. No. 1 grade was specified for superior carcasses, which were graded either U.S. No. 1 or Medium under previous

TABLE 11.4

CHANGES IN USDA GRADES FOR SLAUGHTER BARROWS AND GILTS[1]

Formulated 1918	1930	Tentative 1940	1952[2]	Official 1955	1968[3]
					U.S. No. 1
Formulated for use in market reporting		Choice (fat type)	Choice No. 1	U.S. No. 1	U.S. No. 2
		Choice (meat type)	Choice No. 2	U.S. No. 2	U.S. No. 3
		Good	Choice No. 3	U.S. No. 3	U.S. No. 4
		Medium	Medium	Medium	
		Cull	Cull	Cull	U.S. Utility

Source: USDA (1968B).
[1] Area of spaces occupied by grade names is not intended to be proportional to the relative importance of grades.
[2] Former tentative Choice (meat type) subdivided and renamed Choice No. 1 and Choice No. 2; former tentative Choice (fat type) renamed Choice No. 3.
[3] U.S. No. 1 in 1968 was a new classification for superior carcasses. Former U.S. No. 1, 2, and 3 renamed U.S. No. 2, 3, and 4, respectively. Former Medium and Cull grade names dropped. Utility added for barrows and gilts with characteristics which indicate carcass lean of unacceptable quality. Four numbered grades based on expected combined carcass yield of the four lean cuts.

standards. Under the revision, most of the former U.S. No. 1, 2, and 3 were renamed U.S. No. 2, 3, and 4, respectively, while the former Medium and Cull grades were renamed Utility. The term Utility now has a generally uniform meaning in the grade pattern for all species. Feeder pig grades are of relatively recent origin, and, as with other species, their development has been an attempt to keep feeder grades comparable to grades for slaughter animals (Table 11.5).

TABLE 11.5

CHANGES IN USDA GRADES FOR
FEEDER PIGS[1]

Tentative 1940	1966	Official 1969
		U.S. No. 1
	U.S. No. 1	U.S. No. 2
	U.S. No. 2	U.S. No. 3
	U.S. No. 3	U.S. No. 4
	Medium	U.S. Utility
	Cull	U.S. Cull

Source: USDA (1969A).
[1] Area of spaces occupied by grade names is not intended to be proportional to the relative importance of grades.

The development of lamb grades has had a particularly stormy history. A major source of difficulty arose from using a single set of standards to evaluate diverse types of lamb " . . . western lambs, bred for their ability to use sparse ranges or mountain pastures and for their wool, are different trom native lambs" (Fienup et al. 1963). While federal grade standards recognized differences due to maturity, they did not differentiate between western and native lambs. Western lamb producers felt that early official standards discriminated against their lambs, and in 1959 several sheep industry groups requested a suspension of federal grading. "Much of the pressure on federal grades for lamb in 1959 arose out of a disagreement over the quality levels that were included in U.S. Choice. Federal standards for lamb were designed on the basis of meat-type characteristics more prominent in native lambs. A smaller proportion of western than native lambs met conformation standards for U.S. Choice prior to the 1960 revision. In an attempt to qualify for U.S. Choice by improving quality to offset a lack of conformation, many lambs were fed to heavier weights and discounted in price . . . The lower conformation requirements in the new standards (1960) increased the proportion of western lambs grading U.S. Choice" (Fienup et al. 1963).

A major change in 1969 was the establishment of yield grades for lamb. A chronological picture of changes in slaughter lamb, yearling, and sheep grades is shown in Table 11.6. Thus, cutability (yield of retail cuts) now is an integral factor in the grade standards of cattle, hogs, and lamb.

TABLE 11.6
CHANGES IN USDA GRADES FOR SLAUGHTER LAMBS,
YEARLINGS, AND SHEEP[1]

Formulated 1917	Tentative		Official			
	1936	1940	1951	1957[2]	1960[3]	1969[4]
Formulated for use in market reporting		Prime	Prime[5]	Prime[5]	Prime[5]	Prime[5]
		Choice				
		Good	Choice	Choice	Choice	Choice
		Medium	Good	Good	Good	Good
		Common	Utility	Utility	Utility	Utility
		Cull	Cull	Cull	Cull	Cull

Source: USDA (1969B).
[1] Area of spaces occupied by grade names is not intended to be proportional to the relative importance of grades.
[2] No grade name changes. Quality requirements for Prime and Choice reduced for more mature lambs. Quality requirements for Good lambs increased slightly.
[3] No grade name changes. Quality and conformation requirements lowered for Prime and Choice. Limit placed on the extent superior quality may compensate for deficient conformation.
[4] Yield grades (No. 1, 2, 3, 4, and 5) added to pre-existing quality grades.
[5] Slaughter sheep older than yearlings not eligible for Prime grade.

ANNOTATION OF GRADE STANDARDS [7]

In the previous section a brief description was given of historical developments of the U.S. grading system. In this section emphasis will be placed on standards currently in use. Both aspects are important. A knowledge of the background of grade development affords a better understanding of how and why the system evolved to its current state. This type of information is helpful, if not essential, in further amendments which inevitably will come in the future. Readers who are interested in greater detail on development are referred to the references cited at the end of this chapter.

A general knowledge of current grade standards is essential to everyone engaged in livestock and meat marketing. As mentioned in earlier chapters, extensive use is made of official USDA grades in wholesale meat marketing, even though grading is strictly on a voluntary basis. Many large retail chain buyers insist on USDA graded meat in their wholesale purchasing program. Many retailers carry through by using grade labels on retail cuts.

Live animal grades are not officially applied in the marketing of livestock, but the USDA Market News Service publishes price quotations by grade. In direct selling by carcass grade and weight, USDA standards may be used in grading the carcasses (some packers insist on using their own grading system; others use USDA grades). Even an intelligent interpretation of price quotations calls for some understanding of official grades. Selling (or buying) by carcass grade and weight, or involvement in the wholesale meat trade, makes a knowledge of grade standards a necessity. But a knowledge of grades and grading also is important in buying and selling by liveweight methods. Packer buyers are experienced in estimating the potential carcass grade of live animals. Producers also need to be able to estimate grade to know whether they are getting a price commensurate with the quality and cutability attributes of their livestock. In developing a breeding herd it is imperative to be able to select stock for herd improvement, and this includes improvement in grade of animals produced.

No attempt is made here to present methods and techniques of actual grading. This is a complex problem requiring extensive study and training. An attempt is made, however, to point up the attributes, or characteristics, of live animals and meat upon which grades are based—and indicators used in evaluating these attributes.

In this section both carcass and live animal grades will be discussed. Separate standards are established and published for carcass and live animal grades, but a high correspondence exists between them. Historically, carcass grades have been established first, then slaughter animal grades made to conform to carcass grades. Feeder animal grades also are made to conform to

[7] Material in this section draws heavily upon USDA publications giving official U.S. grade standards and a series of USDA market bulletins which present a more popularized version of grade information.

slaughter animal grades. For example, a U.S. No. 1 feeder pig is evaluated on its potential for feeding out to a U.S. No. 1 slaughter hog which has the potential of producing a U.S. No. 1 carcass.

It is apparent that some of the indicators used to evaluate a carcass may be different, and presumably more precise in application, from those used on the live animal, but the basic attributes which give the carcass value and utility are the same as those of the live animal.

Carcass Beef

Grades of carcass beef are " . . . based on separate evaluations of two general considerations (USDA 1965A): (1) palatability—indicating characteristics of the lean and conformation herein referred to as 'quality,' and (2) the indicated percentage of trimmed, boneless, major retail cuts to be derived from the carcass, herein referred to as 'cutability.' " Note that quality attributes are considered to be (a) palatability—indicating characteristics of the lean, and (b) conformation. "In previous grade standards for beef and in the standards for grades of other kinds of meat, the Department (USDA 1965A) uses the term 'quality' to refer only to the palatability—indicating characteristics of the lean, without reference to conformation."

Standards are established for eight quality grades: Prime, Choice, Good, Standard, Commercial, Utility, Cutter, and Canner. Five cutability (or yield) grades have been defined: No. 1, 2, 3, 4, and 5, with No. 1 representing the highest cutability. Not all classes are eligible for every quality grade. Cows, bulls, and stags are not eligible for Prime grade, and, in addition, bulls and stags are not eligible for Standard grade. All classes are eligible for all yield grades.

Steer, heifer, and cow carcasses are graded and stamped with no reference to sex condition. Separate grade standards are provided for bull and stag carcasses, and when the carcasses are grade stamped they also are stamped as "BULL" or "STAG" as the case may be. Objections have been raised in recent years over the label "BULL" on young bull meat. Some feeders have claimed superiority in feed efficiency and proportion of lean in young bulls, but contend that consumers react unfavorably to the bull label. This probably will be advanced as a matter of potential grade revision in future years.

Quality and cutability are separate considerations. Carcasses may be graded on one, the other, or both at the option of the packer. While the standards for both quality and cutability are defined primarily for carcass beef, the quality standards apply also to certain wholesale and primal cuts—forequarters, hindquarters, rounds, loins, short loins, loin ends, ribs, and chucks. Portions of primal cuts also may be graded if still attached to the primal cut. Although not designated as retail grades, retailers do retain the original grade in cuts fabricated from wholesale and primal cuts. In addition to carcasses, cutability grades may be applied to hindquarters, forequarters, ribs, loins, and short ribs, but not to rounds and chucks.

Carcass Quality Factors.—The quality grade of a beef carcass is based on separate evaluations of two general considerations (USDA 1965A): (1) The quality or the palatability-indicating characteristics of the lean, and (2) the conformation of the carcass.

Determination of quality of the lean is accomplished by considering the degree of marbling and firmness in conjunction with maturity. Maturity is determined by evaluating the size, shape, and ossification of bones and

Quality Grade Marks

cartilages, and by color of the lean. Marbling refers to flecks of fat interspersed among muscle fibers in the lean. The degree of marbling is considered to be positively associated with flavor, tenderness, juiciness, and palatability in general. Marbling requirements for a given grade increase with maturity. Nine different degrees of marbling and five different maturity groupings are recognized in the application of grade standards. Figure 11.2 illustrates the relationship between marbling, maturity, and quality. Marbling requirements for bottom USDA Choice vary from a minimum of the range set up for "small" degree of marbling for the youngest animals, to a maximum of the range set up for "modest" degree for the second stage of maturity. Prime, Choice, Good, and Standard grades are limited to beef from relatively young animals.

"Conformation is the manner of formation of the carcass or primal cut. The conformation descriptions included in each of the grade specifications refer to the thickness of muscling and to an overall degree of thickness and fullness of the carcass and its various parts" (USDA 1965A). Degree of excellence exhibited in conformation is positively correlated to the proportion of meat to bone and to the proportion of weight of a carcass or cut in the more valuable parts.

"The final quality grade of a carcass or cut is based on a composite evaluation of its conformation and quality" (USDA 1965A).

Yield Grade Marks

Carcass Cutability Factors.—Official grade standards provide for five cutability groupings in recognition of the fact that carcasses of identical quality grade and weight can have substantial difference in value due to differences in the percentage of closely-trimmed, boneless, retail cuts obtainable from the carcasses. These groupings, called "yield" grades, are numbered 1 through 5, with No. 1 having the highest percentage of retail cuts and No. 5 the lowest. A test made by the USDA in 1968 showed that differences in yield from adjacent yield grades of a given quality carcass had a difference in retail sale value of about $3.60 per cwt of carcass. Value, of course, varies with the level of market prices, but $3.60 is not unusual—there have been occasions when it amounted to 3 times that much.

The chief factors which account for variation in yield of retail cuts are (1) the amount of fat that must be trimmed, and (2) the thickness and fullness of the muscling. Extensive research has shown that four indicators highly correlated with yield are as follows: (1) amount of external fat, (2) amount of kidney, pelvic, and heart fat, (3) area of the rib eye muscle, and (4) carcass weight. The following mathematical equation for calculating yield grade shows relationships among the four factors:

$$Y.G. = 2.50 + 2.50X_1 + 0.20X_2 - 0.32X_3 + 0.0038X_4$$

where $Y.G.$ = yield grade
X_1 = in. of backfat thickness
X_2 = % kidney, pelvic, heart fat
X_3 = sq in. of ribeye area
X_4 = lb of hot carcass weight

The result is expressed as a whole number (any fractional part is dropped). A simpler means of evaluating objective measurements is by use of a slide-rule

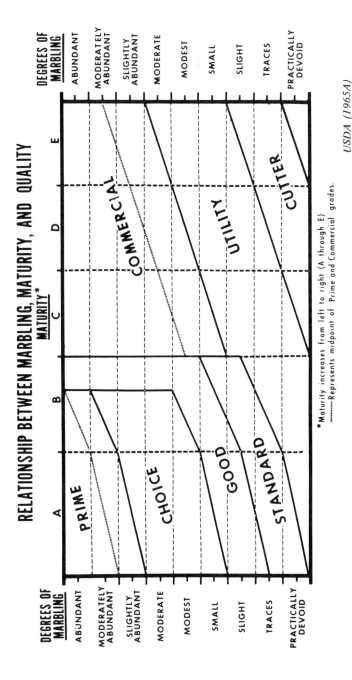

FIG. 11.2. RELATIONSHIP BETWEEN MARBLING, MATURITY, AND QUALITY

type device, designed by the Livestock Division, Consumer and Marketing Service, USDA, called the Beef Carcass Yield Grade Finder. In contrast to quality grade indicators, all of these yield factors can be measured objectively. This was of great help in developing yield grade standards although in application actual measurement is unnecessary. Descriptions given in the standards (USDA 1965A) " . . . facilitate the subjective determination of the cutability group without making detailed measurements and computations. The cutability group for most beef carcasses can be determined accurately on the basis of a visual appraisal."

The establishment of yield grades culminated a long period of discussion and research. It had been known for a number of years that differences existed in cutability. Large wholesale buyers, including buyers for large chains, personally selected carcasses when buying from packers. Many still do this to meet more exact specifications within both yield and quality grades, but as will be pointed out in a following section, a rapid growth has occurred in use of yield grades since their inauguration in 1965.

The economic significance of variation in yield grades is shown by USDA calculations in Tables 11.7 and 11.8. The quantity of carcass beef required to produce 30,000 lb of retail cuts would vary from 36,585 lb for Yield Grade 1 to 47,150 lb for Yield Grade 5. This is a direct reflection of additional fat trim from Yield Grade 5. The retail sales value per 100 lb of carcass weight would vary from $72.77 for Yield Grade 1 to $58.33 for Yield Grade 5, with calculations based on 1968 prices. An efficient marketing system will reflect such differences back to producers. The use of yield grades tends to impart pricing efficiency in the system. The USDA publishes current monthly average retail sales values of 600-lb Choice beef carcasses of various yield grades in their *Livestock, Meat, Wool Market News.*

Table 11.8 points up differences in percentage yield and retail value by cuts of beef from Yield Grade 2 and Yield Grade 4 carcasses. Retail price per pound is not affected by yield grade, but rather by quality grade. In this example, both carcasses are identical in quality. Retail value per cut varies with the yield of retail meat in the cut. The only "cut" in which Yield Grade 4 exceeded Yield Grade 1 in quantity was fat trim—a dubious distinction.

Slaughter Cattle

The term "slaughter cattle" does not include vealers and slaughter calves. Special efforts have been made to make grades for slaughter animals conform directly to the grades of carcasses produced from the live animals. Eight quality grades and five yield grades, identical in name with carcass grades, have been established for slaughter cattle. Eligibility of the various classes for particular grades are identical for both live animals and carcasses.

Quality Grade Factors.—"Slaughter cattle quality grades are based (USDA

TABLE 11.7

RELATIONSHIP BETWEEN BEEF YIELD GRADES AND SELECTED VARIABLES

	No. 1	No. 2	No. 3	No. 4	No. 5
If a retailer sells 30,000 lb of retail cuts and he bought carcasses of these USDA Yield Grades:					
Then he would need to buy this much carcass beef (lb)	36,585	38,760	41,210	43,990	47,170
If, for example, he bought 600 lb carcasses he would need this many carcasses	61	65	69	73	78
After preparing and trimming the retail cuts he would have the following yields of:					
Fat trim (%)	7.5	12.6	17.7	22.8	27.9
Bone and shrink (%)	10.5	10.0	9.5	9.0	8.5
Trimmed cuts (%)	82.0	77.4	72.8	68.2	63.6
At current retail prices, the retail sales value per cwt of carcass would be ($)	72.77	69.16	65.55	61.94	58.33
If all the carcasses were USDA Choice and were bought at $43.00 per cwt, his gross margin as a percentage of sales would be (%)	40.91	37.83	34.40	30.58	26.28

Source: USDA (1968C).
NOTE: Cutting and trimming costs increase as carcasses increase in fatness. If these costs were included, the differences in margins and sales values between yield grades would be even greater than indicated.

TABLE 11.8

COMPARISON OF YIELDS OF RETAIL CUTS AND RETAIL VALUES BETWEEN
USDA YIELD GRADE 2 AND YIELD GRADE 4 CARCASSES—BEEF

Closely Trimmed Retail Cuts[1]	Percentage of Carcass Weight		Price per Lb[2] ($)	Retail Value in Dollars per Cwt	
	USDA Yield Grade 2	USDA Yield Grade 4		USDA Yield Grade 2	USDA Yield Grade 4
Rump, boneless	3.5	3.1	1.12	3.92	3.47
Inside round	4.5	3.7	1.17	5.27	4.33
Outside round	4.6	4.2	1.15	5.29	4.83
Round tip	2.6	2.4	1.19	3.09	2.86
Sirloin	8.7	7.9	1.14	9.92	9.01
Short loin	5.2	5.0	1.36	7.07	6.80
Rib, short cut (7″)	6.2	6.0	1.01	6.26	6.06
Blade chuck	9.4	8.4	.56	5.26	4.70
Chuck, arm, boneless	6.1	5.5	.83	5.06	4.57
Brisket, boneless	2.3	1.9	.93	2.14	1.76
Flank steak	.5	.5	1.14	.57	.57
Lean trim	11.3	9.3	.73	8.25	6.79
Ground beef	12.2	10.0	.53	6.47	5.30
Fat	12.7	22.9	.03	.38	.69
Bone	9.9	8.9	.01	.10	.09
Kidney	.3	.3	.38	.11	.11
Total	100.0	100.0		69.16	61.94

Difference in retail value per cwt between Yield Grade 2 and 4 = $7.22

Source: USDA (1968C).
[1] Cuts trimmed to 1/2 in. of fat.
[2] Average retail prices for Jan. 1968 (including sale priced items) as furnished by a large number of selected retailers throughout the country.

1966) on a composite evaluation of conformation and factors related to the palatability of the lean, herein referred to as 'quality'. . . . Conformation refers to general body proportions of the animal and to the ratio of muscle to bone." In evaluating quality, attention is directed primarily to finish (its amount and distribution), muscling (its firmness and fullness), and physical characteristics associated with maturity. By necessity, appraisal of finish is achieved primarily by observable characteristics of external finish.

From the standpoint of maturity, approximate maximum age limits for steers and heifers, are 42 months for Prime and Choice, 48 months for Good and Standard. If these classes are over 48 months of age, Commercial grade applies. No age limits are recognized for any class in the Utility, Cutter, and Canner grades. In application of the standards, superior quality is permitted to compensate for deficient conformation. However, this compensation is distinctly limited.

Fig. 11.3 illustrates differences in slaughter steers of a partial range in quality grades.

Yield Grade Factors.—The factors used in establishing yield grades for slaughter cattle are identical with those used for carcass beef, i.e., thickness of fat over ribeye; percentage of kidney, pelvic, and heart fat; carcass weight; and area of the ribeye muscle. These characteristics cannot be measured directly.

SLAUGHTER STEERS
U.S. GRADES
(QUALITY)

PRIME ——

CHOICE ——

GOOD ——

STANDARD ——

UTILITY ——

COMMERCIAL, CUTTER, AND
CANNER GRADES ARE OMITTED

Courtesy of USDA

FIG. 11.3. U.S. GRADES OF SLAUGHTER STEERS (QUALITY)

SLAUGHTER STEERS
U.S. GRADES
(YIELD)

YIELD GRADE 1 ——

YIELD GRADE 2 ——

YIELD GRADE 3 ——

YIELD GRADE 4 ——

YIELD GRADE 5 ——

Courtesy of USDA

FIG. 11.4. U.S. GRADES OF SLAUGHTER STEERS (YIELD)

They can be estimated and yield calculated by equation, but "... a more practical method of appraising slaughter cattle for yield grade is to use only two factors normally considered in evaluating live cattle—muscling and fatness.

"In the latter approach, . . . evaluation of the thickness and fullness of muscling in relation to skeletal size largely accounts for the effects of two of the factors—area of ribeye, and carcass weight. By the same token, an appraisal of the degree of external fatness largely accounts for the effects of thickness of fat over the ribeye and the percentage of kidney, pelvic, and heart fat" (USDA 1966).

Fig. 11.4 illustrates differences in steers of the full range in yield grades.

Veal and Calf Carcasses

Veal and calf production has been decreasing for a number of years. It amounted to only 400 million pounds of a total of 18,870 million pounds of beef, veal, and calf slaughter (slightly over 2%) under federal inspection in 1969. However, veal and calf production are important in some areas.

The basic factor which differentiates veal, calf, and beef is maturity, and the three respective sets of standards designed for grading are intended to represent the entire range in bovine maturity. For grading purposes, veal, calf and beef carcasses are distinguished (USDA 1956) "primarily on the basis of the color of the lean, although such factors as texture of the lean; character of the fat; color, shape, size and ossification of the bones and cartilages; and the general contour of the carcass are also given consideration. Typical veal carcasses have a grayish pink color of lean that is very smooth and velvety. . . . By contrast, typical calf carcasses have a grayish red color of lean . . . " Color of the lean in beef carcasses becomes progressively darker red with increasing maturity.

Grade and Class Mark

CALF

Official grade standards recognize three classes of veal and calf carcasses on the basis of sex condition—steers, heifers, and bulls. Standards are established for six grades: Prime, Choice, Good, Standard, Utility, and Cull. Each class is eligible for the full range in grades. In addition to the grade stamp, veal and calf also are stamped "VEAL or "CALF" as the case may be.

Yield grades have not been established for veal and calf carcasses.

"Veal and calf carcasses are graded on a composite evaluation of three general grade factors—conformation, finish, and quality. These factors are concerned with the proportions of the various wholesale cuts and the proportion of fat, lean, and bone in the carcass and the quality of the lean" (USDA 1956). Without explicitly using the term "cutability," this factor is recognized—primarily in the consideration of conformation. Quality of the lean is specified and is identified by consideration of color, texture, firmness, and marbling of the lean. Palatability is recognized, not only in the above-mentioned characteristics of the lean, but also in the degree of finish. Finish refers primarily to the degree of fatness. which is presumed to be associated with marbling and, hence, with palatability.

Vealers and Slaughter Calves

According to USDA (1957), "The basis for differentiation between vealers and calves is made primarily on age and certain evidence of type of feeding. Typical vealers are less than three months of age and have subsisted largely on milk . . . they have the characteristic trimness of middle. . . . Calves are usually between 3 and 8 months of age, have subsisted partially or entirely on feeds other than milk for a substantial period of time, and have developed the heavier middles and physical characteristics associated with maturity beyond the vealer stage."

The three classes of vealers and calves are steers, heifers, and bulls. Eligible grades for each class are Prime, Choice, Good, Standard, Utility, and Cull. Grade is determined by a composite evaluation of conformation, finish, and quality. "Conformation refers to the general body proportions . . . and to the ratio of meat to bone . . . Finish refers to the fatness of the animal . . . Quality in the slaughter animal refers to the refinement of hair, hide and bone and to the smoothness and symmetry of the body. Quality is also associated with carcass yield and the proportion of meat to bone" (USDA 1957). Thus, it is apparent that yield of lean meat (as well as carcass yield) is inherent in the grade standards by considerations of conformation, finish, and quality. The intent of evaluating quality of the meat is explicit in the statement that "the quality, quantity, and distribution of finish are all closely associated with the palatability and quality of the meat" (USDA 1957).

Feeder Cattle

The official distinction between feeder cattle and slaughter cattle is in the intended use. Feeder cattle are intended for futher feeding (growing or finishing) before slaughter. It is recognized that some so-called two-way cattle do not fit exclusively into the feeder or slaughter classification, but this is no obstacle to grading. Any cattle may be graded for slaughter purposes—based on slaughter grade standards. However, if used as feeder animals, they will be graded on feeder cattle grades.

"The term 'cattle' as used in these standards includes bovines of all ages (USDA 1965B). The classes of feeder cattle are identical with those of slaughter cattle: steers, heifers, cows, bulls, and stags. However, bulls and stags are seldom used for feeders. The following discussion is limited to steers, heifers, and cows, with emphasis on steers and heifers.

Grades of feeder cattle are related to slaughter cattle grades in that the primary characteristics considered are the feeder animals' logical slaughter potential as beef. Thriftiness is another factor. The final grade is a composite evaluation of the two with greater weight given to slaughter potential.

FEEDER STEERS
U.S. GRADES

PRIME

CHOICE

GOOD

STANDARD

UTILITY

Courtesy of USDA

FIG. 11.5. U.S. GRADES OF FEEDER STEERS

FEEDER STEERS (CALVES)

U.S. GRADES

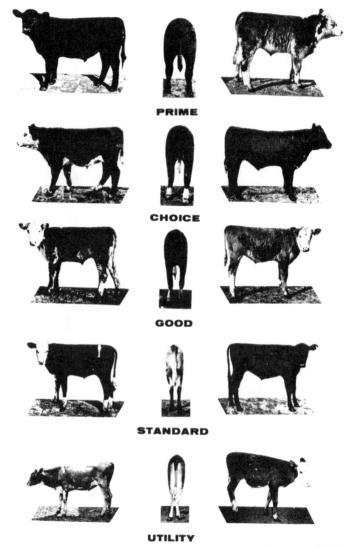

Courtesy of USDA

FIG. 11.6. U.S. GRADES OF FEEDER STEERS (CALVES)

Conformation is a key to slaughter potential. According to USDA (1965B), " . . . conformation or inherent muscular development is the most important single factor affecting the grade of a feeder animal . . . conformation is determined by appraising the development of the muscular system in relation to development of the skeletal system." While degree of fatness is not a grade factor, it affects appearance and is recognized in evaluating conformation.

"Thriftiness (USDA 1965B) refers to the ability of a feeder animal to gain weight and fatten rapidly and efficiently." Shape-for-age and alertness are indicators of thriftiness. This factor, however, is not used in grading except when the animal is less thrifty than normal.

Grade names used for feeder cattle are Prime, Choice, Good, Standard, Commercial, Utility, and Inferior. Fig. 11.5 and 11.6 illustrate differences in a partial range of grades for feeder steers and feeder steer calves.

Pork Carcasses—Barrows and Gilts

Market classes of pork carcasses are barrows, gilts, sows, boars, and stags; however, the following comments are limited to barrows and gilts. In grade standards (and in market prices) no distinction is made between barrows and gilts. Specified grades are U.S. No. 1, 2, 3, 4, and Utility. According to the

revised (USDA1968A) standards of April 1, 1968, "grades for barrow and gilt carcasses are based on two general considerations: (1) quality-indicating characteristics of the lean, and (2) expected combined yields of the four lean cuts (ham, loin, picnic shoulder, and Boston butt)." From the standpoint of quality, two general levels are specified: "acceptable" and "unacceptable." By direct observation of a cut surface, acceptability is based on considerations of firmness, marbling, and color. Indirect indicators are firmness of fat and lean, feathering between the ribs, and color. The degree of external fatness, as such, is not considered in evaluating the quality of the lean (USDA 1968A). Suitability of the belly for bacon (in terms of thickness) also is considered in quality evaluation as is "softness" and "oiliness" of the carcass. Carcasses which have unacceptable quality of lean, and/or bellies that are too thin, and/or carcasses which are soft and oily are graded U.S. Utility.

If a carcass qualifies as acceptable in quality of lean, and belly thickness, and is not soft and oily, then it is graded U.S. No. 1, 2, 3, or 4 " . . . entirely on the expected carcass yields of the four lean cuts . . . " (USDA 1968A.) Carcasses grading U.S. No. 1 are expected to yield 53% or more of the four lean cuts based on chilled carcass weight; U.S. No. 2 carcasses, 50–52.9%; U.S. No. 3 carcasses, 47–49.9%; and U.S. No. 4 carcasses, less than 47%. Variations in yield of the four lean cuts are associated with "variations in their degree of fatness and in their degree of muscling . . . (USDA 1968A). Since many carcasses have a normal distribution of fat and a normal distribution of muscling for their degree of fatness, in determining their grade the actual average thickness of backfat and the carcass length or weight are the only factors considered" (USDA 1968A). Fig. 11.7 illustrates these relationships in objective measurements of the

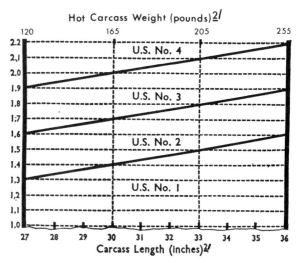

Courtesy of USDA

FIG. 11.7. RELATIONSHIP BETWEEN AVERAGE THICKNESS OF BACKFAT, CARCASS LENGTH OR WEIGHT, AND GRADE FOR CARCASSES WITH MUSCLING TYPICAL OF THEIR DEGREE OF FATNESS

[1] An average of three measurements including the skin made opposite the first and last ribs and the last lumbar vertebra. It also reflects adjustments, as appropriate, to compensate for variations from normal fat distribution.

[2] Carcass weight is based on a hot packer style carcass.

[3] Carcass length is measured from the anterior point of the aitch bone to the anterior edge of the first rib.

variables. Note that carcass weight *or* carcass length may be used but the standards (USDA 1968A) state further that "in cases where length and backfat thickness indicate a different grade than weight and backfat, the grade shall be determined using length." The grade standards also specify the extent to which superior muscling can compensate for greater than average backfat thickness.[8]

Basically, grades for pork carcasses, like those for beef carcasses, are designed to evaluate both quality and yield. The significance of this to the livestock and meat industry follows the same pattern as discussed under the section on beef

[8] For descriptive discussion see USDA (1970A).

carcasses. A USDA (1968A) calculation showed that during July, 1969, the value differences between adjacent grades of 150-lb carcasses averaged nearly $1.25 cwt.

Slaughter Hogs

The classes of slaughter hogs and associated grade names are identical with classes and grades of swine carcasses discussed in the previous section.

SLAUGHTER SWINE

U.S. GRADES

U.S. NO.1

U.S. NO.2

U.S. NO.3

U.S. NO.4

U.S. UTILITY

FIG. 11.8. U.S. GRADES OF SLAUGHTER SWINE

Standards used in grading slaughter animals are consistent with those used in grading carcasses. (A U.S. No. 1 slaughter barrow or gilt is expected to produce a U.S. No. 1 carcass, and so on through the other grades.) The same attributes are evaluated in the live animal as in the carcass: (1) quality of the lean and (2) yield of the four lean cuts. As was the case with carcasses, quality of the slaughter animal includes, in addition to quality per se of the lean meat, a consideration of belly thickness as an indicator of its adequacy for bacon production and a determination of whether the carcass will be soft and oily. "Since carcass indices of lean quality are not directly evident in barrows and gilts, some other factors in which differences can be noted must be used to evaluate quality. Therefore the amount and distribution of external finish, firmness of fat, and firmness of lean are used as quality-indicating factors" (USDA 1968B).

Slaughter barrows and gilts which do not meet standards of acceptable quality are graded Utility. Those which meet the standards for acceptable quality are then assigned grade U.S. No. 1, 2, 3, or 4 on the basis of expected combined carcass yield of the four lean cuts, with U.S. No. 1 representing the highest yield. The reproductions in Fig. 11.8 illustrate the appearance of hogs of the various grades.

Factors used to evaluate yield are average backfat thickness in relation to carcass length *or* live weight. In the live animal only weight can be readily

Courtesy of USDA

FIG. 11.9. RELATIONSHIP BETWEEN AVERAGE THICKNESS OF BACKFAT, WEIGHT OR CARCASS LENGTH, AND GRADE FOR BARROWS AND GILTS WITH MUSCLING TYPICAL OF THEIR DEGREE OF FATNESS

[1] An average of three measurements including the skin made opposite the first and last ribs and the last lumbar vertebra. It also reflects adjustment, as appropriate, to compensate for variations from normal fat distribution.

[2] Carcass length is measured from the anterior point of the aitch bone to the anterior edge of the first rib.

determined. However, with experience these factors can be evaluated visually. Studies have shown objective relationships between these variables, as illustrated in Fig. 11.9, for slaughter barrows and gilts having a normal development of muscling for the degree of fatness. The standards recognize that the degree of muscling varies, and provision is made for superior muscling to compensate for greater fatness (and vice versa) with specified limitations.

Feeder Pigs

Following the revision in grade standards for pork carcasses and slaughter swine in 1968, the grade standards for feeder pigs were revised in 1969. This change was made to keep feeder pig grades consistent with slaughter swine and pork carcass grades. Official standards do not differentiate between barrow, gilt, or boar pigs, but is it assumed boar pigs will be castrated prior to development of secondary physical characteristics of a boar. Sows, stags, and mature boars are seldom used as feeders and are not included in the following. The criteria upon which feeder pigs are evaluated are comparable to those for feeder cattle, namely logical slaughter potential and thriftiness. As pointed out by USDA (1969A), "the logical slaughter potential of a thrifty feeder pig is its expected slaughter grade at a market weight of 220 lb after a normal feeding period ... Thriftiness in a feeder pig is its apparent ability to gain weight rapidly and efficiently."

Designated grades for feeder pigs are U.S. No. 1, 2, 3, 4, Utility, and Cull. Unthrifty pigs are graded Utility and Cull, depending on the degree of unthriftiness, Cull being the lower end. Pigs classed as thrifty are graded U.S. No. 1, 2, 3, or 4 on the basis of logical slaughter potential.

An indication of slaughter potential is derived by a composite evaluation of development of the muscular and skeletal systems. Indicators of thriftiness are size for age, health, and other general characteristics. Fig. 11.10 illustrates the appearance of feeder pigs of all grades except Cull.

Lamb, Yearling Mutton, and Mutton Carcasses

Revision of the grade standards for lamb, yearling mutton, and mutton carcasses in 1969 included establishment of explicit yield grades. This change followed a lengthy period of discussion, conferences, and research. And, as was the case with other meats, not all interests agreed to the change, but USDA investigations indicated a consensus in favor of it.

The groupings of lambs, yearlings, and sheep (which produce the above indicated carcasses) are based on age, or maturity differences—characterized by differences in development of the muscular and skeletal systems. As enunciated by USDA (1969B), "the grade of an ovine carcass is based on separate evaluations of two general considerations: (1) palatability-indicating characteristics of the lean and conformation, herein referred to as quality; and (2) the

FEEDER PIGS

U.S. GRADES

U.S. NO.1   **U.S. NO.2**

U.S. NO.3   **U.S. NO.4**

CULL GRADE IS
OMITTED   **U.S. UTILITY**

FIG. 11.10. U.S. GRADES OF FEEDER PIGS

estimated percentage of closely trimmed, boneless, major retail cuts to be derived from the carcass, herein referred to as yield." The relevant retail cuts are from the leg, loin, hotel rack, and shoulder.

The definitions of such terms as "quality of the lean" and "conformation," as well as the indicators used to evaluate them, are consistent with those used in grading beef carcasses. Quality grades specified are Prime, Choice, Good,

Quality Grade Marks

Utility, and Cull. Mutton carcasses, however, are not eligible for Prime grade. In addition to the grade stamp, yearling mutton and mutton are stamped "YEARLING MUTTON or "MUTTON" as the case may be.

Five yield grades, numbered 1 through 5, cover the range in cutability, with Yield Grade 1 indicating the highest yield. "A carcass which is typical of its yield grade would be expected to yield 3.5% more in total retail cuts than the next lower yield grade, when USDA cutting and trimming methods are followed" (USDA 1970C). Variations in yield are attributed primarily to the same two considerations referred to in the case of beef carcasses—namely, the amount of fat trimmed off in making retail cuts, and the thickness and fullness of muscling.

"The yield grade of an ovine carcass is determined by considering three characteristics: the amount of external fat, the amount of kidney and pelvic fat, and the conformation grade of the legs" (USDA 1970C).

The grade standards include an equation by which yield grade can be calculated. The equation may be written as:

$$\text{Y.G.} = 1.66 - 0.05X_1 + 0.25X_2 + 6.66X_3$$

Where Y.G. = yield grade
X_1 = leg conformation grade code
X_2 = % kidney and pelvic fat
X_3 = adjusted fat thickness over the ribeye in inches

Any fractional part of a yield grade is dropped in this calculation and the result is reported as a whole number. Leg conformation used in the equation is the evaluation used in quality grading, but expressed as a coded number ranging from 1 to 15, with 15 being the most desirable conformation (i.e., conformation applicable to high Prime). The amount of external fat, an indicator of retail trim, can be measured but it also can be accurately estimated. Kidney and pelvic fat cannot be measured without removal from the carcass; however, this too can be evaluated subjectively with an acceptable degree of accuracy.

Yield grades are applicable to wholesale and primal cuts as well as to carcasses.

The economic importance of yield is indicated in Table 11.9 where quality grade and carcass weight are assumed to be constant and the only difference between the two carcasses is two yield grades. The calculated difference in retail sales value is $7.56 per cwt of carcass. This would amount to $3.78 difference between adjacent grades.

TABLE 11.9
COMPARISON OF YIELD OF RETAIL CUTS
AND RETAIL SALES VALUES BETWEEN USDA
YIELD GRADE 2 AND YIELD GRADE 4 CARCASSES—LAMB

Closely Trimmed Retail Cuts[1]	Percentage of Carcass Weight		Price per Lb[2] ($)	Retail Sales Value in Dollars Per Cwt	
	USDA Yield Grade 2	USDA Yield Grade 4		USDA Yield Grade 2	USDA Yield Grade 4
Leg, short cut	22.2	19.4	1.00	22.20	19.40
Sirloin	6.4	5.8	1.50	9.60	8.70
Short loin	10.1	9.5	1.83	18.48	17.38
Rack	7.9	7.5	1.61	12.72	12.08
Shoulder	23.8	21.6	0.93	22.14	20.09
Neck	2.1	1.9	0.51	1.07	0.97
Breast	9.8	9.8	0.39	3.82	3.82
Foreshank	3.4	3.2	0.62	2.11	1.99
Flank (boneless stew)	2.3	2.3	0.84	1.93	1.93
Kidney	0.5	0.5	0.65	0.32	0.32
Fat	8.2	15.4	0.02	0.16	0.31
Bone	3.3	3.1	0.01	0.03	0.03
Total	100.0	100.0		94.58	87.02

Difference in retail sales value per cwt between Yield Grade 2 and 4 $7.56

Source: USDA (1970C).
[1] Cuts trimmed to 1/4 in. of fat.
[2] Average retail prices for Dec. 1969 (including sale priced items) as furnished by a large number of selected retailers throughout the country.

Slaughter Lambs, Yearlings, and Sheep

As with other species, USDA (1970C) specifies "grades of slaughter ovines are intended to be directly related to the grades of the carcasses they produce. To accomplish this, these slaughter ovine grade standards are based on factors which are directly related to the quality grades and the yield grades of ovine carcasses." Quality grade names and yield grade designations for the live animals are identical with those for carcasses. The factors upon which live quality and yield grades are based also are consistent with those of carcass grades. However, the presence of the fleece makes evaluation more difficult and necessitates handling as well as visual observation.

TRENDS IN USE OF FEDERAL GRADES

The trend in percentage of beef, veal, and lamb federally graded under quality grade standards is shown in Fig. 11.11. This service has been on a voluntary basis except during World War II and the Korean War. These periods are easily recognized on the chart. Federal grading was not readily accepted during the 1930's. There was a normal reluctance in the industry to accept something new, and further, this involved an expense since packers pay for the cost of grading. In addition, some packers had vested interests in their own private grading systems and viewed federal grades as detrimental to their interests. Following World War II the proportion of graded meat dropped

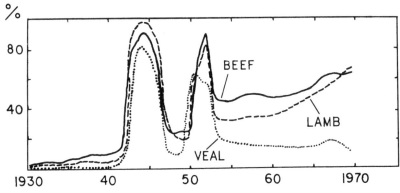

FIG. 11.11. PERCENTAGE OF BEEF, VEAL, AND LAMB FEDERALLY GRADED (QUALITY GRADES), 1930-1969

significantly; but it did not drop back to its former level. The same thing happened following the Korean War. Since the Korean War, the trend in grading of beef and lamb has been steadily upward. In 1969, approximately 2/3 of each of these meats was federally graded for quality. The proportion of veal graded has been less than for other meats, and since the Korean War the trend has been slightly downward. Only 15% of the veal in 1969 was federally graded.

Yield grades for beef have been in effect only since 1965. However, on the basis of experience during the first 5 yr, this service is expanding rapidly. In 1969, 12.8% of the beef was yield graded:

| | Percentage of beef |
Year	yield graded
1965	0.8
1966	2.2
1967	5.6
1968	11.0
1969	12.8

During 1969, slightly more than 20% of the beef that was quality graded also was yield graded.

It is too early to determine a trend on yield grading of lamb, since that procedure only began in 1969.

The trend in the percentage of beef and lamb quality graded is expected to move upward in coming years but at a slower rate than in the recent period. With a major proportion already being graded, further increases will come rather slowly. On the other hand, the rate of increase in yield grading probably will grow. Cutability has an important bearing on carcass value and large chain buyers are insisting on such specifications in their purchasing programs.

IMPROVEMENTS IN GRADES OF LIVESTOCK PRODUCED

An efficiently operating market system is presumed to price products over a period of time in a manner that reflects changing demand and supply characteristics. Theoretically, prices on less preferred products will tend to decline, and production of those products also will tend to decline. The reverse is expected on the more preferred products. Grades and grading provide a means of imparting knowledge which presumably tends to make the system more efficient. The pork market provides evidence that this has occurred in spite of much criticism and impatience with the rate of change.

Fig. 11.12 shows evidence of the market's reaction to the supply-demand situation for fat and for lean cuts. The price for fat has dropped dramatically relative to the price for lean pork cuts. Some over-fat hogs still are being produced, but, in general, producers have responded by equally dramatic changes in production. Through breeding and feeding programs, the average

FIG. 11.12. WHOLESALE PORK PRICES COMPARED WITH LIVE HOG PRICES
Trend since 1960 added by author from USDA data.

lard production per hog has declined. This trend has been underway for several decades, but data for the period 1959-1969 illustrate the point (see Table 11.10). Average liveweight of hogs slaughtered under federal inspection was the same in 1969 as in 1959 (239.5 lb), but dressed weight was higher due to an increase in dressing yield. The pronounced change, however, was in ratio of lard to pork. Lard produced per hundredweight dropped from 14.1 to 9.7 lb. On a per hog basis, lard production dropped from 33.7 to 23.2 lb, while the output of pork increased from 149.8 to 161.9 lb. This type of information indicates general improvement in production of meat-type hogs,

TABLE 11.10

CHANGES IN SELECTED CHARACTERISTICS
OF HOGS SLAUGHTERED UNDER FEDERAL
INSPECTION 1959 AND 1969

Characteristic	1959 (Lb)	1969 (Lb)
Lard per cwt	14.1	9.7
Lard per animal	33.7	23.2
Pork per animal[1]	149.8	161.9
Avg dressed weight	183.5	185.1
Liveweight	239.5	239.5
Dressing yield (%)	76.6	77.3

Source: Data from USDA Livestock and Meat
Statistics
[1] Pounds of pork per animal calculated.

and indirectly suggests that improvements have been made in the grade of hogs, but it does not show changes within the grouping of generally acceptable hogs.

Data are not regularly collected on hog slaughter by grade, since the wholesale trade makes little use of pork grades. However, the USDA made special studies in 1960-1961 and 1967-1968, in which determinations were made of the percentage of barrow and gilt carcasses in each of the various grades. The same grading standards were used in both studies (standards which officially were in effect from July 5, 1955 to April 1, 1968) so results may be compared directly. Table 11.11 shows a marked increase in quality of hogs.

TABLE 11.11

DISTRIBUTION OF BARROW AND GILT
CARCASSES BY GRADE,
1960-1961 AND 1967-1968

Grade	1960–1961 (%)	1967–1968 (%)
U. S. No. 1	33.4	49.9
U. S. No. 2	38.6	35.4
U. S. No. 3	25.9	11.9
Medium	2.0	2.6
Cull	0.1	0.2
All grades	100.0	100.0

Source: Agnew (1969).

This is indicated by a substantial increase in percentage of U.S. No. 1 carcasses and a substantial decrease in percentage of U.S. No. 3 carcasses. In 1967-1968, about 1/2 the carcasses graded U.S. No. 1 while only 1/3 graded that high in 1960-1961. The proportion grading U.S. No. 3 dropped from 25.9 to 11.9% during that 8-yr period. Only slight changes occurred in the proportion of carcasses in other grades.

Information gathered in the study permitted an estimate of the distribution of 1967-1968 carcasses also on the basis of the revised (1968) grade standards which went into effect about the time the study terminated. The results were as follows:

Grade	%	Grade	%
U.S. No. 1	8.13	U.S. No. 4	12.24
U.S. No. 2	42.10	Utility	1.82
U.S. No. 3	35.71		

This not only provides a benchmark for later comparisons, but it also points up differences between the two sets of standards. U.S. No. 1 under the 1968 revision represents a much superior carcass from the standpoint of cutability than the former U.S. No. 1. Only 8.13% of the carcasses slaughtered in 1967-1968 would have graded U.S. No. 1 under the revised standards. It also is evident that under the new standards only a small proportion of carcasses are unacceptable from the standpoint of quality (i.e., Utility grade). Most of the carcasses graded U.S. No. 1 under previous standards were graded U.S. No. 2 under the revised standards, former U.S. No. 2's were graded U.S. No. 3, and former U.S. No. 3's were graded U.S. No. 4 under the revised standards.

Data on distribution of beef by grades have been collected regularly for a number of years. Table 11.12 shows beef production by class as well as by grade. It is worth noting that the proportion of beef obtained from heifers has increased substantially while the proportion from cows has declined and the proportion from steers has remained fairly constant since 1950. From the distribution by grade, it is clear that marked gains have occurred in the quality of beef produced. The slight decline in percentage of Prime does not represent a decrease in absolute quantity since total production increased. The increase in percentage of Choice grade from 34.1 to 55.9% with declines in all other grades represents a substantial increase in beef of more preferred eating quality.

It is not implied that all the improvement in quality of pork and beef can be attributed to the development and use of official grades. Changes in grade standards themselves could affect the distribution if not compensated for in the tabulations. This had no effect on pork carcass grades as standards were constant during the period studied. A revision in beef grades in 1965 slightly relaxed the standards of marbling for more mature beef and may have had a slight tendency to increase the quantity in upper grades, but this was minor. An example of how a change in standards can affect distribution by grade is found in the case of lamb. A revision in 1960 relaxed the requirements for Prime grade. As a result (Fienup et al. 1963), "prime increased from 1% in the 1959 marketing year (March through the following February) to 16% in 1960 and 12% in 1961 . . . Good dropped from 11% in 1959 to 3% in 1960 and 1961. Choice dropped from 87% in 1959 to 81% in 1960 and 82% in 1961." However, in the case of lamb, other factors such as cut-out of retail cuts, tend to confirm a genuine improvement in quality of lamb produced.

TABLE 11.12

BEEF PRODUCTION BY GRADE, 1950–1969

Year	Total Production (Million Lb)	Production by Class			Production by Grade[1]						
		Steer (%)	Heifer (%)	Cow[2] (%)	Prime (%)	Choice (%)	Good (%)	Standard (%)	Commercial[3] (%)	Utility (%)	Canner and Cutter (%)
1950	9,534	57.3	9.2	33.5	6.9	34.1	18.6		14.5	14.6	11.3
1951	8,837	56.8	8.9	34.3							
1952	9,650	59.5	9.4	31.1	5.1	34.3	18.4		16.1	13.0	13.1
1953	12,407	58.7	9.7	31.6			· · ·				
1954	12,963	55.3	11.9	32.8							
1955	13,569	54.2	12.7	33.1							
1956	14,462	56.4	12.8	30.8	4.4	32.8	21.0		15.8	13.0	13.0
1957	14,202	55.5	13.6	30.9							
1958	13,330	60.2	15.0	24.8							
1959	13,580	60.4	19.0	20.6	3.7	36.1	27.4		13.7	9.8	9.3
1960	14,728	59.4	19.1	21.5							
1961	15,300	60.6	20.9	18.5						· · ·	
1962	15,298	60.6	20.1	19.3	2.9	46.8	18.1	11.3	4.4	8.8	7.7
1963	16,428	62.4	20.5	17.1							
1964	18,429	62.4	19.0	18.6	2.6	49.2	16.6	10.5	3.9	8.4	8.8
1965	18,699	55.8	21.4	22.8	3.5	46.5	16.8	8.5	4.5	8.4	11.8
1966	19,694	55.6	23.8	20.6	4.0	48.6	18.4	7.2	4.4	7.6	9.8
1967	20,185	57.6	23.9	18.5	4.6	51.7	17.1	7.0	4.6	7.2	7.8
1968	20,846	56.5	25.1	18.4	4.3	52.4	17.9	6.0	4.4	7.2	7.8
1969	21,126	56.8	24.2	19.0	4.3	55.9	16.7	3.6	4.4	7.2	7.9

Source: USDA (1970D).
[1] Data are 3-yr averages through 1963.
[2] Includes bull and stag beef.
[3] Includes Standard and Commercial grades through 1960.

Factors other than use of grades probably had an effect on grade improvement, but grades and grading provide a means for improvement of market efficiency and an efficient market tends to induce the production of preferred products. The evidence clearly indicates this has happened and use of grades undoubtedly was a beneficial contribution.

COMSUMER PREFERENCES AND KNOWLEDGE OF MEAT GRADES

In most discussions concerned with grades and grading it usually is assumed (explicitly or implicitly) that (1) consumers prefer one grade to another, (2) they are able to distinguish between and among grades, and (3) they act accordingly. Numerous studies have been made to test hypotheses along these lines. This section is not intended to be a comprehensive review of results, but rather to point up some generalizations derived from such studies. The area of consumer preference involves many subjective considerations which are exceedingly complex, and results have not been entirely consistent among studies or with some preconceived notions on the subject.

Consumer preference studies ordinarily are not designed to determine whether consumers can grade meat (place meat of various characteristics in the correct grade). There is clear evidence that consumers are not well-informed in grade names, let alone grade standards. Consumer preference studies are more concerned with a determination of the attributes in meat which consumers prefer, and in consumers' ability to differentiate between meats possessing varying degrees of those attributes.

Consumer evaluation of meat is largely based on (1) visual preferences and (2) sensory preferences—but these are not mutually exclusive. Other possible considerations are situational factors and imaginary differences. Most research has centered on visual and sensory preferences. In studies of visual preferences, consumers usually are shown photographs of cuts of meat (sometimes actual cuts of meat are used) selected in a manner intended to show differences between grades and/or within grades. In most of these studies consumers generally have indicated a preference for leaner cuts whether the meat be beef, pork, or lamb (Branson 1957; Perdue *et al.* 1958; Rhodes *et al.* 1955; Seltzer 1955; Stevens *et al.* 1956).

With beef, the leaner-appearing cuts are the so-called "lower" grades—Commercial, Standard, and Good. A first reaction might be that consumers were irrational, but a more considered judgment is that studies asking consumers' preferences within a range from Commercial to Prime places the respondent in a position not experienced in actual buying.

Most stores carry only one grade of beef—usually Choice, or its equivalent, if not officially graded.[9] The only alternative in this situation (and the only experience) consumers have is selection within the given grade. Many con-

---

[9] Some stores carry other grades, but few advertise the fact.

sumers select the leaner-appearing cuts to avoid trimming waste, with the expectation that eating quality will be relatively uniform. When confronted with Prime grade which has the appearance of more fat, and Good, Standards, and Commercial which appear to be leaner in that order (even though trim specifications may be comparable), many consumers seem to follow the pattern of selecting the leaner, which in these circumstances are cuts of different quality. In this situation their decisions based on visual appearance are rational.

When it comes to sensory tests (eating tests), consumers tend to show a preference for Prime and Choice grades of beef. Kiehl and Rhodes (1956) reported that "the eating preference patterns contradict the visual preferences found by many researchers, including ourselves. Many visual preferences have been made for the leaner grades at equal prices or even some with price differentials against the leaner cuts. Eating preferences were very rarely for the leaner grades."

Consumer studies of pork have shown a consistent preference for lean cuts. However, a substantial variation was apparent among the studies on the degree of preference (Birmingham et al. 1954; Nauman et al. 1959; Stevenson and Schneider 1959; Trotter and Engelman 1959; Vrooman 1952).

Several studies have shown that consumers, by and large, are not familiar with grade names and often confuse inspection with grading. In a study including beefsteak and bacon (along with other nonmeat items) Hutchinson (1970) found that 90% of the persons interviewed said "yes" to the question, "Is there a government grade for beefsteak?" and a like percentage said they usually bought government-graded beefsteak. However, some skepticism arises when 70 and 81%, respectively, of the respondents answered "yes" to the same questions for bacon. Bacon is not sold by government grade. The author (Hutchinson 1970) commented that "possibly a 'halo effect' exists; the consumer reasons that since some beef is graded, all meat is graded. When asked to identify the shape of the USDA grade mark, 21.5% correctly identified the shield-shaped mark, but 29.5% said it was a circle, indicating a high probability that they were confusing the inspection mark with the grade mark.

In summary remarks, Hutchinson (1970) stated, "Most U.S. consumers know little about federal grades for the foods they buy, but those who are aware of grades say they find them helpful in buying decisions . . . the use of both adjective and letter grades for different food items apparently was not confusing."

Weidenhamer et al. (1968), with reference to data collected in a study of opinions about meats reported, "homemakers are indeed confused about inspection and grading. Although virtually all respondents reported that the meat they buy is inspected and that beef is graded, half of the respondents stated that pork is graded; and a considerable number ascribed functions of grading to inspection, and vice versa. A question, therefore, arises about which statements regarding these functions were made on the basis of knowledge, which were based on assumptions, and which stemmed from misrepresentations—such as may be fostered by the way some stores or packers indicate that the meats they sell are inspected or graded." These authors also found homemakers were not well informed on grade names. When confronted with a list of 10 grade names for beef—including 5 correct grade names and 5 spurious grade names—respondents included 1 spurious grade name among the 3 most frequently mentioned.

Despite inconsistencies among some studies and lack of pronounced consensus among consumers on some attributes of meat, consumer preference studies have served, and will continue to serve, an extremely useful purpose. They have pointed up some identifiable preference characteristics, such as preference for leaner cuts and a positive relationship between marbling and palatability. Probably of importance equal to any positive results was the revelation that quality is an extremely complex subject to study. Meat itself is a complex product. Nevertheless, intelligent improvement in grade standards necessitates continued study of quality attributes which consumers can identify with reasonable accuracy and consistency. The ordering of preferences should be immaterial to researchers and public agencies involved in developing grade standards. If consumers were to prefer Standard grade beef over Good, and Good over Choice, this is the consumers' prerogative. From a grading standpoint, it is important that the grades are based on characteristics by which consumers can differentiate between grades regardless of the order of preference.

ADDITIONAL USDA MEAT SERVICES

The USDA provides two additional services closely related to its grading services: (1) Meat Acceptance Service, and (2) Carcass Evaluation Service. Both are voluntary, provided upon request, and paid for by users of the services.

Meat Acceptance Service

This is a service provided for large institutional buyers of meat (hospitals, steamship lines, government institutions, restaurant chains, etc.). Under this program an official USDA grader will certify that meat and meat products are in compliance with the purchaser's specifications. As an assist in the program, USDA's Consumer and Marketing Service has prepared a series of Institutional Meat Purchase Specifications (IMPS) covering some 300 fresh, cured, and processed meat and meat products. Plans call for the inclusion also of frozen canned, and portion control meats. The specifications were developed in conjunction with members of the meat trade; and detail such things as kind of cut, quality grade, size and weight of cut, and style of trim. If the predesigned "specs" do not meet a particular buyer's need, USDA will cooperate in drawing up specifications which meet a particular buyer's need.

With detailed specifications, a buyer is in position to ask suppliers for bids. This facilitates the "bid and acceptance" method of purchasing as mentioned in Chap. 9. After the purchaser has accepted a bid, a USDA grader examines, accepts, and certifies the shipment if it does in fact meet the specifications.

Purchasers and suppliers must make prior arrangements for the service and the USDA is reimbursed for its costs. Normally the supplier pays the cost which presumably is recovered in the price of the meat.

This service has been in operation since about 1960. Almost 1.3 billion pounds of meat were accepted in 1969 as complying with specifications. This is almost 10% of all federally graded meat and about 3.6% of total commercial meat production.

This service can benefit both purchaser and supplier. From the purchaser's standpoint he can obtain (1) assistance, if necessary, in determining specifications which meet his particular needs, and (2) professional assistance which relieves him of employing experts to do the buying (buying can be done by "bid and acceptance") and to examine it upon arrival. The service also can benefit a supplier in that official certification assures him that the shipment will not be rejected upon arrival.

Meat which is accepted is stamped, either directly on the meat if it can be individually stamped, or on the carton containing products that cannot be stamped individually. Stamps used are shown here. Meat which can be individually stamped bears the insignia shown on the left. Cartons which are

Acceptance Stamps

stamped bear both stamps. The letters AC in this example identify the grader who accepted the product.

Beef Carcass Data Service

For a number of years, cow-calf producers and feedlot operators have indicated an interest in obtaining data on carcass characteristics of their cattle after slaughter. This is vital information to a cow-herd operator in his herd improvement program. It is equally vital to a feedlot operator's feeding program. In a very direct way this enters into their marketing programs. Both classes of producers experienced difficulties in obtaining this type of information prior to initiation of the service. Maintaining identity of animals during growing, finishing, and slaughtering is difficult. Without some agreement with packers and graders, producers (and feeders) had problems in lining up all the necessary arrangements. During the early 1960's, the USDA made a move designed to alleviate the latter difficulty.

This was a program designated Beef Carcass Evaluation Service. Packers were informed of the program and graders were instructed to cooperate. It was the producer's responsibility to make arrangements with a packer and with a federal grader and to place an identification on each animal. After slaughter the grader filled out a form giving carcass characteristics and relayed the information to the producer.

The program worked, but from the producer's standpoint it was cumbersome and sometimes frustrating in making arrangements. Participation was limited in spite of the need and desire for carcass information.

In an effort to improve the service, USDA in early 1970 initiated a revised program on an experimental basis—renamed the Beef Carcass Data Service. Under the new setup, producers can purchase bright orange-colored USDA ear tags with identification marks. A cow-herd operator, for example, can tag his calves, and if the ear tag does not become lost or removed, that animal will be positively identified when it reaches a packing plant, even though it may have passed through several different ownerships and may be transported far from the home ranch. Producers have no further responsibilities. Prearrangements have been made with USDA inspectors and graders whereby the inspector will remove the tag from the ear on the slaughter floor and attach it to the carcass. The grader at the plant will examine the carcass for quality grade and yield grade along with such relevant details as the evaluation of conformation; marbling; backfat thickness; ribeye area; and kidney, pelvic, and heart fat. This data, along with tag number, will be forwarded to a clearing center which, in turn, forwards it to the tag owner.

BIBLIOGRAPHY

AGNEW, D. B. 1969. Improvements in grades of hogs slaughtered from 1960-61 to 1967-68. USDA Econ. Res. Serv. Marketing Res. Rept. *849*.

BIRMINGHAM, E. B. *et al.* 1954. Fatness of pork in relation to consumer preference. Missouri Agr. Expt. Sta. Bull. *549*.

BRANSON, R. E. 1957. The consumer market for beef. Texas Agr. Expt. Sta. Bull. *856*.

CLEMEN, R. A. 1923. The American Livestock and Meat Industry. Ronald Press Co., New York.

DOWELL, A. A., and BJORKA, K. 1941. Livestock Marketing. McGraw-Hill Book Co., New York.

ENGELMAN, G. 1961. Livestock and meat grading—the economic whys and wherefores. Paper presented to 11th Stockmen's Short Course, Washington State Univ., Dec.

FARRIS, P. L. 1960. Uniform grades and standards, product differentiation and product development. J. Farm Econ. Febr. 854-863.

FIENUP, D. F. *et al.* 1963. Economic effects of U.S. grades for lamb. USDA Econ. Res. Serv. Agr. Econ. Rept. *25*.

FOWLER, S. H. 1961. The Marketing of Livestock and Meat, 2nd Edition. Interstate Printers & Publishers, Danville, Ill.

HENDRIX, J. *et al.* 1963. Consumer acceptance of pork chops. Missouri Agr. Expt. Sta. Res. Bull. *834*.

HUTCHINSON, T. Q. 1970. Consumers' knowledge and use of government grades for selected food items. USDA Econ. Res. Serv. Marketing Res. Rept. *876*.

KIEHL, E. R., and RHODES, V. J. 1956. Techniques in consumer preference research. J. Farm Econ. *38*, No. 5, 1335-1345.

NATIONAL LIVESTOCK AND MEAT BOARD. 1969. Meat Evaluation Handbook. Natl. Livestock Meat Board, Chicago.

NAUMAN, H. D. *et al.* 1959. A large merchandising experiment with selected pork cuts. Missouri Agr. Expt. Sta. Res. Bull. *711*.

PERDUE, E.J. *et al.* 1958. Some results from a pilot investigation of consumer preferences for beef. Oklahoma Agr. Expt. Sta. Process. Ser. *P-304*.

RHODES, V. J. 1960. How the marking of beef grades was obtained. J. Farm Econ. *42*, No. 1, 133-151.

RHODES, V. J. *et al.* 1955. Visual preference for grades of retail cuts. Missouri Agr. Expt. Sta. Res. Bull. *583*.

RHODES, V. J. *et al.* 1956. Consumer preferences and beef grades. Missouri Agr. Expt. Sta. Res. Bull. *612*.

SELTZER, R. E. 1955. Consumer preferences for beef. Ariz. Agr. Expt. Sta. Res. Bull. *267*.

STEVENS, I. M. *et al.* 1956. Beef consumer use and preference. Wyoming Agr. Expt. Sta. Res. Bull. *343*.

STEVENSON, J., and SCHNEIDER, V. 1959. Consumer reaction to price differentials for meat-type pork. Econ. Marketing Inform. Indiana Farmers Oct. 30.

TROTTER, C., and ENGELMAN, G. 1959. Consumer response to graded pork. Penn. Agr. Expt. Sta. Res. Bull. *650*.

USDA. 1956. Official United States standards for grades of vealers and slaughter calves. USDA Agr. Marketing Serv. Regulatory Announcements *114*.

USDA. 1957. Official United States standards for grades of vealers and slaughter calves. USDA Agr. Marketing Serv. Regulatory Announcements *113*.

USDA. 1965A. Official United States standards for grades of carcass beef. USDA Consumer Marketing Serv. Regulatory Announcements *99*.

USDA. 1965B. Official United States standards for grades of feeder cattle. USDA Consumer Marketing Serv. Regulatory Announcements *183*.

USDA. 1966A. Official United States standards for grades of veal and calf carcasses. USDA Agr. Marketing Serv. Regulatory Announcements *113*.

USDA. 1966B. Official United States standards for grades of slaughter cattle. USDA Agr. Marketing Serv. Regulatory Announcements *112*.

USDA. 1968A. Official United States standards for grades of barrow and gilt carcasses. USDA Consumer Marketing Serv. Reprinted in Federal Register.

USDA. 1968B. Official United States standards for grades of slaughter barrows and gilts. USDA Agr. Marketing Serv. Regulatory Announcements *172*.

USDA. 1968C. USDA yield grades for beef. USDA Consumer Marketing Serv. Marketing Bull. *45*.

USDA. 1969A. Official United States standards for grades of feeder pigs. USDA Consumer Marketing Serv. Regulatory Announcements *189*.

USDA. 1969B. Official United States standards for grades of lamb, yearling mutton, and mutton carcasses; slaughter lambs, yearlings and sheep. USDA Agr. Marketing Serv. Regulatory Announcements *168*.

USDA. 1970A. USDA grades for pork carcasses. USDA Consumer Marketing Serv. Marketing Bull. *49*.

USDA. 1970B. USDA grades for slaughter swine and feeder pigs. USDA Consumer Marketing Serv. Marketing Bull. *51*.

USDA. 1970C. USDA yield grades for lamb. USDA Consumer Marketing Serv. Marketing Bull. *52*.

USDA. 1970D. Handbook of agricultural charts. USDA Agr. Handbook *397*.

VROOMAN, C. W. 1952. Consumer report on pork production. Oregon Agr. Expt. Sta. Bull. *521*.

WEIDENHAMER, MARGARET *et al.* 1968. Homemakers' opinions about selected meats—a preliminary report. USDA Statist. Reporting Serv. *SRS-12*.

WILLIAMS, W. F. 1960. Note on how the marking of beef grades was obtained. J. Farm Econ. *42*, No. 4, 878-886.

CHAPTER 12

Market Intelligence

In a competitive market economy the bargaining position of buyers and sellers is conditioned by the degree to which they are informed. The classical economic concept of a perfectly competitive market assumes perfect knowledge, which of course, is unattainable. Buyers and sellers utilize information which is available, and the relative position of buyers and sellers may be far from equal. Traditionally, agricultural producers have been labelled as "price takers." Part of this stems from lack of effective organization, but part also results from lack of market information, which in a systematic sense may be called market intelligence.

There was always a need for market information, but the urgency has increased with the trend toward more and more direct marketing. Livestock producers are dealing directly with professional buyers in the sale of finished stock and often with professional sellers in the purchase of feeder stock. The concept of competition implies a notion of rivalry, or struggle, and a large share of the struggle is in keeping at least as well informed as other parties. Other parties include competitors in the industry as well as participants in buying and selling transactions. In nationwide and worldwide markets, no single person or firm can possibly make enough observations to keep abreast of the ever-changing economic and political forces which shape the markets. The livestock and meat markets, like many others, are affected by supply-demand trends, import-export regulations, and public policy decisions not only in the United States but in Australia, New Zealand, Argentina, Canada, Ireland, Common Market Countries and many others. Private sources gather and disseminate much information, but it was recognized at an early stage that government services were justified not only from the standpoint of practicality, but also as a matter of public interest.

MARKET DIMENSIONS

Market intelligence needs may be considered in two general dimensions: (1) the short run and (2) the long run. It is impossible to specify short and long run weeks, months, or years, but in general the short run is concerned with informational needs in marketing to best advantage a production output which virtually is complete in quantity and quality (essentially no time remains for altering the product). The long run envisions enough time to adjust production programs which coincidentally are related to marketing programs. The time required for such changes is greater in cow-calf operations than for sow herds; and is still different in a calf wintering program.

A feeder with a pen of livestock about finished out and ready for sale needs to know current price levels for his class, grade, and weight of livestock (implied here is the ability to evaluate grade). He needs to know variations in relevant prices among alternative market outlets. Information on current conditions of supply and demand and market movements help him size up the current market situation, although individually he has no control over them. The market intelligence need in this short-run situation sometimes is referred to as "price and sales information," or as "market news."

The position a producer finds himself in at a given time, however, is, in part, determined by decisions he and others made some months earlier—i.e., when he bought feeder animals, outlined his feeding program or initiated a breeding program. It was then that the wheels were set in motion which largely determined the quantity and quality of livestock which would be available at later dates. Information is needed which assists producers in making wise planning decisions in this longer run context. This type of information also is needed by packers, processors, cold storage interests, wholesalers, and retailers. Consumers, too, have an interest, in that better informed market participants make for a more efficient market system which, in turn, allows consumer demands to guide production. The informational needs in this situation call for data and analyses which project probable supply and demand conditions; information which attempts to look ahead rather than at the present. This type of market intelligence often is referred to as "outlook and situation information," and is construed to include analyses of changing consumer preferences.

DEVELOPMENT OF INFORMATION SERVICES

The history of development of meat and livestock market reporting in the United States is almost as old as the livestock industry itself.[1] The earliest source of market information was newspaper quotations of provisions (meat, lard, and tallow) prices. The press, then as now, recognized the news worthiness of market reports. The reporting of live animal prices followed that of meat by a considerable number of years. The exportation of provisions gave that market a semblance of organized arrangements long before enough consistency was generated in live markets to warrant price reports.

Private market reporting grew with the industry largely in the form of newspapers, magazines, trade publications, and publications sponsored by organized markets. Some of the problems inherent in these reports were mentioned in the last chapter. The heterogenity of terms used among markets, and the inconsistency in use of terms, both within given markets and between markets, seriously hnadicapped the interpretation of reports.

In addition to the reporting of current market information, the need for

---

[1] Two excellent accounts of early historical developments of market information are Dowell and Bjorka (1941) and USDA (1969A).

basic industry data also was recognized at an early date. The merits of turning this job over to the federal government were evident from the beginning. Although the beginning was on an elementary scale, the first Census of Agriculture was taken in 1840 by the U.S. Office of Patents. In later years, responsibility for census enumeration was placed in the Bureau of Census, U.S. Department of Commerce. Early census data did not provide information of immediate application to the marketing of livestock, but it established the federal government as the data collecting and disseminating agency. Subsequent organization of the U.S. Department of Agriculture in 1862 placed additional agricultural data collection, interpretation, and dissemination in that branch of the federal government. However, its early efforts were directed at increasing production rather than improving marketing.

Producer dissatisfaction with market conditions was particularly evident during the latter half of the 1800's and the first decade of the 1900's. Producers, then as now, were troubled by the difference between prices received at the farm and prices charged at retail. Deficiencies in market price reporting were indicated to be one of the major problems. During this period many conferences were held and investigations were carried out. Among the spokesmen for producers, Henry C. Wallace, editor of *Wallace's Farmer*, stands out. Wallace also was secretary of a farmer organization, the Corn Belt Meat Producers Association. This organization, together with another, the American National Live Stock Association, carried on active campaigns in attempts to alleviate what were considered detrimental market reporting practices. The accusations ranged from inadequate and inaccurate reporting to deliberate misrepresentation. Henry Wallace participated in the conferences, carried on discussions in his magazine, and stimulated interest in producer organizations. During the fall of 1915 he published an editorial in which he presented, in some detail, suggestions for investigating the situation and for establishing a federal market reporting service.

A logical branch of government for marketing work was in existence at that time, although it was relatively new. The USDA Office of Markets had been established in 1913, and within it a Division of Livestock, Meats and Wool in early 1915. As a result of studies made by that office and guided extensively by Wallace's work, the federal government in 1915 set up arrangements for collecting market information. Congress appropriated $65,000 in 1916, for collection and dissemination of information on the number and grade of livestock being produced; prices, receipts, and shipments by class and grade at central markets; prices of meat and meat products; and the amount of meat in storage. However, at administrative discretion, the initial emphasis was on meat and lard. The first federal report on meat marketing was issued in December, 1916. Eighteen months later the first livestock marketing report was issued. These early market reports were limited to prices and market conditions at a few central markets. By this time tentative grades had been established on meat and livestock, so for the first time a uniform language was available for use in price quotations. Although the original emphasis was on meat market reporting, this gradually changed over the years. By the early 1940's, major attention was on the live animal market. As the trend toward direct marketing picked up momentum, particularly since World War II, interest again shifted to the meat trade. Direct selling, especially by the carcass grade and weight method, necessitates a good knowledge of conditions in the wholesale meat market. At the same time, interest was high in the live animal market so currently the Federal Market News Service attempts to maintain a balanced reporting of meat, livestock, and wool markets.

Market reporting, as carried on by the Federal Market News Service, primarily is aimed at reporting current prices, movements, and market conditions. This is intended to serve short run informational needs. Many states also carry out market reporting functions—some in cooperation with the federal service, others entirely as a state effort. Private firms and agencies have continued efforts in this area. Newspapers, radio and TV stations, farm magazines, farm organizations, commission firms, auction operators, and private market agencies expend an enormous effort in providing market intelligence to all sectors of the livestock and meat trade. Many of these firms and agencies are engaged only in dissemination of market news, using as their major source the data collected by government agencies. But there are exceptions. The *National Provisioner*'s "Yellow Sheet" is a compilation of privately-collected wholesale meat market information. The American National Cattleman's Association's "CATTLE-FAX" depends almost entirely on privately-collected data and its interpretation.

Comprehensive work in the collection of situation type information followed shortly after that of market news. Following World War I, and continuing to the present, has been a deep interest in knowing the forces behind the market trends. The vast amount of data needed for this type analysis require the services of government. Involved here, in addition to livestock and meat data, are such things as feed supplies, population (by age classifications), incomes (distributed by income levels), prices and supplies of products which compete with meats, trends in consumer preferences, imports, exports, etc. As mentioned earlier, a start on this type information was made in 1940 in the first agricultural census. The agricultural census, however, does not collect nearly all the needed information, and furthermore, it is taken only at 5-yr intervals. In certain data series, the census serves an extremely useful purpose in providing a benchmark with which to check data collected from other sources, but by itself census data are inadequate for outlook and situation analyses. For many analyses, annual, quarterly, and monthly data are required. Although some work was done in this area earlier, the USDA has placed particular emphasis on it following World War II. The office with this responsibility has, over the years, undergone several name changes—currently it is the Statistical Reporting Service (SRS) of the Consumer and Marketing Service (C&MS). While SRS is the major data-collecting agency, several other arms of USDA collect substantial amounts of relevant data in the process of carrying out other functions. Examples are the Meat Inspection Division (MID) of the Agricultural Research Service (ARS) and the Packers and Stockyards Administration (P&S).

The analysis and interpretation of data collected by SRS and others is performed by many governmental agencies, and several merit particular mention. The Economic and Statistical Analysis Division of the Economic Research Service conducts a continuing compilation and interpretation of livestock, meat, and wool marketing factors in an outlook and situation framework. The Marketing Economics Division of the Economic Research Service, and the Transportation and Facilities Division of the Agricultural Research Service carry out programmed research projects on marketing problems as warranted by changing conditions.

PUBLIC AGENCIES AND INSTITUTIONS

Federal-State Market News Service, AMS, USDA[2]

The Federal Market News Service is an arm of the Agricultural Marketing Service within the USDA hierarchy. Individual states may at their option cooperate with the federal agency in activities within their respective states.

The major responsibility of the Federal-State Market News Service is collection and dissemination of current, unbiased, market information. The agency gathers information on many agricultural products, but this discussion is limited to activities in reporting prices, market conditions, and current supplies and demand for livestock, meat, and wool at selected markets throughout the United States.

Organizational Features.–The Federal Market News Service cooperates, where arrangements can be made, with state marketing in setting up Federal-State offices. In other instances, the federal service maintains offices not associated with state agencies. In 1970 there were 21 state marketing agencies cooperating with the federal agency. In total, 55 livestock, meat, and wool field offices were maintained throughout the United States. This provided coverage of 22 terminal livestock markets and 170 auctions. Information was collected on direct sales of livestock from 22 major areas, and wool and wholesale meat sales at a number of points. Information on meat sales were collected from trading in Iowa, Chicago, Omaha, Denver, the East Coast, the West Coast, western Texas, and western Kansas. Marketing data were obtained from Boston, the primary wool market, and for western wool and mohair sales. Arrangements also are operative for collection and dissemination of data

---

[2] Material presented in this section draws heavily from publications of the Federal Market News Service, Consumer and Marketing Service, USDA.

on offal sales, daily slaughter estimates, weekly meat production estimates, and daily pork cut-out values at Chicago.

The Federal Market News Service has attempted to keep pace with changing time, but this is a continuing problem. Funds and personnel are limited, and lags typically occur before changes can be made. The situation was relatively simple when terminals dominated the market scene. A single reporter could personally cover the highly concentrated activities. However, with expansion in auctions and direct marketing, the opposite situation prevails. To maintain the established standards of excellence within the fund restrictions, the reporting of auction sales has been limited to 170 major markets. The expansion in direct selling of livestock presented still another problem. Direct sales from farms are widely scattered, generally nonobservable private transactions. Sales out of commercial feedlots are somewhat more concentrated, but adequate coverage still is a problem. Direct sales of slaughter livestock, of course, involve packing plants which, in effect, are points of concentration, but decentralization of the packing industry presents a widely scattered pattern—and there is no legal compulsion for buyers and sellers to divulge purchase and sale information. This points up an important aspect of the entire governmental marketing intelligence system. Federal Market News Service depends primarily upon voluntary cooperation of all segments of the industry in gathering information and also of the news media in disseminating it.[3] Data are obtained on direct sales—largely by telephone, with some visits by market reporters at points of sale.

At scheduled times the assembled market information is fed into a leased teletypewriter system for dissemination to the press, radio, television, and trade sources; and about 25 offices have automatic self-answering, taped, telephone reports. In addition, mimeographed and printed reports are sent by mail.

Operational Features.—The method of operation is conditioned by the type of market being covered. At most markets, trained, professional reporters personally observe sales, interview buyers and sellers, and check receipts and movements which have a bearing on supplies and demand. Where sales are sparce or distances too great, information is gathered by telephone and teletypewriter with some follow-up personal contacts and inspection of sales records.

Terminal Markets.—Experienced market reporters are stationed at 22 terminal markets. These men are capable livestock graders who tour the yards during trading hours interviewing buyers and sellers, and observing sales. This includes both private treaty and auction sales at terminals which have auction

---

[3] Some data collected by regulatory agencies, e.g., the Meat Inspection Division and the Packers and Stockyards Administration, USDA, is mandatory and finds use in certain aspects of marketing, but these agencies are not a part of the Federal Market News Service.

facilities. Reporters know the market personnel and have working relationships which permit discussions not afforded general market visitors. The actual transaction, ordinarily, is a private affair between buyer and seller, but generally this confidence is shared with market reporters. However, reporters realize that in some instances market personnel may attempt to bias the report for personal gain. An experienced reporter can recognize this and make appropriate adjustments.

Three reports are issued each day at terminals: (1) early morning, (2) mid-session, and (3) market closing. These reports are flashed over the wire network to other livestock markets and to news media. In some cases the reporter may also broadcast directly over a local radio station. The early morning report consists of an estimate of that day's receipts, and evaluation of opening price trends, and observations of early sales. After filing this report on the wire network, the reporter returns to the yards for observations which will comprise the mid-session report. By mid-session a firm report can be made on receipts, price trends, and quotations for the bulk of sales by class, grade and weight. Further observations and checks give indications of possible late changes which go into the closing report.

Auction Markets.—Reporters visit auction markets and take a position which permits an unrestricted view of the sales ring. They use a prepared form for recording sale price and an evaluation of grade and condition of the animals. Weights often can be observed on the auction scales. As is the case at terminals, not all lots are uniform in grade and other value factors. Reporters are trained to recognize these situations and make appropriate adjustments. For the 170 auctions covered, a local report is issued for each sale. In addition, a summary is forwarded to an appropriate central office for dissemination on a statewide or area basis.

Direct Livestock Sales.—Information is assembled on direct sales of slaughter cattle, feeder cattle, hogs, and sheep from 22 major market areas. Contract sales are covered as well as current transactions. Much information is gathered by telephone and teletypewriter, but interviews also are made at feedlots, packing plants, and ranches. Reports are issued daily, semiweekly or weekly, depending upon trading volume.

Wholesale Meat Markets.—Wholesale prices on carcass and primal cuts are reported daily from selected points, including Iowa, Chicago, Omaha, Denver, the East Coast, and the West Coast. Semiweekly reports also are issued covering sales in western Texas and western Kansas. A recent innovation is the collection and reporting of prices on fabricated cuts of beef (wholesale and oven-ready cuts prepared by packers) from Los Angeles, New York, Philadelphia, and Chicago. Chief reliance in this operation is placed on telephone interviews.

Wool.—A weekly wool market report is issued from Boston, the primary U.S. wool market. An experienced market reporter visits the market, observes sales by grade, and interviews buyers and sellers. Reports also are prepared on marketing in western wool and mohair producing areas where reporters collect information by telephone and by visiting with ranchers and local market agents.

Other Products.—The Federal Market News Service also reports offal value from sales points on the East Coast, Chicago, Denver and River Points, and the West Coast. Daily estimates also are made on pork cut-out values. This is the combined value of pork cuts, based on Chicago prices, of 150- and 180-lb hog carcasses grading U.S. No. 1 through U.S. No. 4.

In addition to consistent use of official grade terminology, the Federal Market News Service adheres to uniform use of terms in describing market conditions. Following are the commonly-used terms and their meanings (USDA 1970A).

DEMAND refers not only to a buyer's desire to possess a certain volume, but also refers to his willingness and ability to buy.

Demand is GOOD when buyers are more aggressive than usual, or when large or increased supplies are bringing unchanged to higher prices.

Demand is POOR when buyers are less aggressive than usual, or when decreased supplies are selling at unchanged to lower prices.

SUPPLY refers to the quantity available for current day's trading on the market. It includes any carryover from the previous day.

PRICE refers to specific dollars and cents paid for a given grade and weight selection.

PRICE TREND refers to the direction in which prices are moving compared with prices paid the previous trading session. Five terms used to describe price trends are: HIGHER is used when bulk sale prices are measurably higher than the previous trading session. LOWER is used when bulk sale prices are measurably lower than the previous trading session. STRONG is used when there is a definite, but not quite measurable, leaning toward higher prices. WEAK is used when there is a definite, but not quite measurable, leaning toward lower prices. STEADY is used when prices have not changed from the previous trading session.

TRADING ACTIVITY refers to the pace at which sales are being made compared to normal for that market. The pace can be active, moderately active, or slow.

TRADING MODERATELY ACTIVE means that sales are being made at a normal pace for the particular market.

TRADING SLOW means that sales are being made at a slower than normal pace for the particular market.

Market News Reports.—Figure 12.1 shows the system of approximately 22,000 miles of leased wire facilities over which the Federal Market News Service makes its reports available to communications media. Not all of the office locations shown are concerned with livestock, meat, and wool informa-

Source: USDA, Market News Service

FIG. 12.1. MARKET NEWS SERVICE LEASED WIRE NETWORK

tion, but the network is available for transmission of reports. It will be noted that Kansas City is a critical relay point, connecting the network of the eastern half of the nation with Mountain, Southwest, and West Coast market points. While the widest and most rapid dissemination is over the wire network, Federal Market News Service also makes extensive use of mimeographed, mailed reports.

Each week, data from field offices are summarized and forwarded to Washington where they are compiled in a weekly publication entitled *Livestock Meat and Wool Market News*. This publication is one that by most standards should be on the "must" list for most livestock producers and market personnel. It is useful, not only for relatively up-to-date compilation of data for selected markets, but also for digests of current releases and reports, including outlook and situation reports issued by other government agencies.

Special mention should also be made of the automatic, taped, self-answering telephone service. Unquestionably, this is a valuable improvement in market news reporting. These devices accept long distance as well as local calls. Tapes are updated several times during each day and the service is available on a 24-hr basis.

Statistical Reporting Service, AMS, USDA

Major responsibility of the Statistical Reporting Service is data gathering—as contrasted with analysis and interpretation. Most of the data are collected by state offices which are referred to as (state) Crop and Livestock Reporting Service. The information is forwarded to a Washington office known as the Crop Reporting Board, where, in closed door sessions, the board reviews state and aggregated compilations prior to release.

Vast amounts of data are collected on all aspects of crops and livestock including such general categories as production, distribution, storage, inventories, average prices received by farmers, values, animals slaughtered, meat production, etc. Most of the data are related to marketing.

The type of data collected, and schedules of distribution make the market-related information particularly adapted for outlook and situation analyses. The research and analysis functions, however, are usually carried out in other agencies. The Statistical Reporting Service (SRS) makes the data available, not only to other governmental agencies but also to the public. Many of the findings have considerable newsworthiness (without further analysis) and are widely disseminated by communications media. However, it should be understood that this is not the same current, up-to-the-minute price and market condition information reported by the Federal Market News Service. The market intelligence data collected by the Statistical Reporting Service, as indicated above, is intended for a different purpose from that of Federal Market News Service.

The major livestock, meat, and wool reports published by the Washington, D.C. office are given below (with usual month of release in parentheses).[4] Individual states also distribute mimeographed reports emphasizing data for the respective state

(1) Cattle, Sheep, and Goat Inventory, January 1,_____–(Feb.). Gives (year)
number of livestock on farms Jan. 1, by class and by state.

(2) Calf Crop _____–(Feb.). Gives number of calves born during indi- (year)
cated year, by states. February report gives calves born previous year.

(3) Calf Crop _____–(July). July calf crop report gives estimate of calves (year)
born and to be born during current year, by states.

(4) Hogs and Pigs–(June). Gives inventory of hogs and pigs on farms June 1, an estimate of spring pig crop farrowings that year, and an estimate of intended farrowings for the following fall pig crop, by states.

(5) Hogs and Pigs–(Dec.). Gives inventory of hogs and pigs on farms Dec. 1, an estimate of fall pig crop farrowings that year, and an estimate of intended farrowings for the following spring pig crop, by states.

(6) Hogs and Pigs–(March, June, Sept., Dec.). Provides quarterly estimates of farrowings and inventory for ten important hog-producing states.

(7) Lamb Crop _____–(Feb.). Gives number of lambs saved during the (year)
indicated year, by states. February report gives lambs saved previous year.

(8) Lamb Crop _____–(July). Gives number of lambs saved during the (year)
indicated year, by states. July report gives lambs saved during current year.

(9) Sheep and Lambs on Feed January 1, _____–(Jan.). Gives number of (year)
sheep and lambs on feed, by states.

(10) Sheep and Lambs on Feed and Early Lamb Crop, _____–(March). (year)
Gives number of sheep and lambs on feed Mar. 1 and an estimate of number of early lambs.

(11) Sheep and Lambs on Feed, November 1, _____–(Nov.). Gives (year)
number of sheep and lambs on feed Nov. 1 in seven important feeding states.

(12) Wool and Mohair Production and Value, _____–(April). Gives (year)
number of sheep shorn, wool production, price by month, and value by states; number of goats clipped, mohair production, and value, by states.

(13) Shorn Wool Production _____–(July). Gives number of sheep shorn (year)
and to be shorn during the year and wool production, by states.

[4] From issuance dates and contents of reports released by the USDA Crop Reporting Board.

(14) Meat Animals-Farm Production, Disposition and Income $\overline{\text{(year)}}$ — (April). Gives data on indicated items, by states.

(15) Livestock Slaughter and Meat Production—(Monthly). Gives number of head and live weight of cattle, calves, hogs, sheep and lambs slaughtered in commercial plants, by states; meat production by species, and lard production for the United States.

(16) Cattle and Calves on Feed—(Jan. April, July, Oct.). Gives number on feed at beginning of each quarter, by states; number by class, by weight group, and by length of time on feed for leading states; and number sold for slaughter at selected markets.

(17) Cattle and Calves on Feed—(Monthly). Gives number on feed beginning of each month for seven important feeding states and number sold for slaughter at selected markets.

(18) Shipments of Stocker and Feeder Cattle and Sheep—(Monthly). Gives number received in selected Corn Belt States from public stockyards and shipments of direct sales the preceding month, by states; shipments from public stockyards by market origin and state of destination.

(19) Cattle on Pastures in the Blue Stem (Flint Hills) and Osage Sections of Kansas and Oklahoma—(June). Gives shipments of cattle into these areas as of June 1.

(20) Western Range and Livestock—(Monthly). Gives condition of ranges, cattle and sheep, first of month, by states for western states.

(21) Special Wheat Pasture Report—(Sept., Oct., Nov., Dec.). Gives condition of wheat for pasturing purposes.

In addition to reports listed above, the Statistical Reporting Service issues about mid-year, an annual summary of livestock and meat data for the previous year, along with historical series for several prior years. Each year, adjustments and corrections are made in data of prior years, if necessary. This publication is entitled *Livestock and Meat Statistics* and contains a wealth of basic market-related data. Prior to 1957, these data were published under the title *Livestock Market News Statistics and Related Data*.

Economic and Statistical Analysis Division, ERS, USDA

The Economic and Statistical Analysis Division (ESAD) of the Economic Research Service (ERS) basically is responsible for analysis and interpretation of data in a situation-outlook framework. One of its major activities is the analysis of livestock, meat, and wool data. This agency issues a publication entitled *Livestock and Meat Situation*, about 6 times a year and about 4 times each year it issues the *Wool Situation*. Periodically these situation reports also include special articles on analyses of currently relevant problems in the livestock and meat industry. Once each year an "outlook" issue is prepared.

This agency goes beyond the presentation of data. Its activities include production, demand, and price projections—though somewhat guarded. Retail meat price compilations are given in each issue of the *Livestock and Meat Situation*, and data, with commentary, also are given on imports and exports of livestock and meat. Other relevant publications emanating from this agency are the *Feed Situation*, the *Fats and Oils Situation*, and the *Demand and Price Situation*.

These "Situation" reports are recommended as another "must" among government publications for livestock and meat industry personnel who have an interest in the market situation.

Marketing Economics Division, ERS, USDA

This agency prepares on a regular basis the *Marketing and Transportation Situation*, which contains calculations of marketing margins and marketing costs—an ever popular and informative series of marketing information. Additionally, the Marketing Economics Division conducts a substantial program of research devoted to a wide range of livestock, meat, and wool marketing problems.

States

It was mentioned previously that some states cooperate with the federal government in operation of the Federal Market News Service. Most important agricultural states carry on additional work under a department, division, or an office of marketing. Among the major livestock-producing states, these agencies conduct a variety of programs associated with the marketing of livestock, meat, and wool. No attempt is made here to enumerate individual state activities, but some of the general areas emphasized are promotional programs designed to increase meat consumption, programs designed to improve both quantity and quality of products produced, collection and dissemination of market news not covered by the federal service, and the preparation and dissemination of outlook-type information.

Colleges and Universities

Most Land Grant Colleges and Universities in important livestock-producing states are actively engaged in work related to livestock and meat marketing. This activity is shared by personnel in the Agricultural Experiment Station and in the Cooperative Agricultural Extension Service. The major responsibility of the former is research, while that of the latter is dissemination of information. In most cases these activities are closely coordinated. In some, the personnel hold joint appointments and often are under joint administrative arrangements. Research activities cover every facet of marketing. Virtually no effort is expended in the *collecting* of marketing news, but substantial effort is devoted to preparation and dissemination of outlook and situation type information.

This includes both on-campus and off-campus conferences and meetings, radio and television programs, and published materials. A number of colleges and universities have a long history of work in livestock marketing and regularly issue (monthly or weekly) publications devoted in full or in part to analyses designed to assist producers in both short- and long-run marketing decisions. The emphasis in recent years, however, has shifted to a more analytical approach designed to provide the industry with information which provides a basis for production and marketing decisions within a long-run framework.

Commodity Exchange Authority, USDA

The Commodity Exchange Authority (CEA) is an office of USDA with responsibility for supervising and regulating activities in the futures markets. Among its several functions is the publication of market information and a considerable body of statistics on futures trading. As conditions warrant, this office also makes special surveys and issues reports on trading activities. Monthly reports entitled *Commitments of Traders in Commodity Futures* show aggregate long and short speculative hedging commitments of large traders who are required to report trading positions, and derived unclassified long and short commitments of small traders. This report is available for live cattle, live hogs, frozen pork bellies, and wool, as well as other commodities. A daily report is issued on volume of trading and open interest for wool, and wool top futures, but not for livestock or meat futures. Each year an annual summary of futures market statistics for fiscal years beginning July 1, is usually released in December.

PRIVATE FIRMS, AGENCIES, AND ORGANIZATIONS

Newspapers, Radio, and Television

The management of news media usually respond to the interests of subscribers, listeners, and viewers. But their response is conditioned by the degree of interest shown, the availability of materials with which to satisfy the interest, and personal considerations. Livestock producers continually request more and improved market information—there is no question about producer interest, but that message is not always conveyed to the management. News media, generally, are not organized to collect market information; they depend upon other sources. The Federal-State Market News Service has attempted to fill this need and releases are made available through news wire services.

The available materials are accepted and utilized in all degrees of coverage (from zero to full coverage) by various newspapers, radio, and television stations. Many areas lack local newspapers which give adequate livestock market news, and some of the more remote areas have problems with radio and television reception, yet these media often are listed by producers among the most important sources of information (Bohlen and Beal 1967; Roberts 1959). In most important livestock-producing areas, certain newspapers, radio stations, and television stations have developed a rather respected reputation for livestock market reporting. These sources usually are known among producers and market personnel or can be easily determined by inquiry from experienced stockmen or market representatives.

Farm and Trade Magazines

Farm magazines have been cited as one of the most important sources of livestock marketing information, and a large number of magazines cater to the livestock clientele. (Roberts 1959). The coverage among farm magazines ranges all the way from general farm magazines to those devoted to a single aspect (such as feeding), a single specie, or even to a particular breed. The latter, however, ordinarily are less market oriented than others. Some magazines regularly devote a section to livestock marketing, and some utilize the services of special contributing editors or correspondents for preparing the materials. Others include special articles at irregular intervals.

Trade magazines are oriented to problems and issues of a particular sector of the industry, which may be commodity groups such as wool or meat, or functional groups such as wholesalers or retailers.

The following magazines are cited simply as examples with orientation toward a variety of interest groups: *Beef, Farm Journal, Farm Quarterly, Feedlot, National Hog Farmer, National Livestock Producer, National Provisioner, Successful Farming, Western Livestock Journal, Western Meat Industry, Progressive Grocer*, and *Super Market News*.

Market Agencies

Many market agencies—i.e., commission firms, auction markets, and related organizations (such as livestock market foundations found at some terminals)—prepare and distribute market information. In most cases emphasis is placed upon prices and market conditions of the particular market where the agency is located. A common form of presentation is a weekly market newsletter or card. However, auctions and foundations often sponsor radio and television broadcasts.

Market agencies are frank in acknowledging a dual purpose in their market reporting activities, as follows: (a) a desire to provide informational service, and (b) its use as a competitive tool in market promotion and solicitation of business. From a business standpoint both objectives are perfectly legitimate and tend to increase the degree of competition in the marketing system as long as the information is accurate and methods of presentation are fair.

Personnel of progressive market agencies also personally visit farms and ranches of customers and potential customers and participate in field programs. Again, these may have promotional and solicitation aspects, but at the same time they can be informational.

Market Analysis and Price Reporting Firms

There are a number of market analysis firms which make a business of selling market information—usually on a subscription basis. This class of agency tends to be more specific in forecasts and recommendations than most public agencies. A wide variety of services and reports are offered, ranging from monthly letters to daily private wire reports. The frequency of report, extent of market coverage, and degree of analytical sophistication generally are reflected in the price charged. The following is in no sense a complete listing. The firms named are simply examples of this type of service: *Doanes Agricultural Digest, Kiplinger Agricultural Letter, National Provisioner's Daily Market and News Service* (the Yellow Sheet), and *Pickell Enterprises Livestock Bulletin.* The Yellow Sheet differs from others listed here in two major respects. First, its coverage is devoted entirely to wholesale meat prices, while the others are concerned primarily with livestock. Second, the Yellow Sheet basically reports market prices, rather than performing analyses. The Yellow Sheet is in a class by itself, as an example of a private firm in the livestock-meat industry complex prospering in the area of price reporting—a field almost exclusively in the domain of public agencies.

Industry Organizations

Producer Associations.—The interest of producer organizations in livestock marketing dates back many decades. The Grange considered marketing problems a major issue shortly after the Civil War. Efforts of the Corn Belt Meat Producers Association, and the American National Livestock Association in promoting the establishment of market news reporting was mentioned earlier in this chapter. Every major farm organization has long been concerned with various aspects of marketing. Until recently the efforts of producer organizations have been directed almost exclusively at public policy issues. Several such issues were mentioned in earlier chapters—monopolistic trade practices, and the establishment of federal grade standards. Within recent years, however, several producer organizations have taken a more direct approach to marketing problems. This is an attempt on the part of producers to shift the balance of bargaining power to producers.

Two of these organizations merit special attention. The two organizations prominent in this approach are both utilizing privately-developed market intelligence systems as a basic tool. They are the American National Cattlemen's Association, and the National Farmers Organization. The American National Cattlemen's Association set up a separate corporation, Cattle Marketing Information Services, Inc. (CMIS) to operate their service, appropriately dubbed CATTLE-FAX. Both CMIS and NFO have developed systems for determining, on a relatively local basis, numbers of livestock on feed, potential supplies at future dates, together with current prices, market conditions, and other market factors. In addition to data collected from its own members, each has access to and compiles a great amount of market information made available by many other sources. This, however, is about as far as the similarity goes.

NFO's use of its information is entirely a centralized operation. Information is funnelled into the central office where it is used by this office in contract negotiation with packers and other selling operations for the membership.

CMIS assembles, analyzes, and interprets its information centrally, but transmits it by phone and by mail back to its members. Members then utilize the information individually (or in local pooled arrangements) in negotiating direct sales with packers. CATTLE-FAX subscribers pay a monthly fee—a fixed minimum plus a charge per head up to a stipulated maximum total fee. The CATTLE-FAX service would be rather expensive for a single farm-sized cattle feeder, but pooled arrangements can be set up where several small operators share the cost of an installation which may be located in a bank or business establishment convenient to the group. NFO's cost is included in membership dues.

A number of other producer organizations are active in marketing work and have varying degrees of market information systems, but generally on substantially smaller scales than the two mentioned above. The following are cited as additional examples without elaboration on their programs: The American Farm Bureau Federation (which sponsors the American Marketing Association), the American Sheep Producers Council, the Mid-West Wool Association, the National Swine Producers Council, and the National Livestock Producers Association.

A variety of other industry organizations with interests in market information exists at different levels of the total livestock-meat marketing system. Only four will be cited here. The American Meat Institute is mentioned as representative of the packer-processor sector of the industry, the Super Market Institute, Inc., and the National Association of Retail Grocers as representative of retailers, and the National Livestock and Meat Board, which cuts across all levels of the marketing system.

American Meat Institute.—A group of meat packers met in 1906 and organized the American Meat Packers Association. The name was changed to Institute of American Meat Packers in 1919, and to American Meat Institute (AMI) in 1940. Membership in AMI is composed of packers, processors, and associate members. Its major activities include sponsorship of research, and educational and promotional programs. While the AMI may be classed as a trade organization with primary allegiance to its members, its declared objectives and multidimensional program of activities are of direct and indirect benefit to the entire livestock-meat economy. The central office of this organization maintains a section devoted to continuous development of market information. Among its releases are an annual, *Financial Facts About the Meat Packing Industry*, and a *Weekly Market Supply Information*. The former draws heavily from data collected directly by AMI—data not available from any other source. These original data are supplemented by government information and this publication is available to the public. The weekly release primarily is an AMI staff summary and interpretation of currently relevant government releases. Its distribution is limited to members of the Institute. In 1966 the AMI, under authorship of its Vice President and Director of Marketing, J. Russell Ives, published a book length treatise entitled *The Livestock and Meat Economy of the United States*. This is a comprehensive treatment of economic aspects of livestock production, meat packing, processing, wholesaling, and retailing.

Super Market Institute and National Association of Retail Grocers.—These are trade organizations oriented primarily to interests of their members. The National Association of Retail Grocers has a long history with food retailers, having been organized in 1893. The Super Market Institute was organized in 1937, concurrently with the rapid expansion in super markets. Both carry an extensive informational program covering all phases of retail operation. Super Market Institute is somewhat unique in that it maintains a well-stocked and up-to-date library of informational materials on all aspects of food retailing.

National Livestock and Meat Board (NLMB).—The NLMB is an industry-wide organization. Its directorate includes representatives (through organizations) from all sectors of the livestock-meat economy—livestock producers, market agencies, packers, processors, wholesalers, retailers, and eating establishments. Producer groups, however, hold about half the directorate positions. The NLMB was organized in 1923 as a nonprofit, nongovernmental, service association. Its major activities are (1) sponsorship of research, (2) assembling of information, (3) carrying out of educational programs, and (4) promotion of meat, meat products, and merchandising techniques. Over the years, this organization has financed a wide variety of research ranging from highly technical characteristics of meat to applied techniques in marketing.

From an organizational standpoint, NLMB operates separate beef, pork, lamb, and sausage promotion programs under their respective Beef Industry Council, Pork Committee, Lamb Committee, and Sausage Council. The program of NLMB is financed through voluntary contributions of livestock producers in cooperation with participating marketing firms and by participating meat packers. Marketing firms and packers, in the case of direct sales, assemble the funds from producer sales and forward them to NLMB. However, upon a producer's request the money is returned to him. It is estimated that contributions are made on about 45% of all livestock marketed and slaughtered. The Board also receives some direct contributions from organizations.

The Board's informational and educational activities are directed primarily at promotion of meat, consumer oriented. Demonstrations in meat cutting, merchandising, and cooking are performed by permanently-employed specialists. A wide variety of charts, pamphlets, brochures, and visual aids are prepared by the Board's own experts (marketing specialists, nutritionists, home economists). These are made available to communications media, professional groups (doctors, food specialists, food journalists), educational institutions, the meat trade, etc. Considerable effort is directed toward meat merchandising and toward professional groups whose members are in position to recommend meat as a food item or influence consumer attitudes toward meat.

BIBLIOGRAPHY

ANON. 1965. A half century of Federal Market News. Am. Cattle Producer June, 15.

ANON. 1970. A faster draw on cattle prices. Business Week Apr. 11, 110-112.

BOHLEN, J. M., and BEAL, G. M. 1967. Dissemination of farm market news and its importance in decision making. Iowa Agr. Expt. Sta. Res. Bull. 553.

DIETRICH, R. A. 1967. Price information and meat marketing in Texas and Oklahoma. USDA Econ. Res. Serv. (in cooperation with Texas Agr. Expt. Sta. and Oklahoma Agr. Expt. Sta.) Agr. Econ. Res. Rept. 115.

DOWELL, A. A., and BJORKA, K. 1941. Livestock Marketing. McGraw-Hill Book Co., New York.

ENGELMAN, G. 1956. The role of livestock market news in a free pricing economy. Paper presented to Beef Cattle Breeders' and Herdsmen's Short Course, Univ. Florida, Gainesville.

NEWELL, S. R. 1954. Reporting supplies and markets. USDA Yearbook Agr.

PHILLIPS, V. B. 1961. Price formation and pricing efficiency in marketing agricultural products: the role of market news and grade standards. Proc. 26th Ann. Conf. Natl. Assoc. Sci. Teachers, Washington, D.C., April.

PIERCE, J. C. (undated) The Livestock Division—its programs—its aims. USDA Consumer Marketing Serv. (unnumbered).

ROBERTS, W. P. 1959. Economic information for stockmen; where to find it. Wyoming Agr. Expt. Sta. Bull. 363.

SEUFFERLE, C. H. 1960. Livestock marketing information. Nevada Agr. Expt. Sta. Circ. 28.

SMEBY, A. B. (undated) History of livestock, meat, wool market news. USDA (unnumbered).

STRASZHEIM, R. E. 1968. The how and why of government crop and livestock reports. Econ. Marketing Inform. Indiana Farmers, June 28, Agr. Staff, Purdue Univ.

USDA. 1969A. The story of U.S. agricultural estimates. USDA Statist. Reporting Serv. Misc. Publ. 1088.

USDA. 1969B. Market news keeps pace with livestock industry. USDA Consumer Marketing Serv., Agr. Marketing July, 4-5.

USDA. 1970A. The market news service on livestock, meat and wool. USDA Consumer Marketing Serv. Marketing Bull. 50.

USDA. 1970B. Federal-State market news reports—a directory of services available. USDA Consumer Marketing Serv. 21, Revised Nov.

UVACEK, E., Jr., and GOODWIN, J. (undated) Interpreting livestock and meat market news. Southern Coop. Ext. Serv. Marketing Publ. 69-3.

WASSON, C. R. 1954. The market's nervous system. USDA Yearbook Agr.

CHAPTER 13

Regulatory and
Inspection Measures

The livestock-meat industry is faced with a rather wide array of governmental regulations. Not all were set up specifically for the control of marketing problems (in fact, most were not), but all affect either directly or indirectly various aspects of the marketing system. As in other governmental regulations, whether they be traffic control, drug control, antilittering, registration of firearms, property zoning, licensing, etc., the basic justification for control (or restriction) of individual liberties is enhancement of the general welfare. General welfare is a broad term construed to include such concerns as health, economic well-being, social conditions, aesthetic values, humane consideration, etc. This is not a static situation as human values change over time, technological and economic developments introduce new factors, and new knowledge is gained through study and research. Thus, the establishment of regulatory measures is not a once-and-for-all event. Further changes may be expected. As stated by Brooks (1954), "The regulation of marketing is designed to promote the public welfare and, therefore, is to be modified or altered from time to time to meet the changing needs of the nation."

MEAT INSPECTION

Meat inspection is concerned with the wholesomeness, cleanliness, and truthfulness in labeling of meat and meat products. During the agrarian era when people slaughtered their own livestock, processed the meat, and consumed it themselves, there was little public concern about wholesomeness and sanitation; responsibility was left to individuals. The philosophy of individual responsibility carried over to commerce as the economy moved into the commercial era. The prevailing doctrine was "caveat emptor" or "let the buyer beware."

Some states and cities acted on behalf of the public with food inspection laws long before the federal government. But forces were underway which led to action by the federal government.

The first federal move with respect to meat was prompted by problems in the export trade. By the late 1800's the United States had developed a substantial export market in both pork products and beef. But there was stiff opposition on economic and political grounds, plus alleged presence of diseased beef and incidence of trichinosis from the consumption of imported U.S. pork. A number of countries imposed import restrictions which had a crippling effect on the U.S. livestock-meat industry (Clemen 1923).

Loss of these markets aroused producers and packers to the extent that

Congress enacted an act in 1890 that required "the certification of certain meats processed for exportation. In 1891 and 1895 Congress extended meat inspection to partial protection of domestic consumers by requiring inspection of animals for disease before slaughter" (Crawford 1954).

This act, however, proved inadequate for full protection and was followed by the Meat Inspection Act of 1906. One of the most influential factors at that time was a description by Upton Sinclair of conditions in Chicago packing plants. This appeared in his 1906 novel *The Jungle* and received wide publicity in the newspapers and magazines. Whether the report was fact or fiction, it aroused intense public attention and emotion.

The 1906 act kept the ante-mortem inspection and added a post-mortem inspection along with other features which substantially strengthened its effectiveness. The standards and procedures of the 1906 Act still set the pattern for meat inspection. A major change, however, was made in 1967. Prior to 1967, authority for federal meat inspection was limited only to meat which moved in interstate or foreign commerce. This left authority for inspection of meat moving in intrastate trade up to the individual states. The result was a hodgepodge of state and municipal regulations with adequate inspection in some states, and none at all in others.

Even though nearly 85% of the nation's meat supply was produced in federally inspected plants, Havel (1968) reported that only 5555 of the 14,832 meat facilities operated on an intrastate basis were currently subject to state or local inspection, leaving 9277 plants exempt from any inspection controls.

Congress, over much opposition, passed the Federal Meat Inspection Act, commonly known as the Wholesome Meat Act, in December, 1967. This act specified that by Dec. 1, 1969 each state was to have in operation, inspection standards and procedures for red meat at least equal to those of federal requirements, or submit to federal inspection of meat and plants in which meat was slaughtered for sale within that state's borders.[1] Farm slaughter of meat for home consumption was excluded. Subsequently, an additional year's extension was granted for compliance. Not all states were in compliance by Dec. 1, 1970 but the authority is in force to give the entire country a uniform and effective meat inspection service.

The purpose of meat inspection is to safeguard health by (1) eliminating diseased and otherwise bad meat from human consumption, (2) maintaining sanitary conditions during slaughtering and processing, (3) preventing the addition or use of harmful ingredients, and (4) preventing false or misleading labeling of meat and meat products. This is an important and immense assignment, requiring a large and well-trained group of personnel. The United

[1] The Wholesome Meat Act of 1967 covered inspection of all red meats but did not apply to poultry, fish, or certain wild game animals. Poultry inspection was covered in the Poultry Products Inspection Act of 1968.

States had over 7000 full-time personnel in 1970 working at 1062 plants (including red meat and poultry plants). The basic core of employees are licensed veterinarians who are assisted by trained food inspectors.

The entire regulatory process includes examination of plants before granting approval as an FI plant, ante-mortem and post-mortem inspection of animals and carcasses, inspection of plant operations, checks on ingredients used in processing, checks on the truthfulness of labels, inspection of imported meats, and inspection of plants in foreign countries which export meat to the United States. Operators desiring federal inspection are required to submit plans and specifications of their plants to USDA. Examination of the plans and specifications is followed by examination of the plant. If the plant meets requirements, the operator is granted an official number which appears on the stamp used to mark the meat and meat products produced. The number identifies that particular plant. Shipments of meat bearing that number can easily be traced if the need arises.

Inspection regulations prescribe that animals be examined on the premises before they are brought to the killing floor (i.e., the ante-mortem inspection). This applies to all species. Any animal which shows obvious signs of disease or disorders which are cause for condemnation is immediately tagged "U.S. CONDEMNED." It must be killed, if not already dead, by an official of the establishment and placed in a disposition tank in the presence of an inspector. As the animal is placed in the tank, the inspector removes the tag and reports the disposition. Animals which show some signs of cause for suspicion of disease or disorder that cannot be confirmed during the ante-mortem inspection are tagged "U.S. SUSPECT." These animals are slaughtered separately and are given an extra thorough post-mortem inspection which determines whether they are condemned or passed.

Animals which pass the ante-mortem inspection are cleared for slaughter. At the time of slaughter each carcass and viscera are carefully examined. If evidence of abnormal conditions exist, the carcass is tagged "U.S. RE-TAINED," moved from the regular line, and kept separate until a more detailed examination can be made. "U.S. Retained" meat is kept in a locked compartment pending further examination. Depending upon the results of the examination it either is condemned or passed. Carcasses which pass inspection are stamped with a circular brand bearing the plant number and the abbreviated inscription "U.S. INSP'D & P'S'D" (see below). The imprint is made with a harmless (edible) indelible purple fluid. This mark is imprinted at various places on a carcass so that after breaking, the mark will show on various wholesale cuts. Under certain conditions parts of a carcass may be condemned and the remainder passed.

Processed meats are marked by a circular brand on the container or package, showing the establishment (plant) number and the wording "U.S. INSPECTED AND PASSED BY DEPARTMENT OF AGRICULTURE" (see below).

Inspection continues beyond the killing floor. In the processing departments inspectors check to see that sanitary conditions are maintained, that added ingredients meet specifications, and that labeling is truthful. Periodically, samples of processed products, ingredients, containers and wrapping materials are selected for laboratory analysis.

The meat inspection service also covers imported meats. Before any country is permitted to ship to the United States that country's own inspection system must rate at least equal to that of the United States. The export country designates and certifies which of its plants may ship to the United States. These plants then are inspected at least once a year by a USDA, C&MS, foreign review officer. Inspectors at U.S. ports of entry check inshipments (on a sample basis) for wholesomeness and cleanliness.

Meat inspection is carried out under the Consumer Protection Program of the Consumer and Marketing Service (C&MS), USDA. Evidence that this agency is providing protection is found in the following quotation from USDA (1969A): In 1968 they inspected or reinspected 100 billion pounds of meat and poultry products marketed across State or U.S. borders. They condemned as unfit for food 383 million pounds of poultry and poultry products, 370,000 meat animals, and about 35 million pounds of meat and meat products. They refused entry into the United States or condemned 21 million pounds of foreign meat products; they reviewed about 100,000 different meat and poultry product label designs, rejecting about 2000 that didn't accurately state contents of the package.

Packers sometimes buy slaughter animals from producers "subject to inspection." This is a practice used with animals which show some reason for possible condemnation by the inspectors. The agreement between packer and producer usually stipulates a price that will apply if the carcass (or part of it) passes inspection. Payment usually is withheld pending inspection. This practice has features which are beneficial to both producers and packers.

Without the practice, packers undoubtedly would reduce the offering price enough to compensate for the risk factor involved, or simply refuse to buy such animals. Producers are afforded a market for animals they might not be able to sell otherwise and which they probably would hesitate to slaughter for home consumption.

Almost 88% of all meat during 1969 was produced under federal inspection. Fig. 13.1 shows the trend in number of livestock slaughter and processing establishments receiving federal inspection service. The upward trend started during the early 1940's, dropped slightly following World War II, but then continued upward. This rate of increase undoubtedly will taper off in the years ahead. Most plants now have USDA or equivalent inspection so that further increases will be largely from new plants.

The cost of federal meat inspection is borne by the federal government— except that when plants operate overtime plant owners reimburse the federal government for overtime worked by inspectors. It was estimated in 1969 that federal inspection costs the government about 50¢ per capita. With per capita consumption at 182 lb and approximately 88% of that produced under federal inspection, cost of inspection per pound of federally inspected meat was about one-third cent per pound. By any reasonable standards this must be considered a very nominal cost for insurance of wholesome and clean meat.

FOOD, DRUG, AND COSMETICS ACT

Public concern over wholesomeness of food during the early period mentioned in the previous section was not limited to meat. The separate Meat Inspection Act attests to the particular importance attached to meat, but concurrently with passage of the meat Act, Congress also enacted a Food and Drug Act. Both of these Acts were signed on the same day, June 30, 1906 by President Theodore Roosevelt. This action dealt a *coup de grace* to the doctrine of *caveat emptor*. The major purpose of the Food and Drug Act was to assure the public of wholesome, sanitary, unadulterated and truthfully labelled foods. Changing conditions, new products and new technology necessitated changes and strengthening in the law. This was accomplished by the Food, Drug, and Cosmetics Act of 1938. The 1938 law as amended provides the framework of today's pure food and drug regulations. Administration of these Acts was under the Department of Agriculture from 1906 to 1940 at which time it was transferred to the Federal Security Agency. In 1953, the Federal Security Agency was reorganized and became the Department of Health, Education and Welfare, which currently administers the Act under its Food and Drug Administration (FDA).

The concurrent enactment of a separate meat Act, and food and drug Act, might appear to indicate Congressional intent that the meat Act cover all aspects of regulation with respect to meat. However, changing circumstances

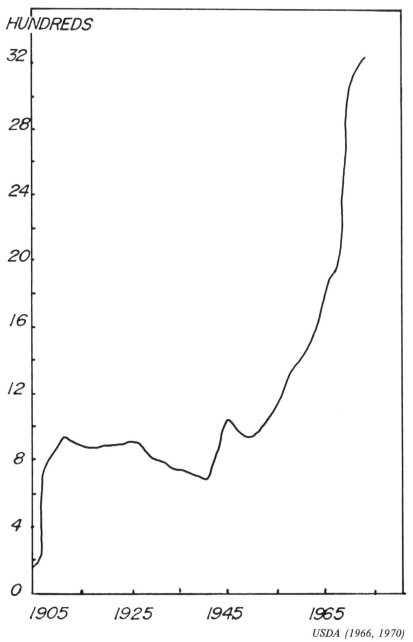

USDA (1966, 1970)

FIG. 13.1. NUMBER OF MEAT ESTABLISHMENTS UNDER FEDERAL IN-
SPECTION, 1905-1969

have introduced new problems. The two agencies cooperate in some areas. One of the areas of recent mutual concern is residues in meat resulting from the use of feed additives, drugs, and pesticides. USDA inspectors test for such residues on a random sampling basis and turn findings over to the FDA for enforcement. FDA has the authority to initiate criminal prosecution of producers who market livestock containing illegal drug and hormone residues.

ANIMAL DISEASE CONTROL

Early U.S. history recorded numerous costly outbreaks of animal disease. Effective veterinary treatments were not available. Quarantines were applied in some areas to restrict the spread of disease and counter quarantines were applied in other areas as retaliatory measures. As a result, "Our system of interstate and export animal transportation was denounced as a disgrace and an outrage on the first principles of humanity. There was a growing demand for protection of the public health in connection with the meat supply" (Van Houweling 1956). A Veterinary Division was established in the USDA in 1883 and was given responsibility of developing information on the prevalence of animal disease and means of controlling and eradicating disease. In 1884, Congress enacted *An Act for the Establishment of the Bureau of Animal Industry*.

Currently, authority and responsibility at the federal level for control and eradication of animal disease is lodged in the Animal Health Division of Agricultural Research Service, USDA. Its programs are carried out in cooperation with states.

An interaction exists between disease control and meat inspection programs. The more effective the degree of control, the fewer animals and carcasses will be condemned during inspection. And disease detection during inspection often assists in disease control. By use of purchase records, brands, tags, etc., authorities often can trace the origin of a disease back to a particular owner or locality where control measures can be applied. Disease control activities, of course, are not limited to connections with meat inspection. Detection of disease also is effected by federal inspectors stationed at designated public markets, by state inspectors at local markets, and by veterinarians in their regular practice.

Detection is followed up by appropriate measures, depending upon the circumstances. With some diseases, e.g., foot and mouth disease, this calls for immediate disposal. In other cases, movement of the animals is restricted— quarantine may be imposed, treatment or immunization may be required, or immediate sale for slaughter may be required (as is the case with brucellosis reactors). Generalization about state restrictions is difficult due to variation among states. At federally inspected public markets, diseased animals are segregated and disposed of under supervision of an inspector. Contaminated vehicles, pens, and premises are disinfected under supervision of an inspector and the state of origin is notified. Outshipments of animals which pass inspection are certified for interstate shipments.

At the international level, a complete embargo is enforced on the importation of live animals or fresh meat from countries infected with especially dreaded diseases, such as rinderpest, and foot and mouth diseases. Livestock may be imported from so-called clean countries, but under strict inspection. Each year substantial numbers of feeder cattle are imported from Mexico and Canada. These cattle must come in through designated ports of entry where they are examined by U.S. inspectors.

Disease control measures of foreign countries still are a factor in U.S. livestock and meat exports. In relation to total U.S. production, the exportation of livestock is relatively small, yet it has increased substantially in recent years. Breeding cattle are by far the major item, with lesser numbers and value of sheep, lambs, hogs, and horses. "The major obstacle that U.S. cattle face is in meeting certain foreign requirements for Blue Tongue disease, once thought to occur only in sheep but now known to affect cattle as well" (Dobbins 1968). The U.S. exports only a minor tonnage of meat, but overseas sales of certain products (lard, tallow, variety meats, hides, and skins) are very important to the industry. It is impractical to attempt to list here detailed restrictions imposed by particular countries on the importation of U.S. products. A number of restrictions are based on presence of animal disease, some are based on hormone residues. Ostensibly, these regulations are enforced in the interest of public health, but in some cases there are strong suggestions that they also are being used to control imports for economic and political reasons.

FEDERAL TRADE COMMISSION

The Federal Trade Commission (FTC) was established in 1914 by enactment of the Federal Trade Commission Act. Conditions which led to establishment of FTC have been discussed in earlier chapters. This was just one step in a series of governmental actions designed to curb unfair trade practices and a tendency toward monopolization of trade by big business. Prior to FTC, there had been the Interstate Commerce Commission Act (1887) and the Sherman Antitrust Act (1890). The Interstate Commerce Commission (ICC) was the first federal regulatory agency empowered to control railroad rates and services. Its purpose was to eliminate rate discrimination among shippers and cut-throat competition among carriers. The Sherman Antitrust Act was designed to curb industrial monopoly. Both had a common purpose of restraining monopoly, but the approaches were substantially different. The ICC Act in effect made public utilities of the railroads. It might be noted parenthetically that a Special Studies Subcommittee of the U.S. House of

Representatives, House Government Operations Committee, in a 1969 study, recommended the creation of a public utility type of commission to regulate the U.S. cattle industry. Opposition in both legislative branches killed that proposal.

The approach under the Sherman Act was an effort to make competition effective by outlawing (1) certain restraints to trade, (2) monopoly, and (3) attempts to monopolize. Due largely to judicial difficulties in defining and interpreting terms, and to administrative apathy, Congress in 1914 tried to clarify the situation by enacting the Federal Trade Commission Act and the Clayton Act. The Clayton Act listed a series of practices which specifically were declared to be unfair and illegal. The FTC was established as the watchdog agency to determine violations. Its major role now is the investigation of unfair trade practices and the issuance of rulings. Major actions are turned over to the courts. One of FTC's early actions was an investigation of practices in the meat packing industry in 1917. This was mentioned in Chap. 7 as a major factor in the Packers Consent Decree of 1920—an agreement whereby the five major packers of that time consented to abide by a number of stringent trade and operational specifications. Those packers have tried periodically to gain modifications of the Consent Decree but the courts and Department of Justice stood firm on all original specifications until 1971. At that time, the Department of Justice agreed to an amendment freeing the remaining four concerned packers (Swift & Co., Armour & Co., Wilson & Co., and Cudahy Co.) from a restriction on production and distribution of more than 100 specified product lines. The amendment allows manufacturing and wholesaling but maintains the original restriction on retailing.

PACKERS AND STOCKYARDS ACT

The Packers and Stockyards Act was enacted in 1921 in an attempt to provide relief for livestock producers who charged packers and market agencies with a variety of unfair and monopolistic practices. It was last amended in 1968. The Act is administered by the Packers and Stockyards Administration of USDA. Major provisions of the act, as they apply to particular types of markets, were discussed in Chap. 6. In general, the Act is designed to regulate business practices of those who engage in the buying and selling of livestock and meat which enters interstate and international trade. Regulations cover the activities of stockyards, companies, market agencies, dealers, packer buyers, and meat packers.

With respect to livestock marketing (USDA 1969B), the act specifically prohibits any stockyard owner, market agency, or dealer subject to its jurisdiction, from engaging in any unfair, unjustly discriminatory, or deceptive practice or device in connection with the receiving, marketing, buying, selling, feeding, watering, holding, delivery, shipment, weighing, or handling of livestock.

By definition, the term meat packer is rather broad. In addition to those who buy livestock across state lines for slaughter, "those who manufacture or prepare meats or meat food products for sale or shipment in interstate commerce are also packers, including wholesalers, fabricators, restaurant and hotel suppliers, and food chains who purchase meat in commerce for fabricating or other processing or preparation" (USDA 1969B). Packers may not (USDA 1969B): (1) Engage in or use any unfair, unjustly discriminatory, or deceptive practice. (2) Make or give any undue or unreasonable preference or advantage to any person or locality, or subject any person or locality to any undue or unreasonable prejudice or disadvantage. (3) Agree or arrange with any other packer to apportion purchase or sale territories or supplies for the purpose or with the effect of restraining commerce or creating a monopoly. (4) Engage in any act for the purpose of or with the effect of manipulating or controlling prices, creating a monopoly, or restraining commerce.

An amendment in 1968 required that payment for livestock purchased on grade and yield basis be made on hot carcass weight. This was a much debated issue. Prior to the 1968 amendment a wide variety of arrangements prevailed in terms for adjusting hot weight to a cold equivalent, with resulting dissatisfaction among producers. A general feeling prevailed that shrinkage adjustments in calculating cold weight tended to favor the packers. This amendment included provisions for tare adjustments for the weight of rollers, gambels, hooks, and other equipment on a uniform basis. Presumably, carcass grade and weight arrangements are now more uniform than previously was the case.

Producers who have reason to believe that they have suffered loss or damage from violations of the P&S Act may petition for reparations. This can be done by filing a written complaint with an area supervisor or directly with the Secretary of Agriculture within 90 days of the wrongful action. Areas and the location of area offices are shown in Fig. 13.2 Some of the more commonly mentioned unfair trade practices which would justify filing a complaint are: dishonest weights, failure to pay for livestock, failure to rectify a mix-up in ownership of livestock, misrepresentation of livestock, etc. Upon receiving a complaint, P&S carries out an investigation without charge.

HUMANE TREATMENT OF LIVESTOCK

The 28-Hour Law

One of the earliest federal laws related to the marketing of livestock was a statute enacted in 1873 intended to alleviate cruelty to livestock while in transit on railroads (Dowell and Bjorka 1941). The Act stipulated that

FIG. 13.2. AREAS AND LOCATIONS OF P&S AREA OFFICES

livestock could not be kept in continuous transit more than 28 hr without a rest stop. At a maximum of 28 hr, the livestock were to be unloaded, fed, watered, and rested for at least 5 consecutive hours. Transportation agencies were made responsible for furnishing the necessary facilities and services. In practice, however, the facilities and services actually furnished were, in many cases, inadequate. Due to aroused sentiment, the 1873 Act was repealed and another, known as the 28-Hour Law, was passed in 1906. The purpose of this Act was similar to the earlier one, but it was more specific with respect to minimum quantity of feed, cleanliness of water, and methods and procedures for handling stock during loading and unloading. In cars that were loaded with sufficient space for each animal to lie down, feeding and watering was permissible without unloading. In addition, the 1906 Act provided for an 8-hr extension, or a total of 36 hr, upon request. This law is still effective.

A limitation of time in continuous transit has economic as well as humane implications. Extended deprivation of feed, water, and rest undoubtedly results in discomfort and suffering. Prior to the Act, periods of 60 hr or more in transit were reported. However, associated costs also are important. Shrinkage, bruising, crippling, and death increase with time in transit. This law was effective in accomplishing both the intended objective of alleviating cruelty and reducing above-mentioned related costs. Need for such a law is considerably diminished now compared to earlier years. Improved, faster freight service makes it possible for many shipments to reach their destination within 36 hr, and with expeditious service shipments from mid-country can reach either coast with 1 rest stop. Trucks were not included in the provisions of the original law. But most buyers of livestock insist on a rest stop in an extended trip, for economic reasons—whether the haul be by rail or truck.

Humane Slaughter Act

Public sentiment over alleged cruelty to livestock during slaughter reached a peak during the 1950's. Methods of handling, shackling, stunning, and killing were considered inhumane and abhorrent by some people. A campaign for modification of slaughter methods culminated in the Humane Slaughter Act of 1958. Provisions of the Act instructed the Secretary of the U.S. Department of Agriculture to prescribe humane methods and made that office responsible for administration. Unlike many laws this Act did not prescribe criminal penalties for noncompliance. However, it did stipulate that government purchases of meat must be from plants using humane methods and this is a persuasive feature. Among other features, this Act provides for keeping animals relatively calm prior to stunning, and using electrical, mechanical, or chemical methods for rendering the animals unconscious prior to killing.

As was mentioned with respect to the 28-Hour Law, humane slaughtering has economic as well as humanitarian aspects. Capital requirements for complying with the recommended mechanical methods are negligible consisting primarily of a captive bolt stunner or small caliber gun device. These devices are faster and use less labor than the previously common use of hammers. The cost of electrical stunners and carbon dioxide tunnel installations (the common chemical method) are offset by elimination of shackling and associated equipment, but probably the most important economic plus is in fewer bruises and damaged parts of pork carcasses that formerly resulted from shackling and hanging prior to sticking of hogs.

Provisions of the Act exempted killing methods used in religious rituals such as kosher slaughtering.

Even though compliance with the law is not mandatory per se, it is reported that most meat is produced under approved methods.

COMMODITY EXCHANGE ACT

Trading in livestock and livestock product futures is regulated under the Commodity Exchange Act (CEA) which is administered and enforced by the Commodity Exchange Authority of USDA. Trading in commodity futures has a long history. As mentioned in Chap. 10, the Chicago Board of Trade was organized in 1848. While the market served a useful economic purpose, a number of abuses were evident from time to time in price manipulation and undue price fluctuations associated with speculative maneuvering. Bills were introduced in Congress as early as 1884 in attempts to provide federal supervision and regulation of trading. However, it was not until 1922 that the first law was passed—the Grain Futures Act. This Act was amended and renamed the Commodity Exchange Act in 1936.

The 1936 Act, with subsequent amendments, remains the basic law for the maintenance of fair and honest trading in commodity futures markets. "Regulation is not directed to the restriction or hampering of legitimate trading, but to the protection of the public interest by safeguards against price manipulation and unfair trading practices" (Kauffman 1956).

Among the functions performed by CEA are: "Market licensing. Brokerage registration. Audits of commodity brokerage firms. Trading surveillance and market analysis. Enforcement of speculative limits. Investigation and compliance activities. Special market surveys and reports. Publication of market information" (Kauffman 1956).

Major emphasis is placed on the detection of attempted speculative price manipulation. Some publications on early efforts at "cornering the market" depict an action-filled, romantic situation, but to a hedger or legitimate speculator who may be caught in a distorted market, the situation is anything but romantic. Attempts to "corner" or "squeeze" the market are rare, but CEA is on the alert and devotes a major share of its work toward the prevention of any abuse which would impair free and open competition.

MEAT IMPORT LAW OF 1964

The question of regulating (either restricting or encouraging) the supply of meat, like any other product, raises extremely complex issues. Conflicts of interest are inherent between producers and consumers, between producers and importers, and within the producing sector itself. At the national level the interest of a particular group may be incompatible with the overall national interest. This point is discussed further in a following chapter on "International Trade." Cattle producers during the early 1960's became deeply concerned over rising imports of beef. Concern had been expressed on previous occasions, but the problem had seemed to ebb and flow without reaching major proportions. Occasionally, imports would increase to about 5% of total beef production, usually in response to relatively high U.S. prices, and then drop back to about 1% as U.S. prices declined. A nominal tariff had been imposed on livestock and meat for many years and this, along with tariffs in general, had been reduced from a high point of the 1930's. As mentioned in an earlier section, a complete ban had been enforced for many years against the importation of fresh meat from countries infected with rinderpest, and foot and mouth disease. But the situation was different in the late 1950's and early 1960's.

Imports of beef in the early 1960's increased to more than 10% of total U.S. production—about twice the level of previous high points (see Fig. 13.3). A number of factors were involved, but a major one was the discontinuance of an agreement in 1958 between Great Britain and Australia whereby Australia no longer was required to ship stipulated quantities of low grade

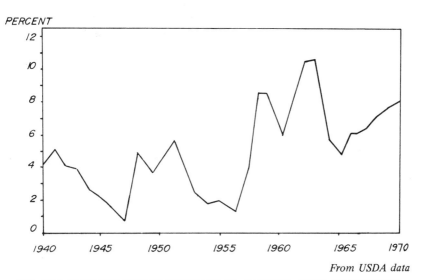

From USDA data

FIG. 13.3. BEEF IMPORTS AS PERCENTAGE OF TOTAL BEEF PRODUCTION beef to Great Britain. The U.S. market was the most lucrative outlet in the world and substantial quantities were coming in, not only from Australia, but from New Zealand, Ireland, and other countries. The situation was compounded by relatively high production in the United States.

Attempts were made during the late 1950's and early 1960's to control the meat import situation through voluntary agreements with major exporters. More stringent types of regulation were viewed unfavorably by State Department officials because an effort was under way to implement a broad tariff liberalization policy. However, spokesmen for the cattle industry did not view voluntary control as a satisfactory solution to the problem. After a series of hearings Congress enacted the Meat Import Law (Public Law 88-482) in August, 1964, to become effective Jan. 1, 1965. This bill provided for import quotas, based on a formula, for fresh, chilled, and frozen beef, veal, mutton, and goat meat. This included both carcass and boneless meat. It did not include lamb or canned meats. The purpose of the law was to limit annual imports of the specified meats to a level comparable to a selected base period (1959-1963) with an annual adjustment ("growth factor") based on changes in domestic production relative to the base period.

The base quota was established as the average annual quantity imported during the base period (1959-1963) which was 725,400,000 lb. Each year the growth factor is determined by calculating the percentage by which the estimated U.S. commercial production of the specified meats in the current calendar year and the 2 preceding years (i.e., a 3-yr average) exceeds (or falls short of) average annual U.S. production during the base period. Thus, to determine the growth factor at the beginning of a given year, it is necessary to estimate production for that year. The calculated growth factor then is multiplied times the base quantity to determine tha amount of increase (or decrease) in the base. This increase (or decrease) added to the base gives an adjusted base quota. With U.S. production on a definitely increasing trend, the annual adjustment has always been upward. The Act allowed a 10% leeway above the adjusted base quota before quotas would be applied to individual countries. Thus a "quota trigger point" is determined at 110% of the adjusted base quota.

In this process, the Secretary of Agriculture is required to estimate at the beginning of each quarter-year the quantity of prospective imports. If the quantity of prospective imports exceeds the trigger point, the President is required to invoke a quota on imports of these meats. In case quotas are imposed, the total import quota would be allocated among exporting countries on the basis of shares supplied by those countries during a representative period.

But the law also contained provisions for extraordinary conditions under which the President could suspend or increase quotas. These were (1) if he determined it necessary because of overriding economic or national security interests, (2) if the supply of meat is inadequate to meet domestic demand at reasonable prices, or (3) if international agreements are entered into after enactment of the Act which have the same effect as the Act.

It is seen that the Meat Import Law provides for a flexible quota. As U.S. production increases, the quota increases. At the time it was passed there was a considerable body of opinion that imports would never reach the trigger point. In the late 1960's, however, it became apparent that imports would reach that point unless some action were taken. In an effort to avert the necessity of invoking mandatory individual quotas, the Secretary of Agriculture, in the fall of 1968, began a program of negotiating voluntary quota agreements with exporting countries, which action is based on provisions of the Agricultural Act of 1956. Among the major exporters, only Canada refused to go along with this program. Most countries abided by the agreements on direct shipments[2] but some exported meat to Canada where it was then transhipped to the United States.

When it appeared in 1970 that the trigger point would be exceeded, President Nixon, under requirements of the act, issued a proclamation, on June 30, " . . . to place a limitation on imports of meats covered by the Act. At the same time, the President suspended the limitation, as authorized by law, after determining that this action was required by the overriding interest of the United States" (USDA 1970B). Thus, it may be said that quotas were triggered, but immediately rescinded. The future effectiveness of the Act is in considerable doubt. It appears that voluntary agreements will be the chief means of controlling imports, but the fact that a law exists may have considerable psychological effect on negotiating processes.

POLLUTION CONTROL

A widespread public concern with environmental degradation reached major proportions during the 1960's. Livestock feedlots, with large numbers of animals in highly concentrated circumstances give rise to air pollution from feedlot odors and water pollution from waste materials carried in water run-off.

Pollution problems are indirectly related to marketing in that regulations designed to control pollution influence the location of feedlots which, in turn, affects transportation costs and competitive position with respect to both feed and feeder livestock procurement and sale of the finished livestock.

A number of states have enacted legislation designed to protect the interests of both the public and feedlot owners. One common form of regulation is the requirement of a license, or permit, for operation of a feedlot. Requirements for obtaining a permit vary, but generally include provision for adequate drainage and control of run-off. One of the most vexatious problems arises

[2] Honduras was an exception and was issued a mandatory quota.

where housing developments expand near the vicinity of a long-established feedlot and then the occupants complain of feedlot odors. Protestations of both water pollution and air pollution have resulted in the closing of some commercial feedlots, notwithstanding valid permits and licenses. Concern with ecological values undoubtedly make feedlot pollution an increasing problem.

The federal government has conducted investigations for a number of years on various aspects of pollution but has not enacted regulatory measures specifically for livestock feedlots.

BIBLIOGRAPHY

ACKER, D. 1963. Animal Science and Industry. Prentice-Hall, Englewood Cliffs, N.J.

BROOKS, N. 1954. The wide range of regulation. USDA Yearbook Agr.

CALLANDER, R. C. 1960. The Commodity Exchange Act and its administration. USDA Commodity Exchange Authority, reprint Forward Markets Bull., Bombay, India, Dec.

CLEMEN, R. A. 1923. The American Livestock and Meat Industry. Ronald Press, New York.

CRAWFORD, C. W. 1954. The long fight for pure foods. USDA Yearbook Agr.

DOBBINS, C. E. 1968. Past and prospects: U.S. livestock in export markets. USDA Foreign Agr. 6, No. 46, 1-3, Nov. 11.

DOWELL, A. A., and BJORKA, K. 1941. Livestock Marketing. McGraw-Hill Book Co., New York.

FOWLER, S. H. 1961. The Marketing of Livestock and Meat, 2nd Edition. Interstate Printers & Publishers, Danville, Ill.

HAVEL, J. T. 1968. Inspection of intrastate meat in Kansas. In Your Government. Univ. Kansas Sept. 15.

GUNDERSON, F. L. et al. 1963. Food Standards and Definitions in the United States. Academic Press, New York.

KAUFFMAN, R. R. 1965. Recent developments in futures trading under the Commodity Exchange Act. USDA Commodity Exchange Authority Agr. Inform, Bull. 155.

LEE, R. F., and HARPER, H. W. 1966. Meat and poultry inspection. USDA Yearbook Agr.

USDA. 1952. The inspection stamp as a guide to wholesome meat. USDA Agr. Inform. Bull 92.

USDA. 1969A. His mission: consumer protection. USDA Agr. Marketing 14, No. 11, 3.

USDA. 1969B. The Packers and Stockyard Act, what it is and how it operates. USDA P&S Admin. PA-399, Revised Aug.

USDA. 1970A. Commodity Exchange Act as amended. USDA Commodity Exchange Authority, Revised Febr. (unnumbered).

USDA. 1970B. Livestock and meat situation. USDA Econ. Res. Serv. LMS-174.

USHEW, 1970. Requirements of the United States Food, Drug and Cosmetics Act. U.S. Health, Education, Welfare, FDA Publ. 2.

VANHOUWELING, C. O. 1956. Our battle against animal diseases. USDA Yearbook Agr.

WILLIAMS, W. F., and STOUT, T. T. 1964. Economics of the Livestock-Meat Industry. Macmillan Co., New York.

ZIEGLER, T. 1965. The Meat We Eat. Interstate Printers & Publishers, Danville, Ill.

CHAPTER 14

International Trade in
Livestock, Meat and Wool

International trade in meat only involves approximately 8% of world production. But this relatively small proportion disguises significant economic and political implications. Two particularly important economic aspects are as follows: (1) at any given time the import-export position of a given country may deviate substantially from the average of the aggregate world situation, and (2) over the years the import-export position of a country can (and does) change.

With regard to the former, the United Kingdom exports virtually no beef, but in recent years has imported nearly 40% of its consumption. On the other hand, Australia and New Zealand import no beef but export approximately 50% of their production. The United States exports substantial quantities of some products and imports others. Many of the less developed countries subsist almost entirely on their own production. Thus, to say that only 8% of the world's meat moves in international trade ignores the fact that some countries are highly dependent upon imports, some are highly dependent upon

FIG. 14.1. U.S. EXPORTS OF BEEF AND PORK (PRODUCT WEIGHT BASIS), 1865-1970

1865-1970 reproduced from Ives (1966); 1964-1970 data from USDA exports, some are dependent upon both, and others are virtually independent.

The United States furnishes a good example of a country whose import-export position has changed drastically over time. As may be seen in Fig. 14.1, U.S. exports of both pork and beef expanded rapidly following the Civil War, reached a peak about World War I, then dropped precipitously, and have remained low since then with the exception of a brief rise during World War II. An equally dramatic change is apparent in imports of beef (Fig. 14.2) which have increased from virtually nothing prior to World War I to almost 2 billion pounds in recent years. Imports of pork, although much less than beef, have picked up significantly since 1950.

Such changes over time, and differences among countries in import-export balances, prompts the question: What gives rise to international trade?

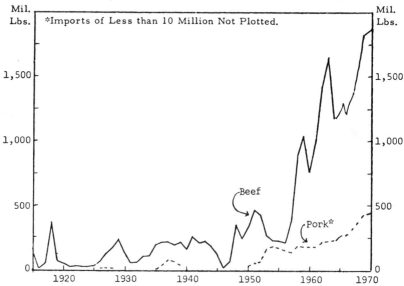

FIG. 14.2. U.S. IMPORTS OF BEEF AND PORK (CARCASS WEIGHT EQUIVA-LENT), 1915-1970

1915-1964 reproduced from Ives (1966); 1965-1970 data from USDA

BASES FOR INTERNATIONAL TRADE

International trade has individual as well as general welfare implications. From the standpoint of individuals, the motive which generates trade is essentially the same whether it be local, regional, or international in scope. That motive is profit. In the absence of artificial restrictions, an incentive exists to move goods internationally if the price in an importing country is high enough to cover production costs as well as cost of moving the product to that country. From the consumer's standpoint, an incentive exists to buy imported goods when such goods can be purchased cheaper than domestically produced products (of equal quality).

But these conditions simply are reflections of more basic, underlying economic conditions. Why are some countries able to produce certain products more cheaply than others? Why doesn't a single low cost country produce the entire world's supply of a given product?

The Principle of Absolute Advantage

The United States can produce cameras, but the cost is higher than the price of cameras shipped in from Japan, for example. Japan can raise hogs, but if they want pork, it can be purchased from the United States at a price less than the cost of producing it in Japan. These blunt statements of apparent fact gloss over some difficult problems in comparing absolute costs, but serve to provide an introduction to basic factors behind specialization and trade.

The following hypothetical example illustrates the gain for each country by specializing and trading. Assume that with 1 unit of labor and capital the United States can produce either 1000 lb of pork or 12 cameras. With an equivalent expenditure of labor and capital, Japan can produce 800 lb of pork or 20 cameras. Now if the United States and Japan each devoted 2 units of labor and capital to production, and if each produced both items, the total output would be:

	Pork Production (Lb)	Camera Production
United States	1000	12
Japan	800	20
Total	1800	32

On the other hand, if each devoted 2 units of labor and capital to production of the product in which it has an absolute advantage, the result would be:

	Pork Production (Lb)	Camera Production
United States	2000	. . .
Japan	. . .	40
Total	2000	40

In total production the gain is 200 lb of pork and 8 cameras. By trading at an exchange of 1000 lb of pork for 20 cameras, each could have pork and cameras as follows:

	Pork (Lb)	Cameras
United States	1000	20
Japan	1000	20
Total	2000	40

It is apparent that in the absence of trade restrictions, each would specialize, trading would follow, and each would benefit. But what makes it possible for one country, or one area to gain an absolute cost advantage over another? Generally the contributing factors can be classified as follows: (1) natural phenomena, such as climate, geographic characteristics, or natural resources; (2) particular attributes or characteristics of the people; (3) capital accumulation and industrial development; and (4) differing proportions of available resources relative to the demands for them.

Many examples could be given where geography, climate, or natural resources give an area an absolute cost advantage in producing certain products compared to other areas. Natural phenomena are particularly important in the production of feed supplies for livestock, and feed is the primary factor in livestock production. Natural forage generally is the cheapest feed for maintaining breeding herds of cattle and ewe flocks, and in producing grass-fed beef. Thus, the vast range areas of the United States, Argentina, Australia, and New Zealand have a decided absolute cost advantage over such areas as central Europe in producing grass-fed cattle or maintaining breeding stock.

In addition to natural phenomena, human skills and capabilities play an important role in costs of production. Education, training, and experience vary greatly around the world. This is true in all industries, including livestock production. Custom and tradition also can be important modifying forces. In Nigeria, for example, the Fulani tribesmen are superb cattle husbandrymen. Yet the century-old tradition of accumulating cattle as a symbol of wealth tends to limit the off-take of their herds. Human characteristics, customs, traditions, and religious beliefs also have varying effects on the demand for goods, and particularly the demand for meat. In India, beef is not eaten by a large segment of the population. In other areas, Moslems and people of the Jewish faith do not eat pork.

Capital accumulation and associated industrial development affect both costs of production and, indirectly (through effects on personal income) the demand for meat and other products. The more highly developed countries have a tremendous head start on less developed countries in capital accumulation. Without this, large-scale enterprises and economies of size would be impossible. Producers in countries with this possibility hold a competitive cost advantage in this factor over their counterparts in less developed countries.

The relative proportions of available resources also influence the use to which those resources may be most profitably utilized. An example in contrast would be Belgium compared to New Zealand. Belgium may be better adapted to lamb production than is New Zealand from the standpoint of soil and climate. But Belgium has a much higher human population density. She must specialize in higher valued land use—high-yielding grain and forage crops, industrial production, etc. New Zealand has relatively less pressure on the land and can utilize it for lamb production.

Cost differences arising from such factors are evident for many goods in many countries. And in many cases, the differences are obvious. Kansas can hardly compete with Honduras in producing bananas. Niger cannot compete with the United States in producing heavy construction equipment. Great Britain cannot produce grass-finished beef as cheaply as Argentina, and so on. Yet a comparison of costs in different countries is a tenuous undertaking, especially in the not-so-obvious cases. Differences exist in monetary units and exchange rates. The applied technology differs greatly, as does the available mix of resources and other factors. Fortunately, it is not necessary to depend upon analyses of absolute costs. Another approach is available: the determination of "comparative costs" or "comparative advantage."

The Principle of Comparative Advantage

Let the following assumption hold for an elementary case of just 2 countries—the United States and a foreign country—and 2 products—grain-finished beef and watches. There are no artificial barriers to trade (such as tariffs, quotas, exchange controls, etc.). Both countries have the natural resources, manpower, skills, and capital to produce either or both products. The cost structure is such that with 1 unit of labor and capital, the United States can produce 1800 lb of fed beef or 6 watches. The foreign country, with 1 unit of labor and capital can produce 600 lb of fed beef or 4 watches. Clearly, the United States has an advantage in the production of both products, but it is apparent that its advantage in the production of beef is greater than in watches. The foreign country is at a disadvantage in both products, but its disadvantage is least in the production of watches.

Suppose each country uses 2 units of resources in producing beef and 1 unit in producing watches. The total quantity produced would be:

	Beef Production (Lb)	Watch Production
United States	3600	6
Foreign country	1200	4
Total	4800	10

Now let the United States specialize and devote all three units of resources to beef production and the foreign country specialize in watch production. Total production would be:

	Beef Production (Lb)	Watch Production
United States	5400	. . .
Foreign country	. . .	12
Total	5400	12

The United States would not be interested in trading unless it could get a watch for something less than 300 lb of beef, for it can produce a watch at that ratio of resource use. The foreign country would not be interested in trading unless it could get more than 150 lb of beef per watch. Assume the bargaining settles at 200 lb of beef for 1 watch. If 1400 lb of beef were exchanged for 7 watches, the distributions of the two goods would be:

	Beef (Lb)	Watches
United States	4000	7
Foreign country	1400	5
Total	5400	12

Both countries in this case would benefit by specialization and trading even though the United States was shown to have an advantage in the production of both products.

A generalization referred to as the "principle of comparative advantage" emerges from this set of circumstances. It may be stated as follows: countries gain by producing the products in which they have the greatest comparative advantage, or those in which they have the least comparative disadvantage.

Does this mean that certain countries would produce the entire world's supply of some products and other countries the entire supply of other products? The answer is qualified. Many countries are at such a decided disadvantage in the production of some goods that no output is feasible. However, it will be advantageous for most countries to produce a variety of goods, particularly when transfer costs are taken into consideration. The relative cost situation also changes as any given country attempts to expand production and exploit its advantage. As production increases, unit costs eventually rise. It is advantageous for countries to expand trade until the cost ratios of producing the commodities are equalized in the respective countries. This is likely to happen before any one country produces the entire world's supply of most products.

Conflicting Interests in International Trade

The above are theoretical concepts—explanations of economic pressures behind international trade in a freely competitive situation. The real world, however, deviates considerably from the perfectly competitive model. For one thing, the competitive model assumes mobility of resources, and resources do not move freely within a country, let alone between countries. In spite of possible gains, governments around the world have instituted a wide array of obstacles to international trade such as tariffs, licenses, quotas, arbitrary control of exchange rates, etc. Among the reasons given for restrictions are the protection of new industries, the shielding of established industries from the rigors of foreign competition, retaliation to another country's restrictions, and the desire to encourage domestic production (in an effort to avoid dependence upon imports in time of war or to avoid a situation of weakness in international politics). Most countries encourage exports through such things as domestic subsidies, overseas promotion, etc. Countries occasionally tax exports in an effort to discourage outmovements and keep the product available for domestic use; and on occasion, countries encourage imports to bolster domestic supplies. Usually, however, governments tend to restrict imports as a measure of protection for home industries. As noted in the previous chapter, the U.S. Meat Import Law of 1964 provided for import quotas as a protective device for the U.S. cattle industry.

Arguments for and against free trade center around three different points of view: (1) its effects on particular industries—or more precisely, individuals within particular industries; (2) its effects on the general national interest, irrespective of the implications to individuals, and (3) its worldwide effects, irrespective of the implications to particular countries or individuals. If "world welfare" were the goal, all barriers to trade and migration of people would be removed. Some workers in traditionally low-wage countries would be expected to move to high-wage countries. The resulting tendency for wages to even out would raise average world wages—to the benefit of some individuals, but to the detriment of others. If national welfare were the goal it might be suggested that relatively cheap beef be imported from Australia. The usual argument is that consumers in general would benefit from the resulting decrease in cost of living. But another result would be a decline in cattle prices to the detriment of cattle producers. Many cattle producers also produce wheat and the export market is vital for wheat. A given individual may find it advantageous to favor import restrictions on beef, but oppose a foreign country's restrictions on wheat imports. Thus, conflicts of interest arise within an industry, between individual and national interests, and between national and world interests. These are exceedingly complex issues, involving political and social as well as economic implications.

Governments have responded over the years to a multitude of pressures and considerations. Broad, general policy objectives set the guidelines within which specific regulations are applied to particular products. And the general policy objectives can, and do, change. In 1930, the Smoot-Hawley Tariff Act culminated a highly protectionist policy—a policy of high tariffs. This policy drew retaliation by trade restrictions of other countries and international trade was choked off. The United States changed its policy in 1934 under the Reciprocal Trade Agreements Program which was aimed at reducing tariffs.

Liberalization of trade has been the general policy since, and tariffs on many products have been substantially reduced. The policy, however, has met opposition where individual industries have felt particular disadvantage. As mentioned, the beef cattle industry is a case in point. Swine and sheep producers also are seriously questioning the rising importation of lamb and pork.

In spite of numerous governmental impediments, large quantities of meat and substantial numbers of livestock do in fact move in international trade. Countries with advantageous cost conditions and various programs of government encouragement maintain constant pressure to export meat to favorably priced markets. Changing cost structures continually alter the production cost ratios among countries. This, together with supply-demand structures, continually alter the price levels. The U.S. beef industry provides an example of such changes and their effect on trade. With the opening of vast range areas during the last half of the 1800's and early decades of the 1900's, the United States possessed both an absolute and comparative advantage in grass-finished beef production. American exporters, in spite of numerous health and tariff restrictions, opened a sizeable market in European countries. Following World War I, trade wars largely in the form designed to protect home industry and combat world-wide depression unemployment, reduced most international movements. Economic recovery during and following World War II brought relative affluence in the United States, and with it, a growing demand for grain-finished beef. The intensity of this demand dried up the supply of grass-finished beef, resulting in a relative shortage and increased price for lower quality beef used in hamburgers and processed meats. In the meantime, producers of the low cost range areas of Australia, New Zealand, Argentina, and other countries not only took over the European market, but began extensive shipments of grass-finished beef into the United States. Partially instrumental in these developments were various subsidies and incentive programs which encouraged production in some of the exporting countries, but the main factors were relative costs of production and meat prices in the respective countries. Export-import activity then and now attests to the importance of economic forces behind international trade.

WORLD PRODUCTION AND TRADE

Leading Meat Producers

The United States is unquestionably the largest producer of meats, producing almost twice as much as the nearest competitor, the Soviet Union. The United States leads in beef, veal, and pork, but is fifth in lamb, mutton, and goat meat production. The ten leading countries in production of each of the meats are shown in Table 14.1.

Table 14.2 shows production by continent and by leading country for the

TABLE 14.1
MEAT PRODUCTION: WORLD'S LARGEST PRODUCERS
BY RANK DURING 1969[1]

Commodity and Rank	Production (Million Lb)	Commodity and Rank	Production (Million Lb)
Beef and veal		Lamb, mutton, and goat meat	
United States	21,843	USSR	1,760
USSR	10,130	Australia	1,488
Argentina	6,063	New Zealand	1,241
Brazil	3,472	Turkey	693
France	3,424	United States	548
Germany, West	2,844	United Kingdom	453
Australia	2,056	Argentina	428
United Kingdom	1,920	South Africa, Republic of	381
Canada	1,915	Spain	284
Italy	1,764	France	262
Pork		Total meat[2]	
United States	12,949	United States	35,340
USSR	6,750	USSR	18,640
France	2,537	Germany, West	7,650
United Kingdom	2,036	Argentina	7,049
Denmark	1,493	France	6,399
Germany, East	1,370	Brazil	4,869
Netherlands	1,296	United Kingdom	4,409
Brazil	1,243	Australia	3,903
Italy	1,209	Poland	3,338
Japan	1,113	Italy	3,138

Source: USDA (1970A).
[1] Carcass weight basis.
[2] Horse meat is included in total where data are available.

several species during recent years. World meat production is increasing in response to a growing demand. This largely reflects increases in population and gains in spendable incomes. Production gains were greatest in beef and veal, with a 22% increase from 1961-1965 to 1969. Beef and veal constituted more than 1/2 of the total world red meat supply. Pork production increased 15%, while lamb, mutton, and goat meat increased only 4.5%. It may be noted that European countries are heavy producers of pork. Japan, which doubled its pork production during the early 1960's, cut back slightly in recent years and increased imports. Australia and New Zealand are undisputed leaders in lamb and mutton production.

Several European countries produce surprisingly large quantities of beef. Most of this beef comes from cattle also kept for milk, but many of the breeds are large-bodied cattle which yield a relatively large proportion of meat. Beef production, generally, is more evenly distributed among continents and countries than are other meats. But as will be seen, the exportable surplus is largely concentrated in a few countries. For the continent of Africa, data are shown only for the Republic of South Africa. Currently, Africa is not much of a factor in international trade. However, if or when she gains control over disease and improves sanitation in packing plants, Africa will make its presence known in the beef trade.

TABLE 14.2

MEAT: PRODUCTION IN SELECTED COUNTRIES, AVERAGE 1961-1965, ANNUAL 1967-1969[1]

Continent and Country	Beef and Veal				Pork[2]			
	Avg 1961-65 (Million Lb)	1967 (Million Lb)	1968 (Million Lb)	1969[3] (Million Lb)	Avg 1961-65 (Million Lb)	1967 (Million Lb)	1968 (Million Lb)	1969[3] (Million Lb)
North America								
Canada	1,618	1,887	1,990	1,915	1,002	1,181	1,181	1,096
Mexico	1,046	1,058	1,174	1,251	453	535	545	549
United States	17,862	21,011	21,610	21,843	11,863	12,581	13,063	12,949
Total	20,526	23,956	24,774	25,009	13,318	14,297	14,789	14,594
South America								
Argentina	4,913	5,666	5,613	6,063	384	478	416	410
Brazil	3,095	3,318	3,417	3,472	1,022	1,228	1,288	1,243
Chile	318	334	364	...	94	106	104	...
Colombia	837	818	874	909	95	88	...	...
Paraguay[4]	256	269	234	...	...	...	...	...
Peru	197	205	198	163	95	90	88	82
Uruguay	691	532	639	525	53	55	48	54
Venezuela	327	417	423	430	62	69	71	82
Total[5]	10,634	11,559	11,762	12,171	1,805	2,114	2,104	2,063
Europe								
Western								
EC:								
Belgium and Luxembourg	482	536	545	564	508	705	772	776
France	3,159	3,492	3,578	3,424	2,370	2,646	2,765	2,537
Germany, West	2,540	2,632	2,734	2,844	3,979	4,328	4,755	...
Italy	1,388	1,569	1,728	1,764	887	1,010	952	1,209
Netherlands	590	606	628	627	923	1,166	1,308	1,296
Total EC	8,159	8,835	9,213	9,223	8,667	9,855	10,552	10,589
Austria[6]	302	346	347	343	540	553	575	593
Denmark	357	481	457	404	1,465	1,620	1,577	1,493
Finland	189	202	195	246	146	200	189	196
Greece	99	153	160	181	67	83	83	95
Ireland	274	491	425	...	262	241	270	307
Norway	124	120	116	127	121	128	136	144
Portugal	113	121	139	...	177	187	185	...

Continent and Country	Lamb, Mutton, and Goat Meat (Million Lb)				Total Meat Production[9] (Million Lb)			
	Avg 1961-65	1967	1968	1969[3]	Avg 1961-65	1967	1968	1969[3]
Spain	410	474	536	560	608	919	924	950
Sweden	330	368	346	364	448	479	502	514
Switzerland	248	259	283	275	291	345	416	426
United Kingdom	1,978	2,031	1,997	1,920	1,796	1,814	1,895	2,036
Total other western[5]	4,424	5,046	5,001	5,000	5,921	6,569	6,752	6,945
Eastern								
Bulgaria	155	216	239	216	270	322	352	317
Czechoslovakia	468	582	646	611	750	798	849	809
Germany, East	456	594	616	646	1,052	1,299	1,349	1,370
Hungary	236	235	..	..	632	646	..	..
Poland	878	1,077	1,172	..	1,826	1,997	1,958	..
Yugoslavia	533	628	760	787	844	859	890	834
Total Eastern[5]	2,726	3,332	3,703	3,770	5,374	5,921	6,098	6,010
Total Europe[5]	15,309	17,213	17,917	17,993	19,962	22,345	23,402	23,544
USSR	6,520	9,560	10,120	10,130	6,250	7,440	6,780	6,750
Africa and Asia								
South Africa, Republic of	998	905	880	864	115	135	142	148
China, Taiwan	14	15	20	..	485	694	711	..
Japan	400	323	353	474	649	1,228	1,147	1,113
Philippines	156	183	166	171	543	744	794	843
Turkey	322	345	364	376	..	..	..	1
Total[5]	1,890	1,771	1,783	1,909	1,792	2,801	2,794	2,825
Oceania								
Australia[7]	1,941	1,937	1,993	2,056	257	313	330	359
New Zealand[8]	614	665	760	830	94	81	84	82
Total	2,555	2,602	2,753	2,886	351	394	414	441
Total selected countries	57,434	66,661	69,109	70,098	43,478	49,391	50,283	50,217
North America								
Canada	30	21	20	16	2,650	3,089	3,191	3,027
Mexico	129	126	124	124	1,654	1,749	1,873	1,954
United States	755	646	602	548	30,480	34,238	35,275	35,340
Total	914	793	746	688	34,784	39,076	40,339	40,321

TABLE 14.2 (Continued)

MEAT: PRODUCTION IN SELECTED COUNTRIES, AVERAGE 1961-1965, ANNUAL 1967-1969[1]

Continent and Country	Lamb, Mutton, and Goat Meat				Total Meat Production[9]			
	Avg 1961-65 (Million Lb)	1967 (Million Lb)	1968 (Million Lb)	1969[3] (Million Lb)	Avg 1961-65 (Million Lb)	1967 (Million Lb)	1968 (Million Lb)	1969[3] (Million Lb)
South America:								
Argentina	344	450	467	428	5,767	6,745	6,686	7,049
Brazil	106	114	118	121	4,226	4,672	4,841	4,869
Chile	74	79	93	...	486	519	561	...
Colombia	5	5	5	5	937	911	968	1,003
Paraguay[4]	...	...	...	...	256	269	234	324
Peru	84	81	82	79	376	376	368	...
Uruguay	113	182	190	191	867	770	877	770
Venezuela	4	6	7	7	393	492	501	519
Total[5]	730	917	962	926	13,308	14,754	15,036	15,341
Europe								
Western								
EC:								
Belgium and Luxembourg	6	6	8	16	1,026	1,264	1,345	1,379
France	238	267	265	262	5,996	6,575	6,773	6,399
Germany, West	28	24	24	24	6,578	6,997	7,524	7,650
Italy	86	90	93	93	2,447	2,740	2,845	3,138
Netherlands	18	19	19	17	1,551	1,802	1,966	1,952
Total EC	376	406	409	412	17,598	19,378	20,453	20,518
Austria[6]	3	3	3	3	855	906	929	943
Denmark	3	6	7	4	1,830	2,112	2,045	1,904
Finland	4	3	2	2	348	416	397	454
Greece	166	157	155	155	332	393	398	431
Ireland	99	100	97	92	639	842	801	844
Norway	34	39	38	38	285	292	295	314
Portugal	51	66	59	59	347	378	385	395
Spain	276	295	289	284	1,337	1,724	1,783	1,828
Sweden	4	6	7	7	800	866	866	894
Switzerland	7	7	7	7	546	611	706	708
United Kingdom	559	577	543	453	4,333	4,422	4,435	4,409
Total other western[5]	1,206	1,259	1,207	1,104	11,652	12,962	13,040	13,124

Eastern								
Bulgaria	134	190	194	174	559	728	785	707
Czechoslovakia	4	3	22	…	1,222	1,383	1,498	1,423
Germany, East	22	22	…	22	1,530	1,915	1,987	2,038
Hungary	19	19	…	…	899	905	994	994
Poland	58	…	…	…	2,805	3,163	3,235	3,338
Yugoslavia	117	119	138	148	1,501	1,609	1,791	1,771
Total Eastern[5]	354	410	438	430	8,516	9,703	10,290	10,271
Total Europe[5]	1,936	2,075	2,054	1,946	37,766	42,043	43,783	43,913
USSR	1,870	1,760	1,760	1,760	14,640	18,760	18,660	18,640
Africa and Asia								
South Africa, Republic of	281	291	342	381	1,394	1,331	1,364	1,393
China, Taiwan	1	2	2	…	500	711	733	746
Japan	5	3	3	3	1,100	1,580	1,534	1,615
Philippines	9	11	11	11	711	942	974	1,028
Turkey	654	657	671	693	976	1,002	1,035	1,070
Total[5]	950	964	1,029	1,090	4,681	5,566	5,640	5,852
Oceania								
Australia[7]	1,310	1,314	1,465	1,488	3,508	3,564	3,788	3,903
New Zealand[8]	1,038	1,148	1,249	1,241	1,746	1,894	2,093	2,153
Total	2,348	2,462	2,714	2,729	5,254	5,458	5,881	6,056
Total selected countries	8,748	8,971	9,265	9,139	110,433	125,657	129,339	130,123

Source: USDA (1970A).
[1] Carcass weight basis; excludes offals, rabbit and poultry meat.
[2] Includes edible pork fat; excludes lard and inedible greases.
[3] Preliminary.
[4] Excludes slaughter for farm use.
[5] Includes an allowance for missing data for countries shown.
[6] Variety meats (offals) included.
[7] Year ending June 30.
[8] Year ending September 30.
[9] Includes horse meat.

Meat Trade

As may be seen in Table 14.3, beef and veal comprise more than 1/2 of total world red meat production, and 9% of the beef produced enters international trade. Pork and lamb, mutton and goat meat trade presents a contrasting situation. A relatively small proportion of pork moves out of the country where it is produced, but almost 1/5 of the lamb, mutton, and goat meat is shipped to foreign customers.

TABLE 14.3

RED MEATS: PERCENTAGE OF TOTAL WORLD PRODUCTION
AND PERCENTAGE MOVING IN INTERNATIONAL TRADE, 1969

Item	Beef and Veal	Pork	Lamb, Mutton and Goat Meat	Total
Percentage each specie is of total world red meat production	54	39	7	100
Percentage of production moving in international trade	9	6	19	8

Source: Calculated from USDA (1970A).

Beef.—Table 14.4 shows the import-export movements of beef and veal for important producing countries. Argentina has been, by a considerable margin, the chief beef exporter. Following in order are Australia, New Zealand, and Ireland. These are the "big four" world suppliers of beef and veal. Other important exporters are France and Uruguay. Brazil has increased beef exports in recent years, but traditionally has not been a major shipper. It is worth noting also that, although Mexico and the Central American countries individually export relatively minor quantities of beef, their shipments have increased significantly in recent years, and collectively, they are assuming a major role in the beef trade.

The United States is the major importer of beef—a position she gained from the United Kingdom during the 1960's. The United Kingdom is a strong second, followed by Italy, West Germany, and Spain. West Germany, like several other European countries, has a sizeable trade in both imports and exports of beef and veal. Generally, these are not identical products. Some countries import wholesale cuts of fresh meat which are processed and reshipped in the processed form.

Pork.—The United Kingdom imports 3 times as much pork as any other country, and in fact takes almost 1/2 of all the pork which moves internationally (Table 14.5). The United States in recent years has assumed a major importing role and now occupies second place. Among the Common Market countries, France, Italy, and West Germany depend heavily upon

TABLE 14.4

BEEF AND VEAL:[1] INTERNATIONAL TRADE IN SELECTED COUNTRIES, AVERAGE 1961-1965, ANNUAL 1967-1969

Continent and Country	Avg 1961-65		1967		1968[2]		1969[2]	
	Exports (Million Lb)	Imports (Million Lb)	Exports (Million Lb)	Imports (Million Lb)	Exports (Million Lb)	Imports (Million Lb)	Exports (Million Lb)	Imports (Million Lb)
North America								
Canada	42.0	54.1	43.3	81.5	70.2	66.2	68.8	192.3
United States	43.8	1236.3	42.2	1327.7	38.2	1518.0	36.7	1640.5
Costa Rica	18.9	...	33.8	0.1	47.5	0.4	52.2	...[3]
Guatemala	13.8	...	26.7	...	28.1	...	36.8	...
Honduras	12.8	...	19.2	...	20.3	...	33.3	...
Mexico	81.1	0.1	66.6	0.3	100.7	0.3	109.2	0.2
Nicaragua	29.6	...	44.6	...	52.1	...	61.2	...
Dominican Republic	0.9	...	0.9	...	12.0	...	13.8	...
Total North America	242.9	1290.5	277.3	1409.6	369.1	1584.9	412.0	1833.0
South America								
Argentina	1216.8	...	1535.7	...	1339.1	0.1	1697.5	...
Brazil	90.5	...	58.3	...	167.3	...	253.2	...
Chile	0.3	17.9	...	28.8	0.6	35.4	...	...
Paraguay	48.7	...	47.9	...	49.2	...	39.0	...
Peru	...	9.8	...	23.0	...	20.8	...	...
Uruguay	215.2	...	121.9	...	234.7	...	245.3	...
Venezuela	...	0.5	...	0.1	...	...	...	0.1
Total South America	1571.5	28.2	1763.8	51.9	1790.9	56.3	2235.6[4]	56.3[4]
Europe								
Western								
EC:								
Belgium and Luxembourg	9.0	41.9	59.1	80.9	67.0	97.2	39.7	65.7
France	250.4	86.0	240.3	92.6	381.4	90.4	288.8	180.8
Germany, West	22.7	240.5	39.7	334.4	76.3	429.9	122.4	500.4
Italy	2.9	421.7	...	767.4	1.1	579.8	3.1	609.4
Netherlands	118.8	55.3	154.1	100.5	194.4	125.9	225.1	141.5
Total EC	403.8	845.4	493.2	1375.8	720.2	1323.2	679.1	1497.8
Austria	3.3	9.9	9.9	5.1	5.3	8.6	6.2	18.1
Denmark	181.9	0.5	269.1	2.2	248.8[3]	2.6	204.8	3.5[3]
Finland	0.8	5.2	2.1	1.1	...	1.2	29.9	...

TABLE 14.4 (Continued)

BEEF AND VEAL:[1] INTERNATIONAL TRADE IN SELECTED COUNTRIES, AVERAGE 1961-1965, ANNUAL 1967-1969

Continent and Country	Avg 1961-65		1967		1968[2]		1969[2]	
	Exports (Million Lb)	Imports (Million Lb)	Exports (Million Lb)	Imports (Million Lb)	Exports (Million Lb)	Imports (Million Lb)	Exports (Million Lb)	Imports (Million Lb)
Greece	...	48.7	...	86.7	...	99.5	...	120.6
Ireland	186.9	0.2	391.9	0.1	318.6	0.3	325.1	0.6
Norway	5.2[3]	3.5	3.2[3]	4.5	2.5[3]	14.3	4.7	2.6
Portugal		20.8		57.9		45.1		21.9
Spain	0.6	101.6	0.6	244.6	0.7	249.0	0.6	254.9
Sweden	24.1	21.0	58.4	15.5	35.3	22.4	54.3	23.7
Switzerland	3.6	60.4	4.0	79.8	7.8	69.8	9.4	85.7
United Kingdom	8.5	1085.5	13.9	993.0	6.3	951.1	16.1	1070.7
Total other Western Europe	414.9	1357.3	753.1	1490.5	625.3	1463.9	651.1	1602.3
Eastern								
Bulgaria	3.0	6.7	15.4	23.9	30.0	24.9		
Czechoslovakia	7.7	81.4	27.3	18.1	41.0	23.9		
Hungary	47.2	36.9	60.4	29.7	58.0	3.2	100.9	
Poland	65.1	20.3	70.2	21.1	83.3	12.4[3]	192.3	8.1[3]
Yugoslavia	149.3	1.1	184.8		193.4			
Total Eastern Europe	272.3	146.4	358.1	92.8	405.7	64.4	422.2[4]	60.1[4]
Total Europe	1091.0	2349.1	1604.4	2959.1	1751.2	2851.5	1752.4[4]	3160.2[4]
USSR	212.7	236.6	396.4	40.8	298.2	33.3	224.9	69.1
Africa								
Ghana	23.1	9.3	27.5	10.3	22.3	3.9	18.1	8.4
Kenya	52.1	0.2	71.3	1.0	42.8		31.4	
South Africa, Republic of	75.2	1.6	98.8	45.7	65.1	42.7	49.5	37.8
Total Africa		11.1		57.0		46.6		46.2
Asia								
Israel	...[3]	34.6	...[3]	52.2	...[3]	82.8	...[3]	80.1
Hong Kong	0.1[3]	7.0	0.1[3]	9.1	0.2[3]	10.4	0.1	10.4
Japan		14.4		31.4		31.8		42.7
Malaysia		3.2		4.2		1.5		
Philippines		32.5		24.3		45.4		41.5
Singapore	2.0	9.6	3.2	10.1	2.8	12.0	2.9	10.9
Total Asia	2.1	101.3	3.3	131.3	3.0	183.9	3.0	185.6

Continent and Country	Avg 1961-65 Exports (Million Lb)	Imports (Million Lb)	1967 Exports (Million Lb)	Imports (Million Lb)	1968[2] Exports (Million Lb)	Imports (Million Lb)	1969[2] Exports (Million Lb)	Imports (Million Lb)
Oceania								
Australia[5]	879.6	...	927.0	...[3]	903.2	0.1	892.9	0.2
New Zealand[6]	355.7	...	372.5	...	420.1	...	498.6	...
Total Oceania	1235.3	...	1299.5	...	1323.3	0.1	1391.5	0.2
Total selected countries	4430.7	4016.8	5443.5	4649.7	5600.8	4756.6	6068.9[4]	5350.6[4]

Source: USDA (1970A).
[1] Carcass weight equivalent basis; excludes fat, offals, and live animals.
[2] Preliminary.
[3] Less than 50,000 lb.
[4] Includes an allowance for nonreporting countries or areas.
[5] Year ending June 30.
[6] Year ending Sept. 30.

TABLE 14.5

PORK:[1] INTERNATIONAL TRADE IN SELECTED COUNTRIES, AVERAGE 1961-1965, ANNUAL 1967-1969

Continent and Country	Avg 1961-65 Exports (Million Lb)	Imports (Million Lb)	1967 Exports (Million Lb)	Imports (Million Lb)	1968[2] Exports (Million Lb)	Imports (Million Lb)	1969[2] Exports (Million Lb)	Imports (Million Lb)
North America								
Canada	65.2	53.4	62.3	36.7	63.2	51.5	58.3	83.0
United States	94.9	245.7	57.9	392.5	93.3	416.1	153.8	408.8
Costa Rica	...	...	...	0.1	...	0.1	...	...
Honduras	...	0.2	...	0.3	...	...	...	...
Mexico	...	0.2	...	0.6	...	0.2	...	0.2
Total North America	160.1	299.5	120.2	430.2	156.5	468.2[3]	212.1	492.4[3]
South America								
Argentina	19.1	...	25.3	...[4]	11.2	...[4]	11.7	...[4]
Brazil	0.9	...	0.5	0.1	0.5	0.1	1.7	...
Chile	...	0.6	...	...	...	...	...	...
Peru	...	0.9	...	2.3	...	0.1	...	...
Uruguay	...	...	0.4	...	...	...	...[4]	...
Venezuela	...	15.4	...	10.3	...	...	...	6.9
Total South America	20.0	16.9	26.2	12.7	11.7	11.0[3]	13.4	9.2[3]

TABLE 14.5 (Continued)

PORK:[1] INTERNATIONAL TRADE IN SELECTED COUNTRIES, AVERAGE 1961-1965, ANNUAL 1967-1969

Continent and Country	Avg 1961-65 Exports (Million Lb)	Imports (Million Lb)	1967 Exports (Million Lb)	Imports (Million Lb)	1968[2] Exports (Million Lb)	Imports (Million Lb)	1969[2] Exports (Million Lb)	Imports (Million Lb)
Europe								
Western								
EC:								
Belgium and Luxembourg	47.4	36.6	122.8	41.7	148.5	22.3	183.6	46.5
France	45.4	148.6	37.5	242.5	19.8	302.0	8.8	438.7
Germany, West	15.7	73.4	12.8	110.0	24.2	153.0	37.5	144.0
Italy	3.1	60.6	16.3	191.8	14.1	144.4	7.3	160.9
Netherlands	314.6	11.0	453.0	7.9	559.9	9.9	504.2	6.2
Total EC	426.2	330.2	642.4[4]	593.9	765.9	631.6	741.4	796.3
Austria	0.5	5.3	...	16.8	0.4	2.0	0.4	2.6
Denmark	1104.7	0.4	1172.2	1.2	1191.2	2.7	1129.7	2.7
Finland	3.9	2.5	28.7	1.3	16.1	1.8	9.9	0.6
Greece	...	3.7	...	2.4	...	11.5	...	4.2
Ireland	103.8	0.2	80.2	0.1	109.1	0.3	136.8	0.4
Norway	3.1	4.7	0.4	10.6	0.8	7.5	4.2	5.9
Portugal	0.7	4.3	0.5	16.2	0.5	7.8		
Spain	0.5	29.5	1.6	12.3	0.5	13.0	0.8	10.3
Sweden	57.4	20.3	74.4	31.3	88.3	35.8	95.5	36.3
Switzerland	3.6	28.5	4.4	27.0	5.6	8.9	7.1	12.9
United Kingdom	14.6	1311.5	13.0	1324.1	8.5	1353.6	26.9	1308.6
Total other Western Europe	1292.8	1410.9	1375.4	1443.3	1,421.0	1444.9	1411.3	1384.5
Eastern								
Bulgaria	16.9	6.3	32.3	28.6	41.2	6.2	...	...
Czechoslovakia	7.0	94.9	...	18.1	...	23.9	...	...
Hungary	42.5	48.3	63.9	138.2	62.2		...	...
Poland	283.8	53.8	297.0	72.1	284.5	161.5	265.3	70.7
Yugoslavia	174.8	1.3	128.7	72.1	83.8	12.3	84.2	3.7
Total Eastern Europe	525.0	204.6	521.9	329.1	471.7	250.6[3]	452.9[3]	151.2[3]
Total Europe	2244.0	1945.7	2539.7	2366.3	2658.6	2327.1[3]	2605.6[3]	2332.0[3]
USSR	39.1	34.1	48.6	13.3	49.7	2.5	45.0	18.1

Africa								
Ghana	..	4.8	..	3.3	..	5.3	..	4.2
Kenya	1.0	0.4	1.5	0.7	1.2	0.2	1.8	0.2
South Africa, Republic of	8.7	0.8	15.7	2.4	12.0	3.5	13.2	4.3
Total Africa	9.7	6.0	17.2	6.4	13.2	9.0	15.0	8.7
Asia								
Hong Kong	0.2	22.6	[4]	46.6	[4]	62.3	[4]	53.6
Japan	0.2 [4]	5.8	0.8 [4]	1.5	1.0 [4]	24.5	1.3	9.6
Malaysia	..	1.7	..	1.6	..	1.4	..	..
Philippines	..	1.0	..	2.3	..	2.3	..	1.2
Singapore	1.0	3.1	0.9	4.4	0.8	5.6	0.8	6.4
Total Asia	1.4	34.2	1.7	56.4	1.8	96.1	2.1	70.8
Oceania								
Australia[5]	2.4	2.7	3.8	0.1	3.1	0.4	4.3	0.6
New Zealand[6]	7.1	..	1.1	..	2.9	..	1.0	..
Total Oceania	9.5	2.7	4.9	0.1	6.0	0.4	5.3	0.6
Total selected countries	2483.8	2339.1	2758.5	2885.4	2897.5	2914.3[3]	2898.5[3]	2931.8[3]

Source: USDA (1970A).
[1] Carcass weight equivalent basis; excludes fat, offals, and live animals.
[2] Preliminary.
[3] Includes an allowance for nonreporting countries or areas.
[4] Less than 50,000 lb.
[5] Year ending June 30.
[6] Year ending Sept. 30.

imported pork. Fortunately for the European importers, the chief sources of supply are nearby.

Denmark, long renowned for superior quality bacon and hams, is the chief exporter; and her neighbors, the Netherlands, Belgium, and Luxembourg, are important exporters. These countries have for many years carried out effective breeding, feeding, and processing programs with rigidly enforced specifications designed to produce bacon, hams, and other pork products that meet the highly discriminating British consumer standards. Two eastern European countries, Poland and Yugoslavia, are surplus pork producers and move substantial quantities in the international market. Ireland is one of the few European countries which has a substantial net surplus of both pork and beef. The determination of these European countries to participate in international meat trade, coupled with the powerful economic forces alluded to earlier, is reflected in the fact that their canned bacon, ham, and other meat products may be found on the shelves of food stores throughout the United States. The United States also exports significant quantities of pork products. These consist primarily of lard, variety meats, casings, etc.

Not included in Table 14.5 are lard and other fats. The United States is the major producer, user, and exporter of these products.

Lamb, Mutton, and Goat Meat.—Import-export movements of lamb, mutton, and goat meat are shown in Table 14.6. Goat meat is a minor fraction of the total, but is an important meat in certain countries—particularly in some Near Eastern and African countries not shown in these tabulations. New Zealand is in a class by itself in the exportation of lamb and mutton—accounting for over 70% of all international shipments. Australia is the next most important exporter. Together, these two "down-under" countries move 85% of the lamb and mutton. However, Argentina also exports sizeable quantities.

The chief importers of lamb, mutton, and goat meat in order are the United Kingdom, Japan, United States, Canada, and Greece.

Horsemeat.—Horsemeat is important in the United States only as a source of pet food, but it is commonly used as human food in northern European countries and in Japan. Japan is the leading importer followed by Belgium, Luxembourg, United States, Netherlands, and France. Argentina is the outstanding source of horsemeat—accounting for almost 60% of international shipments. Other South American countries, Mexico, Canada, and Poland also are major suppliers.

Cattle Hides, Calf and Kip Skins

Often overlooked in discussions of the livestock economy is the extensive and important trade in hides and skins. The production and availability of hides and skins parallels the production of live animals. Expanding world cattle production has increased the availability of these products and in spite

MUTTON, LAMB, AND GOAT MEAT:[1] INTERNATIONAL TRADE IN SELECTED COUNTRIES, AVERAGE 1961-1965, ANNUAL 1967-1969

Continent and Country	Avg 1961-65 Exports (Million Lb)	Avg 1961-65 Imports (Million Lb)	1967 Exports (Million Lb)	1967 Imports (Million Lb)	1968[2] Exports (Million Lb)	1968[2] Imports (Million Lb)	1969[2] Exports (Million Lb)	1969[2] Imports (Million Lb)
North America								
Canada	0.5	37.6	0.2	79.8	0.1	108.7	0.1	130.2
United States	2.0	108.0	2.6	120.9	2.8	146.9	2.3	152.3
Mexico	...	...	...	0.6	...	0.5	...	0.2
Total North America	2.5	145.6	2.8	201.3	2.9	256.1	2.4	282.7
South America								
Argentina	77.7	...	162.6	...	135.0	...[3]	128.5[3]	...
Brazil	0.4	0.3	...	...[3]	...	...[3]	...	...[3]
Chile	2.5	4.2	2.4	...	0.9	...	...	...
Peru	...	...	...	16.9	...	18.7	...	18.7[4]
Uruguay	10.0	0.1	13.5	...	30.2	...	21.3	...
Venezuela	...	...	...	...[3]	...	...[3]	...	...[3]
Total South America	90.6	4.6	178.5	16.9	166.1	18.7	150.7[4]	18.7[4]
Europe								
Western								
EC:								
Belgium and Luxembourg	1.1	4.2	0.9[3]	6.0	4.0[3]	8.4	12.1[3]	10.8
France	2.6	22.9	...	37.5	...	44.1	...	61.7
Germany, West	0.7[3]	4.4[3]	2.0[3]	7.7[3]	4.8	9.3[3]	4.2	10.4
Italy	...	...	...	...	...	2.2	0.4	16.1
Netherlands	13.9	1.1	15.7	2.0	15.7	3.5[3]	14.8	3.1
Total EC	18.3[3]	32.6[3]	18.6[3]	53.2[3]	24.5[3]	67.5[3]	31.5[3]	102.1
Austria	...	0.6[3]	0.2	0.9[3]	0.9	0.9[3]	0.7	0.7
Denmark	...[3]	...	...	...	...	...	...	0.4[3]
Finland	...	...	...	...	...	...	...	...
Greece	...	39.4[3]	...	76.3[3]	...	73.6[3]	...	79.0[3]
Ireland	29.8[3]	...	29.6[3]	...	28.1[3]	...	24.9[3]	...
Norway	...	1.7[3]	...	1.6[3]	...	0.9[3]	...	1.5
Portugal	...[3]	...	...	...	...	...	...	...
Spain	0.9	...	0.2	0.4	0.3	0.5	0.5	0.8

TABLE 14.6 (Continued)

MUTTON, LAMB, AND GOAT MEAT:[1] INTERNATIONAL TRADE IN SELECTED COUNTRIES, AVERAGE 1961-1965, ANNUAL 1967-1969

Continent and Country	Avg 1961-65 Exports (Million Lb)	Avg 1961-65 Imports (Million Lb)	1967 Exports (Million Lb)	1967 Imports (Million Lb)	1968[2] Exports (Million Lb)	1968[2] Imports (Million Lb)	1969[2] Exports (Million Lb)	1969[2] Imports (Million Lb)
Sweden	[3]	1.1	0.3	0.3	[3]	0.2	[3]	0.4
Switzerland		2.1	[3]	8.6	[3]	5.8	[3]	5.7
United Kingdom	4.5	803.3	16.6	777.1	7.8	801.2	17.1	834.4
Total other Western Europe	35.2	848.2	46.9	865.2	37.1	883.1	43.2	922.9
Eastern								
Bulgaria	0.4[3]	2.9	3.9	3.9	11.2	0.4	...	...
Czechoslovakia		4.0	0.6[3]	6.4	2.1	5.3	...	...
Hungary	0.8	1.5					0.9	0.9
Poland	0.8	0.6		1.5		1.5		0.1
Yugoslavia	8.3		10.1		10.4		9.6	
Total Eastern Europe	10.3	9.0	14.6	11.8	23.7	7.2	23.8[4]	6.7[4]
Total Europe	63.8	889.8	80.1	930.2	85.3	957.8	98.5[4]	1031.7[4]
Africa								
Ghana	0.4	3.9	0.1	3.0	0.1	3.5	0.1	4.2
Keyna	1.2	0.1[3]	0.5	0.1	0.8	0.1	1.0	[3]
South Africa, Republic of				2.1				
Total Africa	1.6	4.0	0.6	5.2	0.9	3.6	1.1	4.2
Asia								
Hong Kong	...[3]	1.8	...	2.2	...[3]	2.8	...[3]	2.7
Japan	[3]	92.6	...[3]	215.0	[3]	240.9	...	285.0
Malaysia		3.7		4.5		4.8		
Philippines		0.1		0.4		0.9		0.7
Singapore	2.0	6.6	2.3	7.0	2.8	8.2	2.9	8.8
Total Asia	2.0	104.8	2.3	229.1	2.8	257.6	2.9	297.2
Oceania								
Australia[5]	316.1	...	370.4	...	456.6	1.7	404.6	1.1
New Zealand[6]	804.5	...	873.1	...	957.1	...	1074.4	...
Total Oceania	1120.6	...	1243.5	...	1413.7	1.7	1479.0	1.1
Total selected countries	1281.1	1148.8	1507.8	1382.7	1671.7	1495.5	1734.6[4]	1635.6[4]

Source: USDA (1970A).
[1] Carcass weight equivalent basis; excludes fat, offals, and live animals.
[2] Preliminary.
[3] Less than 50,000 lb.
[4] Includes an allowance for nonreporting countries or areas.
[5] Year ending June 30.
[6] Year ending Sept. 30.

of stiff competition from synthetics, a relatively strong world-wide demand exists for hides and skins.

Prior to the 1960's, Argentina was the leading hide exporter, but in recent years that role has been taken over by the United States. Together, the United States and Argentina dominate exports. Other leading suppliers are Canada, Australia, West Germany, Spain, Yugoslavia, Poland, Czechoslovakia, and the Soviet Union.

In recent years the leading producers of calf and kip skins have been the United States, France, Argentina, West Germany, New Zealand, Australia, and Italy. However, in exports the leaders have been the Netherlands, France, the United States, New Zealand, and West Germany.

A major change among importers of skins has been the recent rapid rise to leadership by Spain. Other important importers are Japan, West Germany, and Italy.

Wool Trade

World wool production continues to increase (Fig. 14.3). At the same time, U.S. production is on a definite downward trend (Table 14.7) despite a government incentive program designed to encourage domestic production. Congress enacted a law in 1954 providing for incentive payments to wool

FIG. 14.3. WORLD PRODUCTION AND COMSUMPTION OF RAW WOOL

TABLE 14.7

WOOL: DOMESTIC PRODUCTION, IMPORTS OF RAW WOOL,
AND THE FOREIGN TRADE IMPORT BALANCE OF WOOL
TEXTILE PRODUCTS, CLEAN BASIS, 1960-1969

| | Domestic Production[1] | | | Imports of Raw Wool[2] | | | Foreign Trade Import Balance of Wool Textile Products[3] | | |
Year	Shorn	Pulled	Total	Dutiable	Duty-free	Total	Apparel Wool	Carpet Wool	Total
				(Million Lb)					
1960	119.4	25.2	144.6	74.3	153.9	228.2	98.9	28.5	127.4
1961	116.6	25.9	142.5	90.3	157.3	247.7	95.2	27.7	122.9
1962	111.0	22.4	133.4	125.8	143.5	269.2	112.3	29.0	141.3
1963	104.6	21.6	126.2	109.2	168.0	277.2	125.4	21.5	147.0
1964	101.3	18.3	119.6	98.4	113.9	212.3	107.1	27.0	134.1
1965	96.1	17.0	113.1	162.6	108.9	271.6	122.6	21.4	144.0
1966	93.0	17.6	110.6	162.5	114.6	277.2	117.9	16.2	134.2
1967	90.1	16.3	106.4	109.1	78.2	187.3	105.4	9.4	114.8
1968	84.7	14.9	99.7	129.7	119.6	249.3	128.1	8.5	136.6
1969[4]	79.1	12.5	91.6	93.5	95.7	189.2	112.7	7.9	120.6

Source: USDA (1970B).
[1] Production as reported converted on basis of 45% yield of shorn wool for 1960 through 1963, 47.7% yield 1964 to date and 75% yield for pulled wool 1960 to 1963, 72.9% yield 1964 to date.
[2] Imports of raw wool for consumption.
[3] Raw wool content of semiprocessed and manufactured wool textile products.
[4] Preliminary.

growers with a stated purpose of maintaining U.S. production at least 300 million pounds a year. This action was prompted by a belief that wool is a strategic war material. But, producers have not responded to the incentives. Lack of labor on the big ranches is given as a chief cause. On family farms, sheep, while consistently returning more income per dollar invested than other livestock, have not been able to stem the drift to other livestock and crop enterprises.

Domestic demand for wool has met strong competition from man-made fibers (domestic and imported) and from imported wool and wool fabrics. Regardless, the demand for imported wool has been relatively strong. Table 14.7 shows that total imports, while somewhat variable from year to year, have about held to a constant trend in the past 10 yr. A significant point, however, is that, in recent years, imports of raw wool have been more than twice domestic production—making the United States highly dependent upon imports. The U. S. import balance is increasing for apparel wool, but declining for carpet wool.

Wool produced in the United States is used chiefly in the fabrication of clothing, blankets, etc. Wool used for rugs is all imported. Australia and New Zealand are the chief suppliers of wool, followed by South Africa and countries of South America.

U.S. MEAT ANIMAL IMPORTS AND EXPORTS

The economics of transporting meat compared to live animals limits the international movement of slaughter animals to trivial numbers. There are, however, small but significant movements of breeding stock and as far as the United States and her neighbors are concerned, varying but often substantial movements of feeder cattle.

Beef Cattle

Imports of beef cattle are shown on Table 14.8. In the past 10 yr imports of breeding cattle have ranged from 11,000 to almost 21,000 head. This includes dairy as well as beef stock. Compared to the current combined 62 million head of breeding stock in the United States, it can be seen that from the standpoint of total numbers, breeding cattle imports are relatively insignificant. Yet for particular herd owners the importation of select stock undoubtedly is of ultimate importance. Were it not for the ban on importation of cattle from foot and mouth disease areas, the importation of breeding cattle would be larger.

TABLE 14.8

IMPORTS OF MEAT ANIMALS, UNITED STATES, 1960-1969

| Year | Breeding Cattle[1] (Hd) | Canada (Hd) | Cattle Other Cattle[2] | | | Sheep and Lambs[1] (Hd) | Hogs[1] (Hd) |
			Mexico (Hd)	Other (Hd)	Total (Hd)		
1960	18,624	233,415	390,517	. . .	623,932	49,767	6,162
1961	19,922	454,717	543,064	. . .	997,781	979	3,151
1962	17,773	464,856	751,885	. . .	1,216,741	20,845	3,277
1963	18,562	236,122	585,342	376	821,840	3,091	4,323
1964	17,735	183,307	330,901	700	514,908	12,680	5,094
1965	17,647	560,105	535,260	. . .	1,095,365	19,073	14,453
1966	18,876	475,587	584,085	327	1,060,002	8,310	22,698
1967	11,387	227,042	500,418	40	727,500	12,403	34,926
1968	14,915	306,117	702,308	27	1,008,452	26,579	21,678
1969	20,855	187,687	810,387	62	998,136	22,805	13,430

[1] Source: USDA (1970C).
[2] Source: USDA (1970D).

Table 14.8 also shows the number of "other" cattle imported in recent years. A majority of these are feeder cattle and came almost entirely from Canada and Mexico, with a substantial predominance from Mexico in most years. When U.S. slaughter cattle prices are attractive, Canada and Mexico are induced to ship in some slaughter animals. The value of such shipments amounted to $64.1 million, $97.4 million, and $103.0 million in 1967, 1968, and 1969 respectively.

Exports of cattle are shown in Table 14.9. The exportation of "other" (i.e., feeder) cattle is negligible. In 1969, most (9420 head) of the breeding cattle

TABLE 14.9

MEAT ANIMAL EXPORTS: NUMBER OF CATTLE, SHEEP
AND HOGS EXPORTED, UNITED STATES, 1962 TO DATE

Year	For Breeding (Hd)	Cattle Other Cattle (Hd)	Total (Hd)	Sheep[1] (Hd)	Hogs (Hd)
1962	18,039	1,273	19,312	37,336	3,330
1963	22,428	727	23,155	31,493	3,899
1964	28,164	33,467	61,631	22,809	16,567
1965	32,380	21,791	54,171	25,315	12,180
1966	26,946	8,371	35,317	59,054	9,649
1967	31,749	23,573	55,322	120,733	12,932
1968	31,917	3,808	35,725	117,677	13,714
1969	34,063	5,123	39,186	106,237	18,620
1970	26,323	61,714	88,037	132,856	25,654

Source: USDA (1970C).
[1] Sheep only for 1962-1964. Beginning 1965 includes sheep, lambs, and goats.

went to Canada. Mexico, Venezuela, Chile, and Guatemala also were major recipients of U.S. cattle. In all, breeding cattle were shipped to 38 different countries, including all continents except Oceania.

Sheep and Hogs

Imports of live sheep and lambs, and hogs are somewhat variable and relatively small in numbers (see Table 14.8). In the early 1960's, wide publicity was given to the importation of slaughter lambs from New Zealand, but this soon dwindled. Most imports of sheep and hogs are breeding animals.

Exports of both sheep and hogs, though small, have increased substantially during recent years (Table 14.9). The United States is the world's leading exporter of breeding hogs. Mexico is the chief importer of American swine—taking almost 1/2 of all foreign shipments in 1969. Other leading destinations were Canada, Venezuela, and Italy.

MAJOR SOURCES OF U.S. MEAT AND LIVESTOCK
PRODUCT IMPORTS

Table 14.10 shows the chief suppliers of meat to the United States. In recent years Australia alone has furnished about 40% of the U.S. imports of beef and veal. New Zealand supplied an additional 18%. Argentina, Brazil, Ireland, and Canada are all important suppliers and, as mentioned earlier, the Central American countries have come up rapidly in recent years. The bulk of imported beef is in frozen, boneless form (see Table 14.11) and is used primarily for processing purposes—including hamburgers. A matter of increasing concern to the U.S. cattle industry, however, has been a recent apparent sharp increase in imports of block beef (fresh meat destined for consumption in unprocessed form). Official data are not regularly reported on

TABLE 14.10

MEAT IMPORTS: UNITED STATES, BY COUNTRIES, 1964 TO DATE

Product and Year	Imports, by Country of Origin, Product Weight in Million Pounds												Total Imports in Million Pounds	
	Canada	Mexico	Argentina	Brazil	Denmark	West Germany	Poland	Netherlands	Ireland	Australia	New Zealand	All Other	Product Weight	Carcass Weight Equivalent
Beef and veal														
1964	28.8	48.9	54.4	10.4	0.1	[2]	0.1	[2]	20.1	377.1	168.3	92.2	800.4	1085
1965	71.4	46.3	54.8	24.5	0.2	0.1	0.1	0.1	7.8	307.5	103.6	84.6	701.0	942
1966	57.2	57.1	80.6	18.3	0.1	[2]	0.1	0.1	38.4	404.1	145.0	92.3	893.3	1204
1967	26.7	47.8	108.1	9.6	0.1	[2]	[2]	[2]	80.6	425.6	170.9	109.6	979.0	1328
1968	46.7	65.6	132.6	31.6	0.1	[2]	0.1	[2]	56.7	444.2	203.1	147.3	1128.0	1518
1969	44.0	66.5	130.0	34.3	0.2	[2]	[2]	[2]	66.0	491.1	223.7	160.8	1216.6	1640
1970[3]	80.6	78.6	141.1	28.8	0.4	[2]	[2]	[2]	69.0	536.1	241.6	174.2	1350.4	1816
Lamb and mutton														
1964	0.7									34.4	8.8	0.8	44.7	79
1965	0.5									30.3	11.4	0.4	42.6	72
1966	0.3									63.8	11.1	0.2	75.4	136
1967	0.2[2]									56.8	9.4	0.2	66.6	121
1968										62.2	0.7	0.1	84.9	147
1969	0.7									73.9	23.4	0.1	98.1	153
1970[3]	0.6									60.1	22.2	0.1	83.0	122
Pork														
1964	50.7	[2]	[2]		66.4	0.7	43.9	38.2	0.2	[2]	[2]	10.5	210.6	268
1965	57.0				85.2	0.9	52.9	46.2	2.2	[2]	[2]	20.9	262.3	333
1966	47.5	[2]	0.3		116.9	1.8	51.6	65.0	1.6	[2]	[2]	13.9	298.3	381
1967	54.8	[2]	[2]	0.1	102.3	1.4	57.2	74.6	0.2	0.1	[2]	16.0	306.9	392
1968	55.5	[2]	0.1		111.9	1.4	55.1	82.2	0.3		[2]	17.6	324.1	416
1969	49.9	[2]	[2]		108.6	1.8	53.6	85.6	0.2	0.2	[2]	15.6	315.6	409
1970[3]	63.2				120.6	1.4	56.0	86.7	0.1	0.3		19.3	347.6	449
Totals[1]														
1964	80.1	48.9	54.4	10.4	66.5	0.7	44.0	38.2	20.3	411.5	176.9	103.8	1055.7	1432
1965	125.9	46.3	54.8	24.7	85.4	1.0	53.0	46.3	10.0	337.7	115.0	105.9	1006.0	1347
1966	105.0	57.1	80.5	18.3	117.0	1.8	51.7	65.1	40.0	467.9	156.1	106.5	1267.0	1721
1967	81.7	47.8	108.6	9.6	102.4	1.4	57.2	74.6	80.8	482.5	180.3	125.6	1352.5	1841

1968	102.2	65.6	132.6	112.1	31.7	55.2	82.2	56.9	203.8	165.0	1544.6	2081
1969	94.6	66.5	130.1	108.8	34.3	53.6	85.6	66.2	247.1	176.5	1639.1	2202
1970³	144.3	78.6	141.1	130.4	28.8	56.1	86.7	69.1	263.9	193.8	1791.5	2387

Source: USDA (1970C).
[1] Includes quantities of other canned, prepared or preserved meat not elsewhere specified, assumed to be mostly beef.
[2] Less than 50,000 lb.
[3] Preliminary.

TABLE 14.11

U.S. IMPORTS OF LIVESTOCK AND LIVESTOCK PRODUCTS, 1965-1970

Item	1965	1966	1967	1968	1969	1970¹
			Million Pounds			
Meat (carcass weight equivalent)						
Beef						
Boneless, fresh or frozen	734.3	986.7	1,116.0	1,224.7	1,348.9	1,483.9
Fresh or frozen	29.3	20.7	11.7	26.8	19.6	24.3
Total fresh or frozen	763.6	1,007.4	1,127.7	1,251.5	1,368.5	1,508.2
Canned	126.8	126.6	136.7	165.2	164.4	167.1
Pickled or cured	.4	.6	1.8	1.3	1.6	1.8
Other processed	32.2	47.6	47.3	81.7	80.3	115.2
Total	923.0	1,182.2	1,313.5	1,499.7	1,614.8	1,792.3
Veal						
Fresh or frozen	18.8	22.0	14.2	18.3	25.7	23.5
Pork						
Fresh or frozen	47.9	42.0	47.4	48.4	42.9	55.5
Hams and shoulders, not cooked	1.9	1.8	1.9	2.4	2.2	1.5
Hams and shoulders, canned	236.7	267.6	284.6	306.5	314.7	339.7
Other	46.5	69.9	58.6	58.8	49.0	51.7
Total	333.0	381.3	392.5	416.1	408.8	448.4
Lamb	12.5	14.9	12.3	22.9	43.9	43.5
Mutton and goat	60.0	121.1	108.6	124.0	108.4	79.0
Total red meat	1,347.3	1,721.5	1,841.1	2,081.0	2,201.6	2,386.7

TABLE 14.11 (Continued)
U.S. IMPORTS OF LIVESTOCK AND LIVESTOCK PRODUCTS, 1965-1970

Item	1965	1966	1967	1968	1969	1970[1]
Variety meats (product weight)	2.2	3.3	3.5	3.8	5.6	9.8
Wool (clean basis)						
Dutiable	162.7	162.5	109.1	129.8	93.5	79.8
Duty-free	108.9	114.6	78.2	119.6	95.7	73.3
Total wool	271.6	277.2	187.3	249.4	189.2	153.1
			1000 Pieces			
Hides and skins						
Cattle	302	221	233	494	276	387
Calf	458	242	481	508	358	191
Kip	607	438	357	286	334	352
Sheep and lamb	29,821	27,893	20,300	30,822	20,715	18,707
			Number			
Live animals						
Cattle[2]	1,110,631	1,081,474	740,448	1,024,235	1,021,054	1,142,900
Hogs[3]	14,453	22,698	34,926	21,678	13,430	67,832
Sheep and lambs	19,073	8,310	12,403	26,579	22,805	11,716

Source: USDA (1971).
[1] Preliminary.
[2] Dutiable: not for breeding.
[3] For years 1965-1966 imports reported in pounds; pounds converted to 200-lb hog equivalent. Beginning 1967 reported in numbers.

TABLE 14.12

MEAT EXPORTS: U.S. EXPORTS AND SHIPMENTS BY COUNTRIES, 1966 TO DATE

Product and Year	Exports, by Destination, Product Weight in Million Pounds											Shipments to Territories[1]	Total Exports and Shipments in Million Pounds	
	Canada	Mexico	France	Bahamas	West Germany	Jamaica	Japan	Nether-lands	Vene-zuela	All Other	Total		Product Weight	Carcass Weight Equivalent
Beef and veal														
1966	13.1	0.2	0.5	4.0	0.2	1.0	0.1	0.3	[2]	9.4	28.8	32.2	61.0	87
1967	17.5	0.2	0.3	5.8	0.1	1.2	0.4	0.2	[2]	5.6	31.3	36.4	67.6	94
1968	11.9	0.4	0.4	7.1	0.1	1.1	0.4	0.1	[2]	5.5	27.0	37.5	64.5	94
1969	10.2	0.4	0.1	7.7	[2]	1.0	0.6	0.1	0.1	5.5	25.7	33.6	59.3	87
1970[4]	11.6	0.4	0.3	7.5	[2]	1.6	1.1	0.2	[2]	6.6	29.3	45.9	75.2	104
Lamb and mutton														
1966	0.6	[2]	[2]	0.4	...	[2]	...	...	[2]	0.6	1.6	1.1	2.7	5
1967	0.2	0.1	[2]	0.5	...	[2]	...	...	[2]	1.0	1.8	1.7	3.5	6
1968	0.3	[2]	[2]	0.7	...	[2]	[2]	...	[2]	0.9	1.9	1.9	3.8	7
1969	0.1	[2]	[2]	0.8	...	[2]	[2]	...	[2]	0.5	1.4	1.6	3.0	6
1970[4]	[2]	0.1	...	0.5	...	[2]	[2]	0.1	0.1	0.4	1.1	3.3	4.4	7
Pork														
1966	28.4	2.2	2.4	2.6	0.3	2.6	0.1	0.3	3.3	8.7	50.9	67.2	118.1	140
1967	27.3	1.9	0.3	3.5	0.2	2.9	0.6	0.2	2.9	10.8	50.6	74.4	125.0	146
1968	36.4	2.9	0.2	4.0	0.1	3.2	25.1	0.2	1.6	11.4	85.1	78.7	163.8	187
1969	64.4	3.9	0.2	4.1	0.4	2.2	57.4	0.1	0.8	11.6	145.1	63.4	208.5	236
1970[4]	23.5	2.7	0.1	3.5	0.1	1.3	16.2	[2]	1.1	12.7	61.2	85.5	146.7	177
Total[3]														
1966	44.2	2.8	3.2	7.6	0.9	4.4	0.6	0.8	3.3	28.8	96.6	130.9	227.5	232
1967	47.8	2.7	0.8	11.6	0.6	5.0	1.4	0.5	3.0	26.6	100.0	142.6	242.6	246
1968	50.9	4.2	0.8	13.7	0.5	5.0	26.1	0.4	1.6	27.9	131.1	153.6	284.7	288
1969	78.1	6.2	0.7	14.5	0.6	3.7	58.6	0.3	1.0	26.3	190.0	138.3	328.3	329
1970[4]	38.9	3.8	0.8	12.9	0.3	3.7	17.8	0.3	1.2	27.9	107.6	258.4	242.4	288

Source: USDA (1971).
[1] Puerto Rico and Virgin Islands, Guam and Wake, Puerto and Virgin Islands only in 1970.
[2] Less than 50,000 lb.
[3] Including sausage, bologna and frankfurters canned and not canned, sausage ingredients, meat and meat products not elsewhere classified.
[4] Preliminary.

the importation of block beef, but unofficial reports place the proportion as high as 40% of the total beef imports during 1970.

Lamb and mutton imports into the United States come almost exclusively from Australia and New Zealand (Table 14.10). And as shown in Table 14.11 the bulk of this is mutton (and goat meat)—largely in boneless form which goes into processed meats. Lamb constitutes less than 30% of total lamb and mutton imports.

Denmark, Poland, Netherlands, and Canada supply most of the U.S. pork imports (Table 14.10). This principally is canned bacon, hams, and shoulders (Table 14.11).

MAJOR DESTINATIONS OF U.S. EXPORTS

As may be seen in Table 14.12, U.S. exports of meat go chiefly to its territories. It is worth noting, however, that pork shipments to Japan and Canada have increased substantially in recent years. Table 14.13 shows that from a dollar standpoint tallow historically has been the biggest money item. However hides and skins carried the highest value of all export items in 1969. Red meats, which go largely to territories, was third high. Variety meats have been steadily increasing while lard, casings, and mohair have lost in dollar value.

TABLE 14.13
LIVESTOCK PRODUCTS: ANNUAL U.S. EXPORTS
(MILLION DOLLARS), 1960-1969

Year	Red Meats (Excluding Offals)	Live Animals	Animal Fats Lard	Animal Fats Tallow	Hides and Skins	Variety Meats (Offals)	Other Animal By-Products Casings, Mohair, etc.	Total
1960	36.3	13.0	60.6	115.2	76.4	25.2	25.9	352.6
1961	35.7	11.6	46.7	134.6	86.1	27.2	29.8	371.7
1962	34.1	10.7	40.6	106.9	82.9	25.5	25.5	326.2
1963	53.0	13.5	48.5	123.7	75.0	31.9	26.7	372.3
1964	65.8	21.0	69.8	179.8	92.7	47.9	12.5	489.5
1965	46.9	21.8	30.2	193.2	108.5	56.0	15.9	472.5
1966	47.6	19.6	19.6	167.9	154.8	58.5	18.0	486.0
1967	47.7	28.3	18.6	157.3	127.4	57.0	13.9	450.2
1968	61.9	21.7	14.2	134.4	120.8	55.0	18.1	426.1
1969	93.9	26.3	25.4	139.0	151.7	61.7	19.9	517.9

Source: USDA (1970B).

Quantities of export items are shown in Table 14.14. While the major items of U.S. export do not constitute a large fraction of the total quantity or value of livestock and meat produced, they nevertheless constitute an important fraction. Generally, these are items with a low demand preference in the United States. Without foreign outlets their value would be considerably less and this would have an adverse effect on U.S. livestock prices.

TABLE 14.14

U.S. EXPORTS OF LIVESTOCK AND LIVESTOCK PRODUCTS, 1965-1970

Item	1965	1966	1967	1968	1969	1970[1]
			Million Pounds			
Meat (carcass weight equivalent)						
Beef						
Fresh or frozen	32.4	17.5	17.1	15.2	16.2	18.3
Canned	2.4	3.0	2.8	2.2	2.0	2.4
Pickled or cured	11.8	12.8	15.9	13.3	10.5	12.3
Other processed	5.5	4.9	5.2	6.3	6.7	5.7
Total	52.1	38.2	41.0	37.0	35.4	38.7
Veal						
Fresh or frozen	1.3	0.5	0.7	0.5	0.6	0.5
Total (includes canned)	1.8	0.9	1.2	1.2	1.3	1.1
Pork						
Fresh or frozen	17.1	17.1	19.2	47.9	98.6	35.0
Hams and shoulders, not cooked	10.5	13.6	12.4	15.5	23.7	7.1
Hams and shoulders, canned	3.3	3.6	3.6	3.0	2.5	2.8
Other canned	3.3	2.8	3.0	3.8	3.8	3.1
Other	21.1	21.3	19.7	23.1	25.2	20.4
Total	55.3	58.4	57.9	93.3	153.8	68.4
Lamb and mutton	2.0	2.3	2.6	2.8	2.3	1.8
Total red meat	11.2	99.8	102.7	134.3	192.8	110.0
Variety meats (product weight)	223.1	213.3	222.3	225.2	239.9	239.5
Animal fats						
Lard	250.9	157.6	188.6	175.3	261.5	365.9
Inedible tallow and greases[2]	2,111.0	1,972.0	2,220.7	2,234.0	1,894.7	2,244.6
Edible tallow and greases[3]	17.0	16.4	17.1	11.2	13.4	20.5
Mohair (clean content)	8.5	10.7	10.3	15.9	12.9	10.9
			1000 Pieces			
Hides and skins						
Cattle	13,309	14,307	11,817[4]	12,879[4]	14,801[4]	15,225[4]
Calf	1,985	2,066	1,906	1,818	1,240	1,075
Kip	474	516	477	390	414	241
Sheep and lamb	2,876	2,422	3,758	3,344	3,931	3,822
			Number			
Live animals						
Cattle	54,171	35,317	55,322	35,745	39,186	88,037
Hogs	12,180	9,649	12,932	13,714	18,620	25,654
Sheep, lambs, and goats	25,315	59,054	120,733	117,677	106,237	132,856

Source: USDA (1971).
[1] Preliminary.
[2] Includes inedible animal oils, greases, fats, and tallow.
[3] Includes oleo oil, oleo stearin, and oleo stock, and edible tallow.
[4] Excludes pieces that are reported in pounds, which were reported in pieces in previous years.

EFFECT OF IMPORTS ON U.S. LIVESTOCK PRICES

As pointed out in Chap. 13, a rise in beef imports during the late 1950's and early 1960's was blamed for depressed cattle prices and led to enactment of the Meat Import Quota Law of 1964. While there is a general consensus that imports are associated with price declines, there is disagreement on the extent of the effect on grain-fed cattle prices as compared to cow prices. The bulk of imported beef is a boned product comparable to U.S. boned cow beef and is used for the same purposes. It is well known, however, that one type of meat can be substituted for another by consumers. In terms of demand concepts discussed in Chap. 3, we are concerned here with the effect that increased quantities of imported beef have, not only on identical or comparable U.S. products, but also on prices of substitute products such as grain-finished beef and hogs. This involves the concepts of price elasticity of demand, cross elasticity of demand, and cross price flexibility.

During the height of discussions over imported beef in 1963 the USDA (1963) published results of a study showing that imports of beef and veal have a greater effect on cow prices than on fed beef prices. More specifically the study indicated that a 20% increase in imports (from 1962 levels) would result in 80–90¢ per cwt reduction in utility grade cow prices. The same increase in imports would cause 50–60¢ decline in choice steer prices. It is generally recognized that, in the short run, changes in the supply of beef are the primary factor affecting prices. The USDA study showed that for the period 1948-1962 a 10% change in steer and heifer beef production was associated with a 13% change in the opposite direction of fed cattle prices, and a 23% change in the opposite direction of cow prices. Furthermore, a 10% change in cow beef production (domestic cow beef plus imported beef) was associated with a 3% change in the opposite direction of fed beef prices and a 7.5% change in the opposite direction of utility grade cow prices. These are average net changes after consideration of other factors which affect prices.

Purcell (1968) estimated the effect of imported beef and veal on prices and revenue for cattle and hogs on an annual basis from 1947 to 1966. Results are shown in Table 14.15. The United States was a slight net importer in 1947 but the effects were not measurable. Since 1948 the United States has been a net importer every year. According to Purcell, imports in 1963 pushed cattle and calf prices down $4.27 per cwt. This is an aggregate average price decline for all classes of cattle and calves. Evidence from the USDA and other studies would indicate that cow prices were depressed more than $4.27 and fed cattle prices less than that amount. Revenues of cattle and calf producers in 1963 were off almost $1.3 billion or 16.7% as a result of imports. In 1966, the effect on cattle and calf revenues again reached $1 billion. Cross relationships are shown in the effects of beef and veal imports on price and revenue of hogs (Table 14.15). The relatively heavy beef imports of the early 1960's depressed hog prices $1.16–$1.17 per cwt and reduced hog revenues to farmers by $235 million, or almost 8% in 1963. Thus, it is apparent why livestock producers were incensed as imports increased in the late 1950's and the early 1960's. Their concern has continued as imports continue to press upon quota levels provided by the Import Quota Act of 1964. This situation

TABLE 14.15

ESTIMATED EFFECT OF NET IMPORTS OF BEEF AND VEAL ON PRICE
AND REVENUE FOR CATTLE AND CALVES, AND HOGS,
UNITED STATES, 1947-1966

| Year | Cattle and Calves | | | Hogs | | |
	Price ($/Cwt)	Revenue[1] (Million $)	(%)	Price[3] ($/Cwt)	Revenue[1] (Million $)	(%)
1947	–	–	–	–	–	–
1948	−1.01	− 201.3	− 3.5	−0.74	−106	−2.6
1949	−0.72	− 143.6	− 2.4	−0.43	− 65	−1.9
1950	−1.06	− 210.7	− 3.4	−0.61	− 97	−2.8
1951	−1.49	− 271.2	− 4.2	−0.98	−169	−4.5
1952	−1.25	− 247.6	− 3.8	−0.68	−119	−3.4
1953	−0.67	− 171.4	− 2.8	−0.36	− 55	−1.5
1954	−0.53	− 142.3	− 2.3	−0.26	− 39	−1.1
1955	−0.48	− 133.2	− 2.1	−0.16	− 27	−1.0
1956	−0.29	− 85.2	− 1.4	−0.07	− 12	−0.5
1957	−0.82	− 234.1	− 3.6	−0.29	− 47	−1.6
1958	−2.45	− 638.3	− 9.1	−1.04	−170	−5.3
1959	−2.78	− 714.3	− 9.7	−0.85	−160	−6.1
1960	−2.02	− 565.0	− 7.8	−0.62	−114	−4.1
1961	−2.69	− 770.0	−10.5	−0.87	−158	−5.3
1962	−3.70	−1,063.3	−13.7	−1.16	−221	−7.2
1963	−4.27	−1,292.1	−16.7	−1.17	−235	−7.9
1964	−2.59	− 880.3	−11.8	−0.67	−136	−4.6
1965	−2.21	− 770.3	− 9.8	−0.78	−142	−3.9
1966	−2.78	−1,004.2	−12.5	−1.05	−198	−4.9

Source: Purcell (1968).
[1] Estimated change in revenue to primary producers in the United States attributed to net imports with actual domestic output (slaughter).
[2] Based on estimated reduction in revenue to primary producers due to imports relative to actual revenue.
[3] Percentage increase in beef and veal due to imports (estimated cross price flexibility −0.91).

is a classic example of conflict of interest between national welfare and that of a particular industry.

TRADE PROMOTIONAL ACTIVITIES

International trade is not a passive proposition. On the contrary, it is a highly competitive, aggressive contest among nations and individual firms. While trade restrictions impede the international flow of meat and other products, most countries with exportable surpluses are actively engaged in efforts to stimulate trade. Among the tactics used are the following: (1) international trade fairs; (2) solo country exhibits; (3) trade missions; (4) in-store promotions—including demonstrations, prizes, etc.; (5) promotional activities by agricultural attachés or other governmental agents stationed in foreign countries; (6) direct contact and selling by representatives of individual firms; (7) governmental manipulation of import-export regulations; (8) export subsidies; and (9) the use of marketing boards or comparable agencies in expediting export movements.

Recipient countries also utilize a number of devices to encourage and/or discourage imports and exports. Among the approaches used are import tariffs, export taxes, import and export licensing, exchange controls, and

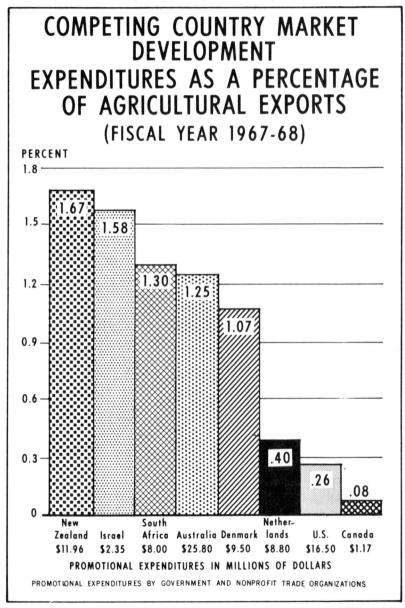

USDA (1969)

FIG. 14.4. COMPETING COUNTRY MARKET DEVELOPMENT EXPENDITURES import trade missions. While exporting countries are busy courting prospective importers, the importers are busy attempting to diversify their sources of supply.

Following is a summary of promotional activities of a group of selected countries.[1] Australia has the largest total expenditure for promotion among the countries studied, but New Zealand has the largest expenditure relative to value of exports (see Fig. 14.4). New Zealand's promotional expenditures amounted to 1.67% of its exports compared to 0.26% for the United States and 0.08% for Canada. These data include all agricultural products. Separate information is not available for livestock products.

Australia

Australia's greatest promotional expenditures are in wool marketing. Out of a total promotional expenditure of $25.8 million in 1967-1968, almost $23.3 million were contributions to the International Wool Secretariat—an international pooled effort in promoting the sale and use of wool. Other principal contributors to this organization are New Zealand and South Africa. In addition, Australia maintained Trade Commissioners in 43 overseas posts in 1967-1968 and participated in trade fairs in a number of importing countries. One of its principal meat promotional agencies is the Australian Meat Board. Operational funds are derived from a levy on livestock slaughtered. The Board maintains offices in London, New York, and Tokyo, and works in conjunction with the Australian Overseas Trade Publicity Committee. The central government matches Board funds for promotional proposals approved by the Committee.

Canada

Canada's promotional efforts in agricultural products are directed primarily at wheat sales. However, livestock and meat receive some attention in trade missions, trade fairs, exhibitions, and advertising and other publicity.

Denmark

Denmark carries on an aggressive overseas marketing program. Her separate commodity activities are not available, but it is reported that direct promotion of pork products and dairy products accounted for 75% of total promotional expenditures (USDA 1969). Although not all of the following agencies spend equal effort on the promotion of livestock products, the listing indicates a well-planned, comprehensive approach to overseas marketing. A Traveling Ambassador for Agriculture was appointed in 1967. A marketing office is maintained in Beirut covering a number of Near East countries. Danish Food Centers are operated in London, Manchester, and Glasgow. These centers are

---

[1] This section draws heavily from USDA (1969).

partially financed by the Danish Bacon Factories Export Association. A Danish Food Festival and Danish Food Fair have operated in Japan. Denmark also has participated in various food fairs in Europe. Use is made of television and press advertising in the United Kingdom, Germany, and Japan.

Netherlands

The Netherlands also maintains a relatively extensive export marketing program. Most of the funds are derived from Marketing Board levies, but the central Ministry of Agriculture also contributes. The Netherlands participates in numerous food fairs, carries out substantial TV advertising programs, and in-store promotions. To foster the sale of breeding stock in less developed countries, the Netherlands sends experienced herdsmen to acquaint local herdsmen with the proper care and feeding of imported stock.

New Zealand

Like Australia, New Zealand is a heavy contributor to the International Wool Secretariat. New Zealand has a Wool Marketing Board but, other than fund contributions to the Secretariat its activities are directed primarily to domestic affairs. A Meat Board is active in promoting overseas sales of meat and meat products. The Board maintains an office in London which covers the United Kingdom and Europe. Promotional activities also are carried on by the Board in Canada and in Far Eastern countries. Activities include press and TV advertising, retail store display materials, demonstrations, and participation in food fairs. An office labeled the Meat Export Department Co., Ltd., is maintained in Canada.

South Africa

South Africa is an important exporter of wool, and of the approximately $8 million expended for overseas promotion, 1/2 went for wool in 1967-1968. Minor amounts are spent for promotion of mohair and meat. The principal activities include trade missions, trade fairs, TV advertising, and in-store promotions.

European Community

The European Community (EC), generally referred to as the Common Market, is an organization of European nations formed under the so-called Treaty of Rome, of January, 1958. Under this agreement, Belgium, France, Italy, Luxembourg, Netherlands, and West Germany formalized a comprehensive arrangement for cooperation in economic, social and political activities. An agreement was reached in 1971 on the admission of Great Britain into the Community. Of particular interest to international trade, the EC plan provides for a common policy whereby barriers are to be removed (over a period of time) for trade among the signatories, but trade with outside countries is strictly regulated. A primary purpose of the regulation is the protection of EC producers and the encouragement of local production. Consumer interests also are considered through various subsidy arrangements.

Imports of livestock products are permitted with varying degrees of regulation depending upon the degree to which the particular product is competitive or complementary to the domestic production and needs of the EC. One of the most potent means of regulating meat and livestock imports is by variable levies. By a complicated series of formula calculations, internal target prices are set up, and so-called sluice-gate prices are calculated for imported products. If the selling price of a third country is less than the sluice-gate price, a levy is imposed to make up the difference. Thus, the lower the outside price, the higher the variable levy. Other restrictions include requirements for import licenses, prior deposits by importers, and quotas. In addition, health regulations are relatively strict on meats.

EC restrictions are more severe on fresh meats than on by-products. Since the United States does not compete actively in the fresh meat trade of EC, the restrictions affect the United States less than other countries. Generally, the EC considers by-products obtained from the United States to be complementary to their production and needs.

United States

The United States works actively through its agricultural attachés—a branch of the diplomatic corp stationed in most countries. These attachés not only promote U.S. products but are valuable in arranging contacts for representatives of private firms in their individual promotional activities. They also work in conjunction with private firms in arranging for displays at trade fairs and in-store displays.

The United States sends meat and livestock trade missions to foreign countries many of which are sponsored jointly by the government and private organizations such as the American Meat Institute, the American National Cattleman's Association, and various breed associations. It should be noted also that the USDA works actively with exporting countries in negotiating voluntary quotas on meat shipments to the United States.

BIBLIOGRAPHY

ALBAUGH, R. 1965. The livestock and meat industry of Australia. USDA Foreign Agr. Serv. *M-164*.
DECOURCY, J. 1967. World production and trade: tallow and greases. USDA Foreign Agr. Serv. *M-182*.
DIRKS, H. J. 1968. World pork trends. USDA Foreign Agr. Serv. *M-197*.

DOBBINS, C. E. 1963. The livestock and meat industry of West Germany. USDA Foreign Agr. Serv. *M-144*.

GERRITY, M. V. 1965. The beef export trade of Central America. USDA Foreign Agr. Serv. *M-168*.

IVES, J. R. 1966. The Livestock and Meat Economy of the United States. Am. Meat Inst., Chicago.

KUTISH, F. A., and SITLER, H. G. 1967. A study of the economics of land use and livestock production in Greece. USDA Intern. Agr. Develop. Serv. IADS *S-16*.

LEIGHTON, R. I. 1970. Economics of International Trade. McGraw-Hill Book Co., New York.

MORGAN, Q. M. 1967A. Uruguay's livestock and meat industry. USDA Foreign Agr. Serv. *M-186*.

MORGAN, Q. M. 1967B. Argentina's livestock and meat industry. USDA Foreign Agr. Serv. *M-188*.

MORGAN, Q. M. 1969A. Denmark's livestock and meat industry. USDA Foreign Agr. Serv. *M-212*.

MORGAN, Q. M. 1969B. Ireland's livestock and meat industry. USDA Foreign Agr. Serv. *M-130*.

MORGAN, Q. M. 1970. New Zealand's livestock and meat industry. USDA Foreign Agr. Serv. *M-184*.

PURCELL, J. C. 1968. Trends and relations in the livestock-meat sector affecting prices and revenue to primary producers. Georgia Agr. Expt. Sta. Res. Bull. *35*.

RAY, J. E. 1960. The market in Japan for U.S. livestock and meat products. USDA Foreign Agr. Serv. *M-78*.

RIESZ, J. E. 1967. Livestock and meat industry of Mexico. USDA Foreign Agr. Serv. *M-185*.

ROURK, J. P. 1969. The beef cattle industries of Central America and Panama. USDA Foreign Agr. Serv. *M-208*.

USDA. 1963. Livestock and meat situation. USDA Econ. Res. Serv. *LMS-158*.

USDA. 1969. Agricultural market development activities of principal competing countries 1967-68. USDA Foreign Agr. Serv. (unnumbered).

USDA. 1970A. Foreign agriculture circular. USDA Foreign Agr. Serv. *FLM-4-70*.

USDA. 1970B. Handbook of agricultural charts. USDA Agr. Handbook *397*.

USDA. 1970C. Livestock and meat statistics. USDA Econ. Res. Serv. Statist. Bull. *333*.

USDA. 1970D. Livestock and meat situation. USDA Econ. Res. Serv. *LMS-173*.

USDA. 1971. Livestock and meat situation. USDA Econ. Res. Serv. *LMS-179*.

WUHRMAN, R. H. 1966. World beef trends. USDA Foreign Agr. Serv. *M-173*.

YOUNG, D. 1970. International Economics. Intext Educational Publishers, Scranton, Penn.

CHAPTER 15

Marketing Costs

The USDA maintains and publishes three series on marketing costs: (1) price spreads, (2) the market basket, and (3) the marketing bill.

MARKETING SPREADS–GENERAL COMMENT

"Marketing spread" is a general term referring to the difference between expenditures by consumers, or prices paid by consumers, and the farm value of an equivalent quantity of products. In other words, marketing spread is the value added in getting the products from the farm gate to consumers at the retail outlet. Alternatively it is viewed as the sum of all costs (middlemen costs) in assembling, processing, transporting, and distributing products- including the profits which middlemen derive for their services.

The marketing spread in 1970 for all food commodities, calculated together, amounted to 62¢ per dollar spent by consumers (USDA 1970A). Commodities which require relatively little processing and other marketing services have a smaller spread, while those which require extensive processing have an even larger marketing spread.

Farmers are prone to emphasize the residual element which shows that they received 38% of the consumer's dollar spent for food in 1970. During 1945, the last year of World War II, the farmers' share was 54%, the highest of record dating back to 1913. The average for all nonwar years since World War II has been about 40%. During the past 10 yr it has ranged from 37 to 41%. As will be shown later, the farmers' share of consumers' expenditures for beef, pork, and lamb differ substantially from this average of all food products.

Farmers tend to equate their relatively low income position to what appears to them to be a slim part of the consumer dollar, and often assume that the larger share going to market agencies is indicative of inefficient marketing, excessive profits, or both. Consumers, generally, are far removed from the agricultural scene and most are not well acquainted with the intricacies of the marketing system. To many, it is simple logic that rising retail prices must be putting profits in farmers' pockets. This notion may be heightened by occasional publicity of government programs which give the impression that farmers are getting rich from federal handouts for not producing.

Obviously, a considerable amount of misunderstanding exists about marketing spreads, their relation to efficiency of marketing, excess marketing profits, retail prices, and producer profits. An understanding of the method of calculating spreads is a first step to their interpretation.

PRICE SPREADS FOR BEEF, PORK, AND LAMB [1]

Price spread, by definition, is the difference between the retail *price per unit* of a commodity and the price received by farmers for an equivalent quantity.

Method of Calculation

The basic data needed for calculating spreads are prices and values at the retail and farm levels, but in the case of beef, pork, and lamb, interest also centers in an in-between level—i.e., carcass or wholesale value. Therefore, for meat price spreads a determination is needed for three levels: (1) retail price; (2) wholesale value equivalent, and (3) farm value equivalent. The word "equivalent" is used because 1 lb of retail meat necessitates somewhat more than 1 lb at wholesale and even more at the farm level. The determination of retail price itself is no small matter, for a carcass is broken down into many cuts by the time it reaches the retail counter. Each cut comprises a different volume of the carcass and each sells at a different price. Cutting methods can affect the volume of meat in various cuts so this also must be standardized for calculation purposes. What is needed at retail, then, is a weighted average price per pound based on standardized yields of the various cuts.

Retail prices for U.S. Choice grade beef are derived from 29 cuts. Prices are obtained weekly by the Animal Products Branch, Marketing Economics Division, Economic Research Service, USDA, in conjunction with the Department of Labor's Bureau of Labor Statistics. A continuing survey is maintained with about 40 retail chains throughout the country in which regular and special prices are obtained. Prices so obtained are applied to standardized proportions of cuts as shown in Column 1, Table 15.1, and in Fig. 15.1. The percentage of total retail cuts from carcass shown in Table 15.1 are not equivalent to carcass cut-out or yield discussed in Chap. 9. The figures shown here are net of retail cutting loss and retail shrink. Cutting losses are accounted for in a conversion to wholesale values. Adjustments are made to take into account the effects of retail shrink and price specials.

Earlier calculations, without these adjustments, prompted criticism from the meat trade and others. Consequently, recent changes were made to improve accuracy of the calculations. Among the improvements at the retail level (Duewer 1970) were an allowance for retail shrinkage due to pilferage, spoilage, refacing, conversion to lower-valued uses, and the extra weight added to the package to allow for dehydration loss. The revised procedure allows a 5% loss for beef. Special prices affect the composite price in two ways. The reduction in price of the cut on "special" reduces the average price of all cuts sold. This decrease is termed the price effect. When the price is reduced,

[1] Material in this section is derived largely from Duewer (1970).

TABLE 15.1

BEEF RETAIL PRICE PER POUND: PROPORTION CUTS ARE OF
TOTAL RETAIL CUTS, AND RETAIL VALUE PER CUT
AND PER 100 LB RETAIL CUTS FROM CARCASS[1]

m	Percentage of Total Retail Cuts from Carcass (%)	Price per Pound ($)	Value/100 Lb ($)
eaks			
Porterhouse, BI[2]	2.1	1.58	3.32
Club, BI	1.3	1.49	1.94
Club, BO[3]	0.5	2.18	1.09
T-Bone, BI	3.6	1.55	5.58
Sirloin, BI	6.6	1.33	8.78
Round fullcut, BI	3.6	1.16	4.18
Round top, BO	3.5	1.28	4.48
Round bottom, BO	2.9	1.32	3.83
Chuck, steak, BI	2.3	0.74	1.70
Rib, BI	2.0	1.24	2.48
Flank, BO	0.7	1.36	0.95
pasts			
Rib, roast, BI	6.0	1.10	6.60
Rib, rolled, BO	1.2	1.57	1.88
Chuck blade, BI	8.2	0.71	5.82
Chuck arm, BI	5.0	0.85	4.25
Chuck roast, BO	5.4	0.94	5.08
Sirloin/round tip, BO	3.5	1.34	4.69
Eye round, BO	1.5	1.53	2.30
Rump, BO	3.8	1.26	4.79
Rump, BI	1.2	0.94	1.13
ther cuts			
Plate, BI	2.1	0.38	0.80
Short rib, BI	3.1	0.59	1.83
Brisket, BO	2.8	1.09	3.16
Ground beef	16.4	0.62	10.17
Ground chuck	2.0	0.83	1.66
Stew, BO	6.0	0.93	5.58
Shin or shank, BO	0.3	0.83	0.25
Shin or shank, BI	2.0	0.60	1.20
Kidney	0.3	0.39	0.12
Total	100.0	. . .	99.64[4]

ource: Duewer (1970).
Prices used were for May, 1969.
Bone in.
Bone out.
In other words, a composite price per retail pound of 99.6¢.

onsumers tend to buy more of that cut than they ordinarily would. As a
esult, a store may sell several times more than the carcass proportion of a cut
hen it is on special (Duewer 1970).

The determination of wholesale value necessitates a conversion factor based
n weight loss from wholesale to retail. In the case of beef, the conversion
ctor used is 1.41. This means that the wholesale value of 1.41 lb of beef is
eeded to make an equivalent comparison with 1 lb at retail.

A recent revision in calculation uses wholesale carlot prices where formerly
ss-than-carlot prices were used. "Most meat now moves by carlot. For beef,

U.S. DEPARTMENT OF AGRICULTURE ■ NEG. ERS 7112-69 (12) ■ ECONOMIC RESEARCH SER

Duewer (1

FIG. 15.1. RETAIL CUTS OF BEEF

icago carlot prices for 600–700-lb Choice steer carcasses are used to resent all U.S. wholesale markets for carcass beef except the West Coast, ere an average of carlot and less-than-carlot prices are used. A transporta-n differential is added to the Chicago price to make it representative of the a for which it is used" (Duewer 1970).

arm level prices are determined (Duewer 1970) from prices of choice steers seven midwestern markets and a California price from which is deducted oducer marketing costs. According to USDA calculations, 2.28 lb of live mal are required to produce 1 lb of retail beef. This, then, is the version factor applied to the farm level price to determine "gross farm ue" of an amount of live animal equivalent to 1 lb of retail beef. However, e animal prices include a valuation of by-products, but retail prices do not. adjustment for this is made by subtracting the current value of hide and al from gross farm value to obtain "net farm value." Value of hide and al is available from a continuing compilation by Federal Market News vice. Price spreads are calculated each month, then aggregated into arterly and annual price spreads.

A simplified hypothetical example of beef price spreads for a given month ght be:

Assume the following prices and values:

	¢/Lb
Composite retail price	85
Wholesale carcass price	45
Farm level price	27
By-product value	6
Equivalent carcass value	45 × 1.41 = 63.4¢
Carcass-retail price spread	85.0 − 63.4 = 21.6¢
Equivalent gross farm value	27.0 × 2.28 = 61.6¢
Equivalent net farm value	61.6 − 6.0 = 55.6¢
Farm-carcass price spread	63.4 − 55.6 = 7.8¢
Farm-retail price spread	85.0 − 55.6 = 29.4¢
Farmers' share of beef dollar	$\frac{85.0 - 29.4}{85.0} \times 100 = 65.4\%$

The approach in calculating pork and lamb price spreads follows the same neral procedure as described for beef. Pork prices and values are determined barrows and gilts, i.e., an average of all grades. Lamb prices are based on S. Choice grade. The 20 retail pork cuts used and the standard percentage at each cut is of the carcass, are shown in Table 15.2 and Fig. 15.2. A 5.5% tail shrink is allowed for pork. Chicago carlot prices, with a transportation fferential, are used to estimate the pork wholesale value (Duewer 1970). is value is multiplied by a wholesale conversion factor of 1.07 to obtain a rcass value equivalent to 1 lb of pork at retail. The average monthly price of rrows and gilts at eight Corn Belt markets is used, along with the deduction

for marketing costs, to obtain the farm price of pork (Duewer 1970). To t
price is applied a conversion factor of 1.97 to obtain gross farm val
equivalent of 1 lb of pork at retail. And from this figure is deducted
allowance for pork by-products. The allowance recently was adjusted
reflect the trend in decreasing yield of lard.

The carcass price for lamb is derived from quotations at New Yor
Chicago, Los Angeles, San Francisco, and the Seattle-Tacoma-Portland area
which a conversion factor of 1.18 is applied to obtain carcass value. Live lar
prices are from quotations for U.S. Choice grade at 13 leading public marke
The average conversion factor is 2.45, but actual monthly factors va
seasonally to allow for changes in the fleece.

TABLE 15.2

PORK RETAIL PRICE PER POUND: PROPORTION CUTS ARE OF
TOTAL RETAIL CUTS, AND RETAIL VALUE PER CUT
AND PER 100 LB RETAIL CUTS FROM CARCASS[1]

Item	Percentage of Total Retail Cuts from Carcass (%)	Price per Pound ($)	Value/100 l ($)
Loin, center chops	2.4	1.07	2.57
Loin, center rib chops	3.2	1.05	3.46
Loin, center cut chops	3.2	1.09	3.49
Loin roast, rib end	4.7	0.65	3.06
Loin roast, loin end	4.3	0.78	3.35
No. 2 chops	1.3	0.69	0.90
Tenderloin	0.9	1.43	1.29
Ham, butt end	6.5	0.65	4.22
Ham, shank ends	8.4	0.56	4.70
Ham, center slices	4.7	1.26	5.92
Whole ham	3.4	0.68	2.31
Butts	8.6	0.66	5.68
Spareribs	4.3	0.76	3.27
Sausage	7.5	0.70	5.25
Neckbones	1.9	0.28	0.53
Pigs feet	2.1	0.30	0.63
Tails	0.3	0.30	0.09
Picnics	10.8	0.51	5.51
Bacon, sliced	17.7	0.83	14.69
Bacon, square	3.7	0.55	2.04
Total	100.0	. . .	72.96[2]

Source: Duewer (1970).
[1] Prices used were for May, 1969.
[2] Or a composite price per retail pound of 73.0¢.

Characteristics of Marketing Spreads

As mentioned above, the total farm-retail spread is composed of tw
components: (1) the farm-carcass (wholesale)[2] spread, and (2) the carca

[2] Prior to 1970, the spread between farm level price and slaughtered meat price w
referred to as the "farm-wholesale" spread. In the case of beef and lamb this was chang
to "farm-carcass" spread in 1970 to more accurately reflect the fact that prices a
values at the wholesale level are for carcasses rather than primal wholesale cuts. The ter
"wholesale" still is used for pork, as prices and values used apply to wholesale pork cu

RETAIL PORK CUTS

% OF RETAIL CUTS

Cut	%
Ham	23.0
Butt end 6.5	
Shank end 8.4	
Center Slices 4.7	
Whole 3.4	
Loin	20.1
Center Chops 2.4	
Ctr. Rib Chops 3.3	
Ctr. Loin Chops 3.2	
Rib End Roast 4.7	
Loin End Roast 4.3	
No. 2 Chops 1.3	
Tender Loin 0.9	
Bacon	17.7
Spareribs	4.3
Butts	8.6
Picnics	10.8
TOTAL MISC. CUTS	15.5
	100.0

Pigsfeet 2.1

Tails 0.3

Lean Trimmings (Sausage) 7.5

Neckbones 1.9

Jowl (Bacon Squares) 3.7

220 lb. Liveweight

148.9 lb. Dressed Weight

Wholesale Cuts

117.9 lb. Total Salable Retail Cuts
1.6 lb. Waste (fat and shrink)
29.4 lb. Lard and Other Edible Byproducts

Total of percentage each salable retail cut is of total salable cuts

DEPARTMENT OF AGRICULTURE ■ NEG. ERS 7113–69 (12) ■ ECONOMIC RESEARCH SERVICE

Duewer (1970)

FIG. 15.2. RETAIL PORK CUTS

(wholesale)-retail spread. Over the years these spreads have exhibited so
common characteristics and some which are peculiar to particular species.

While the spreads have not remained constant, they have been more sta
than farm value. This may be observed in Fig. 15.3 for beef.[3] Farm valu

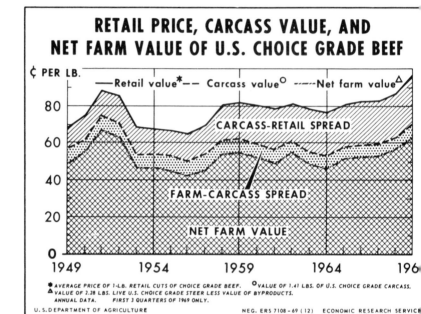

FIG. 15.3. RETAIL PRICE, CARCASS VALUE, AND NET FARM VALUE OF CHO
GRADE OF BEEF

directly related to prices received by producers. As farm price rises and fa
farm value rises and falls, but the spreads tend to be more fixed. This
largely explained by the fact that the elements which comprise slaughteri
processing, wholesaling, and retailing costs (wage rates, rent, taxes, inter
charges, freight rates, profits, etc.) simply do not vary as farm price
livestock varies. The market structure under which these items are determi
is subject to more institutional control than is the market for live animals.

The tendency for the farm-retail spread to remain relatively fixed result:
a decline in the farmer's share of the meat dollar when farm prices fall and
increase when farm prices rise. Assume the farm-retail spread for pork i
constant 30¢ per lb. If the farm value were also 30¢, retail price would be (
and the farmer's share would be 50%. But, if farm value dropped to 2
retail price (if it dropped the same amount) would be 55¢ and the farm
share would be 45%. This has been a matter of contention with produc

[3] Pork and lamb exhibit the same characteristics.

ⁱd what compounds their concern even more is a tendency for retail prices
be rather sticky. Retail prices do change, but usually with a lag, following
ʳm price and wholesale price changes. In the above example, if retail prices
ⁱd remained at 60¢ after farm value dropped to 25¢, the farmer's share
ᵊuld have been 42%, at least temporarily. The reverse happens during rising
ʳm prices (i.e., the farmer's share tends to rise), but if farmers' reactions are
indication of their feelings, this does not seem to balance the situation.
ⁱt of the reason it does not balance out in the eyes of producers is that the
ʳmer's shares, over a period of time, have not averaged out at a constant
ᵛel. As shown in Fig. 15.4 they have tended generally downward, though
ᵐe leveling off is apparent since about the mid-1960's.

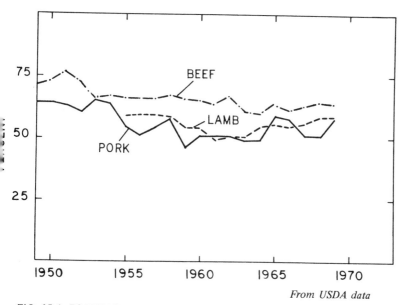

From USDA data

FIG. 15.4. FARMER'S SHARE OF CONSUMER'S MEAT DOLLAR

ᵛer the same period the farm-retail spreads (the costs of marketing) have
ⁱded upward for all three species (see Fig. 15.5, 15.6, 15.7). This is a
ᵉction of the general inflationary trend in most market input items (Fig.
ᵌ). Freight rates were an exception until the late 1960's when that trend
◦ turned upward. Labor is the largest single item among marketing costs,
the pronounced upward trend in hourly wage rates has been partially
ᵉt by increasing labor productivity. However, in spite of productivity
ⁱs, unit labor costs rose 36% from the late 1950's to 1969.
ʰe carcass (wholesale)-retail spreads have exhibited a generally increasing
ⁱd for all three species (Fig. 15.5, 15.6, 15.7). These, basically, are retail

PRICE SPREADS FOR U.S. CHOICE GRADE BEEF
Farm-Retail, Carcass-Retail, and Farm-Carcass

FIG. 15.5. PRICE SPREADS FOR U.S. CHOICE GRADE BEEF

PRICE SPREADS FOR PORK
Farm-Retail, Farm-Wholesale, and Wholesale-Retail

FIG. 15.6. PRICE SPREADS FOR PORK

FIG. 15.7. PRICE SPREADS FOR CHOICE GRADE LAMB

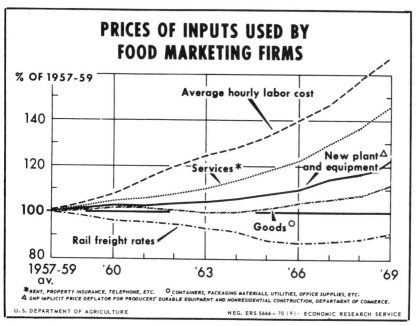

FIG. 15.8. PRICES OF INPUTS USED BY FOOD MARKETING FIRMS

marketing costs, and as calculated by USDA, all cutting, processing, packaging, and merchandising costs of beef and lamb are attributed to the retail level. This is not entirely appropriate as more and more breaking, cutting, and processing is being done at the packer level. However, it does tend to explain why the carcass-retail spread for beef and lamb is greater than for pork. Pork, traditionally, has been broken into wholesale cuts and a considerable share of the processing done by packers which puts this cost in the farm-wholesale spread. Thus, the farm-carcass (wholesale) spread is greater for pork than for beef and lamb. The farm-carcass (wholesale) and the carcass (wholesale)-retail spreads for all species have been on an increasing trend—except the farm-carcass spread for beef (Fig. 15.5). This is attributed to improved technology and increases in efficiency of labor and equipment (Duewer 1970).

Implications with Respect to Marketing Efficiency

The farmer's share of the consumer's dollar spent for beef in 1969 was 65%, during the same time it was 7% for canned beets. There is a tendency for some persons to conclude, on the basis of this evidence, that the marketing of beets must be less efficient than the marketing of beef. This is an unwarranted conclusion. Neither the farmer's share, nor the absolute amount of marketing spread is adequate in itself for evaluating marketing efficiency—either operational efficiency or pricing efficiency. It has been pointed out earlier that price spreads consist of marketing and processing costs, plus profits to participating agencies. The matter of profits will be examined later. Some products simply require more marketing inputs relative to the value of the product itself than do others. This is apparent in the case of beets and beef where processing costs are substantially higher for beets relative to the value of the product.

Some might argue that the marketing costs of both are too high. It is assumed in a competitive economy that astute businessmen are continually looking for ways to reduce costs, but the possibility of further improvements should be a matter of continuing concern for both individual firms and the general public. The public concern is reflected in numerous governmental research and extension projects designed to reduce marketing costs.

It would be possible to reduce the farm-retail price spread to zero (i.e., farmers could get 100% of the consumers' meat dollar if they slaughtered, processed, and delivered meat to the consumers' doors). This, however, is not necessarily the most efficient system. In fact, it was discovered long ago that specialization and trade, based on comparative advantage (as discussed in the previous chapter) would result in a greater total and per capita real income.

The major utility aspects affecting marketing costs and the farmer's share are place, time, and form.

Place.—Transportation costs for meat could be reduced by raising beef cattle near the centers of population. This, however, would increase other costs—feed, labor, pollution abatement, etc.—and negate the comparative advantage of production in the Milo Belt and Corn Belt. It would be less efficient from an overall standpoint and consumer prices would increase.

Time.—Any product which has a seasonal variation in production is faced with a time problem if that product is to be made available to consumers uniformly throughout the year. Beets provide an excellent example of a product with an extreme seasonality of production—the entire crop is harvested within a relatively short period. In processed form, beets may be stored and made available for the remainder of the year. But processing and storage are costly and reduce the farmer's share. This cannot be classed as inefficiency.

Beef is produced more uniformly throughout the year as large commercial feedlots have grown in importance. If year-round production had been attempted when the industry was composed entirely of small family farms, costs undoubtedly would have increased. Net costs probably have not increased with commercial lots since cost gains from economies of scale and more complete utilization of facilities probably offset the cost-increasing tendency of reduced summer gains. However, there still is some seasonality in beef production. This means that slaughtering and processing facilities have unused capacity at times, which causes unit costs to increase and is reflected in marketing spreads and farmers' shares. To reduce this cost by completely leveling out production might increase production costs.

Cold storage is used to alleviate the time factor to a greater extent with pork than for beef or lamb. This increases the marketing spread and reduces the farmer's share, but again, cannot be classified as inefficiency per se.

Form.—Some products require more processing (change in form) than others. Pork is subjected to more processing than beef which goes far in explaining why the farmer's share is smaller for pork than for beef. Canned beets are an extreme example of a product which requires much more processing relative to value than either pork, beef, or lamb. Again, this is not an indictment of marketing efficiency.

Reduction in Farmer's Share Over Time.—As pointed out earlier, the farmer's share has been on a generally declining trend. Inefficiencies cannot be completely ruled out, but studies on market structure of the meat industry have failed to confirm any substantial degree of inefficiency. There is plenty of evidence that consumers are demanding (or merchandisers are selling them) more and more services. This includes such things as more trimming, more boning, better and more attractive packaging, more processing and preparation (e.g., fully cooked meats, TV dinners, etc.) more parking space, air-conditioned stores, carryout service, etc. The cost of all such items end up in the marketing spread and reduces the farmer's percentage of the dollar spent for meat. The recent trend toward discount food stores with a reduction in some services may be partially responsible for the recent leveling off of farmer's share in recent years. However, there is no indication of a slackening in the demand for built-in convenience in meat items.

Implications with Respect to Profits

An increase in marketing profits would show up in the price spread, and, everything else being equal, would result in a decrease in the farmer's share. As has been pointed out, the food industry has been subjected to a number of investigations when monopoly and undue profits were suspected. The Consent Decree was an outgrowth of one such investigation and put some restrictions on the actions of packers involved. Other investigations have been conducted, the most recent being the 1965 National Commission on Food Marketing, which covered the entire food industry, including a complete investigation of the livestock and meat industry. The Commission was critical of some aspects, but ended with a generally favorable conclusion, expressed by Brandow (1966), its executive director, as follows: The Commission concluded its study believing that the contribution of the food industry to a high and rising level of living was fully comparable with that of other leading sectors of the economy. In broadest terms the industry is efficient and progressive. Supplied by a highly productive agriculture, manufacturers and distributors have provided consumers with varied, abundant, and nutritious array of goods at generally reasonable prices.

Some data are available on industry profits. These data are adequate for comparison with other industries, but the question of what constitutes a reasonable or adequate profit level cannot be settled—that requires a value judgment and differences of opinion are to be expected. Data were presented in Chap. 7 (Fig. 7.4, 7.5, 7.6) showing net income after taxes as a percentage of net worth for a number of U.S. industries, including chain food stores and meat packing. The meat packing industry consistently had the lowest returns of the industries shown. "Profits to retail food chains were high relative to other industries during most of the postwar period. These high levels of profits resulted from a rapid rise in popularity of the supermarket. In response to this increase in demand, many thousands of supermarkets were built. As this rapid building program caught up with demand around 1960, profits for food retailers returned to levels comparable to other industries" (National Commission on Food Marketing 1966B).

In 1969 the meat packing industry received profits after taxes of 1.0% of sales and 9.6% of net worth, while the average for all manufacturing companies was 5.4% and 12.5% respectively (Anon. 1969).

What does price spread and farmers' share of the consumers' expenditure reveal about producers' profits? The same generalization applies here as with packer's and retailer's profits discussed above. By itself, the farmer's share (either at a given time or a change over time) is not an adequate indicator of farmers' profit position. It tells nothing about the absolute amount of farm profit or its relation to that of other industries. A 30% share of $1.50 per retail pound of beef would be more dollars than 50% of 70-¢-per-lb beef.

The farmer's profit position can be better evaluated by examining his returns on net worth as was done with the other sectors. Farm management records show that livestock producers' returns are extremely unstable from year to year, and over the long period average about 3–4% of equity. This is substantially lower than other sectors of the meat industry. The effect of relatively low returns has been apparent for many years as livestock production is shifting into fewer and larger units.

Seasonality in Price Spreads

Seasonal variation in meat production leads to a seasonal variation in prices which, in return, affects price spreads. This is illustrated for pork in Fig. 15.9. Production normally drops off during mid-summer and prices rise seasonally.

FIG. 15.9. SEASONAL VARIATION IN PORK PRODUCTION AND PRICE SPREADS

During this period the farm value rises and the farm-retail spread declines slightly. With a lag of about one month, retail prices rise. It may be noted, however, that the farm-retail spread and retail prices are considerably more stable than production and net farm value. Beef and lamb also exhibit seasonal tendencies. The magnitude of seasonal variations associated with beef is considerably less than for either pork or lamb.

MARKET BASKET

Market basket calculations are for a "basket" or a group of products, representative (USDA 1970B) of average quantities of domestic, farm-originated food products purchased annually by wage earners and clerical worker families and single workers living alone. Market basket statistics have three components: (1) retail cost—which actually is somewhat less than an average sized family's expenditure for food since the market basket does not include cost of meals away from the home, imported foods, seafoods, and foods of nonfarm origin; (2) farm value—the gross returns to farmers for the quantity of farm products equivalent to those in the market basket; and (3) farm-retail spread—the difference between retail cost and farm value.

The farm-retail market basket spread is similar in concept to the price spread in that it is an estimate of costs of marketing (assembling, processing, transporting, and distributing). In the case of the market basket, the spread is

TABLE 15.3

THE MARKET BASKET OF FARM FOODS: RETAIL COST, FARM VALUE, FARM-RETAIL SPREAD, AND FARMER'S SHARE OF RETAIL COST, AVERAGED 1947-1949 AND 1957-1959, ANNUAL 1960-1969, MONTHLY 1969-1970[1]

Year and Month	Retail Cost ($)	Farm Value ($)	Farm-retail Spread ($)	Farmer's Share (%)
Average:				
1947-1949	890	441	449	50
1957-1959	983	388	595	39
1960	991	383	608	39
1961	997	380	617	38
1962	1006	384	622	38
1963	1013	374	639	37
1964	1014	374	640	37
1965	1038	408	630	39
1966	1095	443	652	40
1967	1080	414	666	38
1968	1118	435	683	39
1969[2]	1173	477	696	41

Source: USDA (1970B).
[1] Retail cost of average quantities purchased annually per household in 1960-1961 by urban wage-earner and clerical-worker families and single workers living alone, calculated from retail prices collected by the Bureau of Labor Statistics. Data for earlier years are published in Farm-Retail Spreads for Food Products 1947-1964. ERS-226, April, 1965.
[2] Preliminary.

the cost for the entire quantity in the basket, while the price spread discussed earlier was cost for one unit of the product—for meat it was the cost per retail pound.

Table 15.3 shows trends in components of the market basket. Retail costs have advanced at a faster rate than farm value. The farm-retail spread has increased for the same reasons explained under price spreads. The farmer's share is down from 1947-1949 levels, but has remained in the range of 37–41 for the past 10 yr.

In market basket calculations all meat is aggregated into one figure. In all three components, meat is by far the most important item. In recent years meat has comprised about 30% of retail sales, 40% of farm value, and 23% of the farm-retail spread. The next most important food group is dairy products, with about 18%, 22%, and 15% respectively.

Market basket statistics are published quarterly by the USDA.

THE MARKETING BILL

The marketing bill is the total cost of marketing the entire quantity (Findlay and Southard 1970) of U.S. farm-originated foods purchased by civilians. It is the difference between consumer expenditures and farm value.

USDA (1970A)

FIG. 15.10. FARM-FOOD MARKETING BILL AND CONSUMER FOOD EX-PENDITURES

TABLE 15.4

CONSUMER EXPENDITURES, MARKETING BILL, AND FARM VALUE FOR FARM FOODS BY
COMMODITY GROUPS (IN BILLION DOLLARS), 1960-1970

Year	All Farm Foods			Meat Products			Dairy Products			Poultry and Eggs		
	Expenditures	Marketing Bill	Farm Value	Expenditures	Marketing Bill	Farm Value	Expenditures	Marketing Bill	Farm Value	Expenditures	Marketing Bill	Farm Value
1960	65.9	44.2	21.7	18.4	10.2	8.2	12.1	7.5	4.6	5.0	2.2	2.8
1961	67.1	45.1	22.0	18.6	10.3	8.3	12.2	7.6	4.7	5.1	2.4	2.7
1962	69.3	46.9	22.4	19.2	10.5	8.7	12.4	7.8	4.6	5.1	2.4	2.7
1963	71.5	48.9	22.6	19.9	11.4	8.5	12.6	7.9	4.7	5.2	2.5	2.7
1964	74.5	51.2	23.3	20.8	12.3	8.5	12.9	8.1	4.8	5.4	2.6	2.8
1965	77.6	52.1	25.5	21.8	11.9	9.9	13.0	8.1	4.9	5.6	2.7	2.9
1966	82.8	54.7	28.1	24.5	13.2	11.3	13.5	8.1	5.4	6.6	3.1	3.5
1967	84.8	57.5	27.3	25.1	14.0	11.1	13.5	8.1	5.4	6.1	3.2	2.9
1968	90.1	61.1	29.0	26.7	14.8	11.9	14.6	8.9	5.7	6.5	3.3	3.2
1969	95.3	63.2	32.1	28.5	14.8	13.7	15.0	9.0	6.0	7.4	3.6	3.8
1970[2]	101.6	68.5	33.1	30.9	16.7	14.2	15.5	9.3	6.2	7.7	4.1	3.6

Year	Fruits and Vegetables			Grain Mill Products			Bakery Products[1]			Miscellaneous		
	Expenditures	Marketing Bill	Farm Value	Expenditures	Marketing Bill	Farm Value	Expenditures	Marketing Bill	Farm Value	Expenditures	Marketing Bill	Farm Value
1960	14.5	11.0	3.5	2.7	2.1	0.6	6.8	6.0	0.8	6.3	5.1	1.2
1961	14.7	11.2	3.5	2.8	2.2	0.6	7.0	6.2	0.8	6.7	5.3	1.4
1962	15.4	11.8	3.6	2.9	2.2	0.7	7.4	6.5	0.9	6.9	5.6	1.3
1963	15.6	12.0	3.6	3.1	2.4	0.7	7.7	6.8	0.9	7.4	5.9	1.5
1964	16.5	12.4	4.1	3.2	2.5	0.7	7.9	7.0	0.9	7.8	6.3	1.5
1965	17.1	12.7	4.4	3.4	2.7	0.7	8.1	7.1	1.0	8.6	6.9	1.7
1966	17.7	13.4	4.3	3.3	2.6	0.7	8.2	7.1	1.1	9.1	7.2	1.9
1967	18.3	14.0	4.3	3.5	2.8	0.7	8.7	7.6	1.1	9.4	7.7	1.7
1968	19.6	14.9	4.7	3.6	2.9	0.7	8.9	7.9	1.0	10.1	8.4	1.7
1969	20.7	15.8	4.9	3.7	3.0	0.7	9.2	8.1	1.1	10.8	8.9	1.9
1970[2]	21.7	16.9	4.8	4.0	3.2	0.8	10.0	8.8	1.2	11.7	9.5	2.2

Source: USDA (1971).
[1] Farm value of bakery products includes farm values of flour, milk, eggs, fruit, lard, vegetable shortening, and sugar used in bakery products. Farm value of these ingredients are not included in farm values of other groups.
[2] Preliminary.
NOTE: Commodities groups may not add to totals due to rounding.

The marketing bill statistics show the distribution of consumer expenditures between the marketing system and farmers, and the distribution of marketing costs among commodity groups and individual cost components such as labor.

Since marketings costs on a per unit basis have been on an increasing trend, it is no surprise that the total marketing bill also has increased. This is shown in Fig. 15.10 and Table 15.4. Out of total consumer expenditures of 101.6 billion in 1970, the farm value was $33 billion; the marketing bill was the difference, or 68.5 billion. During the past 10 yr, the increase (in marketing bill) is 1/3 chargeable to inflation, 1/6 added to marketing services, and the balance to the increased volume of food an expanding population requires (Siebert 1971).

TABLE 15.5

COST COMPONENTS OF THE MARKETING BILL FOR FARM FOODS
(IN BILLION DOLLARS), 1969-1970

Year	Labor[1]	Packaging Materials	Rail and Truck Transportation[2]	Corporate profits Before Taxes	After Taxes	Business Taxes[3]
1960	18.7	. . .	4.0	2.1	0.9	1.3
1961	18.9	. . .	4.1	2.2	1.0	1.3
1962	19.7	. . .	4.1	2.2	1.0	1.5
1963	20.3	6.1	4.1	2.4	1.1	1.6
1964	21.1	. . .	4.3	2.8	1.4	1.7
1965	22.4	. . .	4.2	3.0	1.6	1.9
1966	23.7	. . .	4.2	3.4	1.8	2.0
1967	25.1	7.3	4.3	3.4	1.8	2.0
1968	27.3	. . .	4.5	3.6	1.8	2.3
1969	29.3	8.3	4.6	4.0	1.9	2.4
1970[5]	32.0	8.8	5.2	4.0	1.9	2.6

	Depre-ciation	Rent (Net)	Adver-tising	Repairs, Bad Debts, Contributions	Interest (Net)	Other[4]	Total
1960	1.5	1.1	1.3	0.7	0.2	13.3	44.2
1961	1.5	1.1	1.3	0.8	0.3	13.6	45.1
1962	1.7	1.3	1.5	0.8	0.3	13.8	46.9
1963	1.7	1.3	1.5	0.9	0.3	8.7	48.9
1964	1.8	1.4	1.6	0.9	0.3	15.3	51.2
1965	1.8	1.5	1.7	1.0	0.4	14.2	52.1
1966	2.0	1.6	1.8	1.0	0.4	14.6	54.7
1967	1.9	1.6	1.8	1.0	0.5	8.6	57.5
1968	1.9	1.8	1.6	1.1	0.7	16.3	61.1
1969	2.0	1.9	1.7	1.2	0.8	7.0	63.2
1970[5]	2.1	2.0	1.9	1.3	0.8	7.8	68.5

Source: USDA (1971).
[1] Includes supplements to wages and salaries such as social security and unemployment insurance taxes and health insurance premiums; also includes imputed earnings of proprietors, partners, and family workers not receiving stated remuneration.
[2] Includes charges for heating and refrigeration; does not include local hauling.
[3] Includes property, social security, unemployment insurance, state income, and franchise taxes, license fees, etc., but does not include federal income tax.
[4] Includes food service in schools, colleges, hospitals, and other institutions; utilities, fuel, promotion, local for-hire transportation, water transportation, insurance, and the cost of packaging materials for years when it is not shown separately.
[5] Preliminary.

The importance of meat is readily apparent; consumers spent almost $30.9 billion for meat out of total food expenditures of 101.6 billion.

Total marketing costs for meat were $16.7 billion or 54% of consumer expenditures for meat. While not showing the meat industry alone, the data in Table 15.5 are heavily weighted by meat due to its importance in the total marketing bill. The outstanding importance of labor costs is obvious—comprising $32.0 billion out of a total of $68.5 billion—and has increased at a substantial rate. The "other" costs are at a significant level and are partially explained in footnote four of the Table.

FACTORS AFFECTING MARKETING COSTS AND SHARE TO FARMERS

The circumstances of an individual producer can vary considerably from the averages presented above, and the share accruing to individuals likewise can vary. The following factors affect a farmer's share: (1) Type of livestock program. A farmer who maintains a cow herd, retains and feeds out his own calves, sells direct to a local packer who, in turn, sells the meat to a local retailer would receive a considerably larger share of the retail dollar than a neighbor who buys yearling feeders, finishes them out and sells to a distant packer who ships the meat to a still more distant retailer. (2) Costs incurred and prices received, which will vary considerably among producers. Cost control is partially a matter of management expertise. Prices paid for feeder animals and received for finished stock are related to market ability, but vagaries of the market can affect profits. (3) Grade of livestock fed, particularly yield grade. This can affect the price and quantity of meat at retail.

Examples are available from studies which illustrate varying shares of returns to producers under several different types of production and marketing programs. The results obtained from these studies are not to be construed as suggestive of average returns which producers could expect from the indicated production or marketing programs. Neither are they suggestive of superiority of any production or marketing program over another.

Results from a S. Dakota report (Schulte undated) are shown in Fig. 15.11. In this study Example No. 1 assumes U.S. Choice grade steer calves were raised in northwestern S. Dakota, marketed as finished steers through the Sioux Falls terminal, slaughtered locally, and the Choice carcasses sold to a New York retail firm. Example No. 2 assumes U.S. Good grade calves were raised and fed out on the same farm in southeastern S. Dakota, sold through the Sioux Falls terminal to a southwestern Minnesota packer who, in turn, sold the U.S. Good grade carcasses to a retailer in Omaha. Example No. 3 assumes U.S. Good grade yearlings in south central S. Dakota were sold through auction to a feeder in eastern S. Dakota, marketed as finished steers through the Sioux Falls terminal to a local packer who shipped the U.S. Good

Schulte (undated)

FIG. 15.11. BEEF: COMPARISON OF THE PERCENTAGE OF
GROSS RETURNS TO PRODUCERS AND MARKETING
AGENCIES

grade carcasses to a retail firm in Philadelphia. The major variation in shares is
in the split between original producer (rancher or producer-feeder) and feeder.
In Example No. 2, producer and feeder are one and the same person who gets
the entire 62.5%. The combined rancher and feeder share in Examples No. 1
and No. 3 is approximately the same, but the division between rancher and
feeder is considerably different in the two examples.

Figure 15.12 shows results of a USDA study (Duewer 1970). The beef
example assumes U.S. Good grade feeder steers from near Casper, Wyo., were
marketed through the Omaha terminal to a feeder near Lincoln, Neb.; sold as
finished Choice grade steers through the Omaha terminal to a local packer
who shipped the carcasses to a retailer in New York. The same program was
assumed for 1967 and 1969. The pork example (again the same program at
two different dates) assumes hogs were raised in western Iowa, sold through
the Sioux City terminal to a local packer, and the wholesale cuts were shipped
to a retail firm in Los Angeles. In the beef example, both the rancher and
retailer shares were less in 1969 than in 1967. Most of the gain was in the
feeder's share. In the pork example, both the retailer and packer-wholesaler
shares declined from 1967 to 1969, with the gain going to the original
producer.

These examples serve to show that shares can vary with different programs
(the S. Dakota study), and that different shares can be obtained from the
same program at different times (the USDA study).

Dissatisfaction exists among producers over the farmer's share, and various
actions have been suggested to alleviate the situation. Farmers have, in some
instances, set up farmer-owned cooperatives to capture a greater share of
marketing profits. In a few instances farmers have organized cooperative
packing plants. Most cooperative packing ventures failed. While several success-

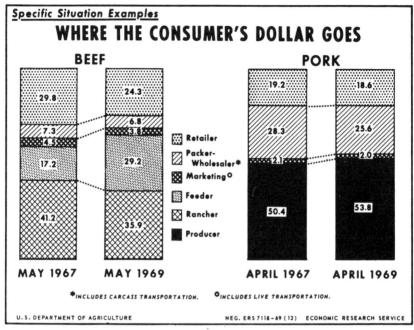

FIG. 15.12. WHERE THE CONSUMER'S DOLLAR GOES

ful plants currently are operating, they are handling a negligible fraction of livestock slaughter.

Farmer organizations on occasion have indicated an interest in ownership and operation of a national retail food chain, but have not made the plunge. Cooperative ventures in retailing to date have been, in general, somewhat less than smashing successes. If the profit rates reported earlier in this chapter are accurate, it appears doubtful that any significant one-shot gain can be squeezed out in favor of farmers. However, this is no excuse for assuming a passive attitude toward marketing costs. Improvements undoubtedly can be made, and a series of small gains could be significant in improving the producer's position.

COMMENT ON SELECTED ITEMS OF MARKETING COST

Live animal shrinkage; transportation; and bruise, crippling, and death losses are selected for particular comment. In the determination of price spreads, account was taken of retail "store shrinkage." In addition, cooler shrinkage was recognized, along with trimming loss, in the conversion factors to carcass weight and live weight equivalent. Neither shrinkage in live animal weight from the feedlot to market place, nor bruise, crippling, and death loss were explicitly considered. Transportation costs were specifically accounted for in spread calculations, but merit additional comment. The total transportation bill for all food products in 1969 was \$4.8 billion (Table 15.5) and the portion attributed to livestock and meat is estimated to be about \$1.28 billion.[4] Transportation is significant not only in the number of dollars involved, but also as a factor in the changing structural characteristics of the livestock-meat industry. These two aspects are related.

Transportation

Early developments in transportation, and their impact upon the livestock and meat industry, were noted in previous chapters. Overland droving in eastern areas, the great cattle trails of the range area, and the era of canal building were all changed as the railroads pushed their steel rails throughout the country. The railroad system set the pattern for concentrated and centralized livestock marketing and meat packing locations. Then came the motor truck and highway system which were instrumental in reversal of the organizational structure (decentralization).

The impact of transportation development was not limited to the livestock-meat sector. Hulbert (1920), writing at the time some of these significant changes were occurring, said, "If the great American novel is ever written, I hazard the guess that its plot will be woven around the theme of American tranportation, for that has been the vital factor in the national development of the United States. Every problem in the building of the Republic has been, in the last analysis, a problem of transportation." In view of subsequent concern with social and environmental problems, undoubtedly many currently would disagree with the attachment of this degree of importance to transportation. Even in the earlier days, concurrent developments in refrigeration, communications, and implementation of grade standards were teamed with transportation in changing the structure of the livestock and meat industry. But there is no question that the central importance of transportation and its significance lies in marketing cost reductions. Conceivably, droving could have continued as the mode of transport as production expanded to mid-continent. But, at what cost? Today, cattle are droved from the southern fringes of the Sahara Desert more than 1000 miles to Lagos, Nigeria, and other west African coastal cities. But consumption is only 8–10 lb per person and not many people can afford the price. Transportation alone would not solve the Nigerian problem, but it would help.

Innovations in Transportation.—It is not enough simply to refer to railroads and trucks as means of transportation. Many improvements have been (and are being) made within each system which sustain a continuous competitive contest between these two types of carriers. In this contest, trucks virtually have taken over all short hauls of both livestock and meat. It is estimated that

[4] Estimated by the author to be 4.5% of consumer expenditures for meat.

more than 80% of all livestock is moved to market by trucks and trailers. The truck advantage in short hauls lies in the faster time, convenience, and flexibility including pickup and delivery at destination. Trucks are vying for long hauls of livestock by increasing capacity, controling temperature, and improving designs that reduce bruising and crippling and expedite loading and unloading. Cross-country, triple-deck trucks haul thousands of hogs from the midwest to the west coast each year. Some of these are equipped with air conditioning units for use in hot weather. Others have sprinkling or fogging devices. Triple-deck trucks also are used for lambs; and double-deck cattle trucks have been in use for a number of years.

Railroads also have made improvements with multideck cars and improved construction for greater animal comfort and reduced bruising. These include such things as improved ventilation, suspension, coupling, and operational procedures that reduce starting and stopping jerks. Most railroads now operate fast, "express" livestock trains to speed delivery.

Some years ago railroads introduced "piggyback" hauling of loaded trucks as a counter measure to truck competition. Piggyback use has increased for meat in refrigerated trucks and is used to some extent for live animals. Significant improvements have been made in refrigeration capacity of rail cars, and in long hauls the railroads are competitive with trucks in meat transportation.

Containerization and palletization of meat shipments has progressed, but much research still is needed to perfect the techniques and maintain quality during shipment. These developments apply to both truck and railroads—and, in fact, extend also to airlines and shipping lines. Lack of standardization in container size is a problem not only for a given mode of transportation, but also especially where trans-shipment involves different modes of transportation.

Types of Motor Carriers.—A first, broad classification of motor carriers is "for-hire" and "private" truckers. Private truckers haul their own products and are subject only to state trucking regulations. For-hire truckers fall into two classes—regulated carriers which are subject to federal regulations and unregulated, or "exempt carriers" which, at the federal level, generally are subject only to regulations concerning the type of commodities that may be hauled, safety specifications, and maximum hour limitations for drivers. The crucial aspects of exemption are freedom in rates charged and routes of operation. Provisions of the Interstate Commerce Act placed regulation of transportation under the Interstate Commerce Commission. However, through a series of administrative rulings, court decisions, and amendments, the hauling of certain commodities by truck was exempt from federal regulation. The major classification of exempt commodities is unmanufactured agricultural products which includes livestock—with certain exceptions. Breeding, racing, and show animals are not exempt. Meat is not exempt on grounds that it has undergone a manufacturing process. The determination of what constitutes manufacturing as applied to agricultural and fishery products has been a matter of contention in establishing the list of exempt products. The exemption does not apply to railroads.

Within the group of regulated carriers a distinction is made between common carriers, which are available to the public generally, and contract carriers, which provide service to shippers under contract. Regulated carriers (railroads and regulated trucks) are subject to numerous federal restrictions including rate charges, routes used, and who may be issued permits. Certain states have regulations (taxes, rates charged, safety requirements, load limits, etc.) which apply to all carriers (exempt or regulated) operating in, or through, that state. However, as a rule, exempt carriers have greater flexibility in rates and in operation than do regulated carriers, and from a competitive standpoint, are in a position to make quicker adjustments to changing competitive situations. Thus, livestock truckers (operating under exempt status) can make quicker adjustments than can railroad officials (operating under regulated status) in the transportation of livestock.

Comparison of Truck and Rail Rates.—A regional study conducted by western states (Capener 1969) indicated that truck rates clearly were less than rail rates on hauls of up to 200–300 miles (Fig. 15.13). The rate for interstate trucks was greater than that for rail on both feeder and slaughter cattle on distances above 300–400 miles. And, rail rates on slaughter cattle were about 15% higher than rail rates on feeder cattle. Rates are important, but other factors must also be considered. Usually, some trucking is required to bring livestock to a rail loading point and take them away from the unloading point. Time in transit also is important and will be discussed later. The adequacy of rest stops is a factor in shrinkage. On this score, railroads have had better facilities than were available for trucks. However, in recent years improvements have been made in privately-operated rest stops.

The Back-Haul Problem.—A factor contributing to livestock transport costs is difficulty in obtaining back-hauls. Established truckers often have contacts for possible return freight, but timing is a problem. At best back-hauls are irregular, inconvenient, or seasonal. Railroads may be able to park cars in freight yards for use at their convenience, but many eventually return empty. Truckers normally must return to their base of operations within a relatively short time whether loaded or empty. The impact of empty returns can be illustrated by a hypothetical example. Assume the cost of operating a diesel powered semitrailer is 60¢ per loaded mile. If return hauls were never available, a 1-way charge of $1.20 per mile would be required to break even (ignoring the fact that costs would be slightly less on the empty return). However, if back-hauls were available 1/2 the time, a charge of 90¢ per mile would give a monetary return equivalent to $1.20 per mile without a back-haul.

FIG. 15.13. COMPARISONS OF REGIONAL RATE FUNCTIONS FOR HAULING CATTLE IN THE WEST

Capener (1969)

An advantage of air-conditioned trucks is their adaptability to back-hauls of perishable products. Truckers operating under exempt status have a problem in that the return load also must be an exempt product if carried for hire. This difficulty may be avoided if the trucker buys (takes title) to the cargo for the return trip. This, however, can be a costly operation unless outlets are prearranged.

Industry Location Related to Transportation Costs.—The transportation rate structure plays a crucial role in industrial location. Other factors, of course, affect packing plant location, but everything else being equal, the relationship between costs of shipping live animals versus the cost of shipping dressed meat is a determining factor. The same situation holds for location of feedyards. The relationship between cost of shipping feed grain versus cost of shipping meat (or livestock) can determine where livestock will be fed.

After a period of relative stability in freight rates, an industry will develop a locational pattern compatible with that rate structure. Subsequent changes of an unequal geographical nature can disrupt the locational pattern. The flour milling industry in parts of the hard red winter wheat area experienced such a disruption during the early 1960's following a reduction in wheat rates to Southeastern states without equivalent reduction in flour rates. As a result, many flour mills ceased operation in the hard red winter wheat area and milling capacity was expanded in Southeastern states. Cattle feeding in the Milo Belt is somewhat vulnerable to the transportation rate structure. A reduction in feed grain rates to the Southwest or West Coast areas without equivalent changes in livestock and meat rates could disrupt cattle feeding and meat packing in the Milo Belt. Western interests have been active in recent years in attempts to effectuate such a change in the rate structure. This is just one aspect of the competitive game.

Shrinkage

Shrinkage is recognized as a loss of weight. Livestock typically shrink during the marketing process, and meat loses weight in marketing channels. Where livestock is sold on a liveweight basis, the number of pounds sold (or paid for) is equally as important as the price. Directly or indirectly, a reduction in weight represents a cost. When meat loses weight in marketing channels, that must be reflected as a cost. In marketing, a distinction is made between the following: (1) "actual" shrink, (2) "pencil" shrink, (3) "cooler" shrink, and (4) "store" shrink. Cooler shrink—a loss due to evaporation of moisture—generally ranges from 1.5–3% by weight. Store shrink is estimated to be 5–5.5%. Both cooler shrink and store shrink were considered in the previous section. This section is devoted to live animal shrinkage, i.e., actual and pencil shrink.

Actual loss in body weight may arise from excretory shrink (the emptying of the digestive and urinary tracts) and tissue shrink (a loss of body tissue). "Tissue shrink occurs on long, extended shipments or during long periods of fast. These two types of shrinkage probably occur as two distinct phases in the shrinkage process. In the early part of shipment only excretory shrink occurs. At an unidentified stage in the movement both excretory and tissue shrinkage occur simultaneously. During the latter part of the shipment, tissue shrinkage is relatively more important" (Harston 1959A).

The economic importance of tissue shrink is readily apparent. A loss in body tissue reduces carcass weight and directly affects value. If buyers (and sellers) were able to precisely evaluate "fill" and if proper allowances were made in the agreed-upon price, excretory shrink would have no economic significance. In slaughter livestock this would involve a precise estimate of carcass yield, and in feeder livestock an estimate of deviation from normal fill condition (i.e., "excess fill" or the opposite, a "shrunk out" condition). Professional marketers are able to average out these estimates over a number of lots with a high degree of accuracy. The occasional buyer or seller usually lacks comparable ability and even the professional may be off on any given lot. In addition to impreciseness of knowledge, inequality of bargaining ability also may result in prices not adequately reflecting shrunk out or excess fill conditions. Therefore, excretory shrink cannot be dismissed as completely noneconomic.

Factors Related to Shrinkage.—A number of studies have been made over the years in attempts to measure the extent of shrinkage and determine the associated factors. Several factors have been isolated, but inconsistency in results points up the fact that shrinkage is a complex phenomenon. Efforts to derive predictive mathematical functions have, in general, been marked with a relatively low degree of accuracy. However, results of the studies do permit some generalizations on explanatory variables and provide some guidelines for manipulation of those variables which are controllable.

Major factors which affect shrinkage are time in transit, distance hauled, degree of fill, weather conditions, weighing conditions, sex, weight of the animals, class of animals, type of feed, mode of transportation, handling procedures, and preconditioning.

Time in Transit and Distance Hauled.—Time in transit and distance hauled may be discussed together as these variables are highly interrelated and have the same general effect on shrinkage. Shrinkage, whether measured in pounds or percentage of body weight lost, increases with distance and time, but not at a constant rate throughout the trip. Shrinkage occurs at a faster rate during the early part of the trip than during the latter part, meaning that shrinkage increases at a decreasing rate with distance and time. Figure 15.14 shows the results of an Indiana study in which shrinkage of hogs increased throughout the distance, but the rate tapered off with distance. The same general type of relationship holds between shrinkage and time in transit, and is consistent also

Stout and Cox (1959)

FIG. 15.14. FARM-WEIGHT TO SALE-(OR CATCH) WEIGHT OF SELECTED HOGS SOLD AT LOCAL AND TERMINAL MARKETS IN RELATION TO DISTANCE TRAVELED, OCT. 31, 1956 TO FEB. 24, 1958

for cattle and sheep. Of these two variables, time in transit probably is the more realistic with which to deal. Two different truckers, hauling identical loads over the same route, might have different times in transit. Over-the-road speeds may differ, length of meal and coffee stops may differ, etc.

The amount of shrinkage to be expected with time or distance cannot be precisely specified because other factors also enter the picture. However, Tables 15.6 and 15.7 show the results of well-planned studies of cattle and hog shrinkage. It may be noted in Table 15.6 that average shrinkage for the group was 3.9% for the entire 200-mile haul and that nearly 1/2 of this occurred during the first 25 miles. Table 15.7 again illustrates a declining rate

TABLE 15.6

PERCENTAGE OF SHRINK FOR 60 FAT CATTLE BETWEEN EACH CHECK WEIGHING DURING 200 MILE TRUCK HAUL (TOTAL ANIMAL WEIGHT EQUALS 100 PERCENT)

| Weight Classes (Lb) | No. Head in Each Class | Avg Weight (Lb) | Miles Traveled Between Weighings | | | | Total Weight Lost (%) |
			0–25 (%)	25–50 (%)	50–100 (%)	100–200 (%)	
Group avg	60	1122	1.8	0.7	0.8	0.6	3.9
Under 1000	11	954	1.5	0.7	0.9	0.8	3.9
1000–1099	10	1056	2.1	0.9	0.8	0.3	4.1
1100–1199	24	1139	1.8	0.8	0.8	0.7	4.1
Over 1200	15	1263	1.9	0.5	0.7	0.5	3.6

Source: Abbenhaus (1951).

TABLE 15.7

RELATIONSHIP OF THE LENGTH OF HAUL
TO SHRINKAGE OF HOGS
(1132 LOTS; 38,303 HOGS)

Miles Hauled	Shrinkage When Not Fed at Market (%)	When Fed at Market (%)
0–5	1.06	[1]
6–15	1.12	1.03
16–25	1.39	1.24
26–35	1.75	1.51
36–45	2.06	1.79
46–55	2.50	1.99
56–65	2.68	2.03
66–75	2.76	2.08
76–85	[1]	2.14
86–95	[1]	2.16

Source: Wiley and Cox (1955).
[1] Sufficient data not available.

of shrinkage for hogs, reaching a maximum of 2.76% where the hogs were not allowed a fill at the market.

Degree of Fill at Destination.—Since excretory shrink results from elimination of the digestive and urinary tracts, it stands to reason that some of this loss will be quickly regained when the animals have access to feed and water. This is shown in Table 15.7. The degree of fill, however, is highly variable depending upon: whether the animals were taken off feed prior to shipping, quantity of feed and water consumed during rest stops, time allowed for fill, and degree of emotional disturbance during transit and during the fill period. Some shippers claim to regain all the shrink, but instances are known where emotional disturbance results in no fill at all.

This is one variable which is at least partially controllable by a shipper. Generally, it is considered desirable to do any necessary sorting several days prior to shipping, withhold feed immediately prior to shipment, handle as quietly and gently as possible during loading (utilizing a pen and loading chute arrangement that facilitates speed with a minimum of excitement), and minimize time in transit consistent with road conditions and general safety considerations. Scheduled time of arrival at the market will depend upon length of haul. On relatively short hauls, arrival 2–3 hr prior to market opening will give the animals time to settle down and partake of water. Then, if sale can be made shortly after the market opens, feeding probably is not economical (Wiley and Cox 1955). On longer hauls it is desirable to schedule arrival the evening prior to day of sale and give access to both feed and water.

Any attempt to gain excess fill is not recommended. Experienced buyers will insist on docking the price of such animals.

Weather Conditions.—Shrinkage tends to increase as temperatures move from moderate levels toward either extreme—heat or cold. This is illustrated in Fig. 15.15 in the case of hogs. "Extreme temperatures have an effect on fat cattle shrinkage during marketing. But other things—wind, rain, snow, humidity, and other weather conditions—seem to have more effect than temperature alone" (Harston 1959B). The effects of temperature extremes can be alleviated by such things as properly adjusting ventilation; using straw bedding and covering open trucks in cold weather; using wet sand for bedding, and spraying and fogging during hot weather; and scheduling hauls during an optimum time of day (this will depend upon weather conditions).

Stout and Cox (1959)

FIG. 15.15. EFFECT OF VARIATION AROUND 50°F OVER TIME ON IN-TRANSIT SHRINKAGE OF SLAUGHTER-WEIGHT MARKET HOGS FROM 232 OBSERVATIONS

Weighing Conditions.—Weighing conditions include such arrangements as holding livestock off water and/or feed for a specified time prior to weighing, and in the case of feeder cattle or lambs, driving the livestock to a specified place for weighing. Weighing conditions affect shrinkage and hence value of the animals. Therefore, weighing conditions need to be considered as an integral part of the bargain, along with price. Harston (1959A) reported overnight shrink—12 hr stand—will vary with the type of feed. Cattle off green grass, wet beet pulp, or silage will generally shrink 4%, while fat cattle off concentrates will shrink about 2.5–3% if no feed and water are available. If feed and water are available, morning weights of fat cattle will be 2% less than evening weights. Range cattle not used to enclosures often shrink more than 5% when held in drylot overnight.

Shrinkage from driving livestock will depend not only on the distance, but also on weather conditions, speed of travel, and handling procedures. Harston (1959B) reported an 8.4% shrink on steers from a 50-mile drive under favorable handling conditions. Under the best of conditions such shrink probably amounts to 3–4% in a 6–8-mile drive.

Sex, Class, and Weight of Animals.–Most studies show that heifers shrink more than steers. However, Harston (1959B) reported the difference was not great except during the summer when heifers shrank 11.5 lb for each 10 lb steers shrank. Much variation occurs in comparison of sex. Bulls usually shrink a lot because of disturbing circumstances and strange animals in nearby pens. Calves also are heavy shrinkers largely because they are often weaned at market time. Finished cattle shrink more during the latter hours of transit (Table 15.8).

TABLE 15.8

COMPARISON OF SHRINKAGE BY FAT
CATTLE AND FEEDER CATTLE

| Time in Transit (Hr) | Rate of Shrink | |
	Fat Cattle (%)	Feeder Cattle (%)
6	5.4	3.8
10–17	6.2	8.2
60	10.8	12.4

Source: Data from Harston (1959B).

Studies relating shrinkage to weight of hogs have been inconsistent (Bjorka 1938; Stout and Cox 1959). In the case of cattle, Harston (1959B) reported that shrinkage was not closely related to weight, except as weight is correlated with degree of fatness.

Mode of Transportation.–The comparative shrinkage by truck versus rail on short hauls is irrelevant since other considerations have given trucks a virtual monopoly on short hauls. The evidence in Fig. 15.16 indicates relatively little difference between rail and truck shrinkage in long hauls of cattle, at least up to 30–40 hr in transit. Factors other than mode of transportation easily could account for the apparent differences.

Preconditioning.–Studies of the effect of preconditioning on shrinkage have been somewhat inconclusive. It appears reasonable that weaning, vaccination, castration, and such operations cause stress. When accomplished as part of preconditioning, subsequent shrinkage would be reduced. However, preconditioning is not standardized and perhaps this has contributed to conflicting results. Additional research is needed to evaluate not only shrinkage, but also other economic aspects associated with preconditioning.

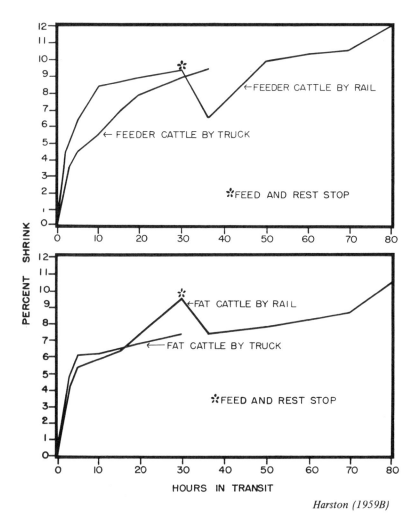

Harston (1959B)

FIG. 15.16. HOW SHRINKAGE DIFFERS WHEN CATTLE ARE SHIPPED
BY TRUCK AND RAIL (FEEDER AND FAT CATTLE)

Pencil Shrink.—Pencil shrink, as defined in Chap. 6, is a negotiated or an agreed upon deduction from scale weight in arriving at pay weight. This is a common practice, particularly in direct cattle sales. Normally, the deduction is specified as a percentage and may range from 2 to 5%, but more generally is 3–4%. The logic of pencil shrink is that some actual shrinkage will take place and the negotiated pencil shrink is an estimate or allowance to compensate the buyer for expected actual loss in weight accompanying the transaction. Everyone is aware that an adjustment could be made in price and accomplish the same results without resorting to pencil shrink, but the custom is well established, and some buyers (and sellers) apparently believe that bargaining advantages accrue to them. The practice is here to stay unless some governmental action is taken to stop it, and, while this has been discussed, it appears unlikely. There is nothing inherently dishonest about the practice, but if both parties are not equally informed and of equal bargaining ability, inequities can result.

In a bargaining situation, the general proposition is one of a trade-off between pencil shrink and price. An equal trade-off occurs where the price adjustment exactly offsets the pencil shrink. This can be illustrated as follows: suppose a rancher wants to realize $38.00 per cwt for his 450-lb steer calves. What price would he need if he agreed to a 4% pencil shrink? In the absence of pencil shrink each calf would be worth $\frac{450}{100} \times \$38.00 = \$171.00$. A pencil shrink of 4% would amount to a deduction of 18 lb per calf or a pay weight of 432 lb. Thus, the trade-off price would need to be $\$171.00 \div \frac{432}{100} =$ $39.58 per cwt. The same result can be obtained by direct calculation as follows:

$$\frac{\$38.00 \div 96}{100} = \$39.58$$

Here the 96 is the difference between 100% and the 4% pencil shrink. If the rancher did not bargain for a higher price to offset the effect of the 4% pencil shrink, but instead settled for $38 per cwt *and* also granted the shrink, he actually would have realized $\frac{\$38.00 \ (432)}{450} = \$36.48$ per cwt for his calves. Again, this result can be obtained more simply as follows: $\frac{(\$38.00)(96)}{100} =$ $36.48. The same general principles apply to any class of livestock. Differences in value received can amount to substantial sums of money. Tables have been prepared showing the trade-off price for various levels of pencil shrink allowance and cattle price level. Two such examples are reproduced in Tables 15.9 and 15.10. These tables are derived by straight arithmetic as illustrated in the examples above. A glance at Table 15.9 shows that with $50.00 calves each 1% shrink amounts to 50¢ per cwt. Few professional marketers carry tables. They have enough experience to make accurate mental estimates. The nonprofessional, occasional trader would do well either to resort to a Table or to make the necessary calculations.

One aspect of the shrinkage-bargaining issue that needs special mention is the combination of pencil shrink and weighing conditions. A set of yearling steers sold with, say, a 3% pencil shrink after an overnight stand and a 10-mile haul before weighing, are likely to sustain at least 5–6% actual shrinkage in addition to the pencil shrink (i.e., a total of 8–9%). This can be offset by adequate consideration in the price. But, as in any other transaction in a competitive market, the "consideration" will depend upon demand and supply conditions for livestock at the particular time and the astuteness and bargaining ability of the participants.

TABLE 15.9
SHRINKAGE TABLE (OFFER) REALIZED PRICES: DOLLARS PER
HUNDREDWEIGHT SHRINKAGE DEDUCTED

OFFER ($)	2%	3%	4%	6%	8%	OFFER ($)	2%	3%	4%	6%	8%
50.00	49.00	48.50	48.00	47.00	46.00						
49.75	48.75	48.26	47.76	46.77	45.77	34.75	34.05	33.70	33.36	32.66	31.97
49.50	48.51	48.02	47.52	46.53	45.54	34.50	33.81	33.46	33.12	32.43	31.74
49.25	48.27	47.77	47.28	46.29	45.31	34.25	33.56	33.22	32.88	32.20	31.51
49.00	48.02	47.53	47.04	46.06	45.08	34.00	33.32	32.98	32.64	31.96	31.28
48.75	47.77	47.29	46.80	45.83	44.85	33.75	33.08	32.74	32.40	31.72	31.05
48.50	47.53	47.04	46.56	45.59	44.62	33.50	32.83	32.50	32.16	31.49	30.82
48.25	47.29	46.80	46.32	45.35	44.39	33.25	32.58	32.25	31.92	31.26	30.59
48.00	47.04	46.56	46.08	45.12	44.16	33.00	32.34	32.01	31.68	31.02	30.36
47.75	46.79	46.32	45.84	44.89	43.93	32.75	32.10	31.77	31.44	30.79	30.13
47.50	46.55	46.08	45.60	44.65	43.70	32.50	31.85	31.51	31.20	30.55	29.90
47.25	46.31	45.83	45.36	44.41	43.47	32.25	31.60	31.28	30.96	30.32	29.67
47.00	46.06	45.59	45.12	44.18	43.24	32.00	31.36	31.04	30.72	30.08	29.44
46.75	45.81	45.35	44.88	43.95	43.01	31.75	31.12	30.80	30.48	29.84	29.21
46.50	45.57	45.10	44.64	43.71	42.78	31.50	30.87	30.56	30.24	29.61	28.98
46.25	45.33	44.86	44.40	43.47	42.55	31.25	30.62	30.31	30.00	29.38	28.75
46.00	45.08	44.62	44.16	43.24	42.32	31.00	30.38	30.07	29.76	29.14	28.52
45.75	44.83	44.38	43.92	43.01	42.09	30.75	30.14	29.83	29.52	28.90	28.29
45.50	44.59	44.14	43.68	42.77	41.86	30.50	29.89	29.58	29.28	28.67	28.06
45.25	44.35	43.89	43.44	42.53	41.63	30.25	29.64	29.34	29.04	28.44	27.83
45.00	44.10	43.65	43.20	42.30	41.40	30.00	29.40	29.10	28.80	28.20	27.60
44.75	43.85	43.41	42.96	42.07	41.17	29.75	29.16	28.86	28.56	27.96	27.37
44.50	43.61	43.16	42.72	41.83	40.94	29.50	28.91	28.62	28.32	27.73	27.14
44.25	43.37	42.92	42.48	41.59	40.71	29.25	28.66	28.37	28.08	27.50	26.91
44.00	43.12	42.68	42.24	41.36	40.48	29.00	28.42	28.13	27.84	27.26	26.68
43.75	42.87	42.44	42.00	41.13	40.25	28.75	28.18	27.89	27.60	27.02	26.45
43.50	42.63	42.20	41.76	40.89	40.02	28.50	27.93	27.64	27.36	26.79	26.22
43.25	42.39	41.95	41.52	40.65	39.79	28.25	27.68	27.40	27.12	26.56	25.99
43.00	42.14	41.71	41.28	40.42	39.56	28.00	27.44	27.16	26.88	26.32	25.76
42.75	41.89	41.47	41.04	40.19	39.33	27.75	27.20	26.92	26.64	26.08	25.53
42.50	41.65	41.22	40.80	39.95	39.10	27.50	26.95	26.68	26.40	25.85	25.30
42.25	41.41	40.98	40.56	39.71	38.87	27.25	26.70	26.43	26.16	25.62	25.07
42.00	41.16	40.74	40.32	39.48	38.64	27.00	26.46	26.19	25.92	25.38	24.84
41.75	40.91	40.50	40.08	39.25	38.41	26.75	26.22	25.95	25.68	25.14	24.61
41.50	40.67	40.26	39.84	39.01	38.18	26.50	25.97	25.71	25.44	24.91	24.38
41.25	40.43	40.01	39.60	38.77	37.95	26.25	25.72	25.46	25.20	24.68	24.15
41.00	40.18	39.77	39.36	38.54	37.72	26.00	25.48	25.22	24.96	24.44	23.92
40.75	39.93	39.53	39.12	38.31	37.49	25.75	25.24	24.98	24.72	24.20	23.69
40.50	39.69	39.28	38.88	38.07	37.26	25.50	24.99	24.74	24.48	23.97	23.46
40.25	39.45	39.04	38.64	37.83	37.03	25.25	24.74	24.49	24.24	23.74	23.23
40.00	39.20	38.80	38.40	37.60	36.80	25.00	24.50	24.25	24.00	23.50	23.00
39.75	38.96	38.56	38.16	37.36	36.57	24.75	24.26	24.01	23.76	23.26	22.77
39.50	38.71	38.32	37.92	37.13	36.34	24.50	24.01	23.76	23.52	23.03	22.54
39.25	38.46	38.07	37.68	36.90	36.11	24.25	23.76	23.52	23.28	22.80	22.31
39.00	38.22	37.83	37.44	36.66	35.88	24.00	23.52	23.28	23.04	22.56	22.08
38.75	37.98	37.59	37.20	36.42	35.65	23.75	23.28	23.04	22.80	22.32	21.85
38.50	37.73	37.34	36.96	36.19	35.42	23.50	23.03	22.80	22.56	22.09	21.62
38.25	37.48	37.10	36.72	35.96	35.19	23.25	22.78	22.55	22.32	21.86	21.39
38.00	37.24	36.86	36.48	35.72	34.96	23.00	22.54	22.31	22.08	21.62	21.16

TABLE 15.9 (Continued)

SHRINKAGE TABLE (OFFER) REALIZED PRICES: DOLLARS PER
HUNDREDWEIGHT SHRINKAGE DEDUCTED

OFFER ($)	2%	3%	4%	6%	8%	OFFER ($)	2%	3%	4%	6%	8%
37.75	37.00	36.62	36.24	35.48	34.73	22.75	22.30	22.07	21.84	21.38	20.93
37.50	36.75	36.38	36.00	35.25	34.50	22.50	22.05	21.82	21.60	21.15	20.70
37.25	36.50	36.13	35.76	35.02	34.27	22.25	21.80	21.58	21.36	20.92	20.47
37.00	36.26	35.89	35.52	34.78	34.04	22.00	21.56	21.34	21.12	20.68	20.24
36.75	36.02	35.65	35.28	34.50	33.81	21.75	21.32	21.10	20.88	20.44	20.01
36.50	35.77	35.41	35.04	34.31	33.58	21.50	21,07	20.85	20.64	20.21	19.78
36.25	35.53	35.16	34.80	34.08	33.35	21.25	20.82	20.61	20.40	19.98	19.55
36.00	35.28	34.92	34.56	33.84	33.12	21.00	20.58	20.37	20.16	19.74	19.32
35.75	35.04	34.68	34.32	33.60	32.89	20.75	20.34	20.13	19.92	19.50	19.09
35.50	34.79	34.44	34.08	33.37	32.66	20.50	20.09	19.88	19.68	19.27	18.86
35.25	34.54	34.19	33.84	33.14	32.43	20.25	19.84	19.64	19.44	19.04	18.63
35.00	34.30	33.95	33.60	32.90	32.20	20.00	19.60	19.40	19.20	18.80	18.40

Source: Wellman (undated).

TABLE 15.10

SHRINKAGE TABLE (ASKING) PRICES: DOLLARS PER HUNDRED-
WEIGHT NEEDED TO COMPENSATE FOR SHRINKAGE

ASKING ($)	2%	3%	4%	6%	8%	ASKING ($)	2%	3%	4%	6%	8%
50.00	51.02	51.54	52.08	53.19	54.36						
49.75	50.77	51.29	51.83	52.93	54.10	34.75	35.46	35.82	36.20	36.97	37.78
49.50	50.51	51.03	51.56	52.65	53.81	34.50	35.20	35.57	35.94	36.70	37.50
49.25	50.26	50.78	51.31	52.39	53.55	34.25	34.95	35.31	35.68	36.44	37.22
49.00	50.00	50.51	51.04	52.12	53.27	34.00	34.69	35.05	35.42	36.17	36.96
48.75	49.75	50.26	50.79	51.86	53.00	33.75	34.44	34.79	35.16	35.90	36.68
48.50	49.49	50.00	50.52	51.59	52.72	33.50	34.18	34.54	34.90	35.64	36.41
48.25	49.24	49.75	50.27	51.33	52.43	33.25	33.93	34.28	34.64	35.37	36.14
48.00	48.98	49.48	50.00	51.05	52.17	33.00	33.67	34.02	34.37	35.11	35.87
47.75	48.73	49.23	49.74	50.79	51.90	32.75	33.42	33.76	34.11	34.84	35.60
47.50	48.47	48.97	49.48	50.52	51.62	32.50	33.16	33.51	33.85	34.57	35.33
47.25	48.22	48.72	49.23	50.26	51.36	32.25	32.91	33.25	33.59	34.31	35.05
47.00	47.96	48.45	48.96	49.99	51.08	32.00	32.66	32.99	33.33	34.04	34.78
46.75	47.71	48.20	48.70	49.72	50.81	31.75	32.40	32.73	33.07	33.78	34.51
46.50	47.45	47.94	48.44	49.46	50.54	31.50	32.14	32.47	32.81	33.51	34.24
46.25	47.20	47.69	48.19	49.20	50.28	31.25	31.89	32.22	32.55	33.24	33.97
46.00	46.94	47.42	47.92	48.93	50.00	31.00	31.63	31.96	32.29	32.98	33.70
45.75	46.69	47.17	47.66	48.66	49.72	30.75	31.38	31.70	32.03	32.71	33.42
45.50	46.43	46.91	47.40	48.40	49.46	30.50	31.12	31.44	31.77	32.45	33.15
45.25	46.18	46.66	47.15	48.14	49.19	30.25	30.87	31.19	31.51	32.18	32.88
45.00	45.92	46.39	46.88	47.87	48.92	30.00	30.61	30.93	31.25	31.91	32.61
44.75	45.67	46.14	46.62	47.60	48.64	29.75	30.36	30.67	30.99	31.65	32.34
44.50	45.41	45.88	46.36	47.34	48.38	29.50	30.10	30.41	30.73	31.38	32.07
44.25	45.16	45.63	46.11	47.08	48.11	29.25	29.85	30.15	30.47	31.12	31.79
44.00	44.90	45.36	45.84	46.81	47.83	29.00	29.59	29.88	30.21	30.85	31.52
43.75	44.65	45.11	45.58	46.54	47.56	28.75	29.34	29.64	29.95	30.59	31.25
43.50	44.39	44.85	45.32	46.28	47.28	28.50	29.08	29.38	29.69	30.32	30.98
43.25	44.14	44.60	45.07	46.02	47.03	28.25	28.83	29.12	29.43	30.05	30.71
43.00	43.88	44.33	44.80	45.75	46.75	28.00	28.57	28.87	29.17	29.79	30.43

TABLE 15.10 (Continued)

SHRINKAGE TABLE (ASKING) PRICES: DOLLARS PER HUNDRED-
WEIGHT NEEDED TO COMPENSATE FOR SHRINKAGE

SKING ($)	2%	3%	4%	6%	8%	ASKING ($)	2%	3%	4%	6%	8%
42.75	43.63	44.08	44.54	45.48	46.48	27.75	28.32	28.61	28.91	29.52	30.16
42.50	43.37	43.82	44.28	45.21	46.20	27.50	28.06	28.35	28.65	29.26	29.89
42.25	43.12	43.57	44.03	44.96	45.94	27.25	27.81	28.09	28.39	28.99	29.62
42.00	42.86	43.30	43.76	44.68	45.66	27.00	27.55	27.84	28.12	28.72	29.35
41.75	42.61	43.05	43.50	44.42	45.39	26.75	27.30	27.58	27.86	28.46	29.08
41.50	42.35	42.79	43.24	44.15	45.12	26.50	27.04	27.32	27.60	28.19	28.80
41.25	42.10	42.54	42.99	43.90	44.86	26.25	26.79	27.06	27.34	27.93	28.53
41.00	41.84	42.27	42.71	43.61	44.57	26.00	26.53	26.80	27.08	27.66	28.26
40.75	41.59	42.02	42.46	43.36	44.31	25.75	26.28	26.55	26.82	27.39	27.99
40.50	41.33	41.76	42.20	43.09	44.03	25.50	26.02	26.29	26.56	27.13	27.72
40.25	41.08	41.51	41.95	42.84	43.78	25.25	25.77	26.03	26.30	26.86	27.45
40.00	40.82	41.24	41.67	42.55	43.48	25.00	25.51	25.77	26.04	26.60	27.17
39.75	40.56	40.98	41.41	42.29	43.21	24.75	25.25	25.52	25.78	26.33	26.90
39.50	40.31	40.72	41.15	42.02	42.93	24.50	25.00	25.26	25.52	26.06	26.63
39.25	40.05	40.46	40.89	41.76	42.66	24.25	24.74	25.00	25.26	25.80	26.36
39.00	39.80	40.21	40.63	41.49	42.39	24.00	24.49	24.74	25.00	25.53	26.09
38.75	39.54	39.95	40.36	41.22	42.12	23.75	24.23	24.48	24.74	25.27	25.82
38.50	39.29	39.69	40.10	40.96	41.85	23.50	23.98	24.23	24.48	25.00	25.54
38.25	39.03	39.43	39.84	40.69	41.58	23.25	23.72	23.97	24.22	24.73	25.27
38.00	38.78	39.18	39.58	40.43	41.30	23.00	23.47	23.71	23.96	24.47	25.00
37.75	38.52	38.92	39.32	40.16	41.03	22.75	23.21	23.45	23.70	24.20	24.73
37.50	38.27	38.66	39.06	39.89	40.76	22.50	22.96	23.20	23.44	23.94	24.46
37.25	38.01	38.40	38.80	39.63	40.49	22.25	22.70	22.94	23.18	23.67	24.18
37.00	37.76	38.14	38.54	39.36	40.22	22.00	22.45	22.68	22.92	23.40	23.91
36.75	37.50	37.89	38.28	39.10	39.95	21.75	22.19	22.42	22.66	23.14	23.64
36.50	37.24	37.63	38.02	38.83	39.67	21.50	21.94	22.16	22.40	22.87	23.37
36.25	36.99	37.37	37.69	38.56	39.40	21.25	21.68	21.91	22.14	22.61	23.10
36.00	36.73	37.11	37.50	38.30	39.13	21.00	21.43	21.65	21.87	22.34	22.83
35.75	36.48	36.86	37.24	38.03	38.86	20.75	21.17	21.39	21.61	22.07	22.55
35.50	36.22	36.60	36.98	37.77	38.59	20.50	20.92	21.13	21.35	21.81	22.28
35.25	35.97	36.34	36.72	37.50	38.32	20.25	20.66	20.88	21.09	21.54	22.01
35.00	35.71	36.08	36.46	37.23	38.04	20.00	20.41	20.62	20.83	21.28	21.74

Source: Wellman (undated).

One overriding consideration in shrinkage is the desirability of having an accurate set of scales at the farm, ranch, or feedlot. Shrinkage is so variable that results of average, or unknown, conditions from other sources are at best only guidelines or approximations. With a good set of scales, an operator can establish shrinkage with a reasonable degree of accuracy for his particular situation. The availability of scales also serves the extremely important function of permitting an operator to check rates of gain and feed consumption for his particular, and often unique, conditions.

Bruising, Crippling, and Death Loss

Bruised carcasses are costly. In the first place, the bruised area, normally, is condemned and must be trimmed away; and secondly, the remainder of the carcass is docked due to a less appealing appearance. Cripples are docked severely on a live basis as some must be condemned, and others may b partially condemned. Dead animals, of course, have virtually no salvage value Livestock Conservation, Inc., a Chicago-based organization which has collected data and carried out educational programs for many years to reduce such losses, estimates that millions of dollars are lost each year. The irony of th situation is that most bruises occur on the higher priced cuts and much of th loss could be prevented by simple and sensible precautions.

Among major causes of bruising are: overcrowding; trampling; striking th animals with clubs, canes, and whips; kicking, prodding, and horning; fork an nail punctures; slipping; lifting sheep and lambs by the wool; and poor loading facilities.

Optimum density of loading depends somewhat on weather conditions, bu too few or too many animals in a truck or rail car will increase the incidenc of bruises. There is little excuse for striking animals to the extent of bruisin (in addition to bruise loss, the associated agitation and excitement wi increase shrinkage). Inadequate and poorly designed pen and loading facilitie can be corrected. Narrow gateways, protruding boards, nails, and sharp edge are frequent causes of bruising and can be corrected.

Many of the factors mentioned above also contribute to crippling and death In addition, inadequate provision for temperature control is a major cause o death. Improper loading density and lack of adequate partitioning togethe with faulty loading and unloading facilities are major causes of crippling. Mos of these things are controllable to a large degree.

Bruising, crippling, and death loss probably cannot be eliminated. Accident will happen. However, this loss certainly could be reduced by prope precautions.

BIBLIOGRAPHY

ABBENHAUS, C. R., and PENNY, R. C. 1951. Shrink characteristics of fat cattl transported by truck. Chicago Union Stockyard and Transit Co., Chicago.

ANDERSON, D. L. (undated) Research to improve transportation of perishable agricul tural commodities. USDA Agr. Res. Serv. (unnumbered).

ANON. 1969. Financial Facts About the Meat Packing Industry. Am. Meat Inst., Chicago

BERMETTLER, E. R. 1964. Interstate transportation of Nevada cattle. Univ. Wyoming Max C. Fleischmann Coll. Agr. Bull. *234*.

BJORKA, K. 1938. Shrinkage and dressing yields of hogs. USDA Tech. Bull. *621*.

BRANDOW, G. E. 1966. Implications for consumers in the work of the Nationa Commission on Food Marketing. Proc. 44th Ann. Agr. Outlook Conf., Washingtor D.C., Nov. 16.

CAPENER, W. N. *et al.* 1969. Transportation of cattle in the west. Wyoming Agr. Expt Sta. Res. J. *25*.

CASAVANT, K. L., and NELSON, D. C. 1967. An economic analysis of the cost o operating livestock trucking firms in North Dakota. N. Dakota Agr. Expt. Sta. Agr Econ. Rept. *55*.

DUEWER, L. A. 1969A. Effects of specials on composite meat prices. USDA Agr. Econ Res., Econ. Res. Serv. *21*, No. 3, 70-77.

DUEWER, L. A. 1969B. Revised beef and pork price spreads. USDA Marketing Transportation Situation, Econ. Res. Serv. *MTS-175.*

DUEWER, L. A. 1970. Price spreads for beef and pork revised series, 1949-69. USDA Econ. Res. Serv. Misc. Publ. *1174.*

FINDLAY, JEANETTE, and SOUTHARD, L. 1970. The bill for marketing farm products. USDA Marketing Transportation Situation, Econ. Res. Serv. *MTS-178.*

FOWLER, S. H. 1961. The Marketing of Livestock and Meat, 2nd Edition. Interstate Printers & Publishers, Danville, Ill.

MARSTON, C. R. 1959A. Cattle shrinkage is important. Montana Agr. Expt. Sta. Circ. *220.*

MARSTON, C. R. 1959B. Cattle shrinkage depends on where, when and what you market. Montana Agr. Expt. Sta. Circ. *221.*

MARSTON, C. R. 1959C. Cattle shrinkage depends on how you market. Montana Agr. Expt. Sta. Circ. *222.*

MARSTON, C. R., and MENZIE, E. L. 1964. Montana cattle movements. Montana Agr. Expt. Sta. Bull. *584.*

MARSTON, C. R., and RICHARDS, J. 1965. Montana Livestock transportation. Montana Agr. Expt. Sta. Bull. *592.*

HENNING, G. F., and THOMAS, P. R. 1962. Factors influencing the shrinkage of livestock from farm to first market. Ohio Agr. Expt. Sta. Bull. *925.*

HULBERT, ARCHER B. 1920. The Paths of Inland Commerce, Vol. 21. Yale Chronicles of America Series. By permission of United States Publishers Assoc., New Rochelle, N.Y.

LINDEBORG, K. H., and PURNELL, G. R. 1963. Economics of transporting Idaho beef cattle. Idaho Agr. Expt. Sta. Bull. *413.*

MADSEN, A. G. 1965. Calf shrinkage under auction market conditions. USDA Consumer Marketing Serv. Res. Rept. *718.*

MIKLIUS, W. 1966. Comparison of for-hire motor carriers operating under the agricultural exemption with regulated motor carriers. USDA Agr. Res. Serv. Marketing Res. Rept. *769.*

MOSER, D. E. 1970. Changes in transportation and their implications for the livestock and meat industry. *In* Long-Run Adjustments in the Livestock and Meat Industry: Implications and Alternatives, T. T. Stout (Editor). Ohio Agr. Res Develop. Center Res. Bull. *1037.* Also, North Central Regional Publ. *199.*

NATIONAL COMMISSION ON FOOD MARKETING. 1966A. Organization and competition in the livestock and meat industry. Natl. Comm. Food Marketing Tech. Study *1.* U.S. Govt. Printing Office, Washington, D.C.

NATIONAL COMMISSION ON FOOD MARKETING. 1966B. Organization and competition in food retailing. Natl. Comm. Food Marketing Tech. Study *7.* U.S. Govt. Printing Office, Washington, D.C.

RICKENBACKER, J. E. 1958A. Causes of losses in trucking livestock. USDA FCS Marketing Res. Rept. *261.*

RICKENBACKER, J. E. 1958B. Losses of livestock in transit in midwestern and western states. USDA FCS Marketing Res. Rept. *247.*

SIEBERT, J. B. 1971. Marketing: This decade's challenge. News Farmer Coop. Mar., 4.

SCHULTE, W. (undated) Beef marketing margins and costs. S. Dakota Coop. Ext. Serv. *FS-209.*

SPERLING, CELIA. 1957. The agricultural exemption in intrastate trucking, a legislative and judicial history. USDA Agr. Marketing Serv., Marketing Res. Rept. *188* .

ST. CLAIR, J. S. 1965. Truck size and weight laws as barriers to the interstate movement of livestock. Wyoming Agr. Expt. Sta. Circ. *213.*

STOUT, T. T., and ARMSTRONG, J. H. 1960. What happens when hogs are fed at market? Purdue Univ. Dept. Agr. Econ., Econ. Marketing Inform. Indiana Farmers Mar. 30.

STOUT, T. T. and COX, C. B. 1959. Farm-to-market hog shrinkage. Indiana Agr. Expt. Sta. Res. Bull. *685.*

THOMPSON, W. H. 1969. Transportation of livestock and meats from Iowa. Iowa Ag Expt. Sta. Spec. Rept. *60*.

ULREY, I. W. 1969. The economics of farm products transportation. USDA Agr. Re Serv. Marketing Res. Rept. *843*.

USDA. 1969. Developments in marketing spreads for agricultural products in 196 USDA Econ. Res. Serv. *ERS-14*. (Reprinted from hearings before Subcommittee of tr Committee on Appropriations, U.S. House Representatives, 91st Congress.)

USDA. 1970A. Handbook of agricultural charts. USDA Agr. Handbook *397*.

USDA. 1970B. Farm-food market basket statistics. USDA Econ. Res. Serv. Marketir Transportation Situation *MTS-179*.

USDA. 1971. Marketing and Transportation Situation. USDA Econ. Res. Serv. *MTS-18.*

WELLMAN, A. C. (undated) Dressed, live price and shrinkage Tables. Nebraska Coo Ext. Serv. *EC 70-839*.

WILEY, J. R., and COX, C. B. 1955. Hog shrinkage—farm to market. Purdue Univ. Dep Agr. Econ., Econ. Marketing Inform. Indiana Farmers Febr. 26.

WILLIAMS, W. F., and STOUT, T. T. 1964. Economics of the Livestock-Meat Industr Macmillan Co., New York.

WYCKOFF, J. B. 1962. Cattle transportation in Washington. Washington Agr. Expt. St Bull. *636*.

CHAPTER 16

Meat Substitutes
and Synthetics[1]

CLARIFICATION OF TERMS

Use of the terms "substitute" and "synthetic" in connection with agricultural products has not been entirely consistent; but, generally, substitutes are considered to be products used in place of conventional natural-form agricultural products. The natural-form agricultural product may, or may not, have undergone processing. Synthetics are products derived from raw materials of nonagricultural origin and used in place of agricultural products. Thus, substitution may involve one agricultural product for another, or it may involve a synthetic for an agricultural product. As used here, then, synthetics are substitutes, but not all substitutes are synthetic.

ASSOCIATED FACTORS

The forces which stimulate development of substitutes, both agricultural and synthetic, may be classified as economic, social, technological, and institutional. In a competitive economy, business men constantly are searching for ways of luring customers from competitors with better, different, or less expensive products. The overriding incentive, from the producer's standpoint, is profit. Consumer demand changes rather slowly, but nevertheless it does change. Personal disposable incomes are increasing, giving people more and more discretionary spending power. Tastes change with affluence, fads, increases in knowledge, and changes in occupational status. An almost continuous stream of technological developments provide sources of knowhow for product and market development. Shifts in the urban-rural distribution of population and intracity shifts to suburbia are related to social changes which impinge upon the preferences of people for agricultural and other products. Institutional factors include governmental concern and action about the health and welfare of the general public. Recent years have witnessed an increase in governmental attention to consumer problems. While the government still recognizes the interests of separate sectors, agriculture's influence has declined and will decline further in the future.

The impact of substitue and synthetic products on agriculture's economic position is a complex phenomenon. Each product must be viewed separately since some agricultural sectors produce substitutes and some sectors utilize them in their productive processes, both of which presumably benefits those

[1] Material in this chapter draws heavily from Moede *et al.* (1969), Swackhamer (1969), and Manley and Gallimore (1971).

sectors. Other sectors find the demand for their products displaced b
substitutes and suffer an adverse effect. A substitute which draws its raw
materials from agriculture may have little effect on agriculture as a whole, but
it may alter intra-agricultural relationships. For example, oleomargarine had an
adverse effect on the dairy sector because of a reduction in demand for
butterfat, but enhanced the demand for vegetable fats, primarily soybean oil
Presumably, in this case one agricultural sector's loss was another's gain. But
expansion in use of soybean oil for oleomargarine affected its availability and
price for other uses. Soybean meal is a joint product which also is affected
Urea, a synthetic product used to replace part of the agriculturally-based
protein supplements in feeds for ruminant animals, has adversely affected the
soybean and cotton sectors by reducing the demand for the respective meals
Presumably, the feeders of urea (the feeding sector) derive some benefit. And
it is likely that some soybean growers also feed urea so that adverse effects to
one enterprise may be at least partially offset by beneficial effects to another
on the same farm. Significant increases in the use of synthetic fibers have
severely cut into the demand for cotton and wool, with no offsetting benefits
to agriculture, and the same has happened to citrus growers with expansion in
use of synthetic citrus drinks. Other examples could be cited, but these
illustrate some of the complexities and conflicts of interest within agriculture
and some between agricultural and nonagricultural industries.

RAW MATERIAL SOURCES

Vegetable Protein Substitutes

Major efforts to date in the development of meat substitutes have centered
in the use of vegetable proteins. Soybeans are the major source of raw
materials, but cottonseed, peanuts, sunflower, and safflower are potential
alternative sources. Soy proteins are used in two general ways: (1) as a
dilutant or extender in processed meat items and in comminuted meats, and
(2) as the major ingredient in a meatless meat product designed to be a total
substitute with characteristics of meat—referred to as a meat analog.

Soy proteins currently are used in four forms: (1) flour and grits, (2)
concentrates, (3) isolates, and (4) textured items (see Table 16.1). Textured
items may be "extruded" or "spun" as described in footnote 2, Table 16.1.
The four forms "differ from each other in protein content, physical and
chemical properties, applications, and prices. From a nutritional viewpoint,
they are comparable to meat in amino acids, although slightly lower in
methionine and lysine. Flour and grits are simplest in form, lowest in protein,
with prices ranging from 5½ to 11½¢ per lb. Concentrates (65–70% protein)
and isolates (90–97% protein) have prices 18–45¢ per lb. These higher prices
result from additional processing costs and lower yields of the finished
products. Textured items may have prices over 50¢ per lb and are the

TABLE 16.1

SOY PROTEIN FOODS

Soy Protein Food	Protein (%)	Prices (¢/Lb)	1970 Volume of U.S. Production (Million Lb)	Current Uses
Flour and grits[1]	40–55	5½–11½	325–500	Ingredients for baked goods, dog foods, sausages
Concentrates	65–70	18–25	25–30	Mfg. textured products; ingredients in processed meats, baby foods, health foods
Isolates	90–97	35–45	20–25	Mfg. analogs such as meatless ham, bacon, hot dogs, etc.
Textured item[2] Extruded Spun	50–55 90+	28 and up 50 and up	25	Simulated bacon bits, bacon strips, and similar food

Source: Manley and Gallimore (1971).
[1] Flour and grits, although handled differently and sold for different uses, are essentially the same product. They are both ground, defatted flakes. Grits are coarse ground (larger than 100 mesh) and flour is fine ground (smaller than 100 mesh).
[2] Textured items are of two distinctly different types. Extruded ones made from flour are textured by high temperature, high-pressure extrusion, using a plastic-type extruder. Spun types made from isolates are spun using somewhat the same technique used in rayon or nylon.

fabricated foods that appear, bite, and taste most like natural animal products" (Manley and Gallimore 1971). Extruded and spun proteins can be textured into a fibrous structure with chewability characteristics (varying degree of tenderness, toughness, and mouth-feel) of meat. They also can be colored, flavored, and molded into characteristic form to simulate meat. In addition to simulating the appearance, color, texture, and flavor of meat, analogs are capable of manipulation with respect to caloric content, cholesterol content, protein content, and additives of various sorts. In other words, meat analogs can be manufactured to desired specifications with complete uniformity of product and without seasonal or cyclical variation in supply. Another appealing factor is no cooking loss or shrink during meal preparation. As will be recalled from earlier chapters, large retail chain and HRI buyers are insisting on a year-round supply of uniform quality product. Meat analogs can satisfy these requirements.

Synthetic Substitutes

Among the leading developments in synthetic substitutes is the use of the single cell protein (SCP)—a microorganism capable of transforming organic carbon compounds into protein. The process involves cultivation (or "feeding") of the organisms in a hydrocarbon medium, then processing the cells to reclaim the protein. Numerous sources of hydrocarbons are available, but petroleum probably is one of the most abundant. A number of petroleum firms in the United States, several western European countries, and the Soviet Union reportedly are carrying on extensive experiments in attempts to develop a practical process for commercial production. Investigations leave no doubt that protein compounds can be produced by SCP. Limited use already is reported in Europe in the production of animal feeds. While, at this time, no known commercial application is being made in human food, technologically it is possible and may be expected if or when economic conditions warrant it.

COMPETITIVE CONSIDERATIONS

Meat substitutes already are on grocery store shelves in a variety of forms—imitation bacon bits or crumbles, bacon strips, products resembling beef and ham, and incorporated in processed and comminuted meats. Institutions are reported to be relatively heavy users in prepared dishes. The extent to which substitutes have replaced meat has not been precisely measured, but at this stage it is relatively minor. What happens in the future will depend upon economic considerations, consumer tastes and preferences, and the impact of groups in position to recommend or influence their consumption.

The economic considerations concern producers, consumers, and retail store operators. Retailers are interested in the total contribution of meat operation to net profit. They will not necessarily push a cheaper product if it contributes a smaller margin to net profit. Not enough experience has been gained yet to know the effect of meat substitutes on retail margins.

From the consumers' standpoint, the price of substitutes compared to meat is one of the controlling factors, but also important is the degree to which substitutes satisfy tastes and preferences. The quantity of substitutes in labeled meat products is relatively small and many consumers probably are unaware of its presence. According to Moede *et al.* (1969), federal standards of identity permit soy protein to be used in meat products up to a 3.5% level. However, regulations do not cover all uses. Manley and Gallimore (1971) report that food served in restaurants is not subject to the same labeling and identification requirements as food sold directly to consumers. Production of soy protein foods in 1970 was 395–580 million pounds (Table 16.1), the bulk of this being flour and grits. At the maximum this would represent only about 1.6% of total meat consumption (carcass weight).

Soy proteins can be readily incorporated into items such as stews, soups, chili, stroganoffs, etc. The least expensive of the substitutes—flour and grits—are generally used. Here the soy proteins can compete with meat and probably will be used to the limit allowed by law, even though the meat they replace in most of these products is from trimmings and the less expensive cuts. Table 16.2 shows the relative cost of net utilizable protein (NPU) from several food sources. "From the information on relative costs, it is obvious

TABLE 16.2

RELATIVE COSTS OF NET UTILIZABLE PROTEIN
COMING FROM SELECTED FOOD SOURCES

Protein Source	Price of the Food[1] ($/Lb)	Cost of the Net Utilizable Protein[2] ($/Lb)
Beef	0.49	3.26
Chicken	0.33	2.47
Fish	0.45	3.07
Whey (dry)	0.09	0.84
Milk	0.07	2.34
Skim milk (dry)	0.22	0.79
Eggs	0.25	2.09
Dry beans	0.07	0.65
Soybean flour	0.08	0.31
Wheat	0.03	0.41
Cottonseed flour	0.35	1.57
Rice	0.09	1.71

Source: Manley and Gallimore (1971).
[1] These prices are for wholesale lots FOB, point of manufacture.
[2] Crude protein values from *Composition of Foods* USDA Agr. Handbook 8. Net utilizable protein (NPU) is the proportion of nitrogen intake that is retained in the human body. The NPU values used to construct this table from *Amino Acid Content of Food and Biological Data on Proteins*, FAO Nutritional Studies Rep. 24.

why users (at this time decision-makers in institutional kitchens) are interested in substituting soy proteins for more expensive animal proteins. If proteins from soy cost 31¢ per lb and proteins from pork cost $3.26 per lb, there is a strong incentive to substitute soy proteins in uses for which the two products are interchangeable. Examples: pizza, sausage, frankfurters, meat loaf, sandwich salami, etc. Add to this the functional advantages of soy preteins (water and fat retention, improvement in keeping quality, browning effects, etc.) and soy proteins appear to have a bright future. These cost and functional advantages will no doubt do much to overcome present deterrents to acceptance identified with consumer prejudices and governmental regulations. Both these barriers are toppling much faster than most people have imagined possible" (Manley and Gallimore 1971).

Attempts to substitute meat analogs for the higher priced cuts involve several considerations, as follows: (1) textured items and isolates, under the present state of the art, are more costly to produce than soy flour or soy concentrate, and (2) consumers are more discriminating where the substitute is an imitation of the total product. A study based on 1967-1968 prices reported that "the textured meat-type products made from soy protein isolate currently available would probably need to be priced at retail near the upper range of prices for red meat. These products are reported to have a relatively high ingredient and production cost, and adding usual marketing markups would result in retail prices that might range as high as those for steaks and other cuts from sirloins" (Moede *et al.* 1969) This relationship is a tenuous one, for if the price of meat rises or the cost of meat analogs decreases, the substitutes could be competitive from a price standpoint. Data in Table 16.1 indicate the situation was more competitive in 1970 than in 1967-1968, but there is little evidence of gains by meat substitutes in other than processed and prepared meat and meat dishes. "For meat products the outlook (to 1980) is not for an actual loss of present volume, but for a loss of potential expansion that would otherwise accrue from population increases" (Manley and Gallimore 1971).

Certain consumers for religious and philosophical reasons, and others in response to transitory fads, welcome imitation meats. The extent to which these groups may influence the total demand for meat is unknown. However, they probably will not have a significant effect, for it is likely most of them have been using some other substitute in the past and, if so, their acceptance of "meatless meat" will not affect the demand for meat.

A group which may already have had some effect and could have considerably more in the future are those with dietary restrictions. Some members of the medical profession recommend that patients with certain cardiovascular problems reduce the intake of animal fat as a measure of control over blood cholesterol levels. Others recommend a restricted fat diet for weight control, or other reasons. Engineering control over the specifications of substitute meat products indicates they are made to order for these situations—and cost may not be the controlling factor.

Thus, it appears that pending futher cost-reducing technological developments in substitutes, the major use of soy proteins is in processed meats and prepared dishes in the hotel, restaurant and institutional trade. Institutions provide a growing market for products such as bacon bits which can be incorporated in scrambled eggs, soups, stews, etc. The elimination of preparatory steps and the ease of storage, along with competitive prices, give soy proteins an advantage in these markets. Manley and Gallimore (1971) predict that by 1980 vegetable protein extenders will probably displace 15–20% of the meat in meat-type food preparations in both the institutional as well as the retail market.

To date, only minor inroads have been made in the market for higher priced cuts, but increased use is expected for certain dietary purposes and if cost-reducing technology is developed along with improved meat-like characteristics, the general demand for meat will be vulnerable. The magnitude of the potential market is so extensive that continued research and development in substitutes is to be expected.

One of the few reported tests in the household market sector was on a bacon substitute (Corkern and Dwoskin 1970). The test product was an analog designed to simulate the form, texture, color, and taste of bacon. This was in the form of bacon strips—not chips or crumbles—and was sold in a frozen state. The experiment was conducted for 6 months in Fort Wayne, Indiana, utilizing 40 supermarkets in national, regional, and local chains. The market test was conducted by a private research firm under contract to the manufacturer of the product, and results were published by the USDA. During the first three months (Phase I) an intensive promotional and advertising program was carried out, consisting of in-store promotion, as well as news-paper and TV advertising. During the latter three months (Phase II) the advertising was similar to that ordinarily carried on for long-established products.

Bacon analog sales amounted to 4% of bacon sales during Phase I and declined to 1.3% of bacon sales as promotion and advertising dropped off in Phase II. Bacon sales also declined during the period of Phase II, but only 1/8 as much as the drop in bacon analog sales. A survey of purchasers showed that, "In general, users expressed a high level of satisfaction. The product's strongest attributes were ease and speed of preparation and good cooking qualities. A large proportion of the users found nothing they disliked about the product" (Corkern and Dwoskin 1970).

There was no clear evidence that bacon analog sales replaced bacon sales during the test period. However, this would hardly be expected in a short, introductory period. The survey showed that many consumers were attracted by the advertised low caloric and cholesterol content, and relatively low price. On an as-served basis, the bacon analog was advertised to cost 1/2 as much as bacon.

Results of the test showed no adverse reaction to the product in the frozen state. "All in all, test market results, though limited, indicate a good chance for further commercial success of the bacon analog" (Corkern and Dwoskin 1970).

IMPLICATIONS FOR FOOD SUPPLIES

As a matter of self interest, the livestock and meat industries are rightfully concerned about competition from substitute and synthetic meats. A dis-cussion of the subject, however, would be incomplete without recognition of food supply problems—domestic and world-wide. People in the United States as a whole are the best fed in the world, but recent studies have shown serious inadequacies in the diets of a substantial number. And on a compara-tive basis the problem is infinitely more serious in less developed countries around the world.

Demographers estimate that the world population will double by about the year 2000. This would mean that within a scant 30 yr, world food production will need to double just to maintain the present inadequate level of supplies. The problem is one not only of total quantity but also—and especially serious—of a lack of high protein foods. There is little doubt that the United

States has the capacity to produce sufficient total food supplies for itself and, with proper economic incentives, to continue to produce sufficient animal protein for domestic needs. However, without some considerable shifts in income distribution, substantial numbers of people probably will not have the purchasing power to buy adequate supplies of animal proteins. It is certain on the world scene that the need will exist for more and less expensive proteins that can be furnished from animal sources.

The pressure on food supplies points up the need to consider the efficiency of protein production from alternative sources. On this score, "The production potential of single-cell proteins is fantastic. Production increases exponentially so that a 1 lb seeded culture would multiply to 2 tons of edible food (1/2 protein, 1/2 carbohydrates and fats) in 24 hr. The SCP yield from 1000 lb of petroleum is approximately 1000 lb of edible product which compares with 500 lb of catfish, 250 lb of dressed poultry, and 75 lb of dressed beef per 1000 pounds of feed" (Swackhamer 1969). On a conversion ratio of 7 lb of grain to produce 1 lb of beef, it would require about 39 lb of grain to produce 1 lb of animal protein.[2] Soybeans average about 37.9% protein (Morrison 1956). While this 37.9% is not all recoverable in the form of protein concentrates, insofar as technical production efficiency is an issue, it is apparent that protein production by way of animal agriculture is less efficient than by either vegetable or synthetic production. Table 16.2 shows that in 1970 the cost of 1 lb of protein from soybean flour was about 1/10 that of protein from beef. From the standpoint of palatability and preferences, it nevertheless remains to be shown that people, even in protein deficient areas, can be induced to consume a new food if that new food constitutes a significant change from traditional consumption patterns.

Several commercial U.S. firms have promoted with some success, vegetable protein-fortified bottled and canned drinks in less developed countries. At this point it is too early to know whether such efforts will have significant effect on the general health of the people of those countries. Any gains made in vegetable or synthetic protein consumption in less developed countries would be little threat to U.S. or international meat industries. Most of the people in such countries consume less than 10 lb of meat per capita. Vegetable or synthetic proteins would not be a substitute, but an addition to their present meat consumption.

ALTERNATIVE LIVESTOCK-MEAT INDUSTRY REACTION

The intrusion of substitute and synthetic products into agricultural markets has prompted various reactions. When oleomargarine began to make inroads into the butter market, dairy farmers attempted to induce legal action prohibiting its manufacture and sale. When this proved ineffective, the

---

[2] This is based on a beef protein content of 17.9% (Moede *et al.* (1969).

approach was switched to taxation by individual states and attempts to prohibit its being colored yellow prior to sale. Some states adopted such measures, but all have now faded away. Agriculture has less political power now than in the days of the oleo battle, and even if farmers and ranchers had the power to induce legal restrictions on meat substitutes, the oleo experience indicates its futility.

The cotton and wool industries have given up a considerable share of their markets to substitute and synthetic fibers. After a somewhat belated start, these industries instituted concerted research efforts to develop processing technology for improved characteristics of their products in line with consumer preferences. Efforts to date have not reversed the trend, but progress has been made in such things as altering the shrink characteristics of wool and cotton fabrics, improving wash-and-wear characteristics, permapress, etc. Technical improvements along with concurrent marketing innovations undoubtedly have reduced the adverse effect of substitute and synthetic fibers.

In a protein deficient world, the livestock and meat industries cannot make an effective case for opposing improved technology for the production of vegetable and synthetic protein foods. Public opinion would not support such a stand, and as pointed out above, it probably would be ineffective anyway. However, the following aspects warrant consideration: (1) The competitive structure necessitates continual efforts to improve the acceptance of meat and meat products through improvements in production, processing, and merchandising. The most effective competitive device is a product which satisfies consumers' tastes and preferences—backed up by an effective merchandising program. (2) The livestock and meat industry also has a responsibility in inducing governmental vigilence with respect to truthfulness in the labeling of substitute and synthetic products so the public will be fully aware of the ingredients and their health-related characteristics. It cannot be assumed that all such products will equal the nutritive qualities of meat.

BIBLIOGRAPHY

ANON. 1968. Food from petroleum. Standard Oil Company SPAN *8*, No. 3, Fall.

CORKERN, R. S., and DWOSKIN, P. B. 1970. Consumer acceptance of a new bacon substitute. USDA Econ. Res. Serv. *454*.

CORKERN, R. S., and POATS, F. J. 1968. Synthetics and substitutes in food and non-food markets. USDA Marketing Transportation Situation, Econ. Res. Serv. *MTS-171*.

MANLEY, W. T., and GALLIMORE, W. W. 1971. Emerging product inroads into agriculture: synthetics and substitutes. Proc. 1971 Natl. Agr. Outlook Conf., Washington, D.C., Febr. 24-25.

MOEDE, H. H. *et al.* 1969. Meat and poultry substitutes. *In* Synthetics and Substitutes for Agricultural Products, a Compendium. USDA Econ. Res. Serv. Misc. Publ. *1141*.

MORRISON, F. B. 1956. Feeds and Feeding, 22nd Edition. Morrison Publishing Co., Clinton, Iowa.

SWACKHAMER, G. L. 1969. Synthetics and substitutes: Challenge to agriculture. Federal Reserve Bank of Kansas City Monthly Rev. Mar., 3-12.

USDA. 1967. Proceedings of International Conference on Soybean Protein Foods. USDA Agr. Res. Serv. *71-35*.

CHAPTER 17

Shape of the Future

As late as the 1950's livestock and meat marketing were criticized as horse-and-buggy operations in a rapidly changing jet age. Criticism still is heard, but the tone is different. Change is the order of the day, so much so that a market news reporter was prompted to say in 1970, "Change is the only constant factor in livestock marketing" (Marshall 1970). While literally a self-contradiction, this statement nevertheless conveys the message—livestock markets truly are in a fluid state.

Not everyone is satisfied with the changes, and a consensus is lacking on exactly what further changes are desirable, but there are few who believe that the forces of change can, or will be, reversed.

Any attempt to anticipate the future is a hazardous endeavor. No one knows with certainty what will happen, but some of the forces which are shaping the future are evident and some generalizations are possible about directions of change. The major factors impinging upon the marketing system are as follows: (1) organizational changes, which are altering the traditional market structure and associated competitive relationships; (2) technological developments, and (3) increasing pressures for greater coordination throughout the marketing system. These factors are exerting influences on the supply of and demand for meat, and on the relative bargaining power of firms (and individuals) within the respective industry sectors. In many respects the factors are interrelated—technological developments are associated with structural changes, structural changes are associated with institutional arrangements used for purposes of vertical coordination, and so on.

Perhaps the most widely discussed and anticipated development in livestock and meat marketing is the trend toward greater coordination in the marketing system. This stems largely from the insistence on a relatively continuous supply of meat of uniform quality and cut-out characteristics. The pressures for this arise from several sources explained by the following: (1) Retailing methods are geared to this type of supply—consumer satisfaction necessitates it and the economic power of large retail buyers is forcing it back through the market system. (2) The HRI trade requires uniformity of product and dependability of supply even more than the retail trade, and demand from this segment is expanding rapidly. (3) The fast food trade has essentially the same requirements as retailing and HRI trade. This segment also is expanding rapidly and, with the growing affluence of U.S. consumers, is likely to be developed to major proportions in the future. Part of the gains in fast foods may come at the expense of the grocery retail trade, but total meat consumption is expanding.

All of these outlets have essentially the same type of need and each, in general, is typified by concentrated buying power which will press for greater market coordination.

STRUCTURAL CHANGES

Among the most economically significant structural changes are those associated with the number and size distribution of primary producing, slaughtering, processing, and retailing firms. The predominant trends have been apparent for a number of years. At the retail level, the concentration of economic power in the hands of a relatively few large buyers dominates the meat trade. The overall degree of concentration among large chains is not likely to change significantly in the foreseeable future. However, several recent developments have demonstrated the fact that no firm in the food industry, regardless of size, can assume the status quo. One such development is discounting, another is the fast food business. Most of the large chains have reluctantly joined the discounters and in all likelihood also will add fast food departments. These movements and the development of chain convenience stores have forced some adjustments within the retail sector. However, the major implication to the livestock-meat industry is a reinforcement of the already existing pressure for a more continuous supply of uniform quality meat.

Processors and packers, caught in the middle of the marketing system, are forced to attempt to meet specifications of retail and HRI buyers. The packing sector, fragmented by decentralization and former lethargy on the part of original large operators, has shown recent signs of possible reversal of deconcentration. Iowa Beef Packers, Inc., which began in 1960 is now the leading beef packer in the United States. Other smaller, well managed packers have made substantial but less spectacular gains. It is not likely that restructuring within the packing industry will significantly alter the dominance of retail buyers, but it is likely that the buying pressures will be passed back to primary producers with greater emphasis.

Number and Size of Farms

The trend toward fewer and bigger primary producing units has been evident, particularly since World War II. In 1970, operators of 1.2% of the cattle feedlots fed more than 1/2 the grain-finished cattle in the 23 most important feeding states (Table 17.1). Hog production has not been commercialized to the extent of cattle production, but there is no question of the increasing scale, with disease control a primary limiting factor. The persistent decline in sheep numbers of an already severely reduced industry has tended to divert research effort from this sector. However, it appears that increasing difficulty in obtaining competent labor is having a more restrictive effect on large-scale ewe flocks than on smaller farm flocks. While the finishing of old

TABLE 17.1

FED CATTLE MARKETED, AND FEEDLOTS, BY FEEDLOT
CAPACITY GROUPS, 23 STATES, 1970

| Feedlot Capacity (Head) | Fed Cattle Marketed | | | Feedlots | |
	No. of Head (1000)	%	No.	As Percentage of Total Feedlots (%)
Under 1,000	11,205	45.0	182,308	98.8
Over 1,000	13,675	55.0	2,242	1.2
1,000–1,999	1,205	4.9	1,004	0.5
2,000–3,999	1,378	5.5	549	0.3
4,000–7,999	1,944	7.8	333	0.2
8,000–15,999	3,138	12.6	210	0.1
16,000–31,999	3,203	12.9	105	0.1
32,000 and over	2,807	11.3	41	[1]
23 States	24,880	100.0	184,550	100.0

Source: USDA (1971).
[1] Less than 1/10 of 1%.

crop lambs has been carried out in relatively large-scale operations for many years, the declining number of lambs available for feeding is limiting the entire activity.

The implications of increasing scale production at the primary producer level are fairly evident. Large-scale producers tend to use direct marketing channels, and many are competent to do so. Packers and processors will look more and more to this segment for continuity in supply of a relatively uniform product, but its accomplishment will require continued change in organizational arrangements as will be discussed later.

The dramatic increase in commercial cattle feeding during the past two decades, continued expansion in size of hog operations, and persistent pressures for more and more vertical coordination in the production and marketing system often leave the impression that farm-sized feeders are virtually out of the picture. This is not the case. The USDA tabulates data on cattle feeding operations of 1000 head or more and on operations of less than 1000 head. There are a considerable number of farmers who have gradually expanded operations beyond 1000 head who consider themselves farm feeders. In addition, there is a considerable variation in trends within the less-than-1000-head size group. A USDA report (Gustafson and VanArsdall 1970) showed that the proportion of cattle fed by Iowa operators handling 100 head or more was increasing. Only in operations of less than 100 head were declines occurring (Table 17.2). A Kansas study showed declines since the early 1960's in operations of less than 400 head, but increases in larger size lots (Fig. 17.1). The difference between Kansas and Iowa probably reflects a tendency toward larger scale operations in the Milo Belt than in the Corn Belt. Both studies indicate that larger size farm cattle feeders still are viable

TABLE 17.2

NUMBER OF FED CATTLE MARKETED AND PERCENTAGE MARKETED
BY VARIOUS MARKETING SIZE GROUPS, IOWA, 1959-1967

Year	No. of Fed Cattle Marketed (1000)	Percentage Marketed by Size Groups (Head)					
		Under 25	25–49	50–99	100–299	300–499	500 and Over
1959	3009	10	16	24	34	8	8
1960	3014	10	16	25	34	8	7
1961	3034	10	16	24	34	8	8
1962	3055	9	14	22	35	10	10
1963	3290	8	13	21	37	10	11
1964	3348	8	12	20	36	11	13
1965	3521	7	11	19	36	12	15
1966	3739	6	10	18	36	13	17
1967	3952	5	9	16	36	14	20

Source: Gustafson and Van Arsdall (1970).

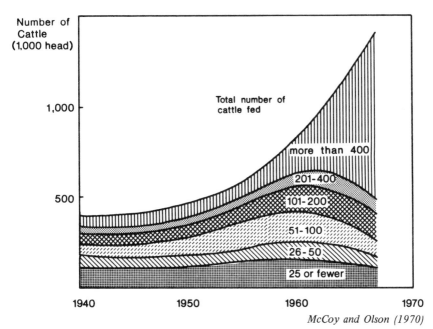

McCoy and Olson (1970)

FIG. 17.1. NUMBER OF CATTLE FED ANNUALLY BY INDICATED SIZE OF LOT,
KANSAS

producers, and even though the smaller ones are fading out as a group, many of them also will be in operation for a long time.

Farm size operators produce approximately 1/2 the fed cattle, the bulk of slaughter hogs, and a substantial proportion of slaughter lambs. It is this segment, including many in the upper end of the size range, which presents the major problems in marketing. The decline in central terminal markets necessitates more direct marketing. Individual production of this group typically is too small in volume and too variable in grade to attract direct buyers to the farms. The operators are so numerous and so diverse in attitude that organization for effective marketing is difficult. Yet, without some means of bringing about more uniformity in production, continuity in delivery, and pooling for aggregating volume, this segment of producers will become increasingly disadvantaged in the marketing process. Outlets will be available, as dealer-type buyers will continue their function of putting together odd lots and, by sorting and combining, build up uniformity and volume. But animals not meeting specification will go to lower valued uses. These buyers, faced with packers who are pressured for a continuous supply of meat of particular specifications, will discount small lots of variable quality.

Problems of Entry and Operation

Entry into the livestock industry has become increasingly difficult with the passage of time, and in all likelihood this will continue in the future. Among the major problems are increasing financial and management requirements, and increasing restrictions with respect to water and air pollution arising from feedlot operations.

Financial Limitation.—Financial requirements are associated with size of operation, degree of mechanization, and inflationary trends. All of these factors are tending to push cost upward. Investment requirements for even a moderately sized grain-livestock farm can exceed 1/2 million dollars. A livestock finishing enterprise of modest proportions can easily necessitate an additional 1/4 million dollars for operating capital. Of course, many family type farms handle small livestock enterprises with virtually no additional fixed capital outlay (where make-do facilities and feeding equipment already are on the farm) and operating costs are limited primarily to the purchases of feeder livestock and feed inventory (where family labor and otherwise unused farm equipment can be used at practically zero opportunity cost). On the other hand, a large commercial cattle feedyard requires several million dollars. There is no question that financial requirements are a constraint on initiation and operation of modern, adequately-sized livestock enterprises, and the situation will be more difficult in the future as size of unit and the degree of mechanization and sophistication increases.

Concern with Environmental Pollution.—Another factor acting as a constraint on livestock operations is concern with problems of environmental pollution. In some cases restrictions take the form of outright prohibition of feedyards in specified areas. In other instances the cost of providing facilities adequate to meet anticipated antipollution requirements may become prohibitory. There is every indication that concern with the environment will be a factor of increasing importance in the future. This is a matter of concern, not only in the construction of a new enterprise, but also in the continuation of long-established operations. There are cases of cattle feedlots, built in what originally were relatively isolated locations, being forced by legal action to close when housing developments expanded to those vicinities. There also are cases where long-established feedlots have been forced to close because of prohibitory costs of controlling run-off which allegedly was contaminating downstream water.

Up to this time, most of the complaint about environmental pollution has arisen from the operation of large commercial feedlots. This will be an increasing source of concern. And, with further increases in population density and increasing size of farm feeding enterprises, this is likely to be a constraining factor in all heavy feeding areas throughout the country.

Financial restrictions on entry and operation are directly related to market structure. Heavy financial requirements limit the number of firms with ownership in an industry. In the case of livestock (and poultry) this factor is linked with attempts by large firms to furnish the capital and contract with farmers for operational services.

Limitations of Managerial Ability.—The ever-increasing complexity of farming and ranching limits the number of persons with qualifications for entry and survival. Management problems increase with size of operation alone, but superimposed on this is a continuous stream of technological developments and changing market organization, all of which present greater and greater demands on management. The breadth and depth of technological requirements (basic knowledge plus the problem of keeping current is such things as disease control, soils, fertilizers, herbicides, insecticides, mechanics, electronics, etc.) are formidable barriers in themselves. But technical knowledge is not enough. Successful management requires a comprehensive grasp of the economic and business aspects of financing the operation, putting the factors together in an optimum combination, developing the most economic sources for input purchases, and devising an advantageous program for product marketing. An acquaintance with the capability of computerized operations is becoming a necessity. Not everyone has the ability or capacity to manage a modern farm or ranch.

With reference to the cattle feeding sector, Gustafson and VanArsdall (1970) say, "A new breed is at work—a new breed of people providing management at a highly professional level, as in large-scale nonfarm enterprises. These people are attracting large amounts of new capital from sources inside and outside of agriculture. This management and money may weigh the heaviest of all factors producing change in cattle feeding." These same forces are pressing on hog and sheep operations and will become more apparent in the future. Both funds and management may be supplied under various ownership and contractual arrangements.

TECHNOLOGICAL DEVELOPMENTS

Significant gains have been made in livestock production efficiency through breeding, feeding, and management innovations. Man-hour requirements per unit of beef output are 45% less than during the late 1930's. Feed conversion ratios have improved, but here the record of the beef sector has lagged behind that of the hog sector. Rates of gain and birth rates have increased. While substantial gains have been made in production efficiency, a considerable latitude remains for further improvement (Warwick 1969). "The question is not whether greatly improved technical performance will occur in the 1970's, but whether enough of it will occur to keep American consumers from turning to increasingly attractive alternatives" (Stout 1970A). Technological improvements cannot be precisely programmed or scheduled, but they are at least partially dependent upon the amount of research effort expended. Future technological improvements will be forthcoming if research is directed to the livestock and meat industry.

Technological developments are important not only in primary production but throughout the entire marketing system. The entire industry is confronted with new technologies in feed production and processing, in animal husbandry, in materials handling, in marketing, and in overall business management (Gustafson and VanArsdall 1970).

A major problem in the wholesale and retail sectors is meat preservation. The high degree of perishability of fresh meat is an important factor in limiting the extent of cutting done by packers and wholesalers. So far, research efforts have not produced an economically feasible breakthrough beyond refrigeration in meat preservation applicable to mass production. From a technological standpoint, freeze drying has many advantages. It is effective and apparently acceptable to consumers, though widespread consumer reaction has not been tested. It requires no subsequent refrigeration. It reduces weight and, hence, transportation costs. Unfortunately, costs under current techniques are relatively high. Experiments with irradiation are still being conducted. At least six countries (Canada, the United States, the Soviet Union, Spain, the Netherlands, and Israel) have cleared irradiation as a means of preservation for various foods. However, at this time only the Soviet Union has approved irradiation for use on meat. Expanded application of this method is expected in the future.

The freezing of fresh meat was hailed as a possible feasible means of preservation at least two decades ago. Consumer reaction was adverse during initial merchandizing attempts and little headway was made with this method.

However, there are indications that the situation is changing. Consumers have become thoroughly familiar with many frozen foods—vegetables, TV dinners, bakery products, dairy products, poultry, and increasing quantities of red meat. Many housewives buy fresh meat and freeze it themselves in home freezers under conditions much less satisfactory than commercial processes. Kansas State University conducted an exhaustive experiment in advanced technologies of wrapping, freezing, and merchandizing frozen red meats during 1969 and 1970. This study included in-store and follow-up surveys of consumer acceptance in urban eastern markets. The appearance of frozen meat cuts under current technology is vastly improved over former techniques. These studies indicate that consumers are more receptive to frozen meat than they were two decades ago. The growing institutional trade is receptive to frozen portion cuts. The evidence at this time indicates a definite, but gradual trend toward frozen retail and institutional cuts.[1]

An acceptable means of preservation which permits a high degree of cutting at the packer and wholesale level has an inherent economic advantage in reducing the quantity of product moved. Bone and excess fat can be trimmed at the source. Some duplication in equipment can be avoided and greater skills can be developed by increased concentration of the cutting. This would free retailers of the necessity of providing cutting space, cutting equipment, cooler hanging facilities, and labor required for cutting. However, there are some obstacles and disadvantages. Labor unions oppose the movement for obvious reasons. The handling of increased quantities of frozen meat will require increased freezer space for store inventory, and meat is a high volume item. Frozen meat has a longer shelf-life than the unfrozen product, but retailer interest in shelf-life is related to the profit margin. Traditionally, fresh meat has been a high turnover item—due to high perishability. An extension of shelf-life, while highly desirable in many respects, may also necessitate a higher retail margin—this remains to be seen.

Organizational arrangements already are prevalent whereby retail buyers deal directly with packers for wholesale shipments. If, or when, packers can supply further-cut and further-processed meat which is acceptable to consumers at competitive prices, retailers will buy it.[2] The trend is moving in this direction and much depends upon successful means of preserving retail cuts. There appears to be no particular bottleneck to institutional acceptance of frozen portion cuts and further-processed cuts, and there are indications that housewives will accept frozen fresh cuts of meat in the near future.

As pointed out in the last chapter, the livestock-meat industry is vulnerable to the development of substitute and synthetic meat products. The economic

---

[1] From a progress report of a Kansas State University Frozen Meat Research Project, March 1971.

[2] "Further processed" is a term used to indicate cutting into individual servings, and, in some cases, the cooking and combining with other ready-to-use foods.

inducements for such development are great and, in less developed parts of the world, the need for high protein foods also is great. There is a high probability that further technological improvements will reduce costs and increase the availability of these products.

VERTICAL COORDINATION

On its way to the final consumer, meat (and the animal it was derived from) passes through a series of stages, each of which adds something to the value of the product. These are the familiar production and associated marketing processes. In a simplified manner, they may be listed as the breeding herd or flock, a growing phase, a finishing phase, slaughtering, processing, wholesaling, and retailing (or restaurant and institutional consumption). Actually, the system also depends upon a number of supplementary components such as feed production and handling, veterinary services, production and processing equipment manufacturing, etc., but the concern here is with livestock and meat operations. Marketing functions are required to move the product through the series of stages.

The term "vertical coordination" refers to the linking of successive stages in a manner designed to accomplish some specific objective. From the standpoint of general welfare, the objective may be optimum production and marketing efficiency. Individual firm objectives may be profit maximization or reduction in uncertainty of price or product. Deficiencies in coordination may result in production of commodities which do not meet consumer preferences, or in the delivery of commodities at the wrong time, the wrong place, or in the wrong form. Traditionally, chief reliance has been placed on the competitive pricing mechanism to do the coordinating, with separate ownership at various stages—at least separate ownership of primary producing, slaughter-processing, and retailing. This approach represents one limit among the possible arrangements. Another limit would be ownership by a single firm of two or more successive stages (Dubov 1969). An example of this is ownership of feedlots by meat packers, or the inverse—ownership of packing plants by feedlot operators. Between the two limits is a wide array of possible contractual arrangements which link successive stages.

Much attention has been directed during the past two decades at "vertical integration." In some writings no distinction is made between integration by ownership and integration by contract. Some authors, however, limit use of the term "vertical integration" to ownership of successive stages (Mighells and Jones 1963). In this discussion vertical coordination is used to indicate control over successive stages by either ownership or contract (formal and informal), including cooperative arrangements. Coordination via the price system was discussed in earlier chapters dealing with price theory.

There are many examples of vertical coordination in the livestock-meat sector. A cow-herd owner who retains ownership of his calves through the growing and finishing phases has coordinated those stages by ownership. This is the typical arrangement among hog producers. In recent years some packers have constructed and operated cattle feedlots. Packers also have contracted for the feeding of cattle and lambs. This was discussed earlier. During the 1950's, a wave of producer agitation accompanied an abortive attempt by packers to develop contractual production and marketing agreements with hog producers. Some feedlot operators own packing plants.

There is a consensus among market analysts that conditions indicate a probable future increase in vertical coordination—especially by contractual arrangements. Coordination by the competitive price system has not entirely satisfied the demand of retail and institutional buyers for a more or less continuous supply of meat measuring up to rather rigid specifications. There is a feeling that greater control is needed over such things as breeding, feeding, and marketing programs to produce an acceptable quality product with delivery on a prescribed schedule. Renewed activity is reported in production and marketing contracts for hogs. Among the major promoters are packers and feed companies. Terms of the contractual arrangements are varied.[3] In some cases, original stock is furnished to relieve the operator of this financial burden. Management techniques usually are specified—partly as a measure to protect the investment, but, again, this may be a recognition of operators' inability to measure up to required management standards. A program promoted by a feed company invariably will specify that that company's feed be used. Feed companies do not attempt to hide the fact that a major objective is increasing the volume of feed sales.

Coordinators who tie in an agreement for the purchase of finished hogs usually stipulate grade price differentials designed to stimulate the production of desired quality. In conjunction with purchase contracts, packers may utilize the futures market for hedging their cash contract position.

Data are not available on the total number of hogs produced under vertically coordinated arrangements, but at present it amounts to a relatively small fraction of total production. Packers are required by P&S regulations to report their feeding activities and in 1969 this amounted to only 43,000 head out of a total commercial slaughter of almost 84 million. This, of course, does not include hogs produced under contract by packers and nonpacker interests.

Vertical coordination programs are more extensive in cattle and lambs than in hogs. Packer feeding of cattle amounted to 6.6% of fed cattle marketed in 1969. If feeding by packer-associated interests were included, the percentage would be in the neighborhood of 11%.[4] Packer feeding of lambs was almost 12% of commercial slaughter in 1969.

[3] For a discussion of various types of contracts see Roy (1963). Terms of current contracts may be found in popular farm magazines; e.g., Seim (1970).

[4] Based on a special USDA study in 1965.

Increased vertical coordination activity is expected in the future for all three species. Forward coordination by packers and processors into retailing is not likely to be extensive. Several of the large national packers are prohibited from retailing under the Consent Decree. With the exception of isolated cases by relatively small operators, other packers have not shown an inclination to enter retailing. And retailers have not exhibited an interest for extensive ownership of packing facilities. Retailers, however, have accomplished a considerable degree of coordination by exercising substantial bargaining power in their purchasing programs. Some have extended coordination backwards by development of central cutting and processing plants. This aspect will grow unless packers expand their activities in this stage, and there are strong incentives for packers to increase their cutting and processing activities. As mentioned above, the increased use of frozen fresh meat, or the development of an alternative process of meat preservation will lead to more cutting and processing by packers.

A greater degree of coordination is almost sure to come in the primary producer-packer stages. Large-scale commercial finishers are in position to produce livestock in volume and are becoming increasingly able to meet packer specifications in quality and delivery. The meeting of these requirements, however, necessitates a supply of feeder livestock capable of meeting the specifications. This is a powerful inducement for finishers to coordinate with growers and with herd and flock owners through contract or ownership. Not only from a quality standpoint, but also in numbers available, an adequate supply of suitable feeder cattle will become a problem of increasing importance in the future. In the past, feeder cattle supplies have been enhanced by a gradual reduction in the slaughter of calves and a gradual switch from dairy to beef cattle in the total cattle population. Most of the gains in beef production from these sources have been exhausted. An increasing pinch in feeder cattle supplies will stimulate vertical coordination by contract and probably, to a lesser extent, by ownership of growing operations and cow-herds by feedlot operators.

Relatively small livestock producers will find themselves in an increasingly disadvantaged position. Kendricks (1970) has suggested a possible organizational arrangement whereby smaller producers might improve their situation by pooling finished livestock. By pooling, producers could provide a volume of relatively uniform quality (sorted by grade) which would be attractive to packers. The plan would require scheduling of deliveries, and for successful operation, some concerted effort in control over quality and numbers of livestock produced. Through organized efforts producers could gain a measure of bargaining power with packers. The National Farmers Organization already is operating as a bargaining association and the American Farm Bureau Federation's marketing association is active in developing greater pricing and operational efficiency in livestock marketing.

Pooling arrangements have worked successfully for many years in the marketing of slaughter lambs, wool, feeder pigs, and feeder calves. However, producers of slaughter cattle and hogs have not shown the same inclination to form marketing pools. Without some pooling arrangement it is doubtful that smaller producers can develop an adequate marketing program.

The effectiveness of producer marketing arrangements will depend in the future on a mutuality of interest among all sectors of the marketing system. As pointed out by Thor (1971), the exercise of bargaining power is constrained by the multinationalization of agriculture. Multinationalization, according to Thor (1971), is defined as joint ownership between U.S. firms and foreign firms of the companies located in foreign countries. This provides many U.S. firms with a worldwide base from which products may be procured, as is evident in the case of meat. While the United States has a law specifying quota restrictions on beef, in practice it is operated on a voluntary agreement basis with extreme pressures to overthrow the law altogether. While multinationalization poses a threat in opening the United States to greater competition from foreign products, it may at the same time offer an opportunity for farmer cooperatives to expand into international marketing. This already is being done by grain, almond, and citrus marketing cooperatives (Thor 1971). However, under current conditions this would appear to offer little opportunity for livestock producers.

Producers have an alternative of coordinating forward stages (packing, processing, retailing) in cooperative organization. While experience from the past does not offer much hope for expansion from previous approaches tried, new approaches are being examined. Land O'Lakes, a diversified producer cooperative active in the North Central States, is involved in turkey production, slaughtering, and further processing (Shoemaker 1971). This cooperative is making an exhaustive study of possibilities in red meats with particular attention to the potential in institutional and fast food outlets. This definitely is a growth area and farmer cooperatives could have a place in its development. However, in terms of the total industry, cooperatives at this time have a very small base in livestock slaughtering and processing upon which to build.

Thor (1971) suggests an alternative of joint ventures between farmer-owned cooperatives and public stock-owned or privately-owned corporations integrated from the farmer to the ultimate consumer. Under such an arrangement, stockholders, including farmers, would share in profits which accrue throughout the entire system. This would appear to satisfy the mutuality of interest and if it could be attained through merger of existing organizations, it would eliminate the almost impossible problem of any one segment gaining coordination throughout the entire system by purchase. "Examples of joint ventures between farmer-owned cooperatives and corporations include a citrus cooperative in Florida joint venturing with Minute Maid, and the major grape growers cooperative in California joint venturing with Heublein, a major bottler and beverage merchandizer" (Thor 1971).

Joint venturing would have to be considered a long-range possibility for the ultimate in vertical coordination with much to offer for all segments of the livestock-meat industry, but with many impediments in the path of accomplishment.

IMPLICATIONS OF DECLINING GROWTH RATE IN POPULATION

Over the years the demand for most agricultural products has been sustained to a high degree by the growth in population. This is true for meat as well as other products. As pointed out in Chap. 5, income levels and other factors also affect demand, but population has the greatest positive impact. A 1% increase in population is associated with a 1% increase in demand for meat. The income elasticity of demand is positive for beef and lamb, but negative for pork (Table 5.13).[5] Thus, the growth in demand for pork is especially dependent upon population growth.

As demographers found out during the 1930's, 1940's, and 1950's, forecasting population trends is difficult and uncertain. During the 1930's conditions indicated a leveling off of U.S. population by the mid-1950's. However, the rate of population growth accelerated following World War II, reaching 1.6–1.8% per year from the late 1940's to early 1960's, then commenced a decline. Currently, the growth rate is about 1% per year. The decline appears temporarily halted as children of the post-World War II baby boom have come into child-bearing age. The average number of children per family, however, continues to decline, and there is every indication this will continue. Strong pressures exist for population control, and advocates claim that this is a prerequisite for conservation of the environment. Some have a goal of population stabilization. This is not likely to be attained in the immediate future, but it is a distinct possibility at some later point. Agricultural interests would do well to plan for this eventuality—it will require considerable adjustments in production, with greater adjustment in products having low income elasticities than in those with higher income elasticities.

BIBLIOGRAPHY

AHALT, J. D., and HERRON, M. J. 1970. Agriculture in the Seventies. USDA Econ. Res. Serv. Demand Price Situation Res. Bull. *124*.

ANDERSON, D. L. 1968. Future distribution methods for meat. Paper presented at Meat Packers and Processors Conf., Fort Washington, Penn., Apr. 16. USDA Agr. Res. Serv. (unnumbered).

ANON. 1969. Vertical coordination in livestock marketing. Workshop Proc. Southern Regional Livestock Marketing Res. Comm., Houston, Mar. 11-14.

[5] See comments in Chap. 5 pointing out limitations in the interpretation of elasticity coefficients calculated at average incomes, and the comments, also, on the possibility that improvements in quality of pork may have improved demand for pork in recent years.

DUBOV, I. 1969. Market hogs and vertical coordination in research. Workshop Proc. Vertical Coordination in Livestock Marketing. Southern Regional Livestock Marketing Res. Comm., Houston, Mar. 11-14.

GUSTAFSON, R. A., and VanARSDALL, R. N. 1970. Cattle feeding in the United States. USDA Econ. Res. Serv. Agr. Econ. Rept. *186*.

KENDRICKS, J. G. 1970. Market organization alternatives–A better way. *In* Long-Run Adjustments in the Livestock and Meat Industry: Implications and Alternatives. USDA North Central Regional Res. Publ. *199*.

LANDSBERG, H. H. *et al.* 1963. Resources in America's Future: Patterns of Requirements and Availabilities 1960-2000. Johns Hopkins Press, Baltimore.

McCOY, J. H., and OLSON, R. 1970. Changes in the livestock economy of Kansas. Kansas Agr. Expt. Sta. Bull. *538*.

MIGHELL, R. L., and JONES, L. A. 1963. Vertical coordination in agriculture. USDA Econ. Res. Serv. Agr. Econ. Rept. *19*.

REIERSON, R. 1970. Special report, lamb and wool industry developments. Western Livestock Marketing Inform. Proj., Denver, Mar.

ROY, E. P. 1963. Contract Farming U.S.A. Interstate Printers & Publishers, Danville, Ill.

SEIM, D. 1970. Sows for rent: big business by the litter. Farm J. Aug., 24B.

SHOEMAKER, K. G. 1971. Land O'Lakes takes research route for progress. News Farmer Coop. Apr., 6.

SIEBERT, J. B. 1971. Marketing: this decade's challenge. News Farmer Coop. Mar., 3-4.

SMITH, S. R. 1965. The forces for change in livestock marketing. Agr. Marketing Sept., 3.

STOUT, T. T. 1970A. The U.S. beef industry in 1980. Proc. 15th Annual Beef Industry Workshop, Canadian Agr. Econ. Soc., Banff, Alberta, Canada June 7-12.

STOUT, T. T. (Editor). 1970B. Long-run adjustments in the livestock and meat industry: implications and alternatives. Ohio Agr. Res. Develop. Center Res. Bull. *1037*. Also North Central Regional Livestock Marketing Res. Comm., North Central Regional Publ. *199*.

THOR, E. 1971. Changing structure of the market. Paper presented at USDA Natl. Outlook Conf., Washington, D.C., Febr. 25

USDA. 1969. Feasibility of a physical distribution system model for evaluating improvements in the cattle and fresh beef industry. USDA Agr. Res. Serv. *52-36*.

USDA. 1971. Cattle on feed. USDA Crop Reporting Board, Statist. Reporting Serv. *MTAn2-1(1-71)*.

VanDUSEN, W. R. 1969. A time for sober thought. Am. Beef Producer Dec., 14-15.

WILLIAMS, W. F., and STOUT, T. T. 1964. Economics of the Livestock-Meat Industry. Macmillan Co., New York.

Index